D1162776

*"It is the great beauty of our science
that advancement in it,
whether in a degree great or small,
instead of exhausting the subject of research,
opens the doors to further
and more abundant knowledge,
overflowing with beauty and utility."*

———*Michael Faraday*

# SILVER BURDETT
## HIGH SCHOOL CHEMISTRY PROGRAM

**For the Student:**

### CHEMISTRY:
**SCIENCE OF MATTER, ENERGY, AND CHANGE**

GREGORY R. CHOPPIN
Professor of Chemistry
Florida State University
Tallahassee, Florida

BERNARD JAFFE
Formerly Chairman, Department of Physical Science
James Madison High School
New York, New York

### INVESTIGATING CHEMISTRY:
**SCIENCE OF MATTER, ENERGY, AND CHANGE**

HAROLD FERGUSON
Chairman, Mathematics and Science Area
Harriton High School of Lower Merion Township
Rosemont, Pennsylvania

JOSEPH S. SCHMUCKLER
Chemistry Coordinator
Haverford Township Senior High School
Havertown, Pennsylvania

IRWIN SIEGELMAN
Chief Science Editor
Silver Burdett Company
Morristown, New Jersey

**For the Teacher:**

Student textbook and
laboratory manual
guides and

### CHEMISTRY:
**REFLECTIONS OF ANOTHER TEACHER**

JAY A. YOUNG
Professor of Chemistry
Kings College
Wilkes-Barre, Pennsylvania

# CHEMISTRY:

**CIENCE OF MATTER,
NERGY, AND CHANGE**

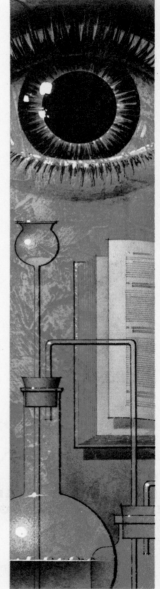

# CHEMISTRY:
## SCIENCE OF MATTER, ENERGY, AND CHANGE

**Gregory R. Choppin**

**Bernard Jaffe**

 **Silver Burdett Company**

The educational publishing subsidiary of Time Inc.

MORRISTOWN, NEW JERSEY
Park Ridge, Ill.     Palo Alto     Dallas     Atlanta

**GREGORY R. CHOPPIN**

*Professor of Chemistry*
*Florida State University*
*Tallahassee, Florida*

**BERNARD JAFFE**

*Formerly Chairman, Department of Physical Science*
*James Madison High School*
*New York, New York*

**THE COVER**

Out of the flickering fires of antiquity and the black magic of medieval alchemy has emerged modern chemical science. Through the ages, as man has learned to investigate his world with increasingly sophisticated tools and reasoning, his superstitions and false notions have given way to understanding. Yet, even with today's deep understandings, the wonder is no less.

© 1965 SILVER BURDETT COMPANY
All Rights Reserved
Printed in the United States of America

Even before the first sputnik was put into orbit in 1957, science educators had begun to do something about the updating and upgrading of our high school chemistry textbooks. In the years following, several government-financed projects, including the CBA and CHEM Study, got under way to modify and enrich the traditional course of study. Out of this science curriculum reform movement also came the writing of this book.

We have tried to give the high school student, whether he is to continue his science education in college or not, (1) a knowledge of the broad concepts and models upon which the edifice of modern chemistry rests and (2) enough of the pertinent facts of the traditional high school chemistry course essential to an understanding of the everyday chemical world in which the student, as an intelligent, well-rounded citizen, lives.

Among the basic generalizations which were to be stressed, we chose the chemical bond, periodicity in the behavior of the chemical elements, the quantum mechanical model of the atom, molecular structure, the mechanics of chemical reactions, and the concept of the mole. These are all fundamental and unifying principles which aid in the proper, logical organization and explanation of modern chemistry as well as in the more sophisticated understanding of the "superficial" facts and applications of descriptive chemistry.

What was needed for a judicious and skillful blending of these two aspects of chemistry was some practical approach which would lighten the introduction of a succession of the new ideas and which would give greater meaning to the best of the descriptive chemistry. To bridge the gap of the two cultures, the humanistic and the scientific, we have made use of the development of chemistry as a slowly evolving science, the saga of men groping for causes and struggling to frame laws. We have touched on the lives and achievements of some of the pioneers of chemistry and on the social impact of their discoveries. This balance of the best of the modern and the most essential of the traditional is even more important in high school than in college. We believe that deep appreciation should go hand in hand with understanding. This approach becomes also an effective way of teaching the methods of science and science as a way of life, by showing how scientists reach their goals and make their contributions.

Difficult concepts have been first introduced lightly and then treated with more sophistication in later chapters. As further aids to understanding, we have made use of a variety of line drawings, illustrations, photographs, and the unique teaching device known as the photographic essay. These aids are found distributed through the textbook where they can best serve. Carefully prepared sets of questions expertly graded, bibliographies (chiefly of inexpensive and easily available paperbacks), and a specially prepared laboratory manual that meshes with the textbook will also help both teacher and student. We have tried to make the style of writing direct and interesting.

Many classroom chemistry teachers and former students have been consulted during the preparation of the manuscript and we are very grateful to them for their help. To the several classroom chem-

istry teachers who kindly served as readers of the manuscript we are
indebted for important suggestions and changes:

Miss Mabel Loo of Hilo High School, Hilo, Hawaii

Mr. Samuel Ascher of Henry Ford High School, Detroit, Michigan

Mr. Herbert Bassow of The Fieldston School, Bronx, New York

Mr. Walter Bowlby of Coral Gables High School, Coral Gables, Florida

Mr. Albert Caro of Morristown High School, Morristown, New Jersey

Mr. Irwin Genzer of Columbia High School, Maplewood, New Jersey

Mr. Till Peters, formerly of Livingston High School, Livingston, New
  Jersey

Dr. Jay Young of Kings College, Wilkes-Barre, Pennsylvania

      Finally, we want to express our deep appreciation to Dr. Irwin
Siegelman, former teacher of chemistry and now Chief Science Editor
of Silver Burdett Company. It was a pleasure to work with him on all
aspects of this book and his contributions in conception, judgment,
and enthusiasm were substantial. We trust that this cooperative effort
will be effective. This is a book for diligent students and enthusiastic
teachers, and we hope it will meet the needs of the new day.

GREGORY R. CHOPPIN
*Tallahassee, Florida, 1965*

BERNARD JAFFE
*Brooklyn, New York, 1965*

## CONTENTS

*It is not in the nature of
things for any one man to make
a sudden, violent discovery;
science goes step by step,
and every man depends on the work
of his predecessors.*

Sir Ernest Rutherford (1871–1937)

**CHAPTER 1** | # Chemistry

Man is a rather new phenomenon on our earth. Recent evidence indicates that he has been in existence for about two million of the more than five billion years since the earth was formed. The first human society and written communication probably developed within the past 10,000 years. That primitive society began to evolve slowly into more complex and more refined civilizations.

The Egyptians, the Greeks, the Romans, and other peoples contributed to the constant development of primitive society: to its art, its literature, and finally its science. Highly developed civilizations resulted. Occasionally, changes in the life of man were revolutionary rather than evolutionary in nature. The great industrial revolution of the late eighteenth century brought about such changes. Machines operated by and for man brought about transformation of the economic life of nations, and thereby of their political and social life.

## MAN'S GROWING DEPENDENCE UPON SCIENCE

Less than one hundred years ago another revolution in man's intellectual and technological development began—the scientific revolution. Many of the discoveries and inventions stemming from the scientific revolution have wrought great changes in the lives of men. Our transportation, our clothing, our housing, our communication, our entertainment—even much of our food—which changed very little in the previous 2000 years, have been rapidly altered. For example, as late as 1900 many Americans still depended upon horses for transportation, just as the Romans had twenty centuries earlier. Today approximately seven million new passenger automobiles are sold annually in the United States.

*2*

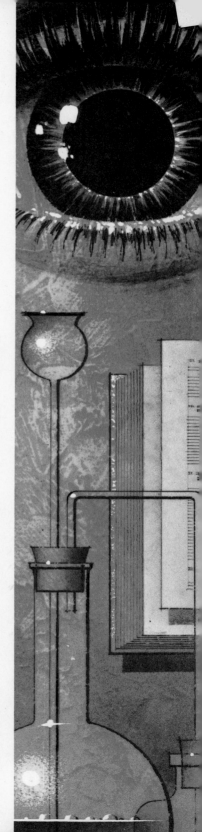

Until 1900 there were few professional scientists, since science played so relatively small a role in human society. With the advent of the scientific revolution, the importance of science grew profoundly greater. Because of this and because science itself became a far more interesting and exciting career, the number of scientists has grown enormously. In fact, it has been estimated that of the total number of scientists that have ever lived, nine out of ten are alive today. Presidents and other government officials frequently consult and are advised by scientists today on questions of national policies, since these are often involved with science.

Because science affects our way of living in almost every detail, and since scientists have increasing influence in all areas of human society, it is necessary for everyone today to understand what science is. Modern man needs to understand the new problems of the nuclear and space age. He must understand them to vote intelligently on legislation bearing on such problems as radiation hazards, space explorations, smog control, the potential harmful effects of food additives, and the indiscriminate use of insecticides. To understand the problems born of great scientific advances means to study and understand the methods of science, its potentialities, its limitations. It is a fascinating study—man's greatest adventure and his greatest achievement.

Just consider the wonder of a single grain of sugar. It appears to be a solid, white cube. Actually, scientists know it is composed of billions of particles called atoms. And even more, these atoms, invisible to the naked eye, are themselves complex little universes of smaller particles known as electrons and nuclei. The nuclei also have a complicated and, as yet, poorly understood structure. However, inside

3

the atomic nucleus is locked the tremendous energy that has already begun to revolutionize our lives.

In this book we hope to give you some understanding of science and scientists. That understanding requires real effort on your part. But if you make the effort, perhaps you will share some of the thrill of scientific discovery. Perhaps, also, the world about you will appear clothed in greater beauty because of your increased comprehension of nature's unity as well as its complexity.

## WHAT IS CHEMISTRY?

Science is like a large mansion with very many rooms. The rooms in this mansion open into each other and have no doors. Our particular concern is with that suite of rooms in the mansion of science that is known as chemistry. Chemistry is the *study of the nature of matter and changes in the composition of matter.* For example, water can be changed into two gases, hydrogen and oxygen. Chemists study what water is like, why and how it can be changed into the two gases, and what hydrogen and oxygen are like. The question of the energy absorbed or released by these changes is also included in the field of chemistry.

### 1.1 What is the difference between a physical and a chemical change?

The changes that matter undergoes may be classified into two broad categories. *In physical changes, the basic chemical nature of the matter is not changed.* The freezing of water is an example of a physical change. Liquid water and ice have basically the same chemical composition. When solid ice melts, it is identical with the liquid that was previously frozen. *In chemical changes (chemical reactions), the basic chemical nature of the material is changed.* The conversion of liquid water into hydrogen gas and oxygen gas is an example of a chemical change. (Fig. 1.1.) More than the form of water has been changed in this process. The basic nature of water is lost in this change and two new substances are formed, hydrogen and oxygen. These gases each have their own set of characteristics, many of which are different from each other and from those of water. Water can be reformed from the oxygen and hydrogen in a chemical reaction.

Another major difference between physical changes and chemical changes is the amount of energy involved. With rare exception, chemical changes either release or absorb much more energy than do physical changes. For example, the chemical formation of 1.00 gram* of liquid water from hydrogen and oxygen gases releases forty-

---

* Units of measurements in the *metric system* are discussed more fully in Appendix II, pages 696–697.

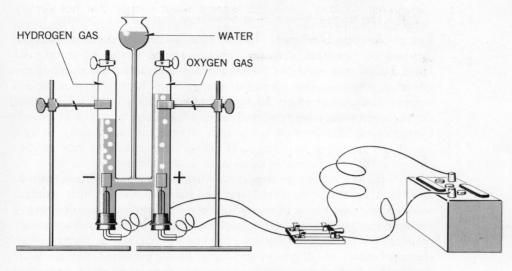

**FIGURE 1.1**   Water is chemically changed by electrolysis. What does *electrolysis* mean? What will happen when the switch is opened?

seven times the energy that is released when 1.00 gram of ice is formed physically from water on freezing.

## 1.2 The law of the conservation of matter

One of the purposes of the study of chemical and physical changes is to discover the basic laws that describe the behavior of matter. Changes in weight, indications of the creation or destruction of matter, have always been a source of study for the chemist. Observations on the chemical and physical behavior of water are examples of what has, so far, always been observed with respect to such weight changes. When 18 grams of water are decomposed to hydrogen and oxygen gases, and these gases are weighed, 2 grams of hydrogen and 16 grams of oxygen are found. When 18 grams of water are frozen, the ice is found to weigh 18 grams, also. On the basis of many such experiments chemists have been led to conclude that in chemical changes the form and composition of matter change but the matter itself cannot be destroyed. In physical changes the physical form of the matter changes but matter cannot be destroyed in the process of changing its form. Evidences such as these are *summarized* in a fundamental law of nature.

**THE LAW OF THE CONSERVATION OF MATTER.**   This most fundamental of natural laws sums up human experience and states that *matter can be neither created nor destroyed.*

### 1.3 The law of the conservation of energy applied to chemistry

Energy can exist in many forms—heat (thermal), light (radiant), mechanical, electrical, magnetic, chemical—and it can be converted from one form to another. The combustion of gasoline in the cylinders of an engine converts chemical energy into heat and mechanical energy. The passage of electricity through the filament of a light bulb converts electrical energy into heat and light energy. In a chemical change, some chemical energy stored in reacting matter may be released and appear as heat and light energy. However, *the sum of the energy in all forms remains a constant in any change.*

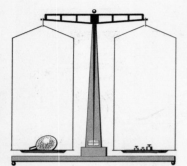

If the heat energy absorbed when 18 grams of ice are melted at 0°C is carefully measured and compared with the heat energy released when 18 grams of water freeze at 0°C, the amounts of energy are found to be identical within the accuracy of the measuring instrument. Likewise, exactly the same amount of energy is absorbed by the conversion of 18 grams of water to 16 grams of oxygen and 2 grams of hydrogen as is released by the formation of 18 grams of water from 16 grams of oxygen and 2 grams of hydrogen. Observations such as these are expressed in another fundamental scientific law.

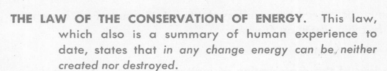

**THE LAW OF THE CONSERVATION OF ENERGY.**  This law, which also is a summary of human experience to date, states that *in any change energy can be neither created nor destroyed.*

### 1.4 The new combined conservation law

In 1905 Albert Einstein, one of history's most eminent scientists, theorized that matter and energy are different forms of the same thing. As a consequence, the conversion of mass to energy and vice versa could be predicted. Careful modern research has proved that minute amounts of matter are indeed destroyed in the spectacular nuclear fusion reactions* which occur in the sun and other stars. There appear in the place of those minute amounts of matter great amounts of energy, hundreds of thousands of times greater than those associated with ordinary chemical changes. The conversion of minute amounts of matter to great amounts of energy during the process called nuclear fission has been the source of great destruction when used as the basis of a weapon. It is the source of great benefit when used today as the basis of power supplies.

In ordinary chemical changes, the amount of transformation of matter to energy is so small that the change in weight of the matter

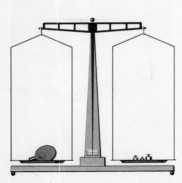

**FIGURE 1.2** Seemingly large amounts of energy are given off by the flashbulb, but the loss of weight is too small to be determined by ordinary laboratory equipment.

---

* Nuclear fusion and fission reactions are considered in more detail in Chapter 32.

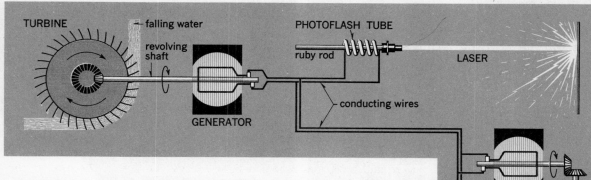

cannot be measured using present instruments, and the individual conservation laws still appear to be valid. However, this is a result of our inability to make sufficiently accurate weight measurements. (Fig. 1.2.) Despite this fact, scientists fully recognize the validity of Einstein's theory and accept a restatement of the separate laws into a unified summary statement of all human experience.

### THE LAW OF THE CONSERVATION OF MATTER AND ENERGY.
*This, now the most fundamental of natural laws, states that matter and energy can be transformed into each other, but the sum total of the matter and energy of the universe can be neither increased nor decreased.*

### 1.5 Chemistry is an experimental science.

The chemist carefully observes the phenomena associated especially with chemical changes. In some cases this observation is with his sense of sight or smell or touch. Far more often he extends his senses through the use of instruments. He observes changes in temperature, in color, and in many other characteristics or properties of matter. More than merely observing these changes, though, a chemist attempts to measure accurately *how much* the temperature or the color changes. In the decomposition of water and in all other chemical changes, the chemist is interested in *how much* energy is absorbed or liberated. He not only cares about *what* products are formed, but *how much* of each. Laboratory observations of a qualitative type and quantitative measurements make up the facts of chemistry.

After accumulating experimental facts, the chemist attempts with an open mind to find relations among these facts. From the similarities and differences he uncovers, the chemist tries to develop a theory to explain why the facts exist. *A theory is a reasonable statement that is in agreement with observed facts and serves to explain those facts.*

Most often theories are based on *model systems* that the chemist first proposes. Such models are *mental images* resulting from the creative leap of the chemist's imagination from his experimental facts

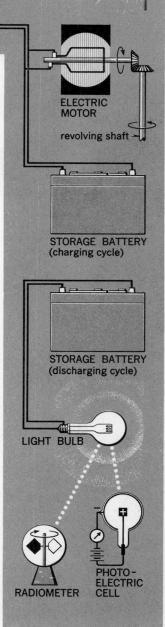

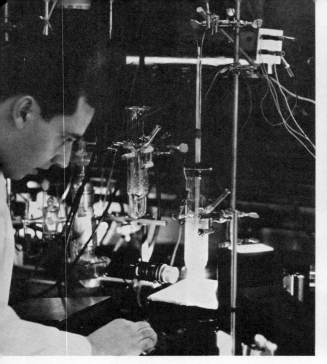

Chemistry: observation, discovery, organization,
thought, creativity, understanding

to an image of how those facts *might* arise. Creative, imaginative leaps
of the mind are characteristic of scientific advances.

The models and theories of science are predictive in nature.
They not only account adequately for known facts but they also
indicate the existence of new ones. Additional experiments to discover
the predicted facts are performed to test theories and models. The
latter change as newly discovered facts may require.

The important thing to keep in mind is that theories are really
guesses, products of human intellect, based on some natural facts.
Most scientific theories are being continually changed—some to a
large extent, others only slightly—as new experiments are performed
and new facts are discovered. But theories and models are very important, as they attempt to bring order to a maze of experimental facts.
Further, they suggest new experiments. By the alternation of experiment and theory, scientists hope to approach more closely an understanding of Nature.

### 1.6 The phlogiston theory: one explanation of burning

Let us illustrate the nature of theories by considering the development
of the explanation for *burning*. One of man's greatest early achievements was the discovery of the use of fire. So strange did fire appear
that for a long time men worshipped it. They considered it the force
responsible for all creation. They pondered over its mystery and made
many attempts to explain it. Alchemists of the sixteenth century, the

medieval mystics who were the forerunners of modern chemists, thought that fire was the result of some vague "sulfur" that burnable substances contain. Later alchemists felt the need for a better explanation—an explanation that took into account more of the facts that had been observed in burning many different substances.

About 300 years ago Joachim Becher (joe AH keem BECK er), a German scientist, advanced the theory that all burnable substances contain phlogiston, or "fire stuff." He said that when a substance burned, phlogiston left it in the form of flame. Becher thought that the ash formed when a substance burned was the substance minus its phlogiston. According to this theory, substances that burn readily, leaving little ash, contain a great deal of phlogiston, while substances that burn with difficulty and leave much ash contain little. The phlogiston theory was the first great theory in chemistry. (Fig. 1.3.)

The phlogiston theory seemed correct to the alchemists because of certain observations they had made. A rising candle flame seemed to tug at the wick. To the alchemists this suggested that phlogiston was escaping from the burning candle. When a small amount of powdered lead is heated in an iron spoon, it melts, burns, and forms a yellow powder. According to the phlogiston theory, this yellow powder is lead ash, or lead minus its phlogiston. Now if some way could be found to add phlogiston to this lead ash, lead should be produced again. Perhaps this could be done by heating the lead ash with some substance that contains a lot of phlogiston, such as carbon. The carbon might give up some of its phlogiston to the lead ash. When this experiment was performed, the final product was actually lead! (Fig. 1.4.)

**FIGURE 1.3** Burning questions of the seventeenth century:

Does something leave?

Does something enter?

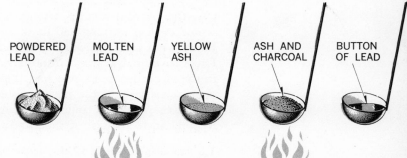

POWDERED LEAD    MOLTEN LEAD    YELLOW ASH    ASH AND CHARCOAL    BUTTON OF LEAD

**FIGURE 1.4** Phlogiston—an answer for the questions? Trace the path of phlogiston in each step shown.

For more than a century the phlogiston theory was considered to be an accurate explanation of burning, and many of the most eminent pioneers of modern chemistry were its ardent supporters.

## 1.7 The first clue to a new theory of burning

Joseph Priestley, an English minister and amateur scientist, was a firm believer in the phlogiston theory but in 1774 he unknowingly paved

**Antoine Laurent Lavoisier** (1743–1794, French). As a young man, Lavoisier abandoned the study of law for the physical sciences. As a result of his brilliant, quantitative studies, he is often referred to as "the father of modern chemistry." Because of his membership in the Ferme Générale, which collected taxes on tobacco, salt, and imports, he was accused of treason during the French Revolution and was beheaded.

the way for its eventual downfall. Priestley was experimenting with a red powder that was formed originally by heating mercury in an open crucible. Priestley was curious. He decided to heat the red powder and collect any gas that was given off. Two startling new facts emerged from his experiments with the strange gas that formed:

1. A mouse when placed in a bell jar containing the new gas lived three times as long as a mouse placed in a jar containing air.
2. A candle burned longer and more brightly when placed in a jar containing this strange gas.

Priestley named his newly discovered gas "dephlogisticated air," air without phlogiston. Let us see how he might have arrived at this name. The gas was similar to air, but possessed some other property that enabled the mouse to live longer. But what was this property that also allowed the candle to burn longer and more brightly? If the candle were simply giving off phlogiston as it burned, why should it burn longer and better? Perhaps the gas was devoid of phlogiston—air without phlogiston; this would enable the phlogiston to escape more easily from the candle. Of course, when the gas became filled with phlogiston the candle would go out.

While Priestley was in Paris, later in 1774, he visited Antoine Lavoisier (AN twon lah vwah zee AY), the most brilliant chemist in France, and told him about his discovery. Priestley's information was a welcome addition to the many facts that Lavoisier had already collected about burning.

Lavoisier accepted the facts, but not the theory. He pondered over the facts for months, trying to formulate an accurate theory that would explain burning and be in keeping with all the observed facts. He was not satisfied with the existing phlogiston theory. Could it be, Lavoisier mused, that when substances burn they *unite* with something in the air, rather than give something off? Here was the creative and courageous leap of the imagination that signaled the rise of modern chemistry. Lavoisier quickly put his tentative working theory, or hypothesis, to the test of experiment.

### 1.8 Lavoisier's classic 12-day experiment that explained burning

"I introduced four ounces of pure mercury into a (sealed) glass vessel," he wrote. "I lighted a fire in the furnace, which I kept up continually for twelve days. On the second day, small red particles already had begun to appear on the surface of the mercury." When most of the mercury had been converted into a red powder, Lavoisier removed the glass vessel and its contents (which he had weighed before the experiment) and weighed them again. There was no increase in weight.

**FIGURE 1.5** Lavoisier "found that all of the red powder was changed back into mercury and that a gas was given off. . . ." What is the answer to the burning questions of the seventeenth century?

Since the glass vessel was sealed, nothing had entered or escaped from it during the heating. Yet when he broke the seal, he noticed that air rushed into the vessel. To him this inrush of air indicated that part of the air in the vessel had been used up during the heating and had left space for more air to enter. After air had entered the vessel, he weighed it once more and determined the increase in weight. He concluded that this increase in weight equaled the weight of something in the air in the vessel that must have combined with the mercury, forming the red powder. (Fig. 1.5.)

Lavoisier's inquiring spirit was not satisfied. He was a scientist in the most modern sense. He refused to jump to a hasty conclusion on the basis of a single experiment. He withheld drawing a conclusion until he had performed many more experiments. As a further precaution, he reversed his original experiment. He took the red powder of mercury and heated it to a higher temperature. He found that all of the red powder was changed back into mercury and that a gas was given off, which he found by a series of tests to be identical with the dephlogisticated air that Priestley had discovered. Hence, he concluded that it was the gas in the air that was responsible for burning. Lavoisier named that gas *oxygen*. Of all the substances he tried, he found none that could burn without oxygen. Every experiment on burning since Lavoisier's time has supported his theory, and we now accept it as the correct explanation of burning.

### 1.9 Scientific method

The story of the development of Lavoisier's theory of burning is illustrative of a way of solving problems. If Lavoisier's approach to the problem of burning is studied carefully, certain characteristics common to the growth of other scientific theories can be tabulated. Lavoisier's approach as a method of science may be briefly summarized as involving the following:

1. The collection of all the available facts related to a problem.
2. The open-minded checking and examination of those facts.
3. The imaginative leap of the mind from those facts to a working hypothesis or model to explain those facts.
4. The experimental testing of the hypothesis or model.
5. The formulation of a theory based on valid experimental testing of the working hypothesis.
6. The predictive use of the theory.

To call these six steps *the* scientific method would be an over-generalization. The six steps represent one way in which scientists may approach a problem. No scientist, however, follows a set pattern in his groping for understanding of Nature. If there is a need to define scientific method, perhaps it can best be defined as the interaction of experiment, ideas, and creative imagination.

## CHEMISTRY: THE STUDY OF MATTER

Now that we have examined briefly the methods of chemistry, let us consider the materials with which chemists work. There are millions of different kinds of chemical materials, but all these commonly exist in only three different *states of matter*—solid, liquid, or gaseous. Water can exist as a solid (ice) if the temperature is below 0°C.* Between 0°C and 100°C it exists mainly as liquid. Above 100°C water is found only in the gaseous state under ordinary conditions of pressure. The state in which a substance exists is dependent partly on the material itself,

---

* °C is the symbol for temperature readings made on the *Celsius* (formerly Centigrade) temperature scale. This temperature scale is, for our purposes, based on 100 equal divisions or degrees between the freezing point and boiling point of pure water at sea level pressure. The freezing and boiling points themselves were arbitrarily designated as 0° and 100°, respectively, by Anders Celsius, a Swedish scientist, in 1742. Since that time the Celsius scale has been the one primarily used by scientists in all countries. It is also widely used for general purposes in most countries other than the United States.

partly on the temperature, and partly on the pressure. For example, water can be kept in the liquid state well above 100°C if the pressure over it is high.

Changes from one state of matter to another by heating or cooling are very common. Iron, which we know as a hard, gray solid, is melted in foundries and changed to a shimmering, silvery liquid. If its temperature is raised high enough, gaseous iron vapor is boiled off.

For a few substances the transformation from solid to gas and vice versa proceeds directly without going through the liquid state. The transition directly from solid to gas is known as *sublimation*. Carbon dioxide is an example of a substance that sublimes. As *dry ice* it exists as a solid, which upon heating transforms to carbon dioxide gas. Iodine is another example.

Molten iron, heated to more than 1500°C, presents a vivid example of a common solid in the liquid state.

A block of dry ice being formed in a hydraulic press. Contrast its physical behavior with that of the wet ice on the outside of the press.

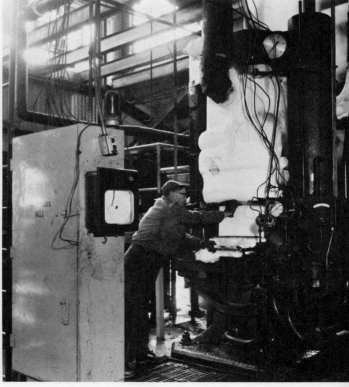

### 1.10 The elements of the ancients

The vast majority of substances found on earth can be either decomposed or transformed by chemical changes. This led the ancient philosophers to speculate on the existence of basic substances that could *not* be decomposed and from which all other substances were formed. Thales (THAY leez), philosopher, astronomer, and geometer, who was born in Miletus in Asia Minor in 640 B.C., noticed that water nourishes crops and that it is found in large amounts in the bodies of men and in other living things. Hence, by deductive reasoning, he suggested the theory that water was the basic substance from which all material things were made.

Later, other philosophers in the same region of western Asia Minor, which was marked by historians as the cradle of Greek science, continued to develop the concept of fundamental substances. Anaximenes (an ax IH muh neez) also of Miletus and who died about 525 B.C., proposed that air was a primary substance. Heraclitus (heh rah KLY tus), philosopher and poet of the early fifth century B.C., postulated fire as an elemental substance.

Finally, in the writings of the great Greek philosopher Empedocles (em PED ah kleez) appeared an idea that was to dominate western scientific thought until the eighteenth century. This wise man, born about 500 B.C. on the south coast of Sicily, was the first to express the idea that all matter was composed not of a single substance, but of "four elements"—*air, earth, fire,* and *water.* This arbitrary hypothesis had very little experimental justification. True, as noted by the ancients, when a stick of green wood was burned, fire was produced, water was forced out and boiled off at the ends of the stick, a smoky vapor or air was given off, and an ash or earth remained. Yet this one observation we would hardly feel is satisfactory support for Empedocles' major theory. That the theory lasted for more than 2000 years, and was considered correct by many otherwise well-informed persons, was due primarily to the fact that quantitative, experimental chemistry did not emerge in full bloom as a science until the eighteenth century.

### 1.11 Today's elements

Scientists now consider that the mountains, the oceans, the air, all living things, and even the stars and the rest of the universe are composed of simple substances that cannot be broken down, or decomposed, into simpler substances by any chemical change. These simple substances are called *elements.* Probably the elements with which you are most familiar are gold, silver, iron, copper, nickel, sulfur, oxygen, carbon, nitrogen, and hydrogen. Examine the list of elements as given on page 85. How many more of these elements do you recognize?

FIRE

Hot          Dry

AIR          EARTH

Wet          Cold

WATER

Aristotle (384–322 B.C.), renowned Greek philosopher, described the four elements of the ancients as combinations of pairs of fundamental properties of matter.

## 1.12 What are compounds?

There are many substances with which the chemist deals that are not elements. Rather, each is composed of two or more elements so combined that (1) only chemical action can tear them apart and (2) the elements of which each substance is composed can no longer be identified by their original individual properties. Such substances are called *compounds*.

Pure cane sugar, for example, is a compound made up of three elements, carbon, hydrogen, and oxygen, chemically combined. The properties of a compound, such as color, odor, taste, form, and ability to dissolve in water, are nearly always distinctly different from the properties of the elements of which it is composed. For example, pure cane sugar, a sweet, white, crystalline solid that dissolves in water, is quite different in properties from any and all of the three elements of which it is composed.

## 1.13 Chemical symbols for the elements

Jöns Berzelius (yearns bear TSAY lee us) of Sweden, a foremost chemist of the nineteenth century, invented a simple system of chemical notation for the elements, which he introduced in 1814. Today it is used by chemists in every country. Berzelius took the first letter of the name of an element for its symbol. Thus, C represents carbon, H represents hydrogen, and U represents uranium.

Since the first letter of the names of several of the elements is the same—eleven elements have names beginning with the letter C, for example—most elements have two-letter symbols. These symbols always begin with the capitalized initial letter of the element's name, followed by a second letter from the name. This second letter is *never* capitalized. The eleven elements whose names begin with the letter C and the symbols for these elements are:

| Name of Element | Symbol |
|-----------------|--------|
| Cadmium         | Cd     |
| Calcium         | Ca     |
| Californium     | Cf     |
| Carbon          | C      |
| Cerium          | Ce     |
| Cesium          | Cs     |
| Chlorine        | Cl     |
| Chromium        | Cr     |
| Cobalt          | Co     |
| Curium          | Cm     |
| Copper          | Cu     |

**Jöns Jakob Berzelius** (1779–1848, Swedish). Considered the most accurate chemical analyst of his day, Berzelius determined the atomic weights of 50 different elements. He also discovered the elements selenium and thorium and was the chief architect of a major theory of chemical combination. Aspects of that *electrochemical theory* are part of modern theories.

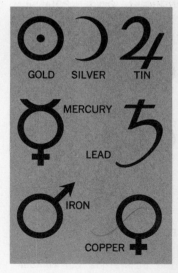

Medieval alchemical symbols of the seven metals known to the ancients

The last element in the list has a symbol that seems to make only partial sense. Copper does, indeed, begin with the letter *C*, but where is there a *u* in its name? The Latin name for copper, *cuprum*, is the clue to the puzzle. Copper, as well as a number of other familiar elements, has its symbol derived from its Latin name. A list of the eleven elements whose symbols are derived from either the Latin (L) or the German (G) name for the element follows.

| ELEMENT | FOREIGN NAME | SYMBOL |
|---|---|---|
| Antimony | *Stibium* (L) | Sb |
| Copper | *Cuprum* (L) | Cu |
| Gold | *Aurum* (L) | Au |
| Iron | *Ferrum* (L) | Fe |
| Lead | *Plumbum* (L) | Pb |
| Mercury | *Hydrargyrum* (L) | Hg |
| Potassium | *Kalium* (G) | K |
| Silver | *Argentum* (L) | Ag |
| Sodium | *Natrium* (G) | Na |
| Tin | *Stannum* (L) | Sn |
| Tungsten | *Wolfram* (G) | W |

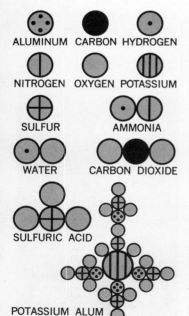

ALUMINUM  CARBON  HYDROGEN

NITROGEN  OXYGEN  POTASSIUM

SULFUR  AMMONIA

WATER  CARBON DIOXIDE

SULFURIC ACID

POTASSIUM ALUM

The picturesque but cumbersome symbolism of John Dalton, which was replaced by the simplified Berzelius system.

## 1.14 Chemical formulas for compounds

The Berzelius system of element symbols is also used for the shorthand notation of compounds. As an element may be represented by its symbol, so a compound may be represented by its formula. The formula for a compound consists of the symbols for the elements that compose the compounds, placed side by side. For example, the formula for zinc oxide, a compound of zinc and oxygen, is $ZnO$; that for zinc chloride, a compound of zinc and chlorine, is $ZnCl_2$; while that for zinc nitride, a compound of zinc and nitrogen, is $Zn_3N_2$. These examples were chosen to indicate clearly the *quantitative* aspect of chemical formulas. A formula tells not merely which elements are combined in the compound, but *how much* of each. A number appearing lowered and to the right of a symbol is called a *subscript*. It represents the number of atoms of the element whose symbol it follows. In the formula $Zn_3N_2$, the subscripts tell us that for every three atoms of zinc in zinc nitride there are two atoms of combined nitrogen. When a subscript is equal to one, as in $Zn_1O_1$ or $Zn_1Cl_2$, it is omitted from the formula.

## 1.15 How does a mixture differ from a compound?

In a compound the elements must be chemically united. But there are other kinds of substances made up of two or more elements or compounds. Although the particles of such a substance are thoroughly intermingled or mixed, each of the original substances can still be identified by most of its original individual properties. Hence, we may conclude that the substances are not chemically joined.

A pinch of salt and a pinch of white sand stirred together make an excellent example of one of these substances. The salt can be identified by its characteristic taste, and the sand by its gritty feel on the tongue and teeth. *A substance composed of two or more elements and/or compounds that are not chemically combined is called a mixture.* The component parts of a mixture *retain most of their individual properties no matter how thoroughly mixed.* Very many of the substances with which you deal each day are mixtures. Examples of familiar mixtures are soil, air, paper, petroleum, coins, milk, and many other foods.

Distillation is the process in which component parts of a mixture are separated by virtue of differences in their boiling points. The laboratory distillation apparatus being used by the scientist has as its industrial counterpart the immense unit in the background.

The properties of a mixture are mostly the same as the properties of the elements or compounds that compose it. A handful of iron powder mixed with a handful of powdered sulfur makes a mixture whose properties resemble both those of the black iron and those of the yellow sulfur. If a magnet is passed through such a mixture, the iron clings to the magnet. If enough liquid called carbon disulfide is added to the mixture, the sulfur is dissolved. But if the mixture of sulfur and iron is heated, these two elements combine, forming a compound known as *iron(II) sulfide**. Iron(II) sulfide does not look like either sulfur or iron. It is not magnetic and does not dissolve in carbon disulfide. The properties of this compound do not resemble those of either sulfur or iron.

Some mixtures are *homogeneous;* that is, their component parts are evenly distributed throughout. For example, salt dissolved in water is such a mixture. Homogeneous mixtures are generally called *solutions*. In *heterogeneous* mixtures the component parts are not evenly distributed.

Substances in mixtures may often be separated from each other rather easily. A mixture of salt and sand, for example, may be separated by adding water. The salt dissolves to form a water solution, and the sand settles to the bottom. The solution may be poured into another vessel, heated to drive off the water, and the original solid salt can be recovered. In what two ways could you separate a mixture of iron and sulfur?

### 1.16 Atoms and molecules and how they differ

Suppose we had a glass of water and we kept dividing the amount of water in half even beyond the limit of visibility. Obviously, there must be a limit to this process. Eventually, a very, very small bit of water is left—this last bit is a molecule of water—which upon further division is no longer water. *A molecule, then, is the smallest particle that can exist as a compound substance.* A molecule is extremely small—in fact, in the glass of water we considered dividing, there would be about $10^{26}$† molecules. The process of dividing the amount of water would go on more than 80 times before a single molecule is reached.

Three representations of the water molecule: at top, symbols; in the middle, a ball and stick model; at the bottom, a scale model

---

* Iron(II) sulfide, or simply iron sulfide, is also, according to older naming procedures, known as ferrous sulfide. Rules for modern nomenclature of chemical compounds will be discussed as the need for such rules arises during your study.
† Very large and very small numbers are conveniently expressed in exponential form. For example:  (a) $0.00000000057 = 5.7 \times 10^{-10}$
(b) $230,000,000,000,000, = 2.3 \times 10^{14}$
Exponential numbers and their arithmetical manipulation are discussed in more detail in Appendix III, pages 698–699.

To gain a better picture of this, take any length of string you wish and begin dividing it. You will find that 10 to 15 is about the limit of the number of times that you can divide the string before it becomes too small to handle. Now imagine dividing it 70 more times to obtain a molecule! (Fig. 1.6.)

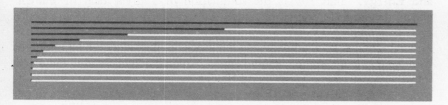

**FIGURE 1.6** Successive division of a line by halves. Can you imagine halving the last segment another seventy times?

A molecule is divisible. When it is divided, however, it is no longer the same substance. A molecule of water can be divided into 3 smaller pieces, but these pieces no longer have either the physical or the chemical properties of water. These smaller, submolecular pieces are called *atoms,* and a molecule of water, $H_2O$, is composed of two atoms of hydrogen, H, and one atom of oxygen, O. (Fig. 1.7.) *An atom is the smallest particle that can exist as an element.*

Molecules and atoms, compounds and elements—the simplest forms of matter—are at the heart of chemistry and will be the natural subject of our interest throughout our study.

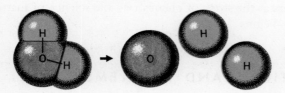

**FIGURE 1.7** Scale-model representation of the composition of water

## SUMMARY

Since the beginning of civilization, science has influenced the progress of man, and man in turn has influenced the progress of science. Chemistry is that branch of science which is concerned with the nature of matter and with the changes in the composition of matter. Two broad categories of material change are evident in nature: (1) physical changes—those that do not involve changes in the basic nature of substances; and (2) chemical changes—those that do involve changes in the basic nature and properties of substances. Accompanying all material changes are energy changes. The purpose of studying all these changes is to discover the basic laws that describe the behavior of matter. Through such study, scientists have evolved the most fundamental of all natural laws—the Law of the Conservation of Matter and Energy. This law is the summation of a great deal of human experience and, like many others, grew out of careful observation and clear thinking.

Chemistry is an experimental science. The chemist attempts to explain the existence of, and relations among, experimental facts by models and theories. Models and theories arise from the interaction of experiment, ideas, and creative imagination. The chemist attempts to be an observant and thoughtful person; he is by no means infallible. Remember the phlogiston theory of burning!

Matter with which the chemist works can exist in three physical states—solid, liquid, and gas. But what are the basic elements of matter? Water, air, fire, and earth? We now know that there are many elements, from which all compounds and mixtures are produced. An atom is the smallest particle that can exist as an element. In compounds, the elements can no longer be identified by their original individual properties. In mixtures, the component parts retain their individual properties no matter how thoroughly mixed. A molecule is the smallest particle that can exist as a compound. Chapter 1 has dealt with how and what the chemist investigates. The stage is set to bring on the players as the story of chemistry—the science of matter, energy, and change—begins . . . .

## QUESTIONS AND PROBLEMS

1.1  What is chemistry?

1.2  In this chapter, science has been likened to a large mansion with very many rooms. The rooms have been described as opening into each other, but doorless. What does this mean to you?

1.3  What is the difference between a physical and a chemical change?

1.4  Indicate whether each of the following involve physical changes, chemical changes, or both:

| | |
|---|---|
| a. a cake baking | g. an egg frying |
| b. a stick breaking | h. a bird flying |
| c. water boiling | i. a bomb exploding |
| d. a man toiling | j. a ship corroding |
| e. a tree growing | k. sulfur burning |
| f. the wind blowing | l. the leaves turning |

1.5  State the Law of the Conservation of Matter in your own words. Describe how the law applies to your experience of eating and growing.

1.6  State the Law of the Conservation of Energy in your own words. Describe how the law applies to your experience of eating and growing.

1.7  Briefly outline the steps the chemist often follows in arriving at a useful theory.

1.8  What observations made by the alchemists led them to believe in the phlogiston theory?

1.9  How was the fact that certain substances gained weight when they burned explained by the phlogiston theory?

1.10  Why did Priestley name the gas he obtained "dephlogisticated air"?

1.11  On what critical point did Lavoisier disagree with the phlogiston theory?

1.12  At the end of the 12-day experiment, how did Lavoisier explain the increase in weight of his glass vessel and its contents after he broke the seal?

1.13  How did Lavoisier explain the fact that a glowing wooden splint burst into flame and burned more brightly in dephlogisticated air than in normal air? What is dephlogisticated air now called?

1.14  On the basis of the modern theory of burning, explain why the ash obtained when wood is burned is lighter than the unburned wood. How could you experimentally test your explanation?

1.15  In what three physical states does matter commonly exist?

1.16  What were the four elements of the ancients? What were some observations that led the ancients to conclude that these were elements?

1.17  What is an element? What is a compound? What is a mixture?

1.18  What is an atom? What is a molecule?

1.19  Indicate whether each of the following substances is an element, a compound, or a mixture.

| | | |
|---|---|---|
| a. air | g. gasoline | m. a nickel |
| b. sea water | h. stone | n. paper |
| c. fresh water | i. wood | o. aspirin |
| d. water | j. iron | p. glass |
| e. steam | k. steel | q. mercury |
| f. ice | l. nickel | r. a flame |

1.20  Give symbols for the following elements:

| | | | |
|---|---|---|---|
| a. hydrogen | e. lead | i. iron | m. mercury |
| b. calcium | f. uranium | j. silver | n. chlorine |
| c. nitrogen | g. oxygen | k. phosphorus | o. copper |
| d. carbon | h. sodium | l. tin | p. potassium |

## SUGGESTED READINGS

In this section, which will appear at the end of each chapter, can be found a list of books or articles from which you may obtain further background and insight into the material covered in a given chapter. Most of the books chosen are available as inexpensive "paperbacks." A fairly complete list of paperback books in chemistry and related sciences will be found in the *Journal of Chemical Education*, April 1965.

There are a number of inexpensive periodicals that appear regularly and may be read with benefit. Two of the best of these are *Scientific American*, which may be purchased from your newsdealer, and *Chemistry*, which may be bought on a subscription basis from the American Chemical Society.

For this chapter, the following are suggested readings:

Bronowski, J. *Science and Human Values* (paperback). Harper, 1959.

Conant, James B. (ed.) *Harvard Case Histories in Experimental Science*, Vol. 2. Harvard University Press, 1957. Overthrow of the phlogiston theory.

Davis, Helen M. *The Chemical Elements* (paperback). Ballantine Books, 1959. Historical account of the discovery of the elements.

Faraday, Michael. *The Chemical History of a Candle* (paperback). Viking Press, 1963. A classic of popular science by one of the greatest scientists in history.

Jaffe, Bernard. *Crucibles: The Story of Chemistry* (paperback). Fawcett, 1962. Chapter 5 tells the story of Lavoisier, and Chapter 7 details Berzelius' development of modern symbolism.

Lapp, Ralph E. and the Editors of LIFE. *Matter* (LIFE Science Library). Time Inc., 1963.

Lucretius. *The Nature of the Universe* (paperback). Penguin Books, 1959. An ancient Roman poet describes the early concept of matter.

Margenau, Henry, David Bergamini, and the Editors of LIFE. *The Scientist* (LIFE Science Library). Time Inc., 1964.

CHEMISTRY

Goran, M., "Scientists Also Make Mistakes." Apr. 1964
Scott, A., "Preparing for a Career in Chemistry." Mar. 1964

SCIENTIFIC AMERICAN

Mauser, B. and J., "A Study of the Anti-scientific Attitude." Feb. 1955
Terman, L., "Are Scientists Different?" Jan. 1955

# Alchemy

## THE PLENTIFUL VINTAGE

In laboratories like this fifteenth-century one recreated at the University of Cracow, Poland, our story begins. Its prologue is the romance of alchemy. Though the alchemists practiced a chemistry that was often more art than science, more fruitless potboiling than productive experimentation, their labors laid the foundations of modern chemical science.

Hermes Trismegistus, legendary founder of Egyptian alchemy, depicted in the *Emerald Tablet*. The tablet summarizes principles of natural change: "The father thereof is the sun, and the mother is the moon; the wind carries it in its belly, and the nurse is the earth."

# EASTERN ALCHEMY

Alchemy began in the East. It was rooted in the Bronze Age cultures of Egypt and Mesopotamia, where metallurgy, dyeing, and glassmaking arose. It was in Alexandria, in the third century B.C., that these technical arts fused with Greek speculative thought, and alchemy came to be. Through conquest and trade, alchemy spread to Arabia, India, and China and became suffused with the practices and philosophies of those Eastern cultures. For example, Jabir ibn Hayyan and al-Razi (Rhazes), Arabic alchemists of the eighth and ninth centuries A.D., first developed the theory that metals were composed of mercury and sulfur, a theory that greatly influenced later European alchemical thought. The Taoism of the fourth-century Chinese alchemist Ko Hung was reflected in the never-ending alchemical search for the elixir of life in succeeding centuries.

*24*

A fundamental doctrine of Alexandrian alchemy was the ultimate unity of matter. It is symbolized on this fifteenth century page by the *ouroboros*, or coiled serpent. Shown also is an ancient still.

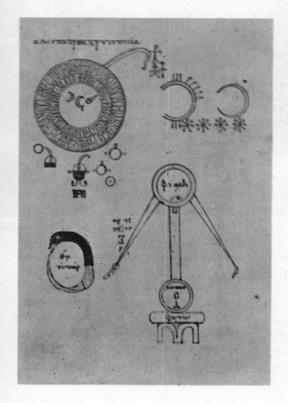

A modern print showing the Chinese alchemist Sun Po making the trees burst into flame. Sun Po was also alleged to have discovered an elixir of life as he worked his magic 2000 years ago.

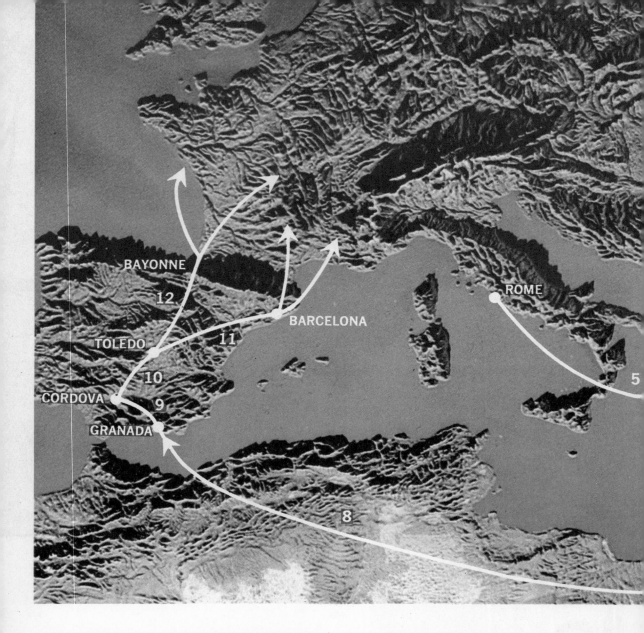

## ALCHEMY REACHES EUROPE

From its early roots in the practical arts of Egyptian (1), Mesopotamian (2), and Persian (3) cultures and in the speculative philosophy that arose in Miletus, Clazomenae, Abdera, and other Aegean towns (4), alchemy came to exist in Alexandria some 22 centuries ago. From the fusion of Egyptian and Babylonian mysticism and astrology with Hellenic thought sprang a profusion of alchemical goals, symbolisms, and practices. Later, commerce between the Roman Empire and the Orient wrought great changes in Alexandrian alchemy. The paganism of Caesar's Rome (5) and the Taoism of China (6) became woven into the mystical patterns of the alchemical arts. Still later, Byzantine savants nurtured and preserved those arts (7). By the eighth century

A.D., less than 200 years after the birth of Mohammed, the sword of Islam had carved out a mighty empire in his name. The Mohammedan empire stretched westward from the borders of India, through Persia, Arabia, Egypt, and all of North Africa, across the Mediterranean, and into the Iberian Peninsula. As the Moslems conquered the ancient lands that spawned alchemy, they adopted, embellished, and carried it along. And so it was that alchemy came to Europe, entering through Granada (8) and flourishing in the splendid Moorish Caliphate of Cordova (9). Mainly through the translations of Arabic texts into Latin, especially at Toledo (10), and the passing of those texts across the Pyrenees through Barcelona (11) and Bayonne (12) did the great scientific legacy of Saracen culture become part of the future history of Europe.

*The Alchemist,* a 1640 painting by Ryckaert that now hangs in the Prado in Madrid. It is but one of many beautiful paintings of medieval alchemists that may be found in museums throughout the world. Portrayed is an aged *adept* with his young assistant amid the clutter of a life's work.

## MEDIEVAL ALCHEMY

Through the efforts of great medieval scholars like Roger Bacon and Albertus Magnus, encyclopedic records of all phases of knowledge were compiled. Thus, alchemy became widely known and appealing to men of all persuasions during the Middle Ages. Bumbling amateurs, or *puffers*, sought quick wealth and fame through alchemy; *adepts* practiced it in pursuit of knowledge; charlatans fraudulently distorted it to reach self-serving goals. Court alchemists toiled vainly to transmute base metals into gold to achieve financial stability for the European monarchies. By the end of the fourteenth century, the medieval surge of alchemical activity had subsided. Much new chemical knowledge and new techniques were recorded. Thereafter, little that was new but much that was obscure became the record of alchemy.

A page from the fifteenth-century *Ordinall of Alchimy*, showing its author, Thomas Norton, and his assistants at alchemical tasks. At the top are portrayed the famous alchemists Geber, Arnold of Villanova, Rhazes, and the legendary Hermes Trismegistus.

Pieter Breughel's famous 1558 engraving of alchemy as practiced by a *puffer*. At the right, he is seen seeding some mixture with his last gold coin. Through the window is his future—the poorhouse.

In SPLENDOR SOLIS is an account of seven ways in which the sun affects the earth. Shown are four allegorical representations from that account. Though some symbols are understood—red, white, and black for spirit, soul, and body—most remain mysteries.

With the glowing yellow liquid in the *cucurbit*, symbolic perhaps of the philosopher's stone, Trismosin begins: "Let us examine the nature of the four elements."

**ALCHEMICAL SYMBOLISM** Throughout its long history, alchemy was filled with mysterious symbolism. Many of the early symbols were derived from mythology. The lance and shield of Mars, ♂, for example, stood for iron. The looking glass of Venus, ♀, represented copper, since Venus had first appeared on the shores of Cyprus, an island famous for its copper mines. As alchemical practices spread throughout medieval Europe, such universal symbolism became lost in the great proliferation of personal symbolism that arose to conceal the meanings of alchemical writings as well as to add mystery and magic to them. In one seventeenth-century Italian manuscript, for example, the element mercury, alone, is represented by twenty different symbols and thirty-five names. Perhaps the most obscure examples of medieval alchemical symbolism can be found in the SPLENDOR SOLIS, the *Splendor of the Sun*, by the sixteenth-century English adept Solomon Trismosin. Though it may be difficult to interpret the alchemy allegorically symbolized in each illustration, the beauty of each shines through. Though Trismosin's science may remain hidden, the life of his times is vividly portrayed.

*30*

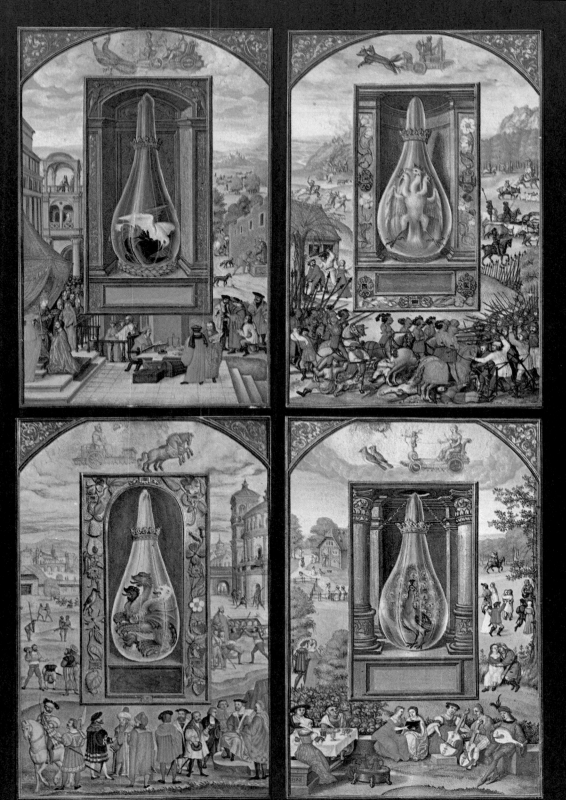

The balance and still, ovens and bellows, mortar and pestle, forceps, funnels, mallet, and lance, retorts, crucible, and flasks—all seen in this French alchemical manuscript of the sixteenth century—remain important artifacts of modern chemical research and technology.

MVLTIPLICACION FERMENTION:

CALCINACION:

FIXATION:

# TECHNICAL ADVANCES OF ALCHEMY

The nineteenth-century chemist J. B. Dumas wrote that "the science of chemistry was born at the potter's wheel, the glazier's workshop, the blacksmith's forge, and the perfumer's salon." Yet each of those artful pursuits could not have existed were it not for the centuries of evolutionary development of technical skills and equipment by the alchemists. In pursuing their elusive goals over the centuries, the alchemists treated all sorts of matter—metals, minerals, plants, flesh, hair, feathers, bones, and excrement—in all sorts of ways—calcination, sublimation, fermentation, amalgamation, reverberation, rectification, and filtration. They went about their tasks using a wide variety of equipment which they devised as the need arose. Many of their crude devices have evolved into pieces that are part of the elaborate laboratory instrumentation and complex industrial apparatus of today. Unquestionably, the most fundamental alchemical procedure was distillation. The most basic apparatus was the still. Even today, distillation is the most important unit process of the chemical industry and the most important separation technique of the research laboratory. Though alchemy is very often thought of in terms of magic and fraud, of mystical incantations and arcane symbolisms, its very tangible contributions to the development of chemical techniques and devices for studying the nature of things constitute a more meaningful chapter in its long history.

Below, at the left, are symbolic representations of three alchemical processes as pictured in THE CROWNE OF NATURE, a sixteenth-century English work. The two pages at the right are from a medieval Italian treatise. The importance of distillation to the alchemist is emphasized. Whether one wished to obtain "heavenly water" (left) or "the quintessence of the water of life" (right), it was through the use of the still that one's goals were realized.

IOÁNES
STRATENSIS
FLANDRVS
1570

The sixteenth-century painting by Stradanus at the left is a magnificent record of the iatrochemical roots of the modern pharmaceutical industry. Plant pressing and distillation are still vital operations. In the German engraving at the right, a sixteenth-century physician is seen consulting with an iatrochemist about a curative potion that is being distilled. Such was the start of today's doctor-druggist relationship.

## MEDICAL ADVANCES OF ALCHEMY

By the sixteenth century, there had been a slow movement away from the fanatical and futile alchemical search for transmutation. Efforts were turned to the preparation of medicines to cure the bodily ills of mankind. This pursuit of *iatrochemistry,* or medicinal chemistry, was most effectively championed by Paracelsus, born in Switzerland in 1493. A renowned physician and surgeon, Paracelsus attacked the medical beliefs and practices of his time with sharp tongue and stinging pen. Those beliefs were grounded in the ideas of the second-century Roman sage Galen, who believed that the body was composed of four *humors*—blood, phlegm, yellow bile, and black bile—and that illness resulted from an imbalance of these. The practices were still those of the tenth-century Arab physician Avicenna. Believing that changes in the body were chemical in nature, Paracelsus experimented to find specific chemical remedies for specific ailments, and met with great success. He was the first European to use opium for its medicinal properties, and the compounds of iron, mercury, and arsenic that he dispensed are still to be found in present-day pharmacopeias. Though much maligned in his own time, Paracelsus is now recognized as the first real practitioner of chemical medicine. Since his time, chemistry has always been an important aspect of medical education and practice.

The life of the German alchemist Böttger is symbolic of alchemy itself. Failing at transmutation, as shown at the left, he turned to more fruitful pursuits. In 1709 he discovered the process for reproducing the white, translucent porcelain of the Chinese, which he is shown demonstrating at the right.

## THE VINTAGE IS PROCURED

We have followed twenty centuries of alchemical toil, from its roots in the Bronze Age antiquity of Egypt and Mesopotamia to its flourishing heights in medieval Europe. Exactly when the romance of alchemy became the adventure of chemistry cannot be fixed. The transition from pseudo-science, magic, and art to the systematic, experimental pursuit of understanding matter, energy, and change was a gradual one. What is certain is that out of their futile searches for physical transmutation to attain the perfect metal and their no less futile striving for spiritual transmutation to become the perfect man, the alchemists left a glorious legacy. Equipment, techniques, and processes of lasting value passed on to the future. In their quest for the seed of gold in the dirt and dross of the centuries, alchemists unearthed at least four new elements—antimony, arsenic, bismuth, and phosphorus—and discovered hundreds of important compounds and mixtures. We might do well to end our prologue and begin our story with the words of the great seventeenth-century English philosopher Francis Bacon:

> Alchemy may be compared to the man who told his sons that he had left them gold buried somewhere in his vineyard; where they by digging found no gold but, by turning up the mold about the roots of the vines, procured a plentiful vintage.

36

In 1669, Hennig Brand, alchemist of Hamburg, Germany, discovered elemental phosphorus. The certain wonderment when the eerie glow of the waxy solid first appeared is re-created in this painting by Joseph Wright, done a century later.

## QUESTIONS AND PROBLEMS

1. Locate in time and place the sources that gave rise to alchemy.
2. Why was Grecian Alexandria a logical place for alchemy to emerge?
3. Determine the possible origin of the word *alchemy*.
4. Describe the growth and dissemination of alchemy after its emergence in Alexandrian Egypt to its appearance in Medieval Europe.
5. What is astrology? Describe the relationship of astrology to astronomy. What similarities are there between this relationship and that of alchemy to modern chemistry?
6. What is Taoism? Relate an important alchemical goal to Taoistic philosophy.
7. Who were the adepts, puffers, and charlatans? Who are their modern counterparts?
8. How does the speculative philosophy of ancient Greece differ from today's scientific inquiry?
9. What is meant by: calcination, sublimation, amalgamation, reverberation, rectification, and filtration? Relate these alchemical processes to modern practice.
10. Determine the possible origins of the medieval alchemical symbols for the seven metals known to the ancients: gold, silver, iron, copper, lead, mercury, and tin. These symbols appear on page 15.
11. Refer to the painting on page 34. What modern drugs are produced from plants?
12. Paracelsus lived in the early Renaissance. Among his contemporaries were: Nostradamus, Vesalius, Agricola, Da Vinci, and Copernicus. Name one contribution to the growth of science made by each of these men.
13. Refer to the illustration at the top of page 32. How many of the devices shown can you locate in modern form in your school laboratory?
14. What were the two major goals of alchemy? In what ways have these goals been realized?
15. How do you interpret the quotation that ends the picture essay on alchemy?

## SUGGESTED READINGS

Canby, C. (ed.) *History of Chemistry* (New Illustrated Library of Science and Invention, Vol. 10). Hawthorne, 1964.

Jaffe, Bernard. *Crucibles: The Story of Chemistry* (paperback). Fawcett, 1962.

Leicester, H. M. *The Historical Background of Chemistry*. John Wiley, 1956.

Pachter, H. M. *Magic into Science*. Henry Schuman, 1951.

Partington, J. R. *A Short History of Chemistry* (paperback). Harper, 1960.

Stillman, John M. *The Story of Alchemy and Early Chemistry* (paperback). Dover Publications, 1960.

*The whole of being consists
of bodies and space ... And
of bodies some are composite,
while some of the elements
of which the composites are made
are atoms and unchangeable. The
atoms are in continual motion.*

*Epicurus* (342–271 B.C.)

CHAPTER 2 | # Atomism and Ideal

Once it is understood that compounds are made up of elements, we might next ask how much of each element is present in a compound. Does the amount change from sample to sample? Let us consider water as a starting compound. If a sample of rain water is caught and then decomposed into the elements of which it is composed, 88.8 grams of oxygen gas and 11.2 grams of hydrogen gas are produced from each 100 gram sample of water. If 100 grams of ice from the Arctic Ocean are melted and the resulting 100 grams of water are decomposed, again 88.8 grams of oxygen gas and 11.2 grams of hydrogen gas result. In fact, the decomposition of 100 grams of water found in any river, ocean, or spring, melted from any sample of ice, or liquefied from any sample of steam has always produced 88.8 grams of oxygen gas and 11.2 grams of hydrogen gas. We can say that the weight composition of water is constant, there always being $\frac{88.8}{11.2}$, or 7.94, times as much oxygen present by weight as hydrogen.

## THE WEIGHT COMPOSITION
## OF COMPOUNDS IS CONSTANT

It would not be sound to draw conclusions about the weight composition of all compounds from our observations of one. So let us proceed further. Huge deposits of quite pure sulfur are found in widely separated parts of the world; in Sicily and in Texas, for example. When 100 gram samples of sulfur from different locations are burned in air,

*40*

# Gases

it has always been found that 200 grams of a choking, colorless gas called sulfur dioxide will form. You could guess from its name that sulfur dioxide is a compound consisting of sulfur and oxygen, and *synthesis* of the compound from its elements has always shown 200 grams of sulfur dioxide formed from 100 grams each of sulfur and oxygen. The weight composition of sulfur dioxide, too, appears to be constant. We may perform another analysis to test our generalization.

Many sulfur compounds called sulfides when heated strongly in air react to produce sulfur dioxide. For example, when mercury(II) sulfide is heated strongly in air, elemental mercury and sulfur dioxide form. When lead sulfide is heated strongly in air, solid lead oxide and sulfur dioxide are formed. When the sulfur dioxide formed from sulfides is decomposed, 200 grams of the gas are always found to produce 100 grams each of sulfur and oxygen. Thus, from both the synthesis of sulfur dioxide from its elements and the decomposition of sulfur dioxide into its elements, the constant weight composition of the compound is an experimental fact.

Water and sulfur dioxide are but two of many thousands of different compounds for which weight composition has been determined. The constancy of composition of those compounds, regardless of where they were found or synthesized and where and by whom they were analyzed, is also an experimental fact. This important generalization or observed regularity is often stated as a fundamental law of chemistry.

**THE LAW OF DEFINITE COMPOSITION.** This law states that *elements in a compound always occur in a definite proportion by weight.* This is another way of saying that the composition of compounds is always the same.

At about the beginning of the nineteenth century, however, chemists seriously debated this point. Claude Berthollet (bear toe LAY), a famous French chemist, prepared zinc oxide in several different ways and obtained varying weight proportions of zinc to oxygen. On the basis of these and other experiments, he believed that the composition of compounds might vary to some extent. In 1803, he published an influential work in which he challenged the Law of Definite Composition.

Joseph Proust (proost), another Frenchman, repeated Berthollet's experiments in a splendidly equipped laboratory in Spain. He used platinum utensils, the purest chemicals, and the most delicate apparatus available. He obtained constant ratios, in contrast to Berthollet, and attributed this difference to the use of impure elements and compounds by Berthollet. For eight long years the difference of opinion persisted. Never, however, did it become anything but an honest, truth-seeking discussion. It is a measure of Berthollet as a scientist that after considering Proust's evidence he admitted his errors and accepted Proust's conclusion that the composition of compounds does not change.

## 2.1 The percentage composition of compounds

We have seen that in any sample of water there is 7.94 times as much oxygen as hydrogen by weight. We have also seen that in any sample of sulfur dioxide there are equal weights of sulfur and oxygen. The chemist finds it convenient to express these facts in simple mathematical terms as the *percentage composition* of the compounds. The percentage composition is calculated from the formula:

$$\% \text{ Composition} = \frac{\text{Weight of the element}}{\text{Weight of the compound}} \times 100$$

From our previously considered examples, we can calculate the percentage composition of water and sulfur dioxide.

**WATER**

$$\% \text{ oxygen} = \frac{88.8 \text{ grams of oxygen}}{100 \text{ grams of water}} \times 100 = 88.8\%$$

$$\% \text{ hydrogen} = \frac{11.2 \text{ grams of hydrogen}}{100 \text{ grams of water}} \times 100 = 11.2\%$$

**SULFUR DIOXIDE**

$$\% \text{ sulfur} = \frac{100 \text{ grams of sulfur}}{200 \text{ grams of sulfur dioxide}} \times 100 = 50.0\%$$

$$\% \text{ oxygen} = \frac{100 \text{ grams of oxygen}}{200 \text{ grams of sulfur dioxide}} \times 100 = 50.0\%$$

Those were simple calculations. Will the results change if we deal with 75.0 grams of water rather than 100 grams? Will the percentage composition of sulfur dioxide be different, based on a 16.8 gram sample instead of on the 200 grams we used in our first calculation? If the elements are present in these compounds always in the same weight ratios, then the percentage composition must also remain the same, no matter what the source or the size of the sample of the compound. (If you think carefully about the meaning of a percentage in terms of a ratio, this conclusion will be clear to you.)

## 2.2 Using percentage composition

We can use percentage composition of compounds to determine weights of elements that are present in samples of those compounds.

**EXAMPLE**

How much oxygen would be produced from the decomposition of 75.0 g of water?

**SOLUTION**

RATIO METHOD

$$\frac{88.8 \text{ g of oxygen}}{100 \text{ g of water}} = \frac{X}{75.0 \text{ g of water}}$$

$$\frac{(88.8 \text{ g of oxygen})(75.0 \text{ g of water})}{(100 \text{ g of water})} = X$$

$$66.6 \text{ g of oxygen} = X$$

PERCENTAGE COMPOSITION METHOD

Weight of oxygen = (weight of water)(percentage of weight
of water that is oxygen)

Weight of oxygen = (75.0 g)(88.8%)

Weight of oxygen = (75.0 g)(0.888)

Weight of oxygen = 66.6 g

(Again, if you understand what a percentage is, you will *clearly* see that the above two methods are one and the same.)

**EXAMPLE**

How much sulfur would be produced from 16.8 g of sulfur dioxide?

**SOLUTION**

RATIO METHOD

$$\frac{100 \text{ g of sulfur}}{200 \text{ g of sulfur dioxide}} = \frac{X}{16.8 \text{ g of sulfur dioxide}}$$

$$\frac{(100 \text{ g of sulfur})(16.8 \text{ g of sulfur dioxide})}{200 \text{ g of sulfur dioxide}} = X$$

$$\boxed{8.40 \text{ g of sulfur} = X}$$

PERCENTAGE COMPOSITION METHOD

Weight of sulfur = (weight of sulfur dioxide) (percentage of
weight of sulfur dioxide that is sulfur)

Weight of sulfur = (16.8 g) (50.0%)

Weight of sulfur = (16.8 g) (0.500)

$$\boxed{\text{Weight of sulfur} = 8.40 \text{ g}}$$

### 2.3 The law of multiple proportions

Sulfur and oxygen can combine to form two entirely different compounds. We have discussed one of these, sulfur dioxide, in which there are equal parts by weight of sulfur and oxygen. In the other compound, known as sulfur trioxide, there is found 40.0% sulfur and 60.0% oxygen by weight.

Carbon and oxygen also form two commonly encountered compounds. Analysis of one, carbon monoxide, shows it to be composed of 42.9 per cent carbon and 57.1 per cent oxygen by weight. The other, carbon dioxide, is composed of 27.3 per cent carbon and 72.7 per cent oxygen by weight. All samples of carbon monoxide show the same composition, and so do all the samples of carbon dioxide. Each compound individually, therefore, illustrates the Law of Definite Composition.

Nitrogen and oxygen when they react with each other have been found to form *five* distinctly different compounds. We will express the weight composition for these compounds in another way. The weight of oxygen in each of these compounds *per 1.00 g of nitrogen* is found to be 0.570, 1.136, 1.734, 2.258, and 2.869 g, respectively. We may wonder what relationship exists among these weights of oxygen that are combined with the same weight of nitrogen. If we divide each of the oxygen weights by the lowest, 0.570 g, we can determine the number ratio among those weights.

$$\frac{0.570 \text{ g}}{0.570 \text{ g}} : \frac{1.136 \text{ g}}{0.570 \text{ g}} : \frac{1.734 \text{ g}}{0.570 \text{ g}} : \frac{2.258 \text{ g}}{0.570 \text{ g}} : \frac{2.869 \text{ g}}{0.570 \text{ g}}$$

or

$$1.00 : 1.99 : 3.04 : 3.96 : 5.03$$

Since any experiment has some unavoidable error in its results, we may round these numbers in keeping with their experimental uncertainty to

$$1 : 2 : 3 : 4 : 5.$$

Thus, we discover that 1.00 g of nitrogen can combine *only* with 1, 2, 3, 4, or 5 times 0.570 g of oxygen. This is indeed an interesting result. If we repeat this process for the two sulfur-oxygen compounds and use percentage composition data, we can determine the oxygen weight ratio *per 1.00 g of sulfur.* (Note that we will use an arbitrary compound weight of 100.0 g, so that weight percentages are converted directly to weights of elements per 100.0 g of compound.)

**SULFUR DIOXIDE**

$$\frac{50.0 \text{ g oxygen}}{50.0 \text{ g sulfur}} = \frac{X}{1.00 \text{ g sulfur}}$$

$$\frac{(1.00 \text{ g sulfur}) \, 50.0 \text{ g oxygen}}{50.0 \text{ g sulfur}} = X$$

$$1.00 \text{ g oxygen} = X$$

**SULFUR TRIOXIDE**

$$\frac{60.0 \text{ g oxygen}}{40.0 \text{ g sulfur}} = \frac{X}{1.00 \text{ g sulfur}}$$

$$\frac{(1.00 \text{ g sulfur}) \, 60.0 \text{ g oxygen}}{40.0 \text{ g sulfur}} = X$$

$$1.50 \text{ g oxygen} = X$$

and

$$\frac{\text{Weight of oxygen/1.00 g of sulfur in sulfur dioxide}}{\text{Weight of oxygen/1.00 g of sulfur in sulfur trioxide}} = \frac{1.00}{1.50}$$

The ratio of the weights of oxygen that are combined with a fixed weight of sulfur in sulfur dioxide and sulfur trioxide is, then, 1.00 : 1.50 or, *in small whole numbers, 2.00 : 3.00.* (When the numbers in the ratio 1.00 : 1.50 are multiplied by 2, the ratio becomes 2.00 : 3.00.)

Let us repeat the process for carbon monoxide and carbon dioxide, again using percentage composition data and arbitrary 100.0 g samples of compounds.

**CARBON MONOXIDE**

$$\frac{57.1 \text{ g oxygen}}{42.9 \text{ g carbon}} = \frac{X}{1.00 \text{ g carbon}}$$

$$1.33 \text{ g oxygen} = X$$

**CARBON DIOXIDE**

$$\frac{72.7 \text{ g oxygen}}{27.3 \text{ g carbon}} = \frac{X}{1.00 \text{ g carbon}}$$

$$2.66 \text{ g oxygen} = X$$

and

$$\frac{\text{Weight of oxygen}/1.00 \text{ g of carbon in carbon monoxide}}{\text{Weight of oxygen}/1.00 \text{ g carbon in carbon dioxide}} = \frac{1.33}{2.66}$$

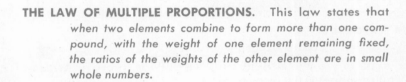

The ratio of the weights of oxygen that are combined with a fixed weight of carbon in carbon monoxide and carbon dioxide is, then, 1.33 : 2.66 or, *in small whole numbers, 1.00 : 2.00.* (When the numbers in the ratio 1.33 : 2.66 are divided by 1.33, the ratio becomes 1.00 : 2.00.)

Results such as those just considered led John Dalton, in early nineteenth-century England, to formulate one of the fundamental laws of chemical composition.

**THE LAW OF MULTIPLE PROPORTIONS.**  This law states that *when two elements combine to form more than one compound, with the weight of one element remaining fixed, the ratios of the weights of the other element are in small whole numbers.*

## A FIRST ATOMIC THEORY OF MATTER

The Law of Definite Composition and the Law of Multiple Proportions suggest strongly that when elements form compounds they do so in definite units or portions. Thus, one portion of carbon can combine with one portion or with two portions, but not with 1.5 portions, of oxygen. Therefore, elements react in definite portions or units—*or atoms.*

Although several of the ancient Greek philosophers, Leucippus (loo SIP us) and Democritus (deh MAH krit us) among them, had postulated about 2500 years ago that matter was composed of invisible, indivisible, indestructible atoms, their arguments were based on the necessity of a stopping point in a hypothetical division of matter. Atomism, however, proved to be the most fruitful scientific speculation that came out of ancient Greece. Even Isaac Newton in the seventeenth century believed in it. "It seems probable to me," he wrote, "that God in the beginning formed matter in solid, massy, hard, impenetrable, movable particles, so very hard as never to wear or break into pieces."

**Democritus** (ca. 470 B.C.–ca. 360 B.C., Greek). Much of the knowledge of Democritus' life is based mainly on tradition. He was primarily a philosopher, who, in trying to make the physical world intelligible, postulated that all matter was made of indivisible particles, or atoms. Thus, he is considered one of the founders of the atomic theory.

Robert Boyle in 1661 wrote in one of the first great books on chemistry, *The Sceptical Chymist,* that "the Universal Matter (of which) the Universe consisted, was actually divided into little Particles of several sizes and shapes. . . ." The revived atomistic beliefs of the seventeenth century remained basically philosophical and nonscientific until the last years of the eighteenth century.

### 2.4  Dalton proposes an atomic theory.

Atomism did not prove of scientific value until John Dalton, an English Quaker schoolteacher, endowed atoms with weight, an experimentally measurable property. Dalton had thought long and hard about the structure of matter. On the basis of some not too accurate experiments and observations that led to the laws of chemical composition, and some indirect evidence from other facts known in his day, he suggested an atomic model and theory of matter to explain them.

Of course, Dalton's original model and theory have been modified and some parts even discarded as thousands of new chemical facts have accumulated. As was mentioned in Chapter 1, this is the fate of scientific theories and is a necessary complement to scientific progress. However, the principal aspects of Dalton's model and theory still are useful and valid. These are:

1. All matter consists of extremely small particles called atoms.
2. The atoms of any one element are similar to each other *particularly in weight,* but different from those of all other elements.
3. Chemical changes are changes in the combinations of atoms with each other.
4. Atoms remain indivisible in even the most violent chemical reaction.

### 2.5  Dalton determines atomic weights.

Dalton believed that the atoms of different elements have different weights. He felt that if he could find the weights of the atoms, the progress of chemistry would be accelerated. He realized, though, that he could not actually weigh a single atom of an element. In fact, it took more than 100 years from the time of Dalton's observations and experiments until accurate methods and precise instruments made it possible to determine *indirectly* the actual weights of single atoms.

However, Dalton knew that elements combine according to fixed ratios by weight. For example, 23.00 g of sodium combine with 79.92 g of bromine to form sodium bromide—a ratio of approximately 1 : 3.5. The two elements never vary in the ratio of their weights in forming this compound. In a similar manner, all elements combine to form compounds in certain specific ratios by weight. Dalton believed that the ratios of these combining weights depended upon the weights of the individual atoms of each element. He believed further that by

The title page of Boyle's book, from the Dutch edition of 1668: "The Sceptical Chymist or Chemical and Physical Doubts and Paradoxes about the Principles of the Spagyrists." The spagyrists believed in a sulfur-mercury-salt theory of the constitution of metals.

**John Dalton** (1766–1844, English). Though surely one of the most influential scientists of his time, Dalton was compelled to give private lessons in arithmetic to earn a living, even after he was long past 60. He was finally awarded a government pension.

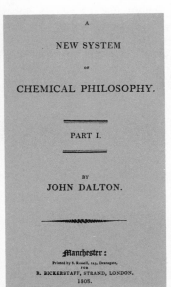

A

NEW SYSTEM

OF

CHEMICAL PHILOSOPHY.

PART I.

BY

JOHN DALTON.

Manchester:
Printed by S. Russell, 125, Deansgate,
FOR
R. BICKERSTAFF, STRAND, LONDON.
1808.

This unassuming title page heralded the publication of Dalton's atomic theory.

studying the ratios of the weights in which elements combine, it would be possible to determine the *relative* weights of single atoms of all the elements.

Dalton selected hydrogen, the lightest element known, to be his standard. *He assigned to each atom* of hydrogen the atomic weight of 1, thus assuring that the atomic weights of all elements heavier than hydrogen would be greater than 1. He then proceeded to analyze the crude weight composition data known in his time to determine those atomic weights relative to that of hydrogen.

## 2.6 Dalton's dilemma

Dalton was faced with a great experimental problem in arriving at relative atomic weights. He knew weight composition of chemical compounds, but had no experimental evidence that indicated atom number ratios in those compounds. For example, Dalton knew that eight parts of oxygen by weight were combined with one part of hydrogen by weight to form water. If the water molecule were composed of one atom each of oxygen and hydrogen (as, indeed, Dalton assumed), then the relative atomic weight of oxygen would be 8. That is, for the case of HO:

$$\frac{8 \text{ parts by weight of oxygen}}{1 \text{ part by weight of hydrogen}} = \frac{X}{1}$$

where 1 equals the *arbitrary* weight of *one* atom of hydrogen, thus,

$$X = 8, \text{ the relative weight of } one \text{ atom of oxygen.}$$

If some other atom ratio existed, then the relative atomic weight of oxygen would not be 8, but rather some multiple or submultiple of 8. For example, if the water molecule contained one oxygen atom for every two hydrogen atoms, the case of $H_2O$, then the relative atomic weight of oxygen would be 16. This results as follows:

$$\frac{8 \text{ parts by weight of oxygen}}{1 \text{ part by weight of hydrogen}} = \frac{X}{2}$$

where 2 equals the arbitrary weight of *two* atoms of hydrogen, thus,

$$X = 16, \text{ the relative weight of } one \text{ atom of oxygen.}$$

If, however, the atom ratio in the water molecule was two oxygens to one hydrogen, the case of $HO_2$, then the relative atomic weight of oxygen would be 4. We find that result in this manner:

$$\frac{8 \text{ parts by weight of oxygen}}{1 \text{ part by weight of hydrogen}} = \frac{X}{1}$$

where 1 equals the arbitrary weight of *one* atom of hydrogen, thus,

$$X = 8, \text{ the relative weight of } two \text{ atoms of oxygen.}$$

Therefore, the relative weight of one atom of oxygen for the case of $HO_2$ is 4.

Surprising though it may seem to you who have always *known* that water has the atom ratio $H_2O$ (and how do you know that?), Dalton did not have *experimental evidence* to know that. Indeed, he had no experimental evidence for the atom ratios of any compounds. Such was his dilemma. His solution was an arbitrary one. He *assumed* atom ratios according to the following scheme.

1. If only a single compound of two elements $A$ and $B$ were known, Dalton assumed they combined in a one-to-one ratio as $AB$. So water was in modern symbolism HO, and not $H_2O$, to Dalton. Ammonia was NH, and not $NH_3$, to him.
2. If two different compounds of the same two elements were known, then Dalton assumed the simplest atom ratios possible, $AB$ and $AB_2$ or $A_2B$, unless the indivisibility of atoms demanded otherwise. Thus, for Dalton, CO and $CO_2$ were the formulas for the two known oxides of carbon. The two oxides of sulfur, however, had to be represented by $SO_2$ and $SO_3$, and not by SO and $SO_{1.5}$.

While Dalton's formulas for the oxides of carbon and sulfur, as well as for other compounds, are now known to be correct, many others based on his assumptions are incorrect. The lack of a firm experimental basis for chemical formulas was an insoluble problem for John Dalton, and it was only in the last years of the nineteenth century that such basis was firmly established to the satisfaction of most chemists.

## 2.7  Dalton prepares a historic table.

From his experimental data on weight composition of compounds, and based on his arbitrary assumptions of atom ratios for those compounds, Dalton prepared the first table of relative atomic weights. It was first made public on October 21, 1802, "before a select group of nine members and friends in the rooms of the Literary and Philosophical Society of Manchester." Although inaccurate because of crude data and, more importantly, because it was based on experimentally unjustified and invalid assumptions of his theory, the table remains, nonetheless, a monument to Dalton's intellect and foresight. His achievement was a crucial advance in chemistry. By attaching so much importance to the *weights* of atoms and by using weights of different atoms to distinguish one atomic species from another, Dalton provided following generations of scientists with the experimental basis for testing and modifying his model and theory.

The next advances, which were to put the determination of relative atomic weights on firmer experimental ground, were made as

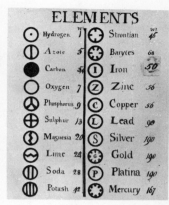

A lecture diagram used by Dalton to illustrate his atomic theory. Atomic weights he gave to elements are shown. What inconsistencies with his own theory are evident in the diagram?

a result of careful studies on the physical and chemical behavior of gases. It is to this chapter in the fascinating evolution of chemistry as an experimental science that we now turn.

## THE BEHAVIOR OF GASES

Dalton's model and theory of atoms as hard, tiny spheres of fixed weight accounts well for the Laws of Definite Composition and Multiple Proportions. This atomic model was soon applied to gases to help account in theory for their experimental behavior.

If we consider carefully our common observations of the three states of matter—the solid, liquid, and gaseous states—certain similarities and differences in properties become apparent. All solid objects have definite shapes and definite volumes. (Fig. 2.1.) All liquids have definite volumes but, as we know, take the shape of the containers that hold them. Thus, unlike solids, liquids have indefinite shapes. (Fig. 2.2.) Gases, quite unlike matter in *condensed* states (solids and liquids), have no definite volume. Atoms or molecules in the gaseous state will occupy any volume open to them. In addition, of course, gases completely fill any volume open to them, regardless of shape. (Fig. 2.3.) Consideration of these common observations of the three states of matter suggests the explanation that *atoms or molecules in the gaseous state are greatly separated from each other, have little effect on each other, and are in constant motion.*

### 2.8  A model for an ideal gas

Our best model for explaining the physical behavior of gases is derived from the Daltonian model of the atom. To that model of tiny, hard, indivisible spheres is added our assumption that gas particles are widely separated and in constant motion. We are creating an *ideal gas* model. We idealize our model, most importantly, by assuming that the gas particles have no effect on each other as they whiz about in space. (Fig. 2.4.) That this is truly an *ideal* property will become apparent to you when you realize that all *real* gases can be made to liquefy. Thus, there must exist interparticle attractive forces in the case of real gases. However, we will begin to consider the properties of real gases from the viewpoint of our ideal gas model. Let us test the predictions to which our ideal model leads.

### 2.9  The effect of concentration of a gas in a container

Suppose we have 10 marbles in a large rectangular box and we shake the box at a constant rate. The marbles will bounce around and will strike the walls of the box with a certain frequency. This frequency or rate will depend on how vigorously the box is shaken. Let us consider that any one wall is struck at an average rate of 30 times per minute.

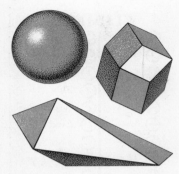

**FIGURE 2.1**   Solids retain their shape.

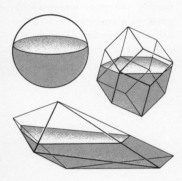

**FIGURE 2.2**   Liquids take the shape of their containers.

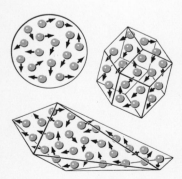

**FIGURE 2.3**   Gases fill any volume open to them.

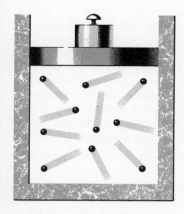

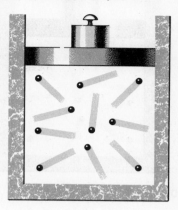

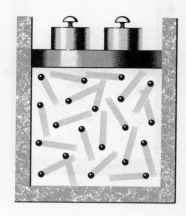

**FIGURE 2.4** A model of an ideal gas

**FIGURE 2.5** Ideal gas model depicting the relationship between gas concentration and gas pressure

Now, if 10 more marbles are added to the box (the number of marbles is thus doubled) and it is shaken at the same rate, we will observe an average rate of 60 hits per minute on each wall. These wall hits constitute a *pressure* on the wall.

If a gas in a container consists of many small particles bouncing around like the marbles in a box, the pressure of the gas is due to the impacts of the gas particles on the container walls. The behavior of the marbles predicts that if we double the number of gas particles, all other conditions remaining constant—that is, if we double the *concentration* of the particles in the container—the pressure should double. (Fig. 2.5.) Experimentally, if 1.00 gram of nitrogen gas exerts a pressure of 1.00 atmosphere* in a certain container, 2.00 grams of nitrogen gas will exert a pressure of 2.00 atmospheres in the same container at the same temperature. Since 1.00 g of nitrogen represents a certain number of gaseous particles, 2.00 g must represent twice that number of particles, according to Dalton's theory. By doubling the concentration of nitrogen molecules—that is, by doubling the number of molecules in a given volume—the pressure exerted is doubled.

---

* Pressures of gases are still most often expressed in millimeters of mercury, mm of Hg, or atmospheres, atm. A pressure of 1.00 atm is equal to 14.7 pounds per square inch or 760 mm of Hg. 760 mm of Hg, or simply 760 mm, is the height to which one atmosphere of pressure raises a column of mercury in an evacuated tube at sea level at 0°C.

Coming into common use as a unit of pressure is the *torr*. It is the pressure unit most often used henceforth in this book. One torr is equivalent to 1 mm of Hg at 0°C and sea level. The torr is named in honor of Evangelista Torricelli (tore ih CHELLY), the seventeenth-century Italian scientist who invented the *barometer*. Pressures are measured with barometers.

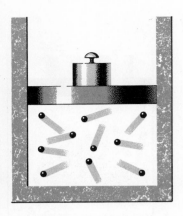

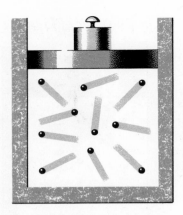

FIGURE 2.6 Ideal gas model depicting the relationship between temperature (molecular motion) and gas pressure *at constant external pressure*. How would the figure appear if the gas *volume* were to be kept constant?

## 2.10 The effect of temperature

This agreement of experiment with the prediction of our model is encouraging. Now suppose we keep 10 marbles in the box but change the rate of shaking. As we increase the rate of shaking, the marbles bounce around faster. The average number of wall collisions per minute is increased; thereby, the "pressure" is increased. In a gas, we can increase the rate of movement by giving the molecules more energy. This is done by raising the temperature. Therefore, we expect the pressure of a gas to increase as its temperature is increased. (Fig. 2.6.) Again, experimental observation of gases agrees with this prediction.

## 2.11 The effect of altering the volume of the container: Boyle's Law

If, instead of doubling the number of marbles, we had put the original 10 marbles in a box whose volume was only one half that of the first box, at the same shaking rate the rate of wall impacts would again double. This leads us to expect to double the pressure of a gas by cutting its volume in half. We can predict the converse behavior as well. (Fig. 2.7.)

The pressure of a gas will be cut in half if its volume is doubled. If the pressure of a gas is 1.00 atmosphere for a volume of

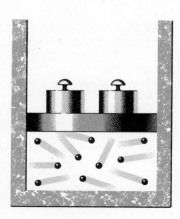

FIGURE 2.7 Ideal gas model depicting the relationship between gas pressure and gas volume

1.00 liter, then we expect 2.00 atmospheres for 0.500 liter or, conversely, 0.500 atmosphere for 2.00 liters. Notice that in all three cases the product of the pressure and volume equals 1.00. *This means that our model predicts that pressure (P) times volume (V) equals a constant (k) for a given sample of gas at a given temperature.* In Table 2–1, the pressure-volume relationship for oxygen at several different pressures confirms this prediction. Again, the slight variations in the $P \times V$ product reflect the experimental errors always present in scientific measurements.

**TABLE 2–1** PRESSURE AND VOLUME OF 16.0 G OF OXYGEN AT 25°C

| Pressure (atm) | Volume (l) | $P \times V$ |
|---|---|---|
| 0.60 | 20.70 | 12 |
| 0.80 | 15.30 | 12 |
| 1.00 | 12.50 | 12.5 |
| 1.20 | 10.10 | 12.1 |
| 1.40 | 8.80 | 12.3 |

Boyle, honored by Englishmen as the father of modern chemistry, first discovered, in 1660, the relationship predicted by our model. He had *no* model. His discovery was a summary of experimental facts.

**BOYLE'S LAW.** This law states that *the volume of a constant weight of gas varies inversely with the pressure exerted on it, if the temperature is maintained constant.*

Mathematically, Boyle's Law is expressed:

$$V \propto \frac{1}{P} \text{ (constant } w, t)^*$$

Therefore:

$$V = k\frac{1}{P}$$

or

$$PV = k \text{ (constant } w, t)$$

**Robert Boyle** (1627–1691, English). This brilliant natural philosopher, who had a command of six languages and, as a child prodigy, went to Eton at the age of eight, is often named as one of the founders of modern chemistry. While chemistry was Boyle's favorite subject, some of his most outstanding achievements were in the field of physics. The gas law that bears his name, his discovery of the role of air in sound propagation, and his work on specific gravity are examples of such achievements.

---

\* This relation is exactly read as: Volume ($V$) of a gas is *directly* proportional to ($\propto$) the inverse of the pressure $\left(\frac{1}{P}\right)$ exerted on the gas for a constant weight of gas ($w$) at constant temperature ($t$). More simply, it is the mathematical equivalent of the statement of Boyle's Law given. The proportional relation is converted by the experimentally determined *proportionality constant, k,* to the equality $PV = k$.

Since for a constant weight of an ideal gas at constant temperature

$$P_1V_1 = k \text{ for state 1 of pressure and volume}$$

and

$$P_2V_2 = k \text{ for state 2 of pressure and volume,}$$

then

$$P_1V_1 = P_2V_2 \text{ (constant } w, t)$$

relates the two states of pressure and volume.

This form of Boyle's Law is most easily used in calculations involving pressure-volume behavior of gases.

**EXAMPLE**

A sample of nitrogen gas occupies 20.0 ml at 27.0°C at a pressure of 800 torrs. What volume will the sample occupy at 27.0°C and 760 torrs?

**SOLUTION**

$$P_1 = 800 \text{ torrs} \qquad P_2 = 760 \text{ torrs}$$
$$V_1 = 20.0 \text{ ml} \qquad V_2 = ?$$
$$P_1V_1 = P_2V_2$$

$$(800 \text{ torrs})(20.0 \text{ ml}) = (760 \text{ torrs})(V_2)$$

$$\frac{(800 \text{ torrs})(20.0 \text{ ml})}{(760 \text{ torrs})} = V_2$$

$$21.0 \text{ ml} = V_2$$

Observation balloon at take-off. How will its appearance change as it rises higher into the atmosphere? Why?

It is neither necessary nor wise to depend on memorized formulas for solving problems. Common sense will often lead you to the correct solution of a problem. In the above case, for example, common observation leads you to recognize that a gas *expands* if the pressure on it is released. Hence, the original volume of 20.0 ml of nitrogen gas will *increase* if its pressure changes from 800 torrs to 760 torrs. Since the new volume of nitrogen gas will be greater than 20.0 ml, common sense dictates that you multiply the original 20.0 ml volume by a factor greater than one, or:

$$V_2 = 20.0 \text{ ml} \left(\frac{800 \text{ torrs}}{760 \text{ torrs}}\right)$$

$$V_2 = 21.0 \text{ ml}$$

## 2.12 The effect of temperature and Charles's Law

A common observation is the fact that gases expand as their temperatures increase. In 1785 Jacques Charles (zhock sharl), a French scientist, first measured that fact quantitatively. He noted that for a constant weight of gas at constant pressure, the *volume of the gas is proportional to the temperature of the gas.* Data exemplifying this relationship, *Charles's Law*, are plotted in Figure 2.8.

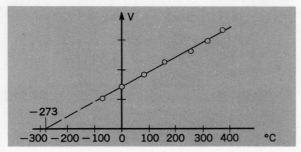

FIGURE 2.8    Volume of a gas as a function of Celsius temperature

Examine the graph carefully. The straight line indicates that the two variables, gas volume and gas temperature, are proportional. Note, however, that the gas volume does not double when the Celsius temperature doubles. The two variables, therefore, *are not directly proportional.*

### 2.13 The absolute temperature scale and Charles's Law

Let us be imaginative. What should happen to our model ideal gas if we continue to cool it? Extrapolating the Charles's Law data in Fig. 2.8 would lead us to predict that at −273°C our ideal gas volume should disappear. This could only come about because all gas particle motion ceases at −273°C. It also comes about because we now further idealize our gas model as consisting of particles whose volume is so infinitesimally small as to be negligible.

No gas volume and no gas particle motion at −273°C imply the lowest energy state and lowest temperature possible. This temperature of −273°C, and not 0°C, might better then be taken as a zero point—as an *absolute zero* point. This temperature is the logical one from which to start a new temperature scale on which all temperatures are positive.

Some sixty years after Charles's discovery, William Thomson, titled Lord Kelvin, on the basis of six decades of increased understanding by scientists of the relationship between temperature and heat, re-examined Charles's Law and invented the *absolute temperature scale* from his interpretations. (Fig. 2.9.) On this scale, all temperature values are indeed positive, and are related to the Celsius scale by the relation

$$°K^* = °C + 273°.$$

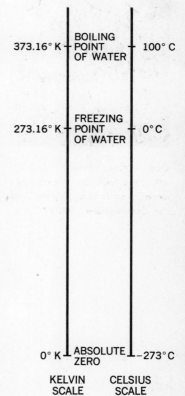

FIGURE 2.9    Temperature scales of the scientist

---

* Absolute or Kelvin temperatures are recorded as °K in honor of Lord Kelvin, though °A (for absolute) is sometimes used. It is general practice to use a capital $T$ when referring to absolute temperature and a lower-case $t$ when referring to Celsius temperature.

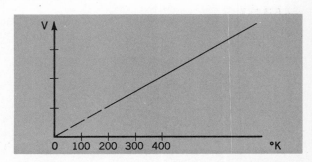

**FIGURE 2.10**  Volume of a gas as a function of absolute temperature

When the Charles's Law data of Fig. 2.8 are replotted in terms of absolute temperatures, Fig. 2.10 results. Now an examination of the proportionality between gas volume and gas temperature is a *direct* one. Double the absolute temperature of a gas sample at constant pressure and the gas volume will double.

**CHARLES'S LAW.**   Finally, then, we can state this relationship as: *The volume of a constant weight of gas varies directly with the absolute temperature, at constant pressure.*

Mathematically, Charles's Law is expressed:

$$V \propto T \text{ (constant } w, P)$$

Therefore:

$$V = k'T \text{ } (k' \text{ is different from } k \text{ in Boyle's Law)}$$

or

$$\frac{V}{T} = k' \text{ (constant } w, P)$$

Since for a constant weight of an ideal gas at constant pressure

$$\frac{V_1}{T_1} = k' \text{ for state 1 of volume and pressure}$$

and

$$\frac{V_2}{T_2} = k' \text{ for state 2 of volume and pressure,}$$

then

$$\frac{V_1}{T_1} = \frac{V_2}{T_2} \text{ (constant } w, P)$$

relates the two states of volume and temperature of the ideal gas.

This form of Charles's Law is most easily used in calculations involving temperature-volume behavior of gases.

**EXAMPLE**

A sample of nitrogen gas occupies 20.0 ml at 27.0°C at a pressure of 800 torrs. What volume will the sample occupy at 0.0°C and 800 torrs?

**SOLUTION**

At the outset, Celsius temperature readings must be converted to Kelvin temperature readings.

$$T_1 = (27.0°C + 273°) = 300°K$$
$$T_2 = (0.0°C + 273°) = 273°K$$

Then with $V_1 = 20.0$ ml, and $V_2$ to be determined:

$$\frac{V_1}{T_1} = \frac{V_2}{T_2}$$

$$\frac{(20.0 \text{ ml})}{(300°K)} = \frac{V_2}{(273°K)}$$

$$\frac{(273°\cancel{K})(20.0 \text{ ml})}{(300°\cancel{K})} = V_2$$

$$\boxed{18.2 \text{ ml} = V_2}$$

Again, approach the problem using common sense, not necessarily with a formula. Gases expand on heating and contract on cooling. Hence, the original 20.0 ml volume of nitrogen gas will decrease when cooled from 300°K to 273°K. Since the new volume of nitrogen gas will be less than 20.0 ml, common sense dictates that you multiply the original 20.0 ml volume by a factor less than one, or:

$$V_2 = 20.0 \text{ ml} \left(\frac{273°\cancel{K}}{300°\cancel{K}}\right)$$

$$\boxed{V_2 = 18.2 \text{ ml}}$$

If we go back to our Daltonian model of particles in the gaseous state, that model always predicts an increase in gas volume with rising temperature at constant pressure. (Fig. 2.6.)

Explosions involve the rapid heating and subsequent expansion of gases. What evidence do you see for gas *expansion* in the deliberate explosive destruction of the building?

## 2.14 Dalton's Law of Partial Pressures

Another check can be made of gas behavior predicted by our modified Daltonian atomic model of an ideal gas. If we have 10 marbles in our box and add 20 more of the same kind, we would expect, and indeed do observe, that the average number of wall collisions per minute and, consequently, the pressure both triple. Now if the original 10 marbles are removed, the number of wall collisions is reduced to two thirds of the previous number, as is also the pressure. (Fig. 2.11.)

Applying these facts to gases allows us to predict that the total pressure exerted by a *mixture* of gases is the sum of the individual pressures of each gas. These individual pressures are termed the *partial pressures*. For example, if 1 liter of oxygen in a flask exerts a pressure of 50 torrs and 1 liter of hydrogen in a flask exerts a pressure of 30 torrs at the same temperature, and if these two gas samples are mixed in one flask with a total volume of 1 liter, the total pressure will be 80 torrs. (Fig. 2.12.)

$$P_{\text{total}} = P_{\text{oxygen}} + P_{\text{hydrogen}} \text{ (in the 1 liter volume)}$$
$$P_{\text{total}} = 50 \text{ torrs} + 30 \text{ torrs}$$

$$P_{\text{total}} = 80 \text{ torrs}$$

However, if we connect the two 1 liter flasks at the same temperature and allow the gases to mix, the total volume is 2 liters. In effect, this doubles the volume of each gas. Consequently, according to Boyle's Law, the partial pressure of each is halved. (Fig. 2.13.)

**OXYGEN**

$$P_1 V_1 = P_2 V_2$$
$$(50 \text{ torrs})(1 \text{ liter}) = (P_2)(2 \text{ liters})$$
$$P_2 = 25 \text{ torrs}$$

**HYDROGEN**

$$P_1 V_1 = P_2 V_2$$
$$(30 \text{ torrs})(1 \text{ liter}) = (P_2)(2 \text{ liters})$$
$$P_2 = 15 \text{ torrs}$$

**GAS MIXTURE**

$$P_{\text{total}} = P_{\text{oxygen}} + P_{\text{hydrogen}} \text{ (in the 2 liter volume)}$$
$$P_{\text{total}} = 25 \text{ torrs} + 15 \text{ torrs}$$

$$P_{\text{total}} = 40 \text{ torrs}$$

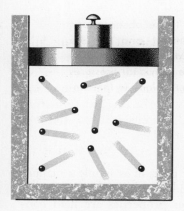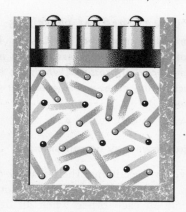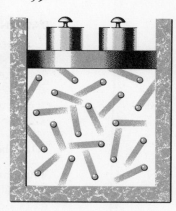

**FIGURE 2.11** Ideal gas model showing independent behavior of molecules. Interpret the drawings.

**FIGURE 2.12** Ideal gas model representation of Dalton's Law of Partial Pressures

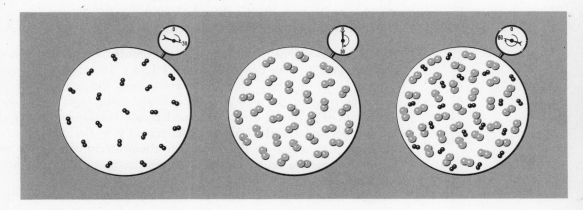

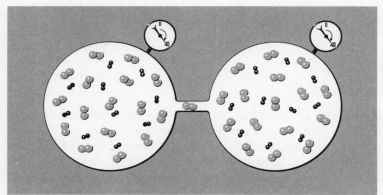

**FIGURE 2.13** Ideal gas model representation of two gases conforming with both Dalton's Law of Partial Pressure and Boyle's Law

**DALTON'S LAW OF PARTIAL PRESSURES.** These observations were first reported by Dalton himself and can be stated as *the total pressure of a mixture of gases is the sum of partial pressures, which are the individual pressures each of the gases would exert if it were alone in the container.*

### 2.15 The gas laws may be combined.

Thus far we have examined the behavior of gases in as simple a manner as possible. What we have done is to consider how two properties of gases depend on each other when all other properties are held constant. What are the properties of gases with which we have been dealing? They have been:

$n$, the number of gas molecules (used to represent the weight of a gaseous sample)
$P$, the pressure exerted by those molecules
$V$, the volume occupied by those molecules
$T$, the absolute temperature of the molecules

What we have done, for example, is to consider $V$ as a function of $P$ when $n$ and $T$ were constant (Boyle's Law). In practice, though, it would be more likely that the pressure and the temperature of a constant mass of gas would change *at the same time*. How do we determine the volume dependence under such conditions? Application of Boyle's and Charles's Laws simultaneously is the answer to this problem. Let us analyze the solution to the problem of how the properties of a gas are related during a change from one state to a second state.

As the diagram indicates, we wish to consider the change of *a constant weight of gas* from one set of conditions of pressure, absolute temperature, and volume, $P_1$, $T_1$, $V_1$, to a second set of conditions, $P_2$, $T_2$, $V_2$.

State 1                                          State 2

$$\boxed{P_1, T_1, V_1, n} \longrightarrow \boxed{P_2, T_2, V_2, n}$$

We will establish the existence of a hypothetical intermediate state between State 1 and State 2. Let us call that intermediate state State $i$. In State $i$ the pressure has changed from $P_1$ to $P_2$, but the absolute temperature remains $T_1$. Since there has been a change in pressure from State 1 to State $i$, there must be a volume change according to Boyle's Law.

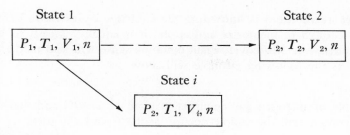

For this change:

$$P_1 V_1 = P_2 V_i$$

$$\frac{P_1 V_1}{P_2} = V_i$$

Now we will assume that the pressure in State $i$ remains constant at the value $P_2$, but the absolute temperature changes from $T_1$ to $T_2$. $V_i$ must change to $V_2$ in accordance with Charles's Law.

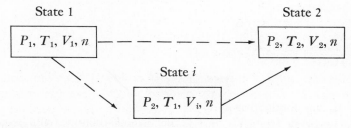

For this change:

$$\frac{V_i}{T_1} = \frac{V_2}{T_2}$$

$$V_i = \frac{V_2 T_1}{T_2}$$

We now have two equations that define $V_i$:

$$V_i = \frac{P_1 V_1}{P_2} \text{ (from State 1} \rightarrow \text{State } i)$$

$$V_i = \frac{V_2 T_1}{T_2} \text{ (from State } i \rightarrow \text{State 2)}$$

We may, therefore, write:

$$\frac{P_1 V_1}{P_2} = \frac{V_2 T_1}{T_2} \text{ (from State 1} \rightarrow \text{State 2)}$$

or

$$\frac{P_1 V_1}{T_1} = \frac{P_2 V_2}{T_2} \text{ (constant } n)$$

The last relationship is known as the Combined Gas Law. While it is easy enough to memorize and apply, it is equally as easy to know how to derive it. Moreover, again common sense will lead to the same results, as the following example will show.

**EXAMPLE**

A sample of nitrogen gas occupies 20.0 ml at 27.0°C and 800 torrs. What volume will the sample occupy at 0.0°C and 760 torrs?

**SOLUTION**

$$P_1 = 800 \text{ torrs} \qquad\qquad P_2 = 760 \text{ torrs}$$
$$V_1 = 20.0 \text{ ml} \qquad\qquad V_2 = ?$$
$$T_1 = (27.0°C + 273°) = 300°K \quad T_2 = (0.0°C + 273°) = 273°K$$

Using the Combined Gas Law:

$$\frac{P_1 V_1}{T_1} = \frac{P_2 V_2}{T_2}$$

$$\frac{(800 \text{ torrs})(20.0 \text{ ml})}{(300°K)} = \frac{(760 \text{ torrs})(V_2)}{(273°K)}$$

$$\left(\frac{800 \text{ torrs}}{760 \text{ torrs}}\right)\left(\frac{273°K}{300°K}\right)(20.0 \text{ ml}) = V_2$$

$$\boxed{19.2 \text{ ml} = V_2}$$

Using common sense:

In going from $V_1$ to $V_2$, the original volume will be multiplied by a pressure factor and temperature factor. Those factors will be fractions less than or greater than one, depending on how gas volume changes with the pressure and temperature changes indicated. In this case, since going from $P_1$ to $P_2$ is a pressure decrease (800 torrs to 760 torrs) and gases expand when pressure decreases, the pressure factor must be a fraction greater than one, or $\frac{800 \text{ torrs}}{760 \text{ torrs}}$. Since going from $T_1$ to $T_2$ is a temperature decrease (300°K to 273°K) and gases contract when cooled, the temperature factor, in this case, must be less than one, or $\frac{273°K}{300°K}$. Thus, to find $V_2$,

$$V_2 = V_1 \text{ (Pressure Factor)(Temperature Factor)}$$

$$V_2 = 20.0 \text{ ml} \left(\frac{800 \text{ torrs}}{760 \text{ torrs}}\right)\left(\frac{273°K}{300°K}\right) \quad \begin{array}{l}\text{(exactly as obtained by using}\\ \text{the Combined Gas Law)}\end{array}$$

$$\boxed{V_2 = 19.2 \text{ ml}}$$

It must be clearly recognized that both the theoretical and the experimental treatments of gases in this chapter have been based on an ideal gas model. We have assumed throughout that gas particles behave independently of each other. We have assumed that interparticle forces of interaction are absent. We have treated gas particles as having no volume of their own. Under laboratory conditions of relatively low pressures and high temperatures, however, many species of gas molecules are moving so rapidly and are, on the average, so far apart from each other that they behave essentially ideally.

The discovery and study of gases came somewhat late in the historical development of chemistry. However, those studies, first begun in the early seventeenth century, propelled chemistry into the vital, ever-growing science that it is today. The primitive studies of the *pneumatic* chemists led to some of the great intellectual achievements in the years that followed. Two of those achievements, *kinetic molecular theory* and the Avogadro Hypothesis, next become the focus of your own development as students of chemistry.

A 1662 engraving of a pneumatic pump.

## SUMMARY

The Law of Definite Composition, which states that elements in a compound always occur in a definite ratio by weight, is a summary statement of an enormous bulk of experimental evidence. This summary of experience led Dalton to suspect that matter was made up of tiny, indivisible particles called atoms. According to Dalton's atomic theory, each element is made up of atoms of that element, all alike and all having a definite weight and definite properties. A chemical reaction involves changes in the combinations of atoms with each other. On the basis of this theory, Dalton was able to account in general for the experimental laws of chemical combination. He postulated relative weights for the atoms of each element, but his dilemma was that he had no way of knowing how many atoms of each element combined to make a specific compound.

The concept of atoms was extended and applied to the study of the physical properties of gases. An ideal model consisting of independently moving, hard masses was postulated to account for the behavior of gases. In the field of gas behavior, as in the field of chemical combination, measurable, observable, sensible behavior could be explained on the basis of tiny, indivisible, invisible masses seen only in the imagination of the beholder. Boyle's Law, $P_1V_1 = P_2V_2$, Charles's Law, $\dfrac{V_1}{T_1} = \dfrac{V_2}{T_2}$, the Combined Gas Law, $\dfrac{P_1V_1}{T_1} = \dfrac{P_2V_2}{T_2}$, and Dalton's Law of Partial Pressures prove to be valid mathematical descriptions of observed gas behavior within the experimental limits that govern the applicability of those laws.

An important feature of the ideal gas model is that at $-273\,°C$ an ideal gas particle theoretically ceases moving and the total gas volume theoretically disappears. The absolute, or Kelvin, temperature scale is based on an absolute zero point that corresponds to $-273\,°C$. For all calculations of gas behavior when temperature is a variable, temperatures must be expressed in absolute units.

## QUESTIONS AND PROBLEMS

2.1  State the Law of Definite Composition in your own words.

2.2  Water may be decomposed into hydrogen and oxygen by means of electricity. If 0.0623 g of hydrogen and 0.4984 g of oxygen are obtained during such a reaction: **a.** What is the percentage of hydrogen and of oxygen in water? **b.** What is the weight ratio of hydrogen to oxygen in water?
Ans.  **b.** 1:8 (approx.)

2.3  When iron combines chemically with sulfur to form a compound, it is found that 1.00 g of sulfur always combines with 1.75 g of iron. If 10.00 g of sulfur are used in making the compound, how many grams of iron will be needed?

2.4  The red powder in Lavoisier's 12-day experiment was mercury (II) oxide. In one experiment, 217 g of the powder is completely decomposed by heat, forming 201 g of mercury. **a.** How many grams of oxygen can be obtained from a 4.34 g sample of the red powder? **b.** What is the weight ratio of oxygen to mercury in this compound?
Ans.  **b.** 2:25 (approx.)

2.5  Common table salt is the compound sodium chloride, NaCl. If 0.230 g of sodium is combined with sufficient chlorine gas to form 0.585 g of salt, how many *pounds* of sodium and chlorine will be needed to produce 10.0 pounds of salt?

2.6  When sulfur burns, a pungent gas called sulfur dioxide is produced. A weight ratio of 1.00:1.00 between the constituents of this gas is obtained. If 26.432 g of the gas are formed, how many grams of sulfur were burned?
Ans.  13.216 g

2.7  Two elements, *A* and *B*, combine to form the compound *AB* in a ratio by weight of 1.008:4.112. If one mixes 3.024 g of *A* with 12.000 g of *B* and combines them chemically, which of the following statements will be true? (More than one may be true.)
   **a.** Some amount of *B* will be left over.
   **b.** Some amount of *A* will be left over.
   **c.** One atom of *A* weighs 1.008 g.
   **d.** 3.024 g of *A* represent three atoms of *A*.
   **e.** All of *A* will combine with all of *B*, since they are chemically forced to do so.

**2.8** Two familiar compounds can be formed from hydrogen and oxygen. These two compounds, water and hydrogen peroxide, have distinctly different chemical properties as well as different weight ratios. If 100.00 g of each compound are decomposed, the following weights are obtained:

|  | WATER | HYDROGEN PEROXIDE |
|---|---|---|
| OXYGEN | 88.80 g | 94.10 g |
| HYDROGEN | 11.20 g | 5.90 g |

a. Does there appear to be any relationship between the weights of oxygen or of hydrogen in the compounds? b. If only 1.00 g of hydrogen is used to form each compound, how much oxygen will be necessary? c. Is there any relationship between the amounts of oxygen needed to combine with the *same* amount of hydrogen in the two compounds? d. What law of chemical composition does this illustrate?

ANS. b. 7.93 g for water; 15.9 g for hydrogen peroxide

**2.9** The percentage composition of carbon and oxygen in the compounds carbon dioxide and carbon monoxide is given below:

|  | CARBON DIOXIDE | CARBON MONOXIDE |
|---|---|---|
| CARBON | 27.3% | 42.9% |
| OXYGEN | 72.7% | 57.1% |

a. If 100.0 g samples of each compound were analyzed, how many grams of carbon and oxygen would be obtained? b. If 1.00 g of carbon were combined with oxygen to form each compound, how many grams of oxygen would be necessary in each case? c. What would you conclude from this evidence?

**2.10**         Law of Definite Composition
                Law of Multiple Proportions
                Law of the Conservation of Mass

The following statements illustrate, describe, or explain *one or more* of the above laws. Briefly discuss the relationship of each statement to the law or laws to which it applies.

a. In one experiment, 6.96 g of lithium combined with 35.44 g of chlorine to form 42.40 g of lithium chloride. In another experiment, 0.87 g of lithium combined with 5.00 g of chlorine to form 5.30 g of lithium chloride and left 0.57 g of chlorine uncombined.

b. 2.016 g of hydrogen combine with 16.00 g of oxygen to form water, but 0.01008 g of hydrogen combines with 0.16000 g of oxygen to form hydrogen peroxide.

c. All matter is composed of fundamental, *indivisible* particles having definite weights. These particles are *exactly* alike for a given element.

**2.11** If the pressure *on* a gas is tripled with the temperature held constant, the volume occupied by the gas will change until the pressure exerted *by* the gas also triples. What volume will the gas occupy at this increased pressure?

**2.12** The external pressure on a gas is supplied by a fixed atmospheric pressure. The gas is held confined to a given volume by a movable piston. **a.** What pressure is being exerted by the gas?

   The confined gas is seen to contract to one half its original volume and remain in this new amount of space with no change in the atmospheric pressure. **b.** What will the new pressure exerted by the confined gas be?

**2.13** **a.** For the above problem, **2.12**, what general statement concerning the Celsius temperature of the gas can you make to help account for the observed change? **b.** What exact statement concerning the absolute temperature of the gas can you make?

**2.14** There are $5.0 \times 10^{23}$ atoms of a gas held in a volume of 1.0 liter by a movable piston located in a 10.0 liter container. The external pressure on the piston is kept constant at one atmosphere. **a.** If the absolute temperature of the gas is doubled, on the average how many atoms will there be in the *original* 1.0 liter of space? **b.** State the observation as a law relating gas *concentration* and absolute temperature.

**2.15** A gas occupies a volume of 1000 ml at a temperature of $x°K$ and a pressure of $p$ torrs. If the pressure of the gas is decreased to $\frac{1}{2} p$ torrs and the temperature is increased to $2x°K$, what volume will the gas occupy?

**2.16** An amount of gas at $0.0°C$ is confined to a 10.0 ml volume at 1.00 atm. If the volume of the gas doubles while the pressure remains the same, which of the following *could* be true?

   **a.** The pressure exerted by the gas at this new position has increased.

   **b.** The temperature of the gas has increased to $273°C$.

   **c.** The temperature of the gas remains at $0°C$, but a reaction has occurred that has broken each particle of gas into two particles.

   **d.** The temperature of the gas has increased to $273°C$, but at this higher temperature there are only half as many particles as there were initially.

**2.17** **a.** An amount of oxygen occupies 4.00 l at a pressure of 740 torrs. If the temperature remains constant, what volume will the same amount of oxygen occupy at standard pressure (760 torrs)? **b.** When the pressure on a confined amount of a gas was changed from 700 torrs to 800 torrs, the final gas volume was 4.37 l. What was the initial volume of the confined gas, the temperature remaining constant? **c.** A balloon is filled with 10.0 l of helium at 760 torrs and 30.0°C. At what pressure will the volume of helium be increased by 2.0 l at 30.0°C? **d.** The volume of a confined gas is 20.0 cu. ft. at 600 torrs and 0.0°C. At the same temperature, what must be the pressure if the volume of the gas changes to 12.0 cu. ft?

Ans. **b.** 5.00 l; **d.** 1000 torrs

2.18 **a.** A mixture of hydrogen and carbon dioxide gases is confined to a 5.00 l tank at STP. The gases are separated from each other and the hydrogen gas alone is found to occupy a volume of 6.00 l at 380 torrs and 0.0°C. What was the partial pressure of the carbon dioxide in the original tank? **b.** The volume of a dry gas is 600 ml at 25.0°C and 750 torrs. What volume will this gas occupy if stored over water at 30.0°C and 730 torrs? (The partial pressure of water vapor at 30.0°C is 31.5 torrs.) **c.** 50.0 ml of a gas are collected over water at 15.0°C and at a pressure of 720 torrs. What is the volume of the dry gas? (The partial pressure of water vapor at 15.0°C is 12.7 torrs.) **d.** 5.000 l of nitrogen are collected over water at 25.0°C and 750.0 torrs. The gas is dried and occupies a volume of 4.841 l at 25.0°C. What is the partial pressure of water vapor at 25.0°C?

Ans. **b.** 655 ml; **d.** 23.8 torrs

## SUGGESTED READINGS

Brock, W. H. "Prout's Chemical Bridgewater Treatise," *Journal of Chemical Education*, December 1963. Discusses Dalton's rule of simplicity and his list of atomic weights.

Conant, James B. (ed.) *Harvard Case Histories in Experimental Science*, Vol. 2. Harvard University Press, 1957. Excellent historical account of the Dalton atomic theory.

Jaffe, Bernard. *Crucibles: The Story of Chemistry* (paperback). Fawcett, 1962. Chapter 6 tells the story of Dalton and his atomic theory.

Leicester, H. M. and H. S. Klickstein. *Source Book in Chemistry*. Harvard University Press, 1956.

Shamos, Morris H. *Great Experiments in Physics*. Holt, 1959. Boyle's original experiment on the relation between volume and pressure of a gas.

SCIENTIFIC AMERICAN

Davis, H., "Low Temperature Physics." June 1949

*...the scales fell from my eyes, doubts vanished, and the feeling of calm certainty came in their place.*

*Lothar Meyer (1830–1895), on reading Cannizzaro's account of the Avogadro Hypothesis*

**CHAPTER 3**

# Avogadro's Hypothesis

Many scientists of the seventeenth, eighteenth, and nineteenth centuries concentrated their efforts on an attempt to understand the properties of gases. Others, independently, strove to develop a theory on the nature of heat. In the nineteenth century these two streams of scientific thought converged into one monumental theory, the *kinetic molecular theory* of gases. Kinetic molecular theory is one of the intellectual milestones in the great progression of human understanding of Nature. It is an achievement of the mind that is filled with a beauty that the nineteenth-century French physicist Henri Poincaré (pwan kah RAY) termed:

> that profounder beauty which comes from the harmonious order of the parts, and which a pure intelligence can grasp.

As with many great scientific theories, kinetic molecular theory had far-ranging influence beyond the fields that created it. And so it was the development of this theory that helped untangle confused chemical ideas of the eighteenth century by leading to a vital extension of the Dalton theory of the atom.

## THE AVOGADRO HYPOTHESIS

The model of ideal gas that we considered in Chapter 2 was derived in an effort to explain the physical properties of gases under ordinary conditions of temperature and pressure. This model is the essential

68

# and the Mole

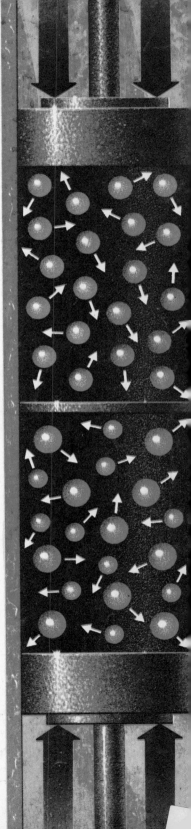

aspect of kinetic molecular theory. The theory has been further developed in very sophisticated mathematical terms. As a result, experimental observations on the physical properties of gases under *all* types of conditions can now be accounted for in *quantitative* detail in terms of model and theory. As we consider the influence of kinetic molecular theory on the development of chemistry, it will be important to recall and understand first the *qualitative* details of that theory.

In the early nineteenth century, observations on the *chemical* properties of gases led to the most important application of kinetic molecular theory to the development of chemistry.

## 3.1  The combining volumes of gases

In 1808 Joseph Gay-Lussac (gay loo SACK), a French scientist, discovered a simple but extremely important chemical property of gases. He observed that when gases combined chemically with each other a simple relationship existed between the *volumes* of reactant gases and product gases. Some experimental observations of Gay-Lussac were:

1 volume of hydrogen + 1 volume of chlorine →
2 volumes of hydrogen chloride

1 volume of nitrogen + 1 volume of oxygen →
2 volumes of nitrogen monoxide

2 volumes of hydrogen + 1 volume of oxygen →
2 volumes of water vapor (steam)

Gay-Lussac's conclusion was that *the volumes of gaseous reactants and gaseous products in a chemical reaction were in small, whole-number ratios.* (Fig. 3.1.) An even more important generalization that he discovered was that gases always combined chemically in small, whole-number ratios no matter what the physical state of the product. Some of his other observations that led to this generalization, the *Law of Combining Volumes,* are, in modern chemical language:

1 volume of ammonia + 1 volume of hydrogen chloride →
solid ammonium chloride

1 volume of ammonia + 1 volume of tetrafluoboric acid →
solid ammonium tetrafluoborate

2 volumes of ammonia + 1 volume of carbon dioxide (moisture
present) → solid ammonium carbonate

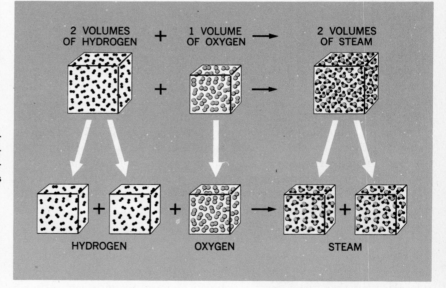

**FIGURE 3.1** A simple, whole-number relationship exists between volumes of gaseous reactants and gaseous products of a chemical reaction.

## 3.2 Dalton disputes Gay-Lussac; Avogadro supports him.

In terms of the Daltonian *atom*, some of these observations were difficult to understand. At the outset, the simple relationship existing between combining *volumes* of gases would suggest that an equally simple relationship should exist between numbers of combining *particles* of gases. Dalton, himself, concluded that Gay-Lussac's observations strongly suggested that equal volumes of gases must contain the same (or simply related) numbers of particles. Dalton, however, made an important assumption about the nature of gaseous particles. He recognized that *compound* gaseous particles, such as carbon monoxide and steam, had to contain atoms of different kinds united chemically. Such particles have been defined as *molecules*. For *elemental* gaseous particles, such as hydrogen, oxygen, and nitrogen, Dalton *assumed* that the particles were, most simply, single atoms. (Dalton and his contemporaries, however, used the word molecule for such particles also.)

For a reaction such as

1 volume of nitrogen + 1 volume of oxygen →
2 volumes of nitrogen monoxide,

the implication, in terms of the Daltonian theory, was that for equal numbers of nitrogen and oxygen atoms to react to form *twice* the number of nitrogen monoxide molecules, nitrogen and oxygen atoms would have to split in half! (Fig. 3.2.) Such an implication was unacceptable to Dalton, and he refused to accept Gay-Lussac's findings. It took the intellectual genius of a brilliant Italian physicist to resolve the inconsistency between Gay-Lussac's experimental data and Dalton's indivisible atom.

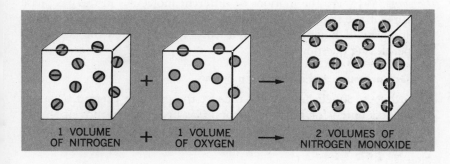

FIGURE 3.2 Gay-Lussac found that some of Dalton's atoms would have to split in half.

In 1811 Amedeo Avogadro (ahmeh DAY o ahvo GAH dro) restated the "equal volumes-equal numbers" idea that Dalton had recognized but rejected. Avogadro was able, though, to give the idea sufficient theoretical justification on the basis of kinetic molecular concepts that he is given full credit for that idea. The "equal volumes-equal numbers" concept is almost always named in honor of the brilliant Italian scientist.

**THE AVOGADRO HYPOTHESIS.** Now fully borne out by a host of experimental facts, this statement asserts that *under the same conditions of temperature and pressure, equal volumes of gases contain equal numbers of particles.*

**Amedeo Avogadro** (1776–1856, Italian). Besides teaching, Avogadro was also very active in civic affairs. Like Lavoisier, he held many public offices. He became involved with public instruction, meteorology, weights and measures, and national statistics.

### 3.3  How reasonable is the Avogadro Hypothesis?

Is the Avogadro Hypothesis plausible? Is it not like stating that if molecules are present in the gaseous state, then regardless of how large or small each molecule might be, under the same conditions of temperature and pressure equal numbers of different molecules take up the same space? Is this not like saying that at the same temperature and pressure 100 grapefruits will occupy the same space as 100 grapes? Surely this is unreasonable. Try to cram 100 grapefruits into a volume that just holds 100 grapes and you will wind up with a good supply of grapefruit juice!

Really, the comparison is not a very good one, for there is a critical difference between solids (grapefruits and grapes) and gases. Gases, unlike solids, can be greatly compressed. Gases, unlike solids, will expand into any volume open to them. So even though molecules in the gas phase do have size of their own, this alone cannot account for the fact that gases occupy space. Why, then, do molecules in the gas phase take up space? The answer is that they are constantly moving!

With great insight, Avogadro was able to deduce that at the same temperature and pressure the same number of molecules of different gases would occupy the same volume *because their motion was the same*. Why are the motions of different molecules in the gas phase the same at the same temperature and pressure? It was the continuing development of kinetic molecular theory that provided the answer to this perplexing question.

### 3.4  Gas pressure and molecular motion

According to kinetic molecular theory, the pressure exerted by a gas can be accounted for by two factors. Gas pressure depends upon (1) the number of molecular collisions per unit area and (2) the force per molecular collision.
That is:

$$\text{Pressure} = \left(\frac{\text{number of molecular collisions}}{\text{unit area}}\right)\left(\frac{\text{force}}{\text{molecular collision}}\right)$$

Carrying through the multiplication, we arrive at the classical definition for any kind of pressure:

$$\text{Pressure} = \frac{\text{force}}{\text{unit area}}$$

Considering each of the two factors separately, we first note that the number of molecular collisions per unit area depends upon molecular velocities. The faster the molecules are moving in a confined volume, the more frequently will they collide with the walls of the container. (Fig. 3.3.) Thus, at the outset, gas pressure, $P$, is proportional to molecular velocity, $v$, or:

$$P \propto v$$

The force of impact per molecular collision depends on how fast a molecule is moving and how heavy it is. In other words, the force per molecular collision is proportional to both molecular mass, $m$, and molecular velocity, $v$. Mathematically, then, force per molecular collision is proportional to the product of molecular mass and molecular velocity, $mv$, a product the physicist calls *momentum*. Recall that gas pressure is proportional to force per molecular collision. Force per molecular collision, we have just seen, is proportional to momentum, $mv$. Therefore, mathematically, gas pressure is proportional to momentum, or:

$$P \propto mv$$

Since gas pressure is proportional to both molecular velocity and molecular momentum, mathematically it is proportional to the product of the two:

$$P \propto (v)(mv)$$

or

$$P \propto mv^2$$

If molecules with *different masses* and *different velocities* have, however, the same value for the product of their velocity and momentum—for the quantity $mv^2$—then they must be exerting the same pressure! (Fig. 3.4.) Is there any condition for which the $mv^2$ values of different molecules are the same? Let us see.

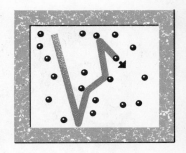

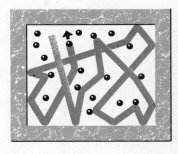

**FIGURE 3.3** The frequency of molecular collisions depends on molecular velocity.

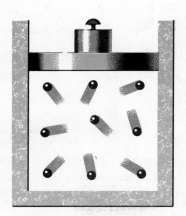

**FIGURE 3.4** Gas pressure depends on both molecular momentum and molecular velocity.

### 3.5 Molecular motion and the meaning of temperature

Gay-Lussac, some twenty years prior to his discovery of the simple combining volumes of gases, made another important discovery concerning the physical behavior of gases.

**Joseph Louis Gay-Lussac** (1778–1850, French). In addition to his classic work with gases, Gay-Lussac did fundamental research in organic and inorganic chemistry. His works on iodine and cyanides are models of experimental research. He obtained boron from boric acid and showed that acids need not contain oxygen as was then believed. Gay-Lussac also carried out work of technical importance that led to improved methods for producing sodium, potassium, and sulfuric acid. He first showed how to flameproof wood by treating it with borax.

**GAY-LUSSAC'S LAW.** This law, in terms of the absolute temperature scale, states that *the pressure of a constant weight of gas varies directly with the absolute temperature, at constant volume.*

Mathematically, Gay-Lussac's Law is expressed:

$$P \propto T \text{ (constant } n, V)$$

therefore

$$P = k''T \text{ (constant } n, V)$$

For our present concern, the importance of this relationship is that it tells us that the pressure of a gas is proportional to its absolute temperature, $T$; that is,

$$P \propto T.$$

Let us now combine all our information. For a given gas for which

$$n = \text{number of gas molecules,}$$
$$m = \text{weight of each gas molecule,}$$
$$v = \text{velocity of each gas molecule,}$$
$$P = \text{total gas pressure,}$$
$$V = \text{volume occupied by gas,}$$
$$T = \text{absolute temperature,}$$

we deduced

$$P \propto mv^2 \text{ (for constant } n, V, T).$$

From Gay-Lussac's Law, we have

$$P \propto T \text{ (for constant } n, V).$$

Mathematically, we may then write

$$mv^2 \propto T \text{ (for constant } n, V, P).$$

This relationship tells us that the $mv^2$ value for a gas is directly proportional to the absolute temperature, $T$. We have found the relationship we sought. The required condition for the $mv^2$ of different molecules to be the same is that those different molecules **be at the same absolute temperature.** Moreover, we conclude from the relationship

$$mv^2 \propto T \text{ (for constant } n, V, P)$$

that at the same absolute temperature equal volumes of *different* gases exerting the same pressure must contain equal numbers of molecules, *n*. This is, indeed, the Avogadro Hypothesis!

### 3.6 Molecular motions and energies are functions of temperature.

Just what is this property of a gas that we have been labeling $mv^2$? It is an energy. For we learn from kinetic molecular theory that the *energy of motion*, or kinetic energy *(KE)*, of a gas molecule is

$$KE = \frac{1}{2} mv^2.$$

Thus, the argument just presented to show the plausibility of the Avogadro Hypothesis rests on a fundamental deduction of the kinetic molecular theory of gases. *The kinetic energies of all gases at the same absolute temperature are equal.* Since, in the first place, different gas molecules have different masses, *m*, they must have different velocities, *v*, in order that their kinetic energies be equal at the same absolute temperature. Qualitatively, heavy molecules move slowly, light molecules move rapidly at the same temperature. You must not, however, be left with the impression that all the molecules of the same mass move with the same velocity at the same temperature. Figure 3.5 shows the velocity *distribution* for molecules of the same mass at the same temperature. This distribution can be experimentally obtained as

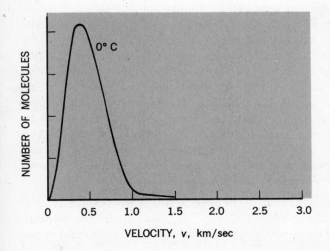

**FIGURE 3.5** Experimentally, all molecules of the same mass, at the same temperature, do not move with the same velocity.

well as *calculated* from kinetic molecular theory. You observe that in a *large* collection of molecules of the same kind, at the same temperature, some few of the molecules move slowly; some few move quite rapidly; most have velocities lying in a narrow range of values.

The velocity distribution of gas molecules changes with temperature as you might expect. Figure 3.6 shows the effect of changing temperature on that distribution.

**FIGURE 3.6** Change in temperature causes a change in the velocity distribution of gas molecules.

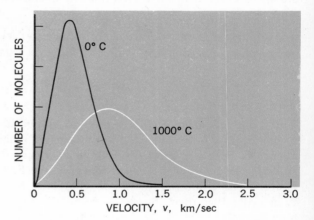

Since the kinetic energy of a gas is a function of molecular velocities, Figures 3.5 and 3.6 can equally as well represent kinetic energy distributions in a collection of gas molecules of the same mass.

### 3.7 Avogadro makes another important contribution.

In his historic paper that appeared in the French *Journal de Physique* (zhure nahl d' fizz EEK) in 1811, Avogadro proposed a second major hypothesis, which history records as a truly original idea of his. Avogadro proposed the existence *for gaseous elements of diatomic molecules*, particles containing two atoms of the same element. Dalton, striving for simplicity in his atomic theory as we noted earlier, had speculated that elemental gases such as hydrogen, oxygen, and nitrogen existed as simple monatomic particles. It was a *speculation* which retarded the growth of his atomic theory for a number of years. Avogadro, on careful analysis of the experimental data of Gay-Lussac, deduced the necessity for the existence of these gases as *diatomic molecules*. Let us consider such a deduction.

In the reaction between hydrogen and oxygen gases to form water vapor (or steam), Gay-Lussac had shown:

2 *volumes* of hydrogen + 1 *volume* of oxygen → 2 *volumes* of steam

From Avogadro's Hypothesis (equal volumes, equal molecules), this can be rewritten in simplest form:

2 *molecules* of hydrogen + 1 *molecule* of oxygen→2 *molecules* of steam

Avogadro's reasoning then followed this line of approach. All of the atoms in two molecules of steam come from two molecules of hydrogen and one molecule of oxygen. In a molecule of steam there must be *at least one whole atom* of combined oxygen. Since two molecules of steam are formed, two whole atoms of oxygen must have been initially present. However, since only *one molecule* of oxygen was originally present, that molecule of oxygen must have contained *two atoms* of oxygen. Thus, elemental oxygen must be represented by the *formula* $O_2$, rather than the symbol O.

What about hydrogen? Avogadro made the simple assumption that it, too, like oxygen, was diatomic, and should be represented by the formula $H_2$, rather than the symbol H. Going back to the reaction between hydrogen and oxygen gases to form steam, it is important to note that this result is not a necessary one, for there is still no means of knowing the formula for steam. The *two* simplest possibilities are:

2 molecules of hydrogen + 1 molecule of oxygen→2 molecules of steam

$$2H \quad + \quad O_2 \quad \rightarrow \quad 2HO$$

or

$$2H_2 \quad + \quad O_2 \quad \rightarrow \quad 2H_2O$$

However, from the experimental observation that

1 volume of hydrogen + 1 volume of chlorine →
2 volumes of hydrogen chloride,

it can be readily deduced that both hydrogen and chlorine most *simply* must exist as diatomic molecules. Therefore, if hydrogen gas is $H_2$ and oxygen gas is $O_2$, steam must have the simplest formula $H_2O$! (Now, you know why the formula for water is $H_2O$. Almost.) Avogadro's reasoning is shown schematically in Figure 3.7.

Avogadro's second great contribution to the development of chemistry was this concept of *polyatomic* molecules for elemental gaseous elements. That such elemental gases as $H_2$, $N_2$, $O_2$, and $Cl_2$ are diatomic, as presented here, is a simplification of the concept Avogadro proposed. Proof of that simplification came later with the verification of diatomicity through the determination of molecular weights. Thus, for the moment, hydrogen could as well be $H_4$ as $H_2$, oxygen could as well be $O_8$ as $O_2$, and water could be $H_4O_2$ instead of $H_2O$.

From the observations of Gay-Lussac, and the Avogadro Hypothesis:

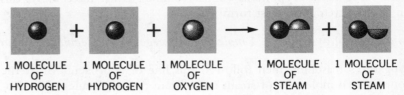

1 MOLECULE OF HYDROGEN + 1 MOLECULE OF HYDROGEN + 1 MOLECULE OF OXYGEN → 1 MOLECULE OF STEAM + 1 MOLECULE OF STEAM

But if in a molecule of steam there must be
*at least one whole atom* of *combined* oxygen, then:

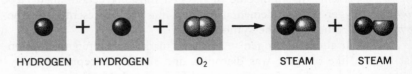

HYDROGEN     HYDROGEN     $O_2$     STEAM     STEAM

Again from experimental observation and the Avogadro Hypothesis:

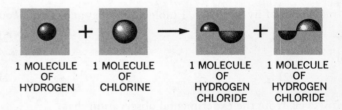

1 MOLECULE OF HYDROGEN + 1 MOLECULE OF CHLORINE → 1 MOLECULE OF HYDROGEN CHLORIDE + 1 MOLECULE OF HYDROGEN CHLORIDE

But if in one molecule of hydrogen chloride
there must be *at least one whole atom* each
of *combined* hydrogen and chlorine, then:

$H_2$ + $Cl_2$ → HCl + HCl

Thus:

**FIGURE 3.7** Diatomicity: Avogadro's resolution of the Dalton–Gay-Lussac controversy

$H_2$ + $H_2$ + $O_2$ → $H_2O$ + $H_2O$

### 3.8 Avogadro's views become universally adopted.

It is an ironic fact of scientific history that Amedeo Avogadro did not live to see his enormous contributions to chemistry take hold. For almost a half-century after the appearance of Avogadro's classical deductions, chemists floundered in uncertainty. This uncertainty arose for a number of complex reasons that caused many reputable chemists to repudiate Avogadro's thinking. For example, a simple, yet profound, objection to diatomicity was raised by the great Berzelius. Berzelius could not conceive of two *like* atoms uniting together.

The pioneering experimental work of the French chemist Jean Dumas (zhon doo MAH) on the vapor densities of phosphorus, sulfur, arsenic, and mercury seemed to disprove the concept of diatomicity. Vapor densities of gaseous substances are derived from the weights that known volumes of gases occupy. That is, as for the density of any substance, vapor or gas density is defined by the relation:

$$\text{Density} = \frac{\text{weight}}{\text{volume}}$$

$$D = \frac{w}{V}$$

**EXAMPLE**

A solid cube of metal, 0.200 cm on edge, weighs 0.180 g. What is the density of the metal?

**SOLUTION**

First, the volume of the metal cube must be calculated.

$$V_{\text{cube}} = e^3$$
$$V_{\text{cube}} = (2.00 \times 10^{-1} \text{ cm})^3$$
$$V_{\text{cube}} = 8.00 \times 10^{-3} \text{ cm}^3$$

The density of the metal is then determined from the formula for density.

$$D = \frac{w}{V}$$

$$D = \frac{0.180 \text{ g}}{8.00 \times 10^{-3} \text{ cm}^3}$$

$$D = 22.5 \text{ g/cm}^3$$

**EXAMPLE**

At a given temperature and pressure 1.26 g of a gas occupy a volume of 900.0 ml. What is the density of the gas?

**SOLUTION**

$$D = \frac{w}{V}$$

$$D = \frac{1.26\,\text{g}}{900.0\,\text{ml}}$$

$$D = 0.00140\,\text{g/ml}$$

$$D = 1.40 \times 10^{-3}\,\text{g/ml}$$

or

$$D = 1.40 \times 10^{-3}\,\frac{\text{g}}{\text{ml}} \times \frac{10^3\,\text{ml}}{1\,\text{l}}$$

$$D = 1.40\,\text{g/l}$$

**Stanislao Cannizzaro** (1826–1910, Italian). Although best remembered among chemists for the reaction in organic chemistry that now bears his name, Cannizzaro's clarification of the concept of atomic weights and of the importance of Avogadro's hypothesis are also among his scientific legacies. Like Avogadro, Cannizzaro was very active in the political life of his country.

Dumas could not know in 1832 that the elements with which he chose to work were complex in structure. Indeed, it is now known that when elemental sulfur vaporizes, such molecules as $S_8$, $S_6$, $S_4$, and $S_2$ are formed. Solid phosphorus and arsenic vaporize to give the tetratomic molecules $P_4$ and $As_4$. Mercury, on the other hand, vaporizes to a simple monatomic particle, $Hg$.

With Berzelius and Dumas, the leading chemical intellects of the early and middle nineteenth century, having refuted Avogadro's deductions, there is little wonder that confusion reigned. By 1860 the situation was so unbelievably confused that nearly every chemist was using his own method of writing formulas. In addition, any number of conflicting tables of atomic and molecular weights existed. In that year, the first International Chemical Congress was held in Karlsruhe, Germany. To that meeting came many chemists, including Stanislao Cannizzaro (STAH niss low connits AH row), professor of chemistry at the University of Genoa. Cannizzaro distributed a small pamphlet called *Sketch of a Course of Chemical Philosophy*. In it he had revived and experimentally justified the Avogadro Hypothesis. When Cannizzaro left the meeting, he had converted a number of influential chemists to the views of his now-dead countryman Avogadro.

The strength of Cannizzaro's arguments in favor of the Avogadro Hypothesis lay in his ability to derive a consistent table of atomic and molecular weights from a host of experimental data by applying Avogadro's ideas. Within a short time, chemists everywhere recognized the debt owed to the almost unknown Italian physicist who first truly understood the "equal volumes-equal numbers" concept and who first recognized the necessity for polyatomic gaseous elements.

## THE MOLE

Between the time when Avogadro first gave logical justification for the "equal volumes-equal numbers" concept in 1811 and the time when this concept was generally adopted by chemists slightly more than fifty years later, there were two great, related problems facing chemists. These were (1) the experimental determination of atomic and molecular weights and (2) the determination of formulas for compound substances. Dalton's dilemma, first posed in 1802, remained a dilemma for the next two succeeding generations of chemists. With the acceptance of Avogadro's ideas the dilemma was resolved, and chemistry burst forth into the last quarter of the nineteenth century as a vigorous quantitative science. Where confusion and even discord had held sway, the light of understanding and cooperation now shone. Let us see how Avogadro's ideas, building on and strengthening the Daltonian atom, became the beacon that gave off that light.

### 3.9 The relative weights of molecules and atoms

A highly developed experimental procedure of the middle nineteenth century was the determination of gas or vapor* densities. In the classical method invented by Dumas, gases or vapors are weighed in sealed bulbs of known volume. The measured weights of the gases or vapors divided by the known volume they occupy lead to derived values of gas and vapor densities.

When measured as just described, the densities of oxygen, nitrogen, and carbon dioxide gases at the same temperature of 25.0°C have the values 1.31 g/l, 1.15 g/l, and 1.80 g/l, respectively. We may then compare the weights of *equal volumes* of these three gases, and find that 1.00 liter of oxygen is $\frac{1.31}{1.15}$, or 1.14, times heavier than 1.00 liter of nitrogen, but is $\frac{1.80}{1.31}$, or 1.37, times lighter than 1.00 liter of carbon dioxide, all measurements being made under the *same conditions of temperature and pressure*. These figures take on much added significance when Avogadro's Hypothesis is applied to them.

Since each of the 1.00 liter volumes of the different gases contains the same number of molecules, the values of 1.31 g/l, 1.15 g/l, and 1.80 g/l represent the weights of equal numbers of molecules of oxygen, nitrogen, and carbon dioxide. The number of molecules, for the moment, is not important. Let us symbolize that number by the letter $N$.

If $N$ molecules of oxygen weigh 1.31 g, then *one molecule* of oxygen weighs $(1.31/N)$ g. For example, if there were only ten molecules of oxygen in the 1.00 liter volume—that is, $N = 10$—then if 10 molecules weigh 1.31 g, one molecule must weigh $(1.31/10)$ g, or

The Dumas bulb is used in the determination of vapor densities. A volatile liquid is completely vaporized by heating it at a constant temperature in the bulb of known volume. Any excess pressure that builds up is released through the stopcock. When the bulb is completely filled with vapor at atmospheric pressure, it is closed off, cooled, and the weight of the vapor is measured. The vapor density *at the temperature of heating* and atmospheric pressure is then calculated.

* The word *gas* is used for a substance that normally exists in the gaseous state. The word *vapor* is used for the gaseous form of a substance that normally exists in a condensed state. Thus, we speak of oxygen, hydrogen, and nitrogen gases and of water and iodine vapors.

0.131 g. Similarly, we can determine the weight of a single nitrogen molecule to be $(1.15/N)$ g. The weight of a single molecule of carbon dioxide is $(1.80/N)$ g.

We may now compare the weights of *single* molecules, and find:

$$\frac{\text{Weight of 1 molecule of oxygen}}{\text{Weight of 1 molecule of nitrogen}} = \frac{(1.31/N) \text{ g}}{(1.15/N) \text{ g}}$$

$$\frac{\text{Weight of 1 molecule of oxygen}}{\text{Weight of 1 molecule of nitrogen}} = \frac{1.14}{1}$$

$$\frac{\text{Weight of 1 molecule of carbon dioxide}}{\text{Weight of 1 molecule of oxygen}} = \frac{(1.80/N) \text{ g}}{(1.31/N) \text{ g}}$$

$$\frac{\text{Weight of 1 molecule of carbon dioxide}}{\text{Weight of 1 molecule of oxygen}} = \frac{1.37}{1}$$

In other words, as a result of applying the Avogadro Hypothesis, **when the experimental weights of equal volumes of gases, under the same conditions of temperature and pressure, are compared, the relative weights of single molecules of those gases are being compared.** (Fig. 3.8.)

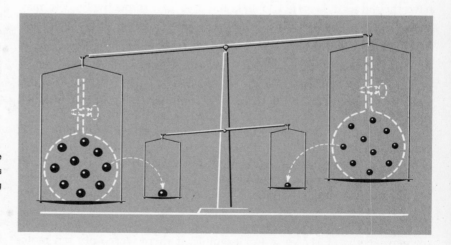

**FIGURE 3.8** . . . relative weights of single molecules of those gases are being compared.

To know that a single molecule of oxygen is 1.14 times heavier than a single molecule of nitrogen, or 1.37 times lighter than a single molecule of carbon dioxide, is very important. Such information enables the chemist to establish *relative atomic and molecular weights.* He is then able to utilize such weights in very important calculations. Before this can be done, however, a *standard for atomic weight* must be chosen.

### 3.10 The atomic mass unit and relative atomic and molecular weights

We recall that Dalton chose to assign, in 1802, the relative atomic weight of 1 to the lightest of atoms, hydrogen. By the late nineteenth century, chemists had far more accurate experimental data than Dalton had. Further, these chemists recognized the necessary existence of diatomic molecules of elemental gases, whereas Dalton, of course, did not. Late-nineteenth-century chemists finally agreed to resolve their differences with respect to a single scale of relative atomic weights. They chose, in international congress, to adopt *as a standard the value of 16.0000 atomic mass units, amu, to be the relative weight of a single atom of oxygen.*\* Thus the relative weight of a single diatomic oxygen *molecule*, by convention, becomes 32.0000 amu. Using the gas density measurements discussed previously, the relative weight of a nitrogen molecule becomes $\dfrac{32.0000 \text{ amu}}{1.14}$, or 28.0 amu. The relative weight of a carbon dioxide molecule is 32.0000 amu × 1.37, or 44.0 amu.

It is important to understand fully the nature of the arbitrary choice for a standard of atomic weight. At the time the standard was chosen, chemists had no means for experimentally determining the weights of single atoms of elements. To be able to do this, even today, means to be able to weigh a very large number of atoms and also to be able to *count* that number. The weight of a single atom can then be *derived* from those two pieces of experimental evidence. *Today chemists can count atoms.* Later on in this book, experimental methods for achieving this will be considered. In the middle of the nineteenth century neither the theoretical basis nor the experimental techniques for counting atoms had been discovered. Thus, chemists had to choose in an arbitrary manner, on which most could agree, a standard for the weights of single atoms.

The atomic mass unit chosen as a *label* for that standard, and for all atomic weights relative to that standard, is a unit without physical meaning. It is simply a label. Quite obviously, a *single* atom of oxygen could not be said to weigh 16.0000 grams, or ounces, or pounds. Such amounts contain vast numbers of oxygen atoms. Thus, the arbitrary unit of relative atomic weight, the atomic mass unit, was created exactly as was the value of 16.0000—by convention and for convenience. The value of 16.0000 amu for the weight of the oxygen atom as a standard was chosen since this led to the relative atomic weights of many of the other elements being whole numbers, or close

The cooperative adoption of standards of measurements is essential to progress. Pictured is the United States' standard kilogram, a carefully machined copy of the international standard kilogram upon which all weights in the metric system are based.

---

\* We are using the words *mass* and *weight* interchangeably. For scientific accuracy it must be noted that mass and weight are different properties of matter. Mass is an *invariable* property of matter. Weight is a *variable* property of matter, which is proportional to mass. While the distinction between mass and weight can be an important one, it is not for the purposes of this textbook.

to whole numbers—again, a matter of convenience. In particular, the value of the relative atomic weight of hydrogen, the lightest of the elements, is very close to one (1.0080 amu), using this definition.

We are now able *to define* the relative atomic weights of the elements in terms of a convention that has served chemists during a century of great progress. *The relative atomic weight of an element is the weight of one atom of that element relative to the weight of one atom of oxygen, which, by convention, has the assigned weight of 16.0000 atomic mass units.* Table 3–1 lists the relative atomic weights of the elements based on *this* definition.*

Molecular weights of compounds must be related to the same standard. Thus, *the relative molecular weight of a compound is the weight of one molecule of that compound relative to the weight of one atom of oxygen, which, by convention, has the assigned weight of 16.0000 atomic mass units.*

### 3.11  The mole

Being eminently practical scientists, chemists of the nineteenth century recognized the need for a larger unit of comparison among atoms and molecules than the atomic mass unit. They also recognized the need for a unit that had physical meaning. Since those chemists could not count atoms and molecules experimentally, they chose to use a *weight* of atoms and molecules to represent a large number of atoms and molecules as their practical unit for comparison. This large unit of comparison is called the *mole*. *The mole was defined to be the number of molecules of oxygen in 32.0000 grams of oxygen.*

If 32.0000 g of oxygen contain one mole of diatomic oxygen molecules, then 32.0000 g of oxygen must contain *two moles* of oxygen atoms. A mole of oxygen *atoms*, then, would be the number of atoms of oxygen contained in 16.0000 g of oxygen.

By virtue of the application of the Avogadro Hypothesis and the choice of $O = 16.0000$ amu as a standard for relative atomic weights, the mole can be defined in other ways. *A mole is the number of atoms contained in the relative atomic weight of any element when that weight is measured in grams.* Thus, 23.0 g of sodium contains a mole of sodium atoms. A mole of iron atoms weighs 55.8 g. *A mole is the number of molecules contained in the relative molecular weight of a compound when that weight is measured in grams.* Thus, 44.0 g of carbon dioxide contains a mole of carbon dioxide molecules. A mole of nitrogen molecules weighs 28.0 g.

---

* In Chapter 8 the necessity for altering the definition of relative atomic weights in light of modern discoveries will become evident. That alteration, however, will have no effect on the values given in Table 3–1, since the change is very small. It is first reflected in the third decimal place.

**TABLE 3-1**  RELATIVE ATOMIC WEIGHTS BASED ON O = 16.0000 AMU

| Element | Symbol | Atomic Weight | Element | Symbol | Atomic Weight |
|---------|--------|---------------|---------|--------|---------------|
| Actinium | Ac | (227)* | Mercury | Hg | 200.61 |
| Aluminum | Al | 26.98 | Molybdenum | Mo | 95.95 |
| Americium | Am | (243)* | Neodymium | Nd | 144.27 |
| Antimony | Sb | 121.76 | Neon | Ne | 20.183 |
| Argon | Ar | 39.944 | Neptunium | Np | (237)* |
| Arsenic | As | 74.91 | Nickel | Ni | 58.71 |
| Astatine | At | (210)* | Niobium | Nb | 92.91 |
| Barium | Ba | 137.36 | Nitrogen | N | 14.008 |
| Berkelium | Bk | (247)* | Nobelium | No | (253)* |
| Beryllium | Be | 9.013 | Osmium | Os | 190.2 |
| Bismuth | Bi | 209.00 | Oxygen | O | 16.0000 |
| Boron | B | 10.82 | Palladium | Pd | 106.4 |
| Bromine | Br | 79.916 | Phosphorus | P | 30.975 |
| Cadmium | Cd | 112.41 | Platinum | Pt | 195.09 |
| Calcium | Ca | 40.08 | Plutonium | Pu | (242)* |
| Californium | Cf | (249)* | Polonium | Po | (210)* |
| Carbon | C | 12.011 | Potassium | K | 39.100 |
| Cerium | Ce | 140.13 | Praseodymium | Pr | 140.92 |
| Cesium | Cs | 132.91 | Promethium | Pm | (145)* |
| Chlorine | Cl | 35.457 | Protactinium | Pa | (231)* |
| Chromium | Cr | 52.01 | Radium | Ra | (226)* |
| Cobalt | Co | 58.94 | Radon | Rn | (222)* |
| Copper | Cu | 63.54 | Rhenium | Re | 186.22 |
| Curium | Cm | (248)* | Rhodium | Rh | 102.91 |
| Dysprosium | Dy | 162.51 | Rubidium | Rb | 85.48 |
| Einsteinium | Es | (254)* | Ruthenium | Ru | 101.1 |
| Erbium | Er | 167.27 | Samarium | Sm | 150.35 |
| Europium | Eu | 152.0 | Scandium | Sc | 44.96 |
| Fermium | Fm | (253)* | Selenium | Se | 78.96 |
| Fluorine | F | 19.00 | Silicon | Si | 28.09 |
| Francium | Fr | (223)* | Silver | Ag | 107.880 |
| Gadolinium | Gd | 157.26 | Sodium | Na | 22.991 |
| Gallium | Ga | 69.72 | Strontium | Sr | 87.63 |
| Germanium | Ge | 72.60 | Sulfur | S | 32.066 |
| Gold | Au | 197.0 | Tantalum | Ta | 180.95 |
| Hafnium | Hf | 178.50 | Technetium | Tc | (99)* |
| Helium | He | 4.003 | Tellurium | Te | 127.61 |
| Holmium | Ho | 164.94 | Terbium | Tb | 158.93 |
| Hydrogen | H | 1.0080 | Thallium | Tl | 204.39 |
| Indium | In | 114.82 | Thorium | Th | 232.05 |
| Iodine | I | 126.91 | Thulium | Tm | 168.94 |
| Iridium | Ir | 192.2 | Tin | Sn | 118.70 |
| Iron | Fe | 55.85 | Titanium | Ti | 47.90 |
| Krypton | Kr | 83.80 | Tungsten | W | 183.86 |
| Lanthanum | La | 138.92 | Uranium | U | 238.07 |
| Lawrencium | Lw | (259)* | Vanadium | V | 50.95 |
| Lead | Pb | 207.21 | Xenon | Xe | 131.30 |
| Lithium | Li | 6.940 | Ytterbium | Yb | 173.04 |
| Lutetium | Lu | 174.99 | Yttrium | Y | 88.92 |
| Magnesium | Mg | 24.32 | Zinc | Zn | 65.38 |
| Manganese | Mn | 54.94 | Zirconium | Zr | 91.22 |
| Mendelevium | Md | (256)* | (Unnamed)† | ? | (260)* |

\* Each of these is a radioactive element. The value in each parenthesis denotes the *mass number* of the *isotope* of the element with the longest known *half-life*. Radioactivity, isotopes, and mass number are introduced first in Chapter 8. Half-life is covered in Chapter 32.

† Discovery of the 104th element was reported in 1964.

The actual number of atoms or molecules that constitute a mole is 602,300,000,000,000,000,000,000. That number is more conveniently expressed as $6.023 \times 10^{23}$ and it is named appropriately the *Avogadro Number*, N. Again, at this stage we are not able to consider how this vastly large number, 602,300 quintillions, is counted experimentally. That will come later. Nor at this stage is the actual number important. It is given as a matter of interest and to honor the man who made the "equal volumes-equal numbers" idea the key to the solution of many perplexing problems in chemistry. Having considered quantitatively the "equal numbers" aspect of Avogadro's Hypothesis, let us now consider the "equal volumes" aspect in the same light.

### 3.12  The mole and the molar volume of gases

If a mole of any gas contains the same number of molecules as a mole of any other gas, then under the same conditions of temperature and pressure a mole of any gas should occupy the same volume as the volume of any other gas. This is experimentally verifiable. An important physical constant of great value to the chemist is the volume occupied by one mole of an *ideal* gas at 0°C and 760 torrs (one atmosphere of pressure) as the particular *standard conditions* of temperature and pressure (symbolized STP). *The experimental value for the molar volume, $V_o$, at STP is 22.4136 liters.* In general practice $V_o$ is used to the first three significant figures* as 22.4 l/mole. (Fig. 3.9.)

### 3.13  Molecular weights and the molar volume of gases

The molar volume has immediate practical importance. If we can determine the weight occupied by a known volume of gas—that is, its vapor density—under given conditions of temperature and pressure, we can then determine the molecular weight of that gas. Let us consider how this can be done.

### EXAMPLE

A volume of 1.36 liters of a gas, measured at 22.0°C and 740 torrs, weighed 2.62 g. What is the molecular weight of the gas?

### SOLUTION

1.  Determine the *volume* the given weight of gas would occupy at STP.

$V_{\text{initial}} = 1.36\,l$          $V_{\text{STP}} = ?$

$T_{\text{initial}} = (22.0°C + 273°) = 295°K$     $T_{\text{STP}} = (0°C + 273°) = 273°K$

$P_{\text{initial}} = 740 \text{ torrs}$         $P_{\text{STP}} = 760 \text{ torrs}$

**FIGURE 3.9**  1.00 liter : 10.0 liters : 22.4 liters

* Significant figures are discussed more fully in Appendix IV, pages 700–702.

Using the Combined Gas Law:

$$\frac{P_{STP}\ V_{STP}}{T_{STP}} = \frac{P_i\ V_i}{T_i}$$

$$\frac{(760\ \text{torrs})(V_{STP})}{(273^\circ K)} = \frac{(740\ \text{torrs})(1.36\ l)}{(295^\circ K)}$$

$$V_{STP} = \left(\frac{740\ \text{torrs}}{760\ \text{torrs}}\right)\left(\frac{273^\circ K}{295^\circ K}\right)(1.36\ l)$$

$$V_{STP} = 1.23\ l$$

2. Determine the weight of the gas that would be present in a molar volume. That is, determine the molecular weight, $M$, of the gas.

$$\frac{\text{Molecular Weight}}{\text{Molar Volume}} = \frac{\text{Weight of the gas}}{\text{Volume at STP}}$$

$$\frac{M}{V_o} = \frac{w}{V_{STP}}$$

or

$$M = \frac{w \times V_o}{V_{STP}}$$

Substituting the known data, we get:

$$M = \frac{2.62\ g}{1.23\ l} \times \frac{22.4\ l}{\text{mole}}$$

$$M = 47.6\ \frac{g}{\text{mole}}$$

Observe carefully that in the above solution to the problem the combined gas laws of Boyle and Charles were used. This implies that the gas in question was ideal and is described by those laws. This implication is not, of course, necessarily true. The more nonideal or real a gas is, the more approximate will be its molecular weight determination by the vapor density method.

### 3.14 The mole and the determination of chemical formulas

The concept of the mole is very importantly extended to the experimental determination of chemical formulas; thus, to the final solution of Dalton's dilemma. The relationship between moles of atoms and the chemical formulas for compounds formed from those atoms may be seen from considering the reaction between hydrogen and chlorine gases to form gaseous hydrogen chloride. The reaction may be described as follows:

1 volume of hydrogen + 1 volume of chlorine →

2 volumes of hydrogen chloride

or

1 molecule of hydrogen + 1 molecule of chlorine →

2 molecules of hydrogen chloride

or

1 mole of hydrogen + 1 mole of chlorine →

2 moles of hydrogen chloride

We have seen previously, from this same reaction, that hydrogen and chlorine gases must both be diatomic, $H_2$ and $Cl_2$. Thus, we can describe the reaction as

$$H_2 + Cl_2 \rightarrow 2\ HCl,$$

where the *symbols* $H_2$ and $Cl_2$ *represent a mole* each of diatomic hydrogen and chlorine gases. In this *chemical equation*, the formula HCl takes on the added significance of representing a mole of hydrogen chloride molecules. Two moles of hydrogen chloride are therefore represented in the equation. Moreover, the formula HCl indicates *clearly* that *one mole* of hydrogen chloride contains *one mole* of hydrogen *atoms* chemically combined with *one mole* of chlorine *atoms*. In Chapter 1 the statement was made that "a formula tells not merely which elements are combined in the compound, but how much of each." We now recognize that *a chemical formula indicates the mole ratio of the atoms combined in a compound.*

With this knowledge, we can proceed to a consideration of the experimental determinations of chemical formulas. Such determinations are based on the constant weight compositions of compounds, a property discussed in Chapter 2. Knowledge of weight compositions and relative atomic weights leads to the mole ratio of atoms combined in the compound. The mole ratio obtained leads to the *simplest formula* for a compound. In many cases the simplest formula for a compound is also its true formula. In many other cases, though, the *true* formula for a compound is different from the simplest formula, and is a multiple of that simplest formula. For example, $CH_4$ is the simplest formula for the compound methane. It is also the true formula for that compound. On the other hand, $CH_3$ is the simplest formula for the compound ethane. The true formula for ethane is $C_2H_6$. (Fig. 3.10.) Thus, while per cent composition data lead importantly to the simplest formula for a compound, further experimental information on molecular weight is needed to determine the true formula. The following examples will illustrate the points just made.

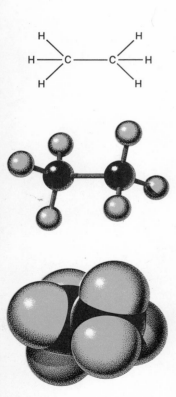

**FIGURE 3.10** Three representations of the ethane molecule

**EXAMPLE**

Find the simplest formula for the gaseous compound that contains
63.6 per cent nitrogen and 36.4 per cent oxygen. ($N = 14.0$
g/mole, $O = 16.0$ g/mole)

**SOLUTION**

1. Convert percentages to weights, *assuming a 100 g sample*, and divide
   by atomic weights to determine number of moles of combined elements.

$$\text{Moles of nitrogen atoms} = \frac{63.6\ \text{g}}{14.0\ \text{g/mole}}$$

$$\text{Moles of nitrogen atoms} = 4.54\ \text{moles}$$

$$\text{Moles of oxygen atoms} = \frac{36.4\ \text{g}}{16.0\ \text{g/mole}}$$

$$\text{Moles of oxygen atoms} = 2.28\ \text{moles}$$

2. Determine the mole ratio among different atoms present by dividing the number of moles of each element present by the
   smallest number of moles present.

$$\text{Mole ratio for nitrogen:}\ \frac{4.54\ \text{moles}}{2.28\ \text{moles}} = 1.99$$

$$\text{Mole ratio for oxygen:}\ \frac{2.28\ \text{moles}}{2.28\ \text{moles}} = 1.00$$

3. Establish the simplest formula, recognizing the indivisibility of
   atoms.

   From step 2, the formula for this oxide of nitrogen is
   $N_{1.99}O_{1.00}$, which becomes simply $N_2O$.

**EXAMPLE**

Find the simplest formula for the oxide of arsenic that contains 75.8
per cent arsenic. ($As = 74.9$ g/mole)

**SOLUTION**

1.

$$\text{Moles of arsenic atoms} = \frac{75.8\ \text{g}}{74.9\ \text{g/mole}}$$

$$\text{Moles of arsenic atoms} = 1.01\ \text{moles}$$

$$\text{Moles of oxygen atoms} = \frac{24.2\ \text{g}}{16.0\ \text{g/mole}}$$

$$\text{Moles of oxygen atoms} = 1.51\ \text{moles}$$

2.

$$\text{Mole ratio for arsenic:}\ \frac{1.01\ \text{mole}}{1.01\ \text{mole}} = 1.00$$

$$\text{Mole ratio for oxygen:}\ \frac{1.51\ \text{moles}}{1.01\ \text{moles}} = 1.50$$

3. From step 2, the formula for this oxide of arsenic is $As_{1.00}O_{1.50}$, which *as a whole-number ratio* becomes simply $As_2O_3$.

$$\left[\left(\frac{1.00}{1.50}\right) \times \left(\frac{2}{2}\right) = \frac{2.00}{3.00}\right]$$

**EXAMPLE**

What is the **true formula** of a compound that contains 92.3 per cent carbon and 7.7 per cent hydrogen, if 2.20 g of its vapor occupy 628 ml at STP? ($C = 12.0$ g/mole, $H = 1.01$ g/mole)

**SOLUTION**

A. Determine the simplest formula for the compound.

1.
$$\text{Moles of carbon atoms} = \frac{92.3\ g}{12.0\ g/\text{mole}}$$
$$\text{Moles of carbon atoms} = 7.69 \text{ moles}$$
$$\text{Moles of hydrogen atoms} = \frac{7.7\ g}{1.01\ g/\text{mole}}$$
$$\text{Moles of hydrogen atoms} = 7.6 \text{ moles}$$

2. Mole ratio for carbon:  $\dfrac{7.69\ \text{moles}}{7.6\ \text{moles}} = 1.0$

   Mole ratio for hydrogen:  $\dfrac{7.6\ \text{moles}}{7.6\ \text{moles}} = 1.0$

3. *Simplest* formula is $C_{1.0}H_{1.0}$, or $CH$.

B. Determine the molecular weight corresponding to the simplest formula, $M_{(CH)}$.

$$\begin{array}{ll} C = & 12.0 \ \text{g/mole} \\ H = & 1.01 \ \text{g/mole} \\ \hline M_{(CH)} = & 13.0 \ \text{g/mole} \end{array}$$

C. Determine the approximate true molecular weight, $M$, from the vapor density data. Remember that 2.20 g of the compound's vapor occupy 628 ml, or 0.628 l, and that the molar volume is 22.4 l/mole. Therefore:

$$\frac{\text{true molecular weight } (M)}{\text{molar volume}} = \frac{\text{weight of given amount of vapor}}{\text{volume of given amount of vapor}}$$

or

$$\frac{M}{22.4 \ \text{l/mole}} = \frac{2.20 \ \text{g}}{0.628 \ \text{l}}$$

$$M = \left(\frac{2.20 \ \text{g}}{0.628 \ \text{l}}\right)\left(\frac{22.4 \ \text{l}}{\text{mole}}\right)$$

$$M = 78.4 \ \text{g/mole}$$

D. Compare the approximate true molecular weight, $M$, with that based on the simplest formula, $M_{(CH)}$, and arrive at the true formula.

$$M = 78.4 \text{ g/mole} \qquad M_{(CH)} = 13.0 \text{ g/mole}$$

$M$ is approximately six times greater than $M_{(CH)}$; therefore, the true formula for this *hydrocarbon* compound is $(CH)_6$ or, in more usual fashion, $C_6H_6$ (benzene).

With an appreciation for the experimental determination of simple and true molecular formulas, we can next turn to a consideration of the use of these formulas to describe chemical changes. Such descriptions, both qualitatively and quantitatively, are the most important concern of chemists. Without them, there would be no chemical science.

## SUMMARY

In this chapter, we learned that one mole of any gas at STP occupies a volume of 22.4 liters and has a weight in grams equal to the relative molecular weight of the gas. For example, an oxygen molecule, $O_2$, has a relative weight of 32.0 atomic mass units, amu. Therefore, in 22.4 liters of $O_2$, a molar volume of the gas, we would expect to find 32.0 grams of the gas. In addition, the 22.4 liters would be the volume occupied by one mole of oxygen molecules. These related facts are true as long as the temperature of the gas is 0°C, and the pressure of the gas is 760 torrs, STP.

To arrive at such a complete description of a gas, we considered Gay-Lussac's experimental observation that the volumes of gases involved in chemical reactions are in small, whole-number ratios. We then followed the careful arguments presented by Avogadro to account for Gay-Lussac's observations. Avogadro postulated the equal volumes-equal numbers of molecules hypothesis. Thus, for the observation that

2 volumes of hydrogen + 1 volume of oxygen →
                                        2 volumes of steam,

Avogadro would have written in simplest explanation

2 molecules of hydrogen + 1 molecule of oxygen →
                                        2 molecules of steam.

Although Avogadro's hypothesis could explain Gay-Lussac's observations, the question was raised as to how it was possible for equal numbers of large, heavy molecules and of small, light ones to occupy the same amount of space. The fact that Avogadro's assumption was consistent with experiment only under the same conditions of temperature and pressure held the clue. By turning to a particle model, we saw that the pressure exerted by equal numbers of gas molecules of different weights can indeed be the same as long as the $mv^2$ of the molecules is the same.

Temperature, we learned, is a measure of the average $mv^2$ of gas molecules. Thus, if the absolute temperature of two different gases is the same, the average $mv^2$ of the different gas molecules is the same. Consequently, the pressure produced by the gases is the same, and equal numbers of molecules can take up equal volumes. We continued to follow the clear logic of Avogadro as he expanded the Daltonian model of matter to include polyatomic molecules.

When the Avogadro Hypothesis became universally adopted, it found very important application in the experimental determination of relative atomic and molecular weights. The experimental weights of equal volumes of different gases, under the same conditions of temperature and pressure, led to the relative weights of single molecules of those gases. Since numbers of molecules of a gas were not experimentally countable, chemists had to establish an arbitrary weight standard to be used with experimental weights of equal volumes of gases to arrive at relative atomic and molecular weights. They chose 16.0000 amu to be the relative weight of a single oxygen atom. They further chose to define a practical unit for comparing equal numbers of atoms or molecules. That unit is the mole, which is defined to be the number of molecules in 32.0000 grams of oxygen.

Finally, we saw that a chemical formula indicates the mole ratio of atoms combined in a compound. We were then able to determine the simplest formula for a compound from weight composition data and relative atomic weights. With gram molecular weight information, we could then determine true molecular formulas.

## QUESTIONS AND PROBLEMS

3.1   The gas ammonia can be formed from nitrogen and hydrogen gas. It is an experimental fact that

1 volume of nitrogen + 3 volumes of hydrogen →
2 volumes of ammonia.

Assume that there are 100 molecules of nitrogen in the 1 volume of nitrogen, and that there are 300 molecules of hydrogen in the 3 volumes of hydrogen gas. Assume also that nitrogen and hydrogen are diatomic, $N_2$ and $H_2$, respectively.

a. State the Avogadro Hypothesis and indicate how the above assumptions illustrate it.

b. The relative molecular weights of nitrogen and hydrogen gases are 28.0 amu and 2.0 amu, respectively. What does this imply with respect to the size of the respective molecules? How would you explain the assumption that equal numbers of nitrogen and hydrogen molecules occupy equal volumes under the same conditions of temperature and pressure?

c. According to Avogadro's hypothesis and the assumptions above, how many molecules of ammonia gas must be formed in the above reaction?

d. On the basis of the Law of the Conservation of Mass, how many *atoms* of hydrogen and nitrogen must there be in the 2 volumes of ammonia formed?

e. On the basis of the above evidence and assumptions, predict the molecular formula for ammonia. $NH_3$

f. How many grams of ammonia would you expect to find in a 22.4 liter volume at STP?

3.2 What gas volume at STP is represented by the following situations?

a. $\frac{1}{2}$ mole of $N_2(N_2 = 28.0$ amu) d. 32.0 g of $CH_4(CH_4 = 16.0$ amu)
b. 8.00 g of $O_2(O_2 = 32.0$ amu) e. 10.0 moles of He(He $= 4.00$ amu)
c. 5.60 g of CO(CO $= 28.0$ amu) f. 11.0 g of $CO_2(CO_2 = 44.0$ amu)

ANS. b. 5.60 l; d. 44.8 l; f. 5.60 l

3.3 a. What volume do 4.00 g of $O_2$ gas occupy at STP? b. How many moles of $O_2$ are present in this volume? c. How many $O_2$ molecules are present in this volume? d. What will the new volume be if the new conditions of temperature and pressure are 273°C and 380 torrs, respectively? e. How many moles of $O_2$ are present in this new volume? f. How many $O_2$ molecules are present in this new volume? g. What property of a gaseous substance determines the number of moles of the gas?

ANS. b. 0.125 moles; d. 11.2 l; f. $7.53 \times 10^{22}$ molecules

3.4 a. How many grams of methane gas, $CH_4$, must be present alone in a 44.8 liter box at 0.0°C and 760 torrs? b. If the same conditions hold, but the box contains 0.500 mole of ethane gas, $C_2H_6$, how many grams of $CH_4$ gas must also be present?

ANS. b. 24.0 g

3.5 The vapor density of steam at 273°C and 760 torrs is 0.400 g/l. What is the weight of 1.00 mole of steam?

3.6 What volume will 11.0 g of $CO_2$ occupy at 68.0°C and 950 torrs?

3.7 How many molecules of carbon monoxide, CO, will be present in a 50.0 liter volume at 100°C and 1520 torrs?

ANS. $1.96 \times 10^{24}$ molecules

3.8 Ten pure chemical compounds, when carefully analyzed, gave the results that follow. Calculate the simplest formula for each compound.

    a. 10.8 g of zinc; 5.3 g of sulfur

    b. 71.4% calcium; 28.6% oxygen

    c. 1.77 g of phosphorus; 2.29 g of oxygen

    d. 46.5% iron; 53.5% sulfur

    e. 2.50 g of uranium; 0.45 g of oxygen

    f. 81.8% carbon; 18.2% hydrogen

    g. 76.59% carbon; 6.38% hydrogen; 17.03% oxygen

    h. 14.0% potassium; 9.7% aluminum; 30.2% silicon; 46.1% oxygen

    i. 29.1% sodium; 40.5% sulfur; 30.4% oxygen

    j. 19.3% sodium; 26.9% sulfur; 53.8% oxygen

    Ans.   b. $CaO$;  e. $U_3O_8$;  g. $C_6H_6O$;  i. $Na_2S_2O_3$

**3.9** The vapor density of elementary chlorine gas is 3.17 g/l at STP. Show by calculation that chlorine exists as diatomic molecules.

**3.10** A gaseous hydrocarbon consists of 92.30% carbon and 7.70% hydrogen. At STP, 100.0 ml of the gaseous compound weigh 0.347 g. What is the true formula for the hydrocarbon?
    Ans.  $C_6H_6$

**3.11** A gaseous hydrocarbon consists of 85.7% carbon and 14.3% hydrogen. At 27.0°C and 740 torrs, 0.505 l of the compound weighs 0.840 g. What is the true formula for the hydrocarbon?

**3.12** On the basis of Gay-Lussac's Law of Combining Volumes: a. Would 623.6 ml of hydrogen gas combine with 311.8 ml of oxygen gas to produce 623.6 ml of liquid water? Explain. b. Would 623.6 ml of hydrogen gas at STP combine with 311.8 ml of oxygen gas at STP to produce 1246 ml of water vapor at a temperature of 273°C and at standard pressure? Explain.

**3.13** How does the following evidence support the Avogadro Hypothesis?

| Gas | Formula | Weight of hydrogen from gas samples of equal volume at same temperature and pressure |
|---|---|---|
| hydrogen chloride | HCl | 0.1 g |
| hydrogen | $H_2$ | 0.2 |
| water vapor | $H_2O$ | 0.2 |
| ammonia | $NH_3$ | 0.3 |
| methane | $CH_4$ | 0.4 |
| acetylene | $C_2H_2$ | 0.2 |
| propane | $C_3H_8$ | 0.8 |
| ethylene | $C_2H_4$ | 0.4 |
| ethane | $C_2H_6$ | 0.6 |

**3.14** On the basis of the evidence presented in problem 3.13, how would it be possible to determine whether the true formula for a compound was HX, or $H_2X_2$, or $H_3X_3$, and so forth.

**3.15** A sealed container filled with 1.0 liter of compressed gas is heated from 300°K to 1200°K. As a result of the temperature increase: **a.** By what factor is the average molecular kinetic energy increased? **b.** By what factor has the average speed of the molecules increased? **c.** By what factor has the internal gas pressure increased? **d.** What fraction of the number of gas molecules would have to be released at 1200°K to reduce the internal gas pressure to its original value at 300°K? **e.** If the container were originally cooled to 150°K, by what factor would the average molecular speed decrease?

ANS. **b.** 2; **d.** $\frac{3}{4}$

**3.16** Two containers of equal volume contain unequal numbers of moles of the same gas. Container *B* has four times as many moles as container *A*. If both containers are at the same temperature: **a.** What is the ratio of the density of the gas in *B* to the gas in *A*? **b.** What *must* the ratio of gas pressures be? **c.** Which variables fully describe the physical condition of a gas? **d.** How many *independent* variables are there in the description of the physical condition of a known amount of gas? **e.** What are the independent variables and the dependent variable in this problem?

ANS. **b.** 4 : 1; **d.** 2

## SUGGESTED READINGS

Conant, James B. (ed.) *Harvard Case Histories in Experimental Science*, Vol. 2. Harvard University Press, 1957. Excellent historical account of the contributions of Avogadro and Cannizzaro.

Cowling, T. G. *Molecules in Motion* (paperback). Harper, 1960. Discusses the kinetic theory of gases.

Hildebrand, Joel H. *An Introduction to Molecular Kinetic Theory* (paperback). Reinhold, 1963.

MacDonald, D. K. C. *Near Zero: The Physics of Low Temperature* (paperback). Doubleday, 1961. Chapter 1 discusses heat, motion, and the absolute temperature scale.

*If from any art that which
concerns weighing and measuring
and arithmetic is taken away,
how little is left of that art.*

Plato (427–347 B.C.)

**CHAPTER 4**

# The Mole and the

We learned earlier of a simple shorthand notation for elements and compounds. The use of symbols and formulas to represent the *names* of elements and compounds is a great convenience to the community of chemists. With the total adoption of the Avogadro Hypothesis and all of its consequences by chemists, symbols and formulas became more than just a convenience, however. They became *quantitative* tools for communicating knowledge.

## THE CHEMICAL EQUATION

Basic to a sound understanding of the science of chemistry is a clear understanding of the language of the science. When chemical symbols and formulas are understood in terms of what they mean *quantitatively*, they take on much added significance. Just as nouns, verbs, adjectives, and adverbs in proper order yield meaningful language, the basic vehicle for communicating human knowledge, so the proper ordering of chemical symbols and formulas leads to chemical equations. Chemical equations are the chemist's basic language for communicating his particular contribution to human knowledge.

### 4.1  Symbols and formulas and what they mean

What does the symbol Fe mean? Most simply, it stands for the name of the element iron. When iron reacts chemically, though, large numbers of iron atoms are involved. Fe, then, might stand for a *standard* large number of iron atoms. Indeed it does. Fe, for chemists, represents *one mole of iron atoms*. Since a mole of iron atoms weighs 55.85 g, the symbol Fe also represents 55.85 g of iron.

*96*

# Chemical Equation

What does the formula $S_8$ mean? S, most simply, stands for the name of the element sulfur. The subscript in $S_8$ tells us that sulfur exists naturally as an octatomic (eight atoms) molecule. $S_8$ also will represent *one mole of sulfur molecules* and the eight moles of sulfur atoms therein. Since a mole of sulfur atoms weighs 32.07 g, the symbol $S_8$ represents $8 \times 32.07$ g, or 256.56 g, of sulfur.

As mentioned in Chapter 1, when a mixture of powdered iron, Fe, and sulfur, $S_8$, is heated, a reaction occurs. The product of the reaction is a black, solid compound called iron(II) sulfide. Analysis of the compound shows it to be composed of 63.5% iron and 36.5% sulfur. We may, therefore, determine the formula for iron(II) sulfide. Again, we begin by assuming a 100 g sample and calculate the number of moles of atoms of each element present.

$$\text{Moles of iron atoms} = \frac{63.5 \text{ g}}{55.85 \text{ g/mole}}$$

$$\text{Moles of iron atoms} = 1.14 \text{ moles}$$

$$\text{Moles of sulfur atoms} = \frac{36.5 \text{ g}}{32.07 \text{ g/mole}}$$

$$\text{Moles of sulfur atoms} = 1.14 \text{ moles}$$

The numbers of moles of iron atoms and sulfur atoms in iron(II) sulfide are in the ratio of 1.14 : 1.14, or 1 : 1. Therefore, the experimentally determined simplest formula for iron(II) sulfide is FeS.

What does the formula FeS mean quantitatively? It tells us that in *one mole* of iron(II) sulfide there are combined one mole of iron atoms and one mole of sulfur atoms. Since we know the weights

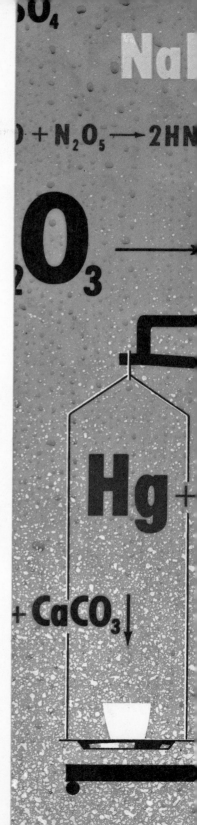

associated with one mole each of iron and of sulfur atoms, FeS must represent $(55.85 \text{ g} + 32.07 \text{ g})$, or 87.92 g, of iron(II) sulfide. Thus, the formula for a compound allows us to calculate the weight of a mole of that compound easily.

### 4.2 Determining the weight of a mole of a compound from its formula

**EXAMPLE**

What is the weight of one mole of potassium sulfate, the formula for which is $K_2SO_4$?

**SOLUTION**

1. Determine the weight per mole of atoms for each element in the compound.
2. Multiply each weight by the number of moles of atoms of each element present in one mole of the compound.
3. Total all the weights.

$$
\begin{array}{lll}
\text{For } K_2, & 2 \times K = 2 \times 39.10 \text{ g/mole} = & 78.20 \text{ g/mole} \\
\text{For } S, & 1 \times S = 1 \times 32.07 \text{ g/mole} = & 32.07 \text{ g/mole} \\
\text{For } O_4, & 4 \times O = 4 \times 16.00 \text{ g/mole} = & 64.00 \text{ g/mole} \\
\hline
K_2SO_4 & & = 174.27 \text{ g/mole}
\end{array}
$$

The example just studied was stated in terms of the "weight of one mole" of potassium sulfate. Some of you may be wondering why the problem was not simply stated in terms of the "molecular weight" of $K_2SO_4$. If the problem had been stated in this manner, the existence of *molecules* of $K_2SO_4$ would have been implied. *These do not exist*. Potassium sulfate is one of thousands of crystalline solids in which molecules cannot be experimentally identified. Potassium sulfate is a *nonmolecular compound*. In fact, $K_2SO_4$ represents the *simplest formula* for potassium sulfate. The compound has no *true formula* in the same sense that $C_6H_6$ is the true formula for benzene while CH is its simplest formula. For $K_2SO_4$, then, and thousands of compounds in which the *chemical bonding* between atoms is of a similar nature, it is proper to speak of "formula weight" but not molecular weight.

As there are thousands of nonmolecular compounds, so, experimentally, there are some two million(!) molecular compounds in which the nature of the *chemical bonding* between atoms leads to the existence of molecules. For such molecular compounds as $CO_2$, $CH_4$, HCl, $P_4O_{10}$, and even $C_{254}H_{377}N_{65}O_{75}S_6$ (the hormone insulin), it is proper to speak of *molecular weights*. The distinction between molecular and nonmolecular compounds is a distinction in the nature of chemical bonding, a distinction that will be discussed in major detail in Chapter 11. For the moment, if we continue to think in terms of a mole of a compound, as represented by its formula, the molecular or nonmolecular nature of the compound will not matter.

## 4.3  Chemical equations and what they mean

Recognizing the fact that chemical symbols and formulas can represent a fixed number of atoms—that is, a mole or multiple thereof—the
use of these symbols to describe chemical changes becomes our next
concern.

Chemical changes occur during chemical reactions. The chemical equation is the symbolic language used to describe a chemical
reaction. The word *equation,* itself, is a clue to the proper writing of
chemical equations. Something must be *equal* in a chemical reaction.
Let us consider the reaction between powdered iron, Fe, and sulfur,
$S_8$, to find the equality we seek. The reaction in words is:

iron reacts with sulfur to form iron(II) sulfide

or, more simply,

iron plus sulfur → iron(II) sulfide

or, more simply yet,

$$Fe + S_8 \rightarrow FeS$$

Something is wrong with this last symbolic description of the
reaction. As it stands, it states that eight moles of elemental sulfur
atoms react to produce but one mole of combined sulfur atoms. This
is in fundamental disagreement with the Law of the Conservation of
Matter. How can eight moles of elemental sulfur atoms, 256.56 g, lead
to but one mole, 32.07 g, of combined sulfur? They cannot. The symbolic description must be altered immediately to read:

$$Fe + S_8 \rightarrow 8FeS$$

While it might seem the easy way out to write $Fe + S_8 \rightarrow FeS_8$, this
cannot be done. The formula for the *sulfide* formed is FeS. We determined that fact from weight composition data. **The formula, FeS, may
not be tampered with. It is an experimental fact!** $FeS_8$ does not exist,
in fact.

Now, quite obviously, we have created eight moles of combined iron atoms, or 446.80 g, from but one mole, or 55.85 g. Again,
this is not possible. The symbolic picture must, therefore, be altered
again. It now reads

$$8Fe + S_8 \rightarrow 8FeS$$

and states *eight moles of iron atoms combine with eight moles of sulfur
atoms (one mole of molecular sulfur) to form eight moles of iron(II)
sulfide.* That is the same as stating that the number of reacting iron
atoms *is equal to* the number of combined iron atoms. The number of
reacting sulfur atoms *is equal to* the number of combined sulfur atoms.
We have discovered the fundamental equality we sought. *Atoms are*

*equal in number before and after reactions.* This fact is yet another statement of the *Law of the Conservation of Matter.*

The last symbolic representation we wrote,

$$8Fe + S_8 \rightarrow 8FeS,$$

is, then, *a balanced chemical equation* and can also be written:

$$8Fe + S_8 = 8FeS$$

Some details concerning this and all other equations may be usefully covered here. The numeral 8 before the symbol Fe and the formula FeS is called a *coefficient*. (The analogy between chemical and algebraic equations is extended thereby.) *Writing a correct equation involves changing coefficients but not subscripts* to preserve the Law of the Conservation of Matter.

### 4.4 Balanced chemical equations and how they are written

The writing of balanced chemical equations for chemical reactions simplifies to two simple rules:

1. Know the correct symbols and formulas for reactants and products.
2. Preserve the Law of the Conservation of Matter by conserving atoms.

**EXAMPLE**

Write the balanced chemical equation for the thermal decomposition of potassium chlorate to form potassium chloride and oxygen gas.

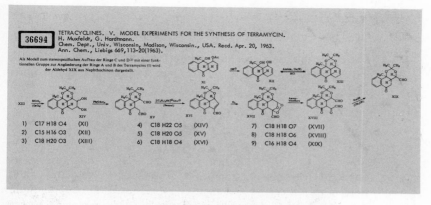

TETRACYCLINES. V. MODEL EXPERIMENTS FOR THE SYNTHESIS OF TERRAMYCIN.
H. Muxfeldt, G. Hardtmann.
Chem. Dept., Univ. Wisconsin, Madison, Wisconsin., USA. Recd. Apr. 20, 1963.
Ann. Chem., Liebigs 669,113–20(1963).

Als Modell zum stereospezifischen Aufbau der Ringe C und D²⁷ mit einer funk-
tionellen Gruppe zur Angliederung der Ringe A und B des Terramycins (I) wird
der Aldehyd XIX aus Naphthochinon dargestellt.

1) C17 H18 O4   (XI)
2) C15 H16 O3   (XII)
3) C18 H20 O3   (XIII)
4) C18 H22 O5   (XIV)
5) C18 H20 O5   (XV)
6) C18 H18 O4   (XVI)
7) C18 H18 O7   (XVII)
8) C18 H18 O6   (XVIII)
9) C16 H18 O4   (XIX)

The chemical equation is the fundamental tool for communicating chemical information. This is so in graduate education in chemistry (left), and in the research laboratories (above), just as it is in this book.

## SOLUTION

1. The formulas for the reactants and products are:*

$$KClO_3 = \text{potassium chlorate}$$
$$KCl = \text{potassium chloride}$$
$$O_2 = \text{oxygen gas}$$

2. a) $KClO_3 \rightarrow KCl + O_2$

   The potassium and chlorine atoms "balance," but there are three moles of oxygen atoms as reactants and only two moles as products. The least common multiple of 3 and 2 is 6; hence we multiply the reactant oxygen atoms by 2 and the product oxygen atoms by 3:

   b) $2KClO_3 \rightarrow KCl + 3O_2$

   Now the oxygen atoms are balanced, but there is imbalance between reactant potassium and chlorine atoms and the product potassium and chlorine atoms. This is easily solved by multiplying the product KCl by 2, and:

   c) $2KClO_3 = 2KCl + 3O_2$

---

* Soon you will be required to be able to produce the formulas for many different compounds. Lest this disturb you, be assured that this will require remembering a *few* facts. Those few facts will lead to your ability to write *hundreds* of chemical formulas.

**ALTERNATE SOLUTION**

$$KClO_3 \rightarrow KCl + O_2$$

The three moles of reactant oxygen atoms can be *most directly* converted to three moles of product oxygen atoms by multiplying the product $O_2$ by $1\frac{1}{2}$, and:

$$KClO_3 = KCl + 1\frac{1}{2}O_2$$

or

$$KClO_3 = KCl + \tfrac{3}{2}O_2$$

Since the formula $O_2$ stands for a *mole* of oxygen molecules, there is *absolutely no reason* why a fractional number of moles cannot be considered. Either of the last two equations meets both criteria established for writing equations and is as correct as the one resulting from the first method of solution. Just as in algebra $2x = 2y + 3z$ is identical with $x = y + \tfrac{3}{2}z$, so in chemistry $2KClO_3 = 2KCl + 3O_2$ is identical with $KClO_3 = KCl + \tfrac{3}{2}O_2$.

**EXAMPLE**

Write the balanced chemical equation for the complete combustion of benzene in air to form carbon dioxide and steam.

**SOLUTION**

1. The formulas for the reactants and products are:

$$C_6H_6 = \text{benzene}$$
$$O_2 = \text{oxygen gas}$$
$$CO_2 = \text{carbon dioxide}$$
$$H_2O = \text{steam}$$

2. a) $C_6H_6 + O_2 \rightarrow CO_2 + H_2O$

The *six* moles of carbon atoms, "$C_6$," and *six* moles of hydrogen atoms, "$H_6$," present in the *one* mole of reactant benzene, $C_6H_6$, *must* lead to *six* moles of carbon atoms in *six* moles of carbon dioxide and *six* moles of hydrogen atoms in *three* moles of steam, as:

b) $C_6H_6 + O_2 \rightarrow 6CO_2 + 3H_2O$

For six moles of carbon dioxide and three moles of steam to form, a total of fifteen moles of oxygen atoms as reactants are required (twelve moles of oxygen atoms in $6CO_2$ and three moles of oxygen atoms in $3H_2O$). Since elemental oxygen is diatomic, this is accomplished as:

c) $C_6H_6 + 7\frac{1}{2}O_2 = 6CO_2 + 3H_2O$

or

$C_6H_6 + \frac{15}{2}O_2 = 6CO_2 + 3H_2O$

or, multiplying through by 2,

$2C_6H_6 + 15O_2 = 12CO_2 + 6H_2O$

## 4.5 Making chemical equations more informative

We have already hinted at the great quantitative information communicated by chemical equations. Before proceeding in depth to a fuller understanding of that aspect of chemical equations, let us consider ways of making chemical equations more useful qualitatively.

On reconsidering each of the two balanced chemical equations just worked out in detail,

$$2KClO_3 = 2KCl + 3O_2$$

and

$$C_6H_6 + \tfrac{15}{2}O_2 = 6CO_2 + 3H_2O,$$

it would be of interest to know the *physical state* of each reactant and product. Now this interest may be simply, but importantly, a matter of curiosity. In a later chapter, in which we will also be concerned with energy changes during chemical reactions, knowledge of physical states of reactants and products will be a necessity. Is potassium chlorate, $KClO_3$, a solid, liquid, or gas? What about potassium chloride, $KCl$, and benzene, $C_6H_6$? From now on, each chemical equation given in this book will indicate the physical state of the chemical substances involved in chemical reactions. Immediately following each symbol or formula in a chemical equation will be one of the following abbreviations to indicate the physical state of a given substance:

$(s)$ = solid
$(l)$ = liquid
$(g)$ = gas or vapor
$(aq)$ = aqueous (water) solution

Thus, the two chemical equations we have been studying are, more informatively:

$$2KClO_3(s) = 2KCl(s) + 3O_2(g)$$

and

$$C_6H_6(l) + \tfrac{15}{2}O_2(g) = 6CO_2(g) + 3H_2O(g)$$

Let us now proceed to the quantitative meaning of the chemical equation. But first, for practice work, change the following to balanced chemical equations:

1. $P_4(s) + O_2(g) \rightarrow P_4O_{10}(s)$
2. $Zn(s) + HCl(aq) \rightarrow ZnCl_2(aq) + H_2(g)$
3. $SiO_2(s) + C(s) \rightarrow SiC(s) + CO(g)$
4. $NaHCO_3(s) \rightarrow Na_2CO_3(s) + CO_2(g) + H_2O(g)$
5. $Cu(s) + AgNO_3(aq) \rightarrow Cu(NO_3)_2(aq) + Ag(s)$
6. $C_2H_5OH(l) + O_2(g) \rightarrow CO_2(g) + H_2O(g)$
7. $BaCl_2(aq) + Na_2SO_4(aq) \rightarrow BaSO_4(s) + NaCl(aq)$
8. $HNO_3(aq) + Al(OH)_3(s) \rightarrow Al(NO_3)_3(aq) + HOH(l)$
9. $Pb(s) + H_3PO_4(aq) \rightarrow Pb_3(PO_4)_2(s) + H_2(g)$
10. $CO_2(g) + CaCO_3(s) + H_2O(l) \rightarrow Ca(HCO_3)_2(aq)$
11. $Al(s) + Fe_3O_4(s) \rightarrow Al_2O_3(s) + Fe(s)$
12. $MgO(s) + H_2SO_4(aq) \rightarrow MgSO_4(aq) + H_2O(l)$

## CALCULATIONS FROM CHEMICAL EQUATIONS

Basic to our understanding of how chemical equations are written is our understanding of the concept of the mole. Inherent in the writing of correct chemical formulas for compounds is the experimental determination of mole ratios of atoms combined in those compounds. Only with correct knowledge of chemical formulas can correct chemical equations describing chemical reactions be written.

Full understanding of the mole concept will allow us not only to write correct chemical equations but to interpret them quantitatively. Full understanding of the mole concept allows us the freedom to handle fractions of moles in a typical laboratory situation, exact small numbers of moles theoretically, and vast numbers of moles in the typical industrial process.

### 4.6 The quantitative meaning of chemical equations

Just as chemical symbols and formulas have distinct quantitative meaning, so it must be that chemical equations based on those symbols and formulas must take on equally precise quantitative meaning.

For the reaction

$$2KClO_3(s) = 2KCl(s) + 3O_2(g)$$

the equation tells us that *exactly* two moles of potassium chlorate will decompose to yield *exactly* two moles of potassium chloride and *exactly* three moles of oxygen. But a mole of $KClO_3$ is 122.56 g of that compound; a mole of $KCl$ is 74.56 g of that compound; a mole of $O_2$ is 32.00 g or a molar volume of 22.4 l at STP of that element. Thus, we can interpret the equation in a number of ways:

$$2KClO_3(s) = 2KCl(s) + 3O_2(g)$$

2 moles → 2 moles + 3 moles (Note carefully that there is no "law of the conservation of moles.")

or, $2 \times 122.56$ g → $2 \times 74.56$ g + $3 \times 32.00$ g

i.e., 245.12 g → 149.12 g + 96.00 g

245.12 g = 245.12 g (Note, though, that the law of the conservation of matter always holds.)

or, 245.12 g → 149.12 g + $3 \times 22.4$ l *at STP*

i.e., 245.12 g → 149.12 g + 67.2 l

Again, as another example, for the complete combustion of benzene a similar quantitative analysis of the reaction would be:

$$C_6H_6(l) + \tfrac{15}{2}O_2(g) = 6CO_2(g) + 3H_2O(g)$$

1 mole + $\tfrac{15}{2}$ moles → 6 moles + 3 moles

or, 78.12 g + $\tfrac{15}{2} \times 32.00$ g → $6 \times 44.01$ g + $3 \times 18.02$ g

i.e., 78.12 g + 240.00 g → 264.06 g + 54.06 g

318.12 g = 318.12 g

or, 78.12 g + $\tfrac{15}{2} \times 22.4$ l → $6 \times 22.4$ l + $3 \times 22.4$ l *at STP*

i.e., 78.12 g + 168 l → 134 l + 67.2 l *at STP*

or, 78.12 g + $\tfrac{15}{2}$ *volumes* → 6 *volumes* + 3 *volumes*

(when $O_2$, $CO_2$, and $H_2O$ are *all* in the gaseous state, all at the same conditions)

Careful consideration of the detailed quantitative study just made on two different chemical equations leads to the fact that chemical equations yield (1) *weight-weight*, (2) *weight-volume*, and (3) *volume-volume* relations among the chemical reactants and products involved. These quantitative relations are termed *stoichiometric* (stoy key o MEH trick) relations by chemists and chemical engineers, from the Greek words that mean "to measure an element." Examples of stoichiometry (stoy key OM e tree), that branch of chemistry dealing with exact mass and volume relations among substances involved in a chemical reaction, follow.

## 4.7 Weight-weight problem calculations

Two "methods" for solving problems involving weights of reactants and products are the "mole" method and the "weight-weight" method.

They are basically the same. Each begins with the balanced chemi
equation for the reaction.

**EXAMPLE**

What weight of oxygen gas will be produced from the thermal
decomposition of 1.226 g of $KClO_3$? ($KClO_3$ = 122.6 g/mole)

**SOLUTION**

MOLE METHOD

1. Determine the number of moles of $KClO_3$ present in the 1.226 g of
   this compound.

$$\text{Number of moles} = \frac{\text{number of grams given}}{\text{number of grams/mole}}$$

For convenience, let $n$ = number of moles

$\quad w$ = number of grams given

$\quad M$ = number of grams/mole (In the case of $KClO_3$,
$\quad\quad M$ is the formula weight.)

These three quantities are simply related. The weight, $w$, of a compound divided by its formula or molecular weight, $M$, equals the
number of moles, $n$, of the compound. That is:

$$\frac{w}{M} = n$$

That this relationship is correct can be tested by examining the units
for each quantity.

$$\frac{w \text{ in grams}}{M \text{ in grams/mole}} = n \text{ in moles}$$

For this problem, then:

$$n_{KClO_3} = \frac{w_{KClO_3}}{M_{KClO_3}}$$

$$n_{KClO_3} = \frac{1.226 \text{ g}}{122.6 \text{ g/mole}}$$

$$n_{KClO_3} = 0.01000 \text{ mole}$$

$$n_{KClO_3} = 1.000 \times 10^{-2} \text{ mole}$$

2. Now find what weight of oxygen gas (in grams) will be produced
   from $1.000 \times 10^{-2}$ mole of $KClO_3$.

From the equation for the reaction:

$$2KClO_3(s) = 2KCl(s) + 3O_2(g)$$
$$2 \text{ moles} \xrightarrow{\hspace{3cm}} 3 \text{ moles}$$

*Either* of the following mole ratios is indicated:

$$\frac{2 \text{ moles } KClO_3}{3 \text{ moles } O_2} = \frac{1.000 \times 10^{-2} \text{ mole } KClO_3}{n_{O_2}}$$

or

$$\frac{2 \text{ moles } KClO_3}{1.000 \times 10^{-2} \text{ mole } KClO_3} = \frac{3 \text{ moles } O_2}{n_{O_2}}$$

Solving for $n_{O_2}$, both lead to the *same* next step:

$$n_{O_2} = (1.000 \times 10^{-2} \text{ mole } KClO_3) \left( \frac{3 \text{ moles } O_2}{2 \text{ moles } KClO_3} \right)$$

and

$$n_{O_2} = 1.500 \times 10^{-2} \text{ mole } O_2$$

Now, using the relationship between moles, weight, and molecular weight we determined previously for this case, we see that:

$$n_{O_2} = \frac{w_{O_2}}{M_{O_2}}$$

$$w_{O_2} = n_{O_2} M_{O_2}$$

or

$$w_{O_2} = 1.500 \times 10^{-2} \text{ mole} \times 32.00 \text{ g/mole}$$

$$w_{O_2} = 48.00 \times 10^{-2} \text{ g}$$

$$w_{O_2} = 0.4800 \text{ g}$$

## WEIGHT-WEIGHT METHOD

1. For convenience, put the given weight of $KClO_3$ and $w_{O_2}$ for the weight of $O_2$ to be found *above* the formulas for the substances involved. Place the stoichiometric weights *below* the same formulas in the balanced equation.

$$\begin{array}{cc} 1.226 \text{ g} & w_{O_2} \\ 2KClO_3(s) = 2KCl(s) + 3O_2(g) \\ 2(122.6 \text{ g/mole}) \longrightarrow 3(32.00 \text{ g/mole}) \end{array}$$

2. Set up indicated ratio and solve.

*Either* of the following ratios is indicated:

$$\frac{1.226 \text{ g}}{2(122.6 \text{ g/mole})} = \frac{w_{O_2}}{3(32.00 \text{ g/mole})}$$

or

$$\frac{1.226 \text{ g}}{w_{O_2}} = \frac{2(122.6 \text{ g/mole})}{3(32.00 \text{ g/mole})}$$

Solving for $w_{O_2}$, both lead to the *same* next step:

$$w_{O_2} = \frac{3(32.00 \text{ g/mole})(1.226 \text{ g})}{2(122.6 \text{ g/mole})}$$

and

$$w_{O_2} = 0.4800 \text{ g}$$

Prove that each of the above methods is basically the same.

### 4.8 Weight-volume problem calculations

Again, two methods for solving problems involving weights and volumes of reactants and products will be applied. Basic, again, is the necessity of knowing the correct chemical equation for the reaction involved. In any problem involving the measurement of gas volumes, another significant factor is involved. The need to specify conditions of temperature and pressure is demanded. For any conditions other than STP, an additional calculation involving the Combined Gas Law will usually be necessary. The following sample problem will be solved first for STP conditions. This will be followed by a change in conditions making necessary a new solution to the problem.

**EXAMPLE**

What volume of dry oxygen gas, measured at STP, will be produced from the thermal decomposition of 1.226 g of $KClO_3$? ($KClO_3 = 122.6$ g/mole)

**SOLUTION**

MOLE METHOD

1. Find the number of moles of $KClO_3$.

$$n_{KClO_3} = \frac{w_{KClO_3}}{M_{KClO_3}}$$

$$n_{KClO_3} = \frac{1.226 \text{ g}}{122.6 \text{ g/mole}}$$

$$n_{KClO_3} = 1.000 \times 10^{-2} \text{ mole}$$

2. Determine the number of moles of $O_2$.

$$\underset{2KClO_3(s)}{\overset{1.000 \times 10^{-2} \text{ mole}}{}} = 2KCl(s) + \underset{3O_2(g)}{\overset{n_{O_2}}{}}$$

2 moles $\longrightarrow$ 3 moles

$$\frac{2 \text{ moles } KClO_3}{3 \text{ moles } O_2} = \frac{1.000 \times 10^{-2} \text{ mole } KClO_3}{n_{O_2}}$$

$$n_{O_2} = (1.000 \times 10^{-2} \text{ mole } KClO_3)\left(\frac{3 \text{ moles } O_2}{2 \text{ moles } KClO_3}\right)$$

$$n_{O_2} = 1.500 \times 10^{-2} \text{ mole } O_2$$

3. Find the volume at STP occupied by the number of moles of $O_2$ present. This volume is found by multiplying the molar volume, $V_o$, by the number of moles. That is:

$$V_{O_2(STP)} = V_{o(O_2,STP)} \times n_{O_2}$$
$$V_{O_2(STP)} = 22.4 \text{ l/\cancel{mole}} \times 1.500 \times 10^{-2} \text{ \cancel{mole}}$$
$$V_{O_2(STP)} = 33.6 \times 10^{-2} \text{ l}$$
$$\boxed{V_{O_2(STP)} = 0.336 \text{ l}}$$

## WEIGHT-VOLUME METHOD

1.
$$\overset{1.226 \text{ g}}{\underset{}{\phantom{x}}} \qquad \overset{V_{O_2(STP)}}{\phantom{x}}$$
$$2KClO_3(s) = 2KCl(s) + 3O_2(g)$$
$$2(122.6 \text{ g/mole}) \longrightarrow 3(22.4 \text{ l/mole}) \text{ (STP)}$$

2.
$$\frac{1.226 \text{ g}}{2(122.6 \text{ g/mole})} = \frac{V_{O_2(STP)}}{3(22.4 \text{ l/mole})}$$

or

$$\frac{1.226 \text{ g}}{V_{O_2(STP)}} = \frac{2(122.6 \text{ g/mole})}{3(22.4 \text{ l/mole})}$$

and

$$V_{O_2(STP)} = 3(22.4 \text{ l/\cancel{mole}}) \left[ \frac{1.226 \text{ \cancel{g}}}{2(122.6 \text{ \cancel{g}/\cancel{mole}})} \right]$$
$$\boxed{V_{O_2(STP)} = 0.336 \text{ l}}$$

If the problem had been stated, "What volume of dry oxygen gas, measured at 25.0°C and 735 torrs, will be produced from the thermal decomposition of 1.226 g of $KClO_3$?" the final answer would be obtained by converting $V_{O_2(STP)}$ to $V_{O_2}$ (25.0°C, 735 torrs). Determine the answer to the problem as newly stated.

### 4.9 Volume-volume problem calculations

With an understanding of Avogadro's Hypothesis, the stoichiometric calculations involving volumes alone are simplest of all. The *coefficients* appearing before the formula for each *gaseous* substance in a chemical equation can be read directly as a general *volume*. For example, in the reaction

$$H_2(g) + Cl_2(g) = 2HCl(g),$$

we may state that, *under any fixed conditions of temperature and pressure*, one volume of hydrogen gas reacts with one volume of chlorine gas to yield two volumes of gaseous hydrogen chloride. The general volumes can be made specific by actual measurement. So the above reaction tells us any of the following, and more:

| $H_2(g)$ | $+ Cl_2(g)$ | $= 2HCl(g)$ |
|---|---|---|
| 1 volume | + 1 volume | → 2 volumes |
| 1.00 liter | + 1.00 liter | → 2.00 liters |
| 40.00 cubic feet | + 40.00 cubic feet | → 80.00 cubic feet |
| 12.00 quarts | + 12.00 quarts | → 24.00 quarts |

It is the nature of the reaction chosen as an example that volume seems to be conserved. However, just as there is no "law of the conservation of moles," so, too, there is no "law of the conservation of volumes." The following sample problem will make this clear.

### EXAMPLE

(a) What volume of oxygen, $V_{O_2}$, is required for the complete combustion of benzene, $C_6H_6$, to produce 36.0 l of carbon dioxide, $CO_2$, under certain conditions of temperature and pressure? (b) What volume of water vapor, $V_{H_2O}$, will be produced under the same conditions?

### SOLUTION

1. For convenience, place the given volume of $CO_2$ and $V_{O_2}$ and $\dot{V}_{H_2O}$ *above* the formulas for the substances involved. Place the coefficients for the substances in the balanced equation *below* their formulas.

$$V_{O_2} \qquad 36.0 \text{ l} \qquad V_{H_2O}$$

$$C_6H_6(l) + \tfrac{15}{2}O_2(g) = 6CO_2(g) + 3H_2O(g)$$

$$\tfrac{15}{2} \text{ volumes} \rightarrow 6 \text{ volumes} + 3 \text{ volumes}$$

2. Set up the ratios indicated and solve.

a) $\dfrac{V_{O_2}}{\tfrac{15}{2} \text{ volumes}} = \dfrac{36.0 \text{ l}}{6 \text{ volumes}}$    or    $\dfrac{V_{O_2}}{36.0 \text{ l}} = \dfrac{\tfrac{15}{2} \text{ volumes}}{6 \text{ volumes}}$

$$V_{O_2} = (36.0 \text{ l})\left(\dfrac{\tfrac{15}{2} \text{ volumes}}{6 \text{ volumes}}\right)$$

$$V_{O_2} = 45.0 \text{ l}$$

b) $\dfrac{V_{H_2O}}{3 \text{ volumes}} = \dfrac{36.0 \text{ l}}{6 \text{ volumes}}$    or    $\dfrac{V_{H_2O}}{36.0 \text{ l}} = \dfrac{3 \text{ volumes}}{6 \text{ volumes}}$

$$V_{H_2O} = (3 \text{ volumes})\left(\dfrac{36.0 \text{ l}}{6 \text{ volumes}}\right)$$

$$V_{H_2O} = 18.0 \text{ l}$$

The three basic calculations of stoichiometry have been considered in some detail. Knowledge of those calculations, and the full understanding of chemical equations that such knowledge implies, is one of the hallmarks of progress in understanding underlying principles of chemical thought and achievement. To be able to solve a problem in stoichiometry *with understanding*, and not from memorized rules, means that you understand such concepts and principles as the Daltonian atom, the Avogadro Hypothesis, and kinetic molecular theory, of which the chemical equation and stoichiometry are ultimate expressions.

## SUMMARY

A chemical equation is a symbolic shorthand representation of experimental facts. In place of the statement,

> When heated together, the gaseous diatomic element hydrogen and the gaseous diatomic element oxygen combine to produce the compound water in the gaseous state,

we can write:

$$H_2(g) + O_2(g) \rightarrow H_2O(g)$$

This symbolic statement represents the substances involved in the reaction but does not tell the whole story. Matter appears to have been lost in the formation of the product from the reactants. An oxygen atom is missing. According to the Law of the Conservation of Matter, this is not possible; therefore, chemical equations must symbolically represent not only what is happening but also how much of what is happening. A balanced chemical equation does both. Applying the Law of the Conservation of Matter (or atoms) to a reaction leads to a balanced chemical equation:

$$2H_2(g) + O_2(g) = 2H_2O(g)$$

or

$$H_2(g) + \tfrac{1}{2}O_2(g) = H_2O(g)$$

The coefficients do not alter the basic statement of what is happening, but they do offer the additional information of how much is happening.

Chemical equations may be interpreted in terms of reacting atoms or molecules, or weights, or volumes. A most basic interpretation is in terms of moles. The mole relationships symbolized by the chemical equation for a reaction are then the basis for all further quantitative interpretations of the reaction. A summary of these interpretations that stem from an understanding of the Avogadro Hypothesis and the mole is:

| | $2H_2(g)$ | $+$ | $O_2(g)$ | $=$ | $2H_2O(g)$ |
|---|---|---|---|---|---|
| moles | 2 | | 1 | | 2 |
| grams | 4 | | 32 | | 36 |
| liters (STP) | 44.8 | | 22.4 | | 44.8 |
| molecules | $2(6.02 \times 10^{23})$ | | $6.02 \times 10^{23}$ | | $2(6.02 \times 10^{23})$ |
| atoms | $4(6.02 \times 10^{23})$ | | $2(6.02 \times 10^{23})$ | | |

Experimentally verifiable quantitative interpretations of chemical reactions lie in the knowledge and intelligent use of chemical equations.

## QUESTIONS AND PROBLEMS

**4.1**  Using relative atomic weights listed in Table 3–1, page 85, determine the weight in grams of each of the following:

    **a.** 1.0 mole of $Na_2S_2O_3$  **c.** $1.00 \times 10^{-3}$ mole of $C_{254}H_{377}N_{65}O_{75}S_6$
    **b.** 0.500 mole of $CO_2$  **d.** 3.60 moles of $Pb(NO_3)_2$

    Ans.  **b.** 22.0 g; **d.** $1.19 \times 10^3$ g

**4.2**  What is the weight percentage of oxygen in each of the compounds of problem 4.1?

    Ans.  **b.** 72.7%; **d.** 29.0%

**4.3**  Change the following to balanced chemical equations:

    **a.** $As_4(s) + O_2(g) \longrightarrow As_4O_6(s)$
    **b.** $H_2S(g) + O_2(g) \longrightarrow H_2O(g) + SO_2(g)$
    **c.** $Al_2O_3(s) + HCl(aq) \longrightarrow AlCl_3(aq) + H_2O(l)$
    **d.** $Na(s) + H_2O(l) \longrightarrow NaOH(aq) + H_2(g)$
    **e.** $AgNO_3(aq) + MgCl_2(aq) \longrightarrow AgCl(s) + Mg(NO_3)_2(aq)$
    **f.** $CaCO_3(s) \longrightarrow CaO(s) + CO_2(g)$
    **g.** $HCl(aq) + NaOH(aq) \longrightarrow H_2O(l) + NaCl(aq)$
    **h.** $Al(s) + Fe_2O_3(s) \longrightarrow Al_2O_3(s) + Fe(s)$
    **i.** $NaNO_3(s) \longrightarrow NaNO_2(s) + O_2(g)$
    **j.** $AgNO_3(aq) + Ba(OH)_2(aq) \longrightarrow Ag_2O(s) + Ba(NO_3)_2(aq) + H_2O($
    **k.** $Al(s) + H_3PO_4(aq) \longrightarrow H_2(g) + AlPO_4(s)$
    **l.** $MnO_2(s) \longrightarrow Mn_3O_4(s) + O_2(g)$
    **m.** $Ca(OH)_2(aq) + CO_2(g) \longrightarrow Ca(HCO_3)_2(aq)$
    **n.** $C_8H_{18}(l) + O_2(g) \longrightarrow CO_2(g) + H_2O(g)$
    **o.** $AgNO_3(aq) + Na_2S(aq) \longrightarrow Ag_2S(s) + NaNO_3(aq)$
    **p.** $C(s) + Al_2O_3(s) \longrightarrow Al_4C_3(s) + CO(g)$
    **q.** $SiO_2(s) + HF(aq) \longrightarrow SiF_4(g) + H_2O(l)$
    **r.** $K_2CrO_4(aq) + HCl(aq) \longrightarrow K_2Cr_2O_7(aq) + KCl(aq) + H_2O(l)$
    **s.** $Pb(C_2H_5)_4(l) + O_2(g) \longrightarrow CO_2(g) + H_2O(g) + PbO(s)$
    **t.** $(CH_3)_3BO_3(l) + O_2(g) \longrightarrow CO_2(g) + H_2O(g) + B_2O_3(s)$

**4.4** Give quantitative interpretations in terms of reactant and product —(i) moles, (ii) weight in grams, (iii) volume at STP if a gas is involved, and (iv) molecules if a molecular substance is involved —for each of the following reactions. Formulas of molecular substances appear in bold type.

$$\text{a. } \mathbf{P_4}(s) + 3\mathbf{O_2}(g) = \mathbf{P_4O_6}(s)$$
$$\text{b. } Fe(OH)_3(s) + 3HCl(aq) = FeCl_3(aq) + 3\mathbf{H_2O}(l)$$
$$\text{c. } \mathbf{NH_3}(g) + \tfrac{5}{4}\mathbf{O_2}(g) = \mathbf{NO}(g) + \tfrac{3}{2}\mathbf{H_2O}(g)$$
$$\text{d. } \mathbf{Pb(CH_3)_4}(g) + \tfrac{15}{2}\mathbf{O_2}(g) = PbO(s) + 4\mathbf{CO_2}(g) + 6\mathbf{H_2O}(g)$$

**4.5** Phosphorus trichloride, $PCl_3$, can be made by reacting white phosphorus, $P_4$, with chlorine gas according to the equation:

$$P_4(s) + 6Cl_2(g) = 4PCl_3(s)$$

**a.** How many grams of phosphorus are required to produce 5.49 g of $PCl_3$? **b.** What volume of chlorine, measured at STP, will be used in the process?
Ans. **b.** 1.34 l

**4.6** **a.** What volume of oxygen, measured at STP, is needed for the complete combustion of 20.0 g of hydrogen? **b.** What weight of water will be produced? **c.** What volume will the product water occupy at 317°C and 12.0 atmospheres?
Ans. **b.** 180 g

**4.7** **a.** How many moles of oxygen are required to prepare 142 g of $P_4O_{10}$ from elemental white phosphorus? **b.** What weight of oxygen is this? **c.** What volume of oxygen, measured at STP, is this?
Ans. **b.** 80.0 g

**4.8** If 2.17 g of HgO are thermally decomposed to elemental mercury and oxygen, **a.** what weight of mercury will be produced? **b.** How many oxygen molecules will be produced?
Ans. **b.** $3.01 \times 10^{21}$ molecules

**4.9** Carbon dioxide and water vapor are the only products formed during the complete combustion of propane gas, $C_3H_8$. **a.** What volume of $CO_2$ will be formed from the complete combustion of $2.00 \times 10^2$ l of $C_3H_8$, all volumes being measured at STP? **b.** If the propane was bottled under 20.0 atmospheres at 0.0°C, what volume of $CO_2$, measured at STP, will be formed from the complete combustion of $2.00 \times 10^2$ l of $C_3H_8$? **c.** What weight of water vapor will be formed in the second case?
Ans. **b.** $1.20 \times 10^4$ l

**4.10** In the thermal decomposition of solid potassium nitrate, $KNO_3$, oxygen gas and solid potassium nitrite, $KNO_2$, are the products.

**a.** What weight of solid will remain after the thermal decomposition of 5.05 g of $KNO_3$? **b.** What volume of oxygen will be collected *over water* at 27.0°C and 753 torrs of atmospheric pressure? (The partial pressure of water vapor at 27.0°C is 26.7 torrs.)

ANS. **b.** 6.45 × 10² ml

**4.11** The experimental fact that lead burns forming an ash that in turn can react with carbon to form lead again was erroneously submitted as evidence in support of the phlogiston theory of burning. (See Fig. 1.4, page 9.) **a.** Write two balanced equations illustrating how this same evidence can be used to support the oxygen theory of burning. **b.** On the basis of your equations, if 20.7 g of lead are burned, how many grams of carbon will be necessary to recover the lead again? **c.** How many liters of carbon dioxide, measured at STP, will be formed in this reaction?

**4.12** A mixture of 16.3 g of zinc and 21.6 g of bromine, $Br_2$, was heated until the reaction was completed. **a.** How many grams of zinc bromide, $ZnBr_2$, were formed? **b.** How many grams of zinc oxide, $ZnO$, could be formed from the remaining zinc? **c.** What volume of oxygen gas, measured at STP, would be required in the reaction with the remaining zinc? **d.** What weight of mercury(II) oxide, $HgO$, would have to be thermally decomposed to produce that volume of oxygen?

ANS. **b.** 9.3 g;   **d.** 25 g

**4.13** Hydrochloric acid, $HCl(aq)$, is a water solution of the very soluble gas hydrogen chloride, $HCl$. Zinc metal reacts with hydrochloric acid to produce hydrogen gas and the soluble solid zinc chloride, $ZnCl_2$. **a.** How many grams of zinc metal are required to produce 4.48 l of dry hydrogen at 27.0°C and 748 torrs? **b.** What minimum volume of hydrogen chloride, measured at STP, must be dissolved in water to account for the noted production of hydrogen? **c.** To what weight of hydrogen chloride does that minimum volume correspond?

ANS. **b.** 8.04 l

**4.14** When 19.5 g of Zn are dropped into a solution of HCl, a reaction occurs (see problem 4.13) and stops when 6.5 g of the Zn has been consumed. **a.** What weight of HCl was originally in the solution? **b.** What volume of dry $H_2$, measured at STP, is produced? **c.** What minimum additional volume of HCl, measured at STP, should be added to react with the remaining Zn? **d.** What additional weight of $H_2$ will be produced?

ANS. **b.** 2.2 l;   **d.** 0.398 g

**4.15 a.** If 4.50 l of $N_2$ were reacted with 4.50 l of $H_2$, both at 140°C and 720 torrs, what volume of ammonia gas, $NH_3$, could be produced at 140°C and 720 torrs? **b.** If 4.50 l of $N_2$ at 140°C and 720 torrs are reacted with 4.50 l of $H_2$ at 280°C and 1440 torrs, what volume of ammonia gas, $NH_3$, could be produced at 140°C and 720 torrs?

Ans.  **b.**  4.50 l

**4.16** Air is approximately 20% oxygen by volume. Approximately what volume of air at room temperature (approximately 27°C) and one atmosphere of pressure would be necessary to burn 342 g of wood (mostly cellulose of simplest formula $C_{12}H_{22}O_{11}$) completely to form $CO_2$ and $H_2O$?

Ans.  Approximately 1500 l

**4.17** The chemical equation indicating the initial reactants and final products for the complex photosynthesis reaction is:

$$6CO_2(g) + 6H_2O(g) \rightarrow C_6H_{12}O_6(s) + 6O_2(g)$$

The solid product is a sugar for which the simplest formula is given. During the photosynthesis reaction, radiant energy from the sun is converted by the green plant to chemical potential energy. The reverse of this reaction, occurring in body cells, is a source of animal energy. If you ate a candy bar containing 180 g of the sugar, what volume of oxygen would have to be transported to your cells at body temperature (37.0°C) and pressure (one atmosphere) so that the chemical potential energy stored in the sugar could be released?

**4.18** One liter of octane vapor, $C_8H_{18}$, is added to a reaction chamber of variable volume at 100°C and one atmosphere. Exactly enough $O_2$ for the complete combustion of the octane is added to the chamber *with the pressure held at one atmosphere*. The mixture is then compressed to one tenth of *its* volume and ignited. The temperature in the reaction chamber rises to 473°C as the volume of the chamber is held fixed. **a.** What is the total pressure of the mixture of product gases $CO_2$ and $H_2O$? **b.** What is the partial pressure of the $CO_2$?

Ans.  **b.**  18.8 atm

## SUGGESTED READING

Kieffer, W. F. *The Mole Concept in Chemistry* (paperback). Reinhold, 1962.

*The peaks of (theoretic)
science may appear to be floating
in the clouds, but their
foundations are in the hard
facts of experience.*

*R. B. Braithwaite (1900–        )*

**CHAPTER 5**

# Oxygen, Valence,

We have now considered in some detail the *general* behavior of elements and compounds, particularly in the gaseous state. We now turn to a specific chemical element and its compounds. Some of the properties we examine we will be able to understand from what we have learned. Other properties will raise the inevitable question WHY, and we will understand that there is more to learn.

## OXYGEN

On our earth, oxygen is easily the most abundant element. In fact, as Table 5–1 indicates, slightly more than 60 per cent of the number of atoms in the earth's crust are oxygen atoms. The discovery of oxygen was a turning point in the development of chemistry. It is one of the unusual facts of history that this element, which surrounds us everywhere and without which life is impossible, was not obtained pure until about 190 years ago.

### 5.1 The discovery of oxygen

On the first of August, 1774, Joseph Priestley was working in his laboratory. He placed a red powder [mercury(II) oxide] in a bell jar so arranged that any gas that might be formed on heating the powder would pass out of the jar through a tube and be collected in a bottle. To heat the powder, Priestley used a large magnifying glass (burning lens) to concentrate the rays of the sun on it. "I presently found," he reported, "that *air* was expelled from it readily."

# and Formula Writing

**TABLE 5–1**  ABUNDANCE OF ELEMENTS IN THE EARTH'S CRUST

| Rank | Element | Atom Per Cent |
|---|---|---|
| 1 | oxygen | 60.50 |
| 2 | silicon | 20.45 |
| 3 | aluminum | 6.25 |
| 4 | hydrogen | 2.70 |
| 5 | sodium | 2.58 |
| 6 | calcium | 1.89 |
| 7 | iron | 1.87 |
| 8 | magnesium | 1.79 |
| 9 | potassium | 1.38 |
| 10 | titanium | 0.27 |
| 11 | phosphorus | 0.086 |
| 12 | carbon | 0.055 |
| 13 | manganese | 0.038 |
| 14 | sulfur | 0:034 |
| 15 | fluorine | 0.033 |
| 16 | chlorine | 0.028 |
| 17 | chromium | 0.015 |
| 18 | barium | 0.0075 |

Priestley studied the behavior of burning substances in this "air." He reported somewhat dramatically: "A candle burned in this air with an amazing strength of flame; and a bit of red-hot wood

crackled and burned with a prodigious rapidity exhibiting an appearance something like that of iron glowing with a white heat and throwing out sparks in all directions."

Priestley was unable to explain what had happened. He was such a firm believer in the phlogiston theory that he did not associate this new gas with the burning process. As we learned in Chapter 1, it was Lavoisier who showed that Priestley's "air" was really an element, which he named oxygen.*

### 5.2 Some physical properties of oxygen

Oxygen is a colorless, odorless gas. It is slightly heavier than air and is slightly soluble in water. (About four quarts of oxygen gas will dissolve in 100 quarts of water under standard conditions.) Oxygen, as we have learned, exists naturally as a diatomic molecule. Oxygen liquefies and freezes only at very low temperatures; therefore, these molecules must have only very slight attraction for one another. At one atmosphere of pressure, oxygen condenses to a liquid at $-183.0°C$. Pale-blue liquid oxygen freezes to a bluish-white solid at $-218.8°C$.

### 5.3 The chief chemical property of oxygen

Oxygen is a very reactive element forming compounds directly with every element except the so-called "rare" gases, which we will study later. The simple compounds that oxygen forms with other elements are called *oxides*. The chemical reaction whereby oxygen combines with another element to form oxides is called *oxidation*. A much broader concept of oxidation will be discussed in Chapter 18. The formation of calcium oxide and of water are examples of two oxidation reactions:

$$2Ca(s) + O_2(g) = 2CaO(s)$$
$$2H_2(g) + O_2(g) = 2H_2O(g)$$

A familiar example of oxidation is the slow formation of rust [hydrated iron(III) oxide] when iron is exposed to oxygen for long periods of time in the presence of moisture:

$$4Fe(s) + 3O_2(g) + 6H_2O(g) = 2Fe_2O_3 \cdot 3H_2O(s)^†$$

**Joseph Priestley** (1733–1804, English). As a result of a very active and stormy life, this dissenting minister was forced to emigrate to America. Among his friends here were Washington, Jefferson, and Franklin. While living in Pennsylvania, Priestley continued his researches, and he made the first careful study of carbon monoxide gas. The highest honor accorded by the American Chemical Society is called the Priestley Medal.

---

* Karl W. Scheele (SHAY leh), the Swedish druggist who discovered chlorine, also prepared oxygen and is credited as its codiscoverer. Scheele's discovery actually came three years before Priestley's work, but he did not publish his results until several years later.

† $Fe_2O_3 \cdot 3H_2O$ is an example of a *hydrate*. In such *solids*, water is part of the compound. For hydrated iron(III) oxide, the oxide and water are present in the definite mole ratio of 1 : 3. The dot in the formula may be treated as a plus sign. In any chemical equation the coefficient before the formula for a hydrate applies to the whole formula. Hydrates are discussed more fully in Chapter 6.

If iron is first heated until it glows, and then placed in a bottle of oxygen, the oxidation reaction is so vigorous that the iron burns brilliantly, throwing off sparks of glowing magnetic iron oxide:

$$3Fe(s) + 2O_2(g) = Fe_3O_4(s)$$

Oxidation reactions are usually accompanied by the liberation of energy. During *slow* oxidation, such as the rusting of iron or the decaying of wood, no light is given off, nor can we easily detect heat evolved because it is given off so slowly. Delicate measurements, however, have proved beyond doubt that the total energy liberated is the same whether the oxidation of a substance takes place slowly or rapidly. Again, this is experimental verification of the Law of the Conservation of Energy. When a substance reacts rapidly with oxygen, with a noticeable liberation of heat and light, the substance is said to be *burning*. (*Combustion* refers to *any* chemical reaction that produces light and heat. *Burning* is only *one* kind of combustion.)

### 5.4 Why some substances catch fire more easily than others

In starting a log fire we often begin by burning paper, which sets fire to kindling wood, which sets fire to the logs. The heat given off by the burning paper causes the wood to catch fire; the heat given off by the burning wood in turn causes the logs to ignite. *The lowest temperature at which a substance catches fire and continues to burn is called the kindling temperature of that substance.*

The kindling temperature of a substance depends upon the size of its particles or its state of *subdivision*. A solid piece of iron has a high kindling temperature, but powdered iron, because of the large surface that is exposed to the oxygen of the air, will burn readily in air. Many dust explosions in flour mills, starch factories, grain elevators, and coal mines are caused by the very rapid oxidation of explosive mixtures of air and finely divided materials. A spark resulting from static electricity or friction often sets off the explosion. (The rates of chemical reactions will be discussed more fully in Chapter 14.)

Fires have been caused by painters' rags saturated with linseed oil. As the linseed oil slowly oxidizes, heat is given off. Unless there is a sufficient circulation of air to remove this heat, the oily rags can become hot enough so that their kindling temperature is reached and they begin burning. Materials igniting in this way are said to undergo *spontaneous combustion*.

### 5.5 Preparation of oxygen in the laboratory

Mercuric oxide may be used, as Priestley showed, to prepare oxygen. The equation for that preparation is:

$$HgO(s) \overset{\triangle}{=} Hg(l) + \tfrac{1}{2}O_2(g)$$

This coal dust explosion, set off deliberately, may have flashed through the mine shaft at more than 5000 miles per hour.

Why is this a safe action?

(The $\Delta$ stands for the fact that the reactant[s] must be heated for the reaction to begin. It is often used in this way.) It is more common, however, to use the white crystalline solid potassium chlorate, $KClO_3$.* The balanced equation for this reaction is, as we have seen:

$$2KClO_3(s) \overset{\Delta}{=\!\!=} 2KCl(s) + 3O_2(g)$$

The oxygen is liberated when the $KClO_3$ is heated, and collected by displacement of water in the collecting bottle. (Fig. 5.1.)

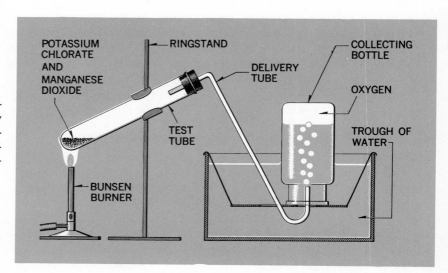

**FIGURE 5.1** Generating oxygen, in a laboratory, by thermal decomposition of potassium chlorate. Why is oxygen collected by the displacement of water?

This method of preparing oxygen has one serious drawback. Unless a very high temperature is reached, oxygen is liberated very slowly. However, when a small amount of powdered manganese dioxide, $MnO_2$, is added to the potassium chlorate before heating, oxygen is liberated more quickly and at a lower temperature.

At the end of the chemical reaction, when oxygen is no longer given off, the *same amount of manganese dioxide with which the experiment started remains*. The weight of manganese dioxide has not been changed in any way. Since manganese dioxide remains unchanged at the end of the reaction, it is not included in the stoichiometric equation. It can be indicated qualitatively as follows:

$$2KClO_3(s) \underset{MnO_2(s)}{\overset{\Delta}{=\!\!=}} 2KCl(s) + 3O_2(g)$$

---

* Though $KClO_3$ is still commonly used in the laboratory preparation of oxygen, its use can be hazardous. $KClO_3$ should never be mixed with combustible materials, such as paper or wood. Under some conditions such mixtures can be explosive.

*A substance that changes the speed of a chemical reaction is called a catalyst, or a catalytic agent.* A catalyst itself may undergo some temporary change, but at the end of the reaction it is present in the same quantity as at the beginning. Catalysis will be discussed more fully in Chapter 14.

Other methods for the laboratory production of oxygen include:

a) The electrolysis of water (Fig. 1.1, page 5)

$$2H_2O(l) \overset{\text{D.C.}}{=} 2H_2(g) + O_2(g)$$

(The D.C. stands for direct electrical current.)

b) The thermal decomposition of *certain dioxides*

$$2PbO_2(s) \overset{\Delta}{=} 2PbO(s) + O_2(g)$$

c) The decomposition of *peroxides* (Fig. 5.2)

$$2Na_2O_2(s) + 2H_2O(l) = 4NaOH(aq) + O_2(g)$$

or

$$H_2O_2(aq) \overset{\text{MnO}_2}{=} H_2O(l) + \tfrac{1}{2}O_2(g)$$

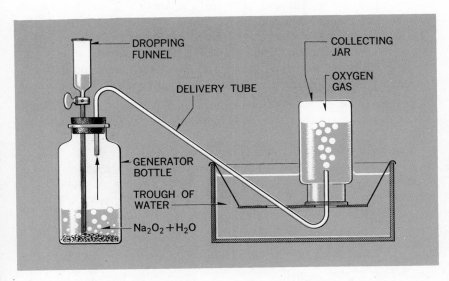

DROPPING FUNNEL

COLLECTING JAR

OXYGEN GAS

DELIVERY TUBE

GENERATOR BOTTLE

TROUGH OF WATER

$Na_2O_2 + H_2O$

**FIGURE 5.2** Generating oxygen, in a laboratory, by decomposition of sodium peroxide

In *peroxides*, two oxygen atoms are chemically bonded to each other as well as to other elements. In *dioxides*, two oxygen atoms are chemically bonded only to another element. (Fig. 5.3.) The reaction between solid peroxides and water to liberate $O_2$ spontaneously could

CARBON DIOXIDE

HYDROGEN PEROXIDE

**FIGURE 5.3** Models of a *di-oxide* and a *peroxide*. Which of the above models would $SO_2$ most closely resemble?

be used as a *test* for peroxides. Simple oxides and dioxides do not react with water to produce $O_2$.

### 5.6  How can we test for oxygen?

When Priestley prepared oxygen from mercuric oxide, he tested the gas by placing burning and glowing substances in it. In each case, the substance burned more vigorously. This method is still used to identify oxygen. A *glowing* wooden splint is thrust into a bottle of the gas. It bursts into flame at once.

No other *odorless* gas will cause a glowing splint to burst into flame in this way. Hence, we can distinguish oxygen from any other odorless gas by this simple procedure. We call such a method of iden-tifying a substance a *test* for that substance. Chemical tests to identify unknown substances play an important part in chemical research.

### 5.7  Oxygen and life

One of the chief chemical changes that occur in the body of any animal is slow oxidation. The oxygen of air that is breathed in passes from the lungs into the blood stream, where it is absorbed by the red blood cells. It is carried by the blood to all parts of the body. Very complicated, catalytically controlled, slow and steady oxidations occur within body cells. These reactions supply a steady amount of internal energy. This energy is necessary for the successful completion of many other complex biochemical reactions that are the basis of life. The inhaled oxygen is eventually exhaled combined in carbon dioxide and water vapor, the final products of the slow oxidations.

When the normal oxygen supply is lowered, a person becomes less alert and may even lose consciousness. Consequently, high-altitude

Scuba gear permits man to extend his environment.                    A controlled atmosphere may aid in survival.

airplanes are pressurized to maintain the same oxygen concentration as at low levels. Balloonists, mountain climbers, divers, and patients with respiratory diseases also often require special oxygen breathing equipment. Lack of oxygen for more than a few minutes will lead to the irreparable damage of brain cells and to death.

### 5.8 Oxides are sources of acids and bases.

The simplest reaction involving oxygen is in the oxidation of elements to form *oxides*. Some further examples of this type of reaction are:

$$P_4(s) + 5O_2(g) \overset{\Delta}{=} P_4O_{10}(s)$$

$$C(s) + O_2(g) \overset{\Delta}{=} CO_2(g)$$

$$S_8(s) + 8O_2(g) \overset{\Delta}{=} 8SO_2(g)$$

$$4Na(s) + O_2(g) = 2Na_2O(s)$$

$$2Sr(s) + O_2(g) = 2SrO(s)$$

When the products of the above reactions are added to water, important secondary effects occur. Solid $P_4O_{10}$, which reacts with a violent evolution of heat, and the gaseous oxides of carbon and sulfur react with water to form solutions having some important similar properties. For example, water solutions of these oxides liberate hydrogen gas when treated with zinc and certain other metals. Each of these solutions tastes sour and causes the blue form of the plant dye *litmus* to turn to the red form. Solutions that have these properties are traditionally called *acids*. *The soluble oxides of nonmetals form acid solutions or, simply, acids.* We call soluble nonmetal oxides *acid anhydrides*. The oxides of phosphorus, carbon, and sulfur we have considered form acids according to the following:

$$P_4O_{10}(s) + 6H_2O(l) = 4H_3PO_4(aq)$$
phosphoric<br>acid

$$CO_2(g) + H_2O(l) = H_2CO_3(aq)$$
carbonic<br>acid

$$SO_2(g) + H_2O(l) = H_2SO_3(aq)$$
sulfurous<br>acid

What about soluble metal oxides? When $Na_2O$ and $SrO$, for example, are added carefully to water (much heat is evolved as a result), solutions having important similar properties result. Water solutions of these and other soluble metal oxides feel slippery to the touch, taste bitter, and *neutralize* the effects of acid. Thus, for example, the red form of litmus reverts to the blue form in the presence of these solutions, which are traditionally called *bases* or *alkalis*. *The soluble oxides of metals form basic or alkaline solutions or, simply, bases.* We call such oxides *basic anhydrides.* The oxides of sodium and strontium we have considered form bases according to the following:

$$Na_2O(s) + H_2O(l) = 2NaOH(aq)$$
$$\text{\small sodium}$$
$$\text{\small hydroxide}$$

$$SrO(s) + H_2O(l) = Sr(OH)_2(aq)$$
$$\text{\small strontium}$$
$$\text{\small hydroxide}$$

Compounds containing the (OH) group are called *hydroxides.* Metal hydroxides, then, are bases.

It is important to recognize that acid and basic solutions can be prepared in other ways than by dissolving nonmetal and metal oxides. In some cases, in fact, acids and bases have no relationship to a parent oxide. For example, hydrochloric acid, $HCl(aq)$, results when gaseous hydrogen chloride, $HCl(g)$, dissolves in water. Ammonium hydroxide, $NH_4OH(aq)$, results when gaseous ammonia, $NH_3(g)$, dissolves in water.

### 5.9 Acids and bases neutralize each other.

We have indicated that bases neutralize the effects of acid. The acid-base neutralization reaction is one of the classical reactions of chemistry, and was known to the ancients. Some examples are:

$$H_3PO_4(aq) + 2NaOH(aq) = Na_2HPO_4(aq) + H_2O(l)$$
$$\text{\small sodium}$$
$$\text{\small monohydrogen}$$
$$\text{\small phosphate}$$

$$H_2CO_3(aq) + Sr(OH)_2(aq) = SrCO_3(s) + 2H_2O(l)$$
$$\text{\small strontium}$$
$$\text{\small carbonate}$$

or

$$HCl(aq) + NH_4OH(aq) = NH_4Cl(aq) + HOH(l)$$
$$\text{\small ammonium}$$
$$\text{\small chloride}$$

Each of the compounds $Na_2HPO_4$, $SrCO_3$, and $NH_4Cl$ is called a *salt,* and the general reaction is, then,

$$\text{acid} + \text{base} = \text{salt} + \text{water.}$$

Our considerations of acids and bases thus far have been based mainly on their formation from *soluble* nonmetal and metal oxides. Most metal oxides are, however, insoluble. Insoluble metal oxides usually have counterpart insoluble hydroxides. These insoluble bases may be formed when a soluble salt and a soluble base react. For example:

$$ZnCl_2(aq) + 2NaOH(aq) = Zn(OH)_2(s) + 2NaCl(aq)$$
$$\text{\small zinc} \qquad\qquad\qquad\qquad \text{\small zinc}$$
$$\text{\small chloride} \qquad\qquad\qquad\qquad \text{\small hydroxide}$$

Insoluble metal oxides not only have their counterpart insoluble hydroxides—$Al_2O_3/Al(OH)_3$, $CuO/Cu(OH)_2$ are other examples—but such oxides behave similarly to those hydroxides in the presence of acids. For example,

$$2HCl(aq) + Zn(OH)_2(s) = ZnCl_2(aq) + 2H_2O(l)$$
$$2HCl(aq) + ZnO(s) = ZnCl_2(aq) + H_2O(l)$$

or

$$6HCl(aq) + 2Al(OH)_3(s) = Al_2Cl_6*(aq) + 6H_2O(l)$$
$$6HCl(aq) + Al_2O_3(s) = Al_2Cl_6*(aq) + 3H_2O(l)$$

Thus, another general chemical reaction is

$$acid + metal\ oxide = salt + water.$$

This reaction is carried on industrially and consumes vast quantities of hydrochloric and sulfuric acids in the removal of oxide scale from iron and steel:

$$6HCl(aq) + \underset{\text{``oxide scale''}}{Fe_2O_3(s)} = 2FeCl_3(aq) + 3H_2O(l)$$

and

$$3H_2SO_4(aq) + Fe_2O_3(s) = Fe_2(SO_4)_3(aq) + 3H_2O(l)$$

Industrially, the process is called *pickling*.

### 5.10 Industry uses immense quantities of oxygen.

Commercial production of high-purity oxygen (99.5% pure or better) in the United States is more than 10,000 tons a day. Almost all of this oxygen is produced from liquid air. (See page 146.) It is estimated that more than 50 per cent of the oxygen produced is used in the manufacture of steel. (See the photographic essay that begins on page 519.)

Oxygen is also used in *oxyacetylene* and *oxyhydrogen* torches, which are employed in the welding of metals such as aluminum and steel.

With the oxyacetylene torch, a flame temperature of about 3400°C may be easily produced. The principle of operation of the oxyacetylene torch is shown in Figure 5.4. The oxygen used in the torch is stored under high pressure in steel cylinders. The acetylene, $C_2H_2$, however, is not under high pressure but is dissolved in a liquid called acetone. The primary reaction which occurs is:

$$2C_2H_2(g) + 5O_2(g) \overset{\Delta}{=} 4CO_2(g) + 2H_2O(g) + heat$$

---

* Note that the true formula for aluminum chloride is $Al_2Cl_6$. Its simplest formula is $AlCl_3$.

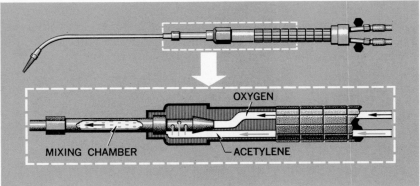

"Scarfing"—an oxyacetylene torch being used to remove surface imperfections from steel.

**FIGURE 5.4** The oxyacetylene torch. How does it differ in use and operation from the Bunsen burner?

Oxygen is used in a variety of other ways, from the manufacture of chemical compounds to the oxidizing of fuels that power rocket engines into outer space.

### 5.11 Ozone

Ten years after Priestley's discovery of oxygen, another form of oxygen gas was reported. Unlike the common and stable form of oxygen, the new gas possessed a peculiar odor and tarnished the metal mercury under normal conditions. It was not until 1840 that Christian F. Schönbein (SHURN bine), a German chemist, isolated this gas. He named it *ozone*, from the Greek word meaning "to smell." Its sharp odor is noticeable around electrically driven machines that are sparking in operation.

Ozone is a pale-blue gas, one and one half times as dense as oxygen. It is much more soluble in water than is oxygen and is more active chemically.

This species of oxygen is prepared by passing electric discharges through either dry air or pure oxygen itself. About eight per cent of the oxygen is converted into pure ozone, although slightly larger yields can be obtained if the temperature is kept low. Molecular weight determinations indicate that ozone is triatomic. Thus, the equation for the conversion of oxygen to ozone is:

$$3O_2(g) = 2O_3(g)$$

Ozone is chemically unstable; it spontaneously changes to oxygen, two volumes of ozone changing into three volumes of oxygen. (Fig. 5.5.) Thus, ozone cannot be stored for long periods of time and is usually produced at the point of its use.

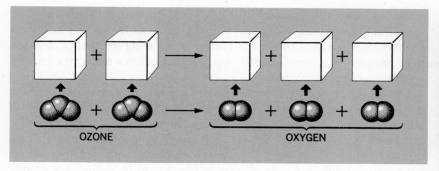

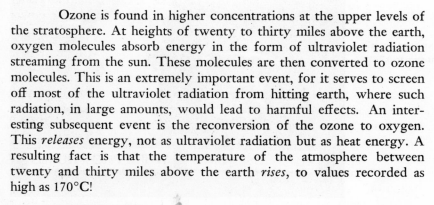

OZONE          OXYGEN

**FIGURE 5.5** Spontaneous decomposition of ozone. How is the Law of Combining Volumes illustrated?

15,000-volt discharges in each of the 204 aluminum-coated glass tubes convert oxygen to ozone in this industrial *ozonator.*

Ozone is found in higher concentrations at the upper levels of the stratosphere. At heights of twenty to thirty miles above the earth, oxygen molecules absorb energy in the form of ultraviolet radiation streaming from the sun. These molecules are then converted to ozone molecules. This is an extremely important event, for it serves to screen off most of the ultraviolet radiation from hitting earth, where such radiation, in large amounts, would lead to harmful effects. An interesting subsequent event is the reconversion of the ozone to oxygen. This *releases* energy, not as ultraviolet radiation but as heat energy. A resulting fact is that the temperature of the atmosphere between twenty and thirty miles above the earth *rises*, to values recorded as high as 170°C!

### 5.12 Uses of ozone

Because of its extreme chemical activity, ozone is used to a limited extent in purifying water. It kills bacteria and other microorganisms in water by reacting with them. In high concentrations it is equally toxic to man. Ozone is also used in purifying air in homes, refrigerators, tunnels, and zoos by reacting with compounds having objectionable odors to form odorless compounds. Small ultraviolet lamps change some of the oxygen in the air into ozone for this deodorizing task. Ozone is also used in the rapid aging of wood and in the drying of varnishes and inks.

### 5.13 What is allotropy?

As we have just learned, oxygen exists in two forms: ordinary oxygen and ozone. *The existence in the same physical state of two or more forms of the same element is a phenomenon called allotropy.* The various allotropic forms of an element have different physical and chemical properties. Ozone, for example, has a higher energy content than oxygen. We have learned that ozone liberates this extra energy on decomposing to oxygen.

Allotropy is not confined to the gaseous state. For example, solid phosphorus commonly occurs in two allotropic forms: white phosphorus and red phosphorus. White phosphorus is poisonous, the red form is not. White phosphorus undergoes spontaneous combustion. Red phosphorus must be heated to reach its kindling temperature. Such unusual differences in allotropic forms will be more understandable when chemical bonding differences in allotropes are considered in later chapters.

The allotropes of phosphorus exposed to air. How would you store white phosphorus?

## VALENCE AND THE WRITING OF FORMULAS

Thus far we have encountered the formulas of many different compounds. Formulas such as $H_2O$, $HCl$, $NaOH$, $Fe_2O_3$, $H_3PO_4$ are just a few. Perhaps you have wondered how it is ever possible to remember all these formulas? You already know how chemical formulas may be determined experimentally. Perhaps you wonder if there is any way to predict what the experiment will show.

### 5.14 The meaning of valence

Consider the *simplest* formulas for the oxide, hydroxide, and chloride of aluminum. They are $Al_2O_3$, $Al(OH)_3$, and $AlCl_3$, respectively. What about the oxide, hydroxide, and chloride of iron considered in this chapter? Their formulas were $Fe_2O_3$, $Fe(OH)_3$, and $FeCl_3$, respectively. If you are told that the formula of an oxide of gallium is $Ga_2O_3$, what do you predict to be the formulas for gallium hydroxide and gallium chloride? If your answers are $Ga(OH)_3$ and $GaCl_3$, you are right.

Consider the formulas for the oxide, hydroxide, and chloride of magnesium. They are $MgO$, $Mg(OH)_2$, and $MgCl_2$. Given the formula of zinc hydroxide to be $Zn(OH)_2$, what do you predict to be the formulas for the oxide and chloride of zinc? Again, if your answers are $ZnO$ and $ZnCl_2$, then you have reasoned correctly. That is, if $Zn(OH)_2$ is similar in formula to $Mg(OH)_2$, then $ZnO$ and $MgO$, and $ZnCl_2$ and $MgCl_2$, are probably similar in formulas.

Finally, consider that $Na_2O$, $NaOH$, and $NaCl$ are the formulas of sodium oxide, sodium hydroxide, and sodium chloride, respectively. What are the formulas of lithium oxide and lithium hydroxide if lithium chloride is $LiCl$? Again, logic demands $Li_2O$ and $LiOH$ to be the answers. Let us tabulate the formulas just considered.

| OXIDES | HYDROXIDES | CHLORIDES |
|---|---|---|
| $Al_2O_3$ | $Al(OH)_3$ | $AlCl_3$ |
| $Fe_2O_3$ | $Fe(OH)_3$ | $FeCl_3$ |
| $Ga_2O_3$ | $Ga(OH)_3$ | $GaCl_3$ |
| $MgO$ | $Mg(OH)_2$ | $MgCl_2$ |
| $ZnO$ | $Zn(OH)_2$ | $ZnCl_2$ |
| $Na_2O$ | $NaOH$ | $NaCl$ |
| $Li_2O$ | $LiOH$ | $LiCl$ |

How might we state the regularities observed? We may say that the chemical combining capacities of aluminum, iron, and gallium are the same *in the compounds given*. The combining capacities of magnesium and zinc are the same, and so are those of sodium and lithium, *in the compounds given*. Do you also see, however, that the combining capacities of chlorine *in chlorides*, and the hydroxyl group *in hydroxides*, are the same?

The combining capacity of an element *in a compound* is called, traditionally, the *valence* of the element. Knowledge of the valences of the elements will be the key to writing correct chemical formulas for compounds of the elements.

### 5.15 Valences have number values.

In order to be able to use valences conveniently to write formulas, it is necessary to establish arbitrary number values for such valences.

For example, let us consider the compound magnesium oxide first. We note a 1:1 atom ratio between magnesium and oxygen atoms in MgO. Clearly, the combining capacities or valences of magnesium and oxygen for each other are the same in this compound. We might, therefore, arbitrarily give the *number value* of 1 for the valence of both magnesium and oxygen in MgO. Using these arbitrary number values, let us now turn to sodium oxide, $Na_2O$. Clearly, from the 2 : 1 atom ratio between sodium and oxygen, the combining capacity or valence of sodium must be *half* that of oxygen. It takes two sodium atoms to satisfy the valence of one oxygen atom. However, if the arbitrary number value for oxygen's valence is 1, then it must be that the number value for sodium's valence is $\frac{1}{2}$. What could have happened had we begun with a consideration of sodium oxide instead of magnesium oxide? The experimental fact that two sodium atoms are required for each oxygen atom in sodium oxide, $Na_2O$, remains unchanged. Thus, looking at the formula $Na_2O$, we can state with certainty that the valence of sodium must be half that of oxygen. Now we might arbitrarily choose as number values for the respective valences the value of 1 for sodium and of 2 for oxygen. Now turn to magnesium oxide, MgO, where it is still apparent that the valences of the two combined elements are identical. In this case the number value for the valence of magnesium must be 2 since in this case the valence of oxygen is 2. So we see that while *the true combining capacity of an element in a compound is fixed*, the arbitrary number value for that combining capacity can vary depending upon an arbitrary starting place. Chemists of the nineteenth century, still strongly influenced by the indivisible atom of Dalton's theory, chose not to have valence number values of a fractional nature.

The number value scheme decided upon by nineteenth century chemists is based on the following definition. *The valence of an element is the number of atoms of hydrogen equivalent to one atom of the element.* Some examples will make this clearer. Consider the following compounds: $HCl$, $H_2O$, $Na_2O$, $FeCl_3$. In the case of hydrogen chloride, $HCl$, and water, $H_2O$, the definition of valence leads directly to valence number values of 1 for chlorine in $HCl$ and 2 for oxygen in $H_2O$. For sodium in $Na_2O$, since the oxygen atom is equivalent to two hydrogens (from $H_2O$), then, indirectly, two sodium atoms in $Na_2O$ are equivalent to two hydrogen atoms. More simply, one sodium atom is equivalent to one hydrogen atom; hence the valence of sodium is, by definition, 1. For iron $FeCl_3$, since the three chlorine atoms are equivalent to three hydrogen atoms (from $HCl$), then, indirectly, the one iron atom must be equivalent to three hydrogen atoms. The valence of iron in $FeCl_3$ is then, by definition, 3. (Fig. 5.6.)

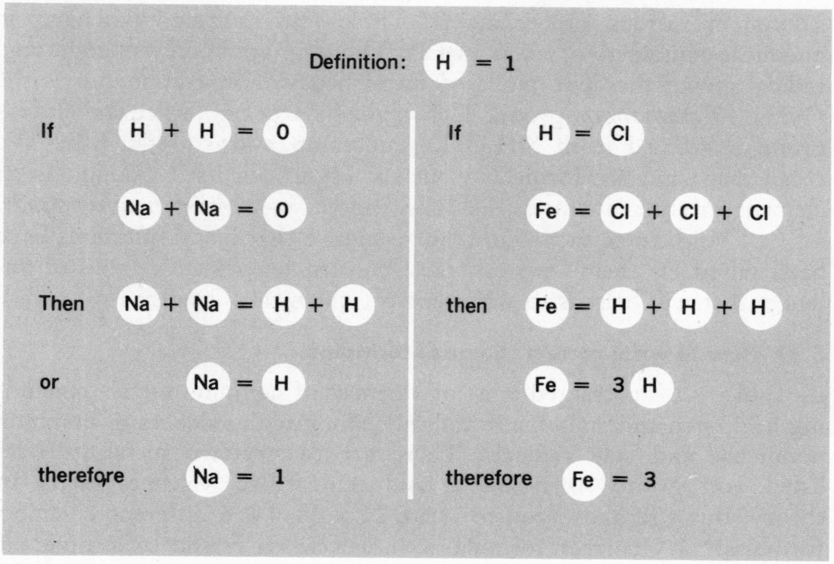

Definition: H = 1

If H + H = O

Na + Na = O

Then Na + Na = H + H

or Na = H

therefore Na = 1

If H = Cl

Fe = Cl + Cl + Cl

then Fe = H + H + H

Fe = 3 H

therefore Fe = 3

**FIGURE 5.6** The valence of an element is the number of atoms of hydrogen equivalent to one atom of the element.

## 5.16 A brief look at the nature of compounds

Before we can go on to write chemical formulas based on the valence of the elements, we must consider briefly some facts about compounds. Quite simply, most chemical compounds we have studied and will study are composed of two types of elements or groups of elements. Most simply, a compound consists of a metal atom combined with a nonmetal atom. Examples of this type of compound are $FeS$, $NaCl$, $Al_2O_3$, and $Zn_3N_2$. Were such *binary compounds*, compounds containing *two* different elements, the only ones possible, the rich variety of chemistry would be lost to us. Fortunately, many thousands of other compounds result from the existence of oxygen-containing acids.

Acids, like nitric acid, $HNO_3$, sulfuric acid, $H_2SO_4$, and carbonic acid, $H_2CO_3$, lead to a host of *salts* in which metal atoms are combined with *groups* of nonmetal atoms derived from the acids. The $(NO_3)$ or *nitrate* group behaves very often as a chemical unit and is found in such salts as $Na(NO_3)$, $Zn(NO_3)_2$, and $Fe(NO_3)_3$—all called nitrates. Observe that the $(NO_3)$ group in $H(NO_3)$ is *equivalent* to one hydrogen atom; hence, its valence is one. The $(SO_4)$ or *sulfate* group and the $(CO_3)$ or *carbonate* group may be similarly considered. What are the valences of the $(SO_4)$ and $(CO_3)$ groups? Carbonic acid, $H_2CO_3$, is the source of not only the $(CO_3)$ group, but also the $(HCO_3)$ or *hydrogen carbonate* (bicarbonate) group. What is the valence of the $(HCO_3)$ group?

Groups of atoms such as $(NO_3)$, $(SO_4)$, $(CO_3)$, and $(HCO_3)$ are often called *radicals* or *acid radicals*. Their true nature will be considered in various later chapters. These acid radicals all behave, in chemical combination, as nonmetals. The only commonly encountered radical giving the appearance of metal behavior in compounds is the $(NH_4)$ or *ammonium* group. This might be expected, since the $(NH_4)$ group is derived from $NH_4OH$, ammonium hydroxide—a base. We recall that bases are formed by metals. Hydrogen itself, though as an element surely a nonmetal, likewise appears metal-like *in compounds*.

With these facts—and we recognize that many questions have been raised by them—we can now construct a valuable table of valences that will help us to write correct chemical formulas.

### 5.17  How to write correct chemical formulas

In Table 5–2 is presented a list of valences of common metals (including hydrogen and ammonium radical), along with valences of common nonmetals and acid radicals. There are twenty-two metal valences listed, and twenty-six nonmetal and acid radical valences listed. In theory, this will allow you to write $22 \times 28 = 616$ different chemical formulas!* [A correct formula is, however, no reason to assume the actual existence of the compound having that formula. For example, $Hg_2O$ is a correct formula for the nonexistent compound mercury(I) oxide.]

### How do we proceed?

1. Write the symbol for the metal element part of the compound first, followed by the symbol for the nonmetal element or acid radical part of the compound. Include the valence numbers for each of the species. These are to be written as *Roman numerals* to the upper right of the symbols; that is, as *superscripts*, $Fe^{II}S^{II}$.

2. If the valences (valence numbers) are equal, no *subscripts* are added. The simplest formula for the compound will then depict a 1 : 1 atom or radical ratio; $Fe^{II}S^{II} = FeS$.

3. If the valences (valence numbers) are not equal, then *Arabic numeral subscripts* will be necessary to equalize combining capacities. This is most simply achieved by writing as a subscript to the symbol of one part of the compound the valence number of the symbol for the other part of the compound. The crossed arrows show the derivation of the subscripts. Again, the subscript 1 is never written in a final formula.

$$Fe_1^{II} \diagdown\!\!\!\!\diagup Cl_2^{I} = FeCl_2$$
$$As_2^{III} \diagdown\!\!\!\!\diagup S_3^{II} = As_2S_3$$

---

* Actually, though $H_2O$ and $HOH$ appear to be different, they are both the formula for water.

**TABLE 5–2** IMPORTANT COMMON VALENCES

| | Monovalent (I) | | Divalent (II) | | Trivalent (III) | |
|---|---|---|---|---|---|---|
| **METALS** | ammonium | $(NH_4)$ | barium | Ba | aluminum | Al |
| | hydrogen | H | calcium | Ca | antimony (III) | Sb |
| | copper (I) or cuprous | Cu | copper (II) or cupric | Cu | arsenic (III) | As |
| | lithium | Li | iron (II) or ferrous | Fe | chromium (III) | Cr |
| | potassium | K | lead (II) or plumbous | Pb | iron (III) or ferric | Fe |
| | silver | Ag | magnesium | Mg | | |
| | sodium | Na | mercury (I) or mercurous | $(Hg_2)$* | | |
| | | | mercury (II) or mercuric | Hg | | |
| | | | tin (II) or stannous | Sn | | |
| | | | zinc | Zn | | |
| **NONMETALS AND ACID RADICALS** | acetate (from acetic acid) | $(CH_3COO)$ | carbonate (from carbonic acid) | $(CO_3)$ | arsenate (from arsenic acid) | $(AsO_4)$ |
| | bromine (*in* bromides) | Br | chromate (from chromic acid) | $(CrO_4)$ | nitrogen (*in* nitrides) | N |
| | chlorate (from chloric acid) | $(ClO_3)$ | dichromate (from dichromic acid) | $(Cr_2O_7)$ | phosphate (from phosphoric acid) | $(PO_4)$ |
| | chlorine (*in* chlorides) | Cl | monohydrogen phosphate (from phosphoric acid) | $(HPO_4)$ | phosphorus (*in* phosphides) | P |
| | cyanide (from hydrocyanic acid) | CN | oxalate (from oxalic acid) | $(OOCCOO)$† | | |
| | dihydrogen phosphate (from phosphoric acid) | $(H_2PO_4)$ | oxygen (*in* oxides) | O | | |
| | fluorine (*in* fluorides) | F | oxygen (*in* peroxides) | $(O_2)$ | | |
| | hydrogen carbonate (from carbonic acid, also called bicarbonate) | $(HCO_3)$ | sulfate (from sulfuric acid) | $(SO_4)$ | | |
| | hydrogen sulfate (from sulfuric acid, also called bisulfate) | $(HSO_4)$ | sulfite (from sulfurous acid) | $(SO_3)$ | | |
| | hydroxyl [from water as H(OH)] | $(OH)$ | sulfur (*in* sulfides) | $(S)$ | | |
| | iodine (*in* iodides) | I | | | | |
| | nitrate (from nitric acid) | $(NO_3)$ | | | | |
| | nitrite (from nitrous acid) | $(NO_2)$ | | | | |
| | permanganate (from permanganic acid) | $(MnO_4)$ | | | | |

* Mercury(I) compounds contain two mercury atoms acting *together* with a valence of II, e.g., mercury(I) chloride, $Hg_2Cl_2$; mercury(I) nitrate, $Hg_2(NO_3)_2$, and mercury(I) chromate, $Hg_2CrO_4$. The corresponding mercury(II) compounds are $HgCl_2$, $Hg(NO_3)_2$, and $HgCrO_4$.

† The oxalate radical is more usually written as $(C_2O_4)$.

4. The symbol for a radical is placed in parentheses only if followed by a subscript greater than one.

$$Fe_1^{II}(SO_4)_1^{II} = FeSO_4$$

$$Fe_1^{II}(NO_3)_2^{I} = Fe(NO_3)_2$$

**EXAMPLE**

What is the formula for copper(I) chloride?

**SOLUTION**

1. Copper has a valence of one, as does chlorine in chlorides. The symbol for copper appears first in the formula, since it is a metal and chlorine is a nonmetal.

$$Cu^I Cl^I$$

2. Since the valence numbers are equal, no subscripts are written, and the subscript for each symbol is understood to be one.

3. The simplest formula for copper(I) chloride is, therefore, CuCl. (The true formula is experimentally determined to be $Cu_2Cl_2$. Use of the valence table will not allow such a prediction to be made.)

**EXAMPLE**

What is the formula for zinc phosphate?

**SOLUTION**

1. Zinc has a valence of 2 and is a metal. The phosphate acid radical has a valence of 3. Zinc appears first in the formula.

$$Zn^{II}(PO_4)^{III}$$

2. Since the valences are unequal, subscripts are required.

$$Zn_3^{II}(PO_4)_2^{III}$$

3. The formula for zinc phosphate is $Zn_3(PO_4)_2$.

The table of valences is a summary of the results of many experiments on the per cent composition of compounds. If you learn the contents and use of that table well, you will be able to begin communicating as a chemist. The use of *correct* chemical formulas will save you great amounts of time and effort as you continue on in your study of chemistry.

To see how well you can use the table of valences, write the formulas for the following compounds. Until you are adept at formula writing, it is strongly suggested that you follow step by step the procedure outlined above.

1. sodium fluoride
2. calcium acetate
3. tin(II) carbonate
4. aluminum sulfate
5. potassium dichromate
6. magnesium bromide
7. zinc phosphide
8. barium peroxide
9. silver chromate
10. arsenic(III) sulfide
11. chromium(III) oxide
12. mercury(II) nitrate
13. calcium oxalate
14. copper(II) hydrogen carbonate
15. iron(III) hydroxide
16. barium dihydrogen phosphate
17. magnesium arsenate
18. lithium aluminum hydride

## 5.18 Some elements have variable valences.

The rich variety of chemistry is further enhanced by the fact that a large number of elements exhibit variable valences. The table of valences given indicates the existence of two valence forms of copper, mercury, iron, and oxygen. The Roman numerals associated with a number of other metal species, Sn(II) and Pb(II), for examples, should imply the existence of other valence forms for those metals. Indeed, Sn(IV) and Pb(IV) are, for example, well-characterized though less common valence forms of tin and lead. The existence of more than one combining capacity for a given element should add further to the list of questions you have compiled in reading and learning about valence. The answers to many of those questions will slowly unfold in the next few chapters.

## 5.19 The names of chemical compounds of metals with nonmetals

We have read about, talked about, and used so many different compounds thus far that it might be useful to summarize a few simple rules of *chemical nomenclature*, the systematic ways of naming compounds. Since most of this chapter has been concerned with compounds formed between metals and nonmetals or acid radicals, we will first consider how such compounds are named.

1. All *binary* compounds, compounds containing *no more than two elements*, have names that end in *-ide*. The compound is named as a derivative of the nonmetal element present in it. Examples are $NaCl$, $Na_2S$, $Na_3N$—sodium chloride, sodium sulfide, and sodium nitride, respectively.

2. Compounds containing metals combined with acid radicals will be *ternary* (three element) or *quaternary* (four element) compounds. Examples of ternary compounds are $NaCN$, $Fe_2(SO_4)_3$, and $Ag_2CrO_4$. Examples of quaternary compounds are $Pb(HSO_4)_2$, $KH_2PO_4$, and $Mg(CH_3COO)_2$. Compounds containing acid radicals are named from the names of the acid radicals.

$NaCN$ = sodium *cyanide* (Note *-ide* ending for a nonbinary compound.)

$Fe_2(SO_4)_3$ = iron(III) *sulfate*

$Ag_2CrO_4$ = silver *chromate*

$Pb(HSO_4)_2$ = lead(II) *hydrogen sulfate*

$KH_2PO_4$ = potassium *dihydrogen phosphate*

3. If the metal element part of the compound has more than one valence form, the name of the formula must clearly indicate which form is present. The modern, and more acceptable, way of achieving this is based on a system of nomenclature first devised by Alfred Stock, a Polish-born American chemist who died in 1946. The Stock System indicates the valence form of an element by a *Roman numeral*, which follows the name in parentheses. Examples are: FeS, iron(II) sulfide; $CrCl_3$, chromium(III) chloride; $TiO_2$, titanium(IV) oxide.

An older nomenclature system uses the stem of the metal's name plus the suffixes *-ous* and *-ic*. The *-ous* ending indicates a lower valence form, the *-ic* ending a higher one. Examples are: $Cu_2O$, cuprous oxide; CuO, cupric oxide; $Hg_2Cl_2$, mercurous chloride; $HgCl_2$, mercuric chloride. In the Stock System, these are more simply called copper(I) oxide, copper(II) oxide, mercury(I) chloride, and mercury(II) chloride.

### 5.20 The names of chemical compounds of nonmetals with each other

In addition to compounds of the type just considered, we will also consider the nomenclature of binary compounds of nonmetals *with each other*. We have come across a number of these in our studies, such as $SO_2$, $CO_2$, and $P_4O_{10}$. These compounds are most simply named according to the *numbers* of atoms of each nonmetal element present. Greek prefixes are used:

| | | | |
|---|---|---|---|
| *mono-* | one | *hexa-* | six |
| *di-* | two | *hepta-* | seven |
| *tri-* | three | *octa-* | eight |
| *tetra-* | four | *ennea-* | nine |
| *penta-* | five | *deca-* | ten |

Some examples:

$SO_2$ = sulfur *dioxide* (*mono*sulfur is understood)

$SO_3$ = sulfur *trioxide*

$P_4O_{10}$ = *tetra*phosphorus *deco*xide (*deca*oxide is not as easy to say)

$S_4N_4 = tetra$sulfur *tetra*nitride

$IF_7 =$ iodine *hepta*fluoride

Another question to be added to the "wondering why" list developed in your reading through this chapter revolves about which nonmetal is written first in a binary compound between nonmetals. Why, for example, do we write $S_4N_4$ instead of $N_4S_4$? Since this and many other questions raised in this chapter will be answered in following chapters, we move on.

## SUMMARY

Oxygen was discovered independently by Scheele and by Priestley, but it was Lavoisier who first showed its relationship to burning. Oxygen is chemically a very active element and combines with most other elements, forming compounds called oxides. During these oxidation reactions, heat is usually evolved. Oxidations occur slowly or rapidly, depending upon the mechanism of the reaction and the state of subdivision of the materials involved. A burnable substance, oxygen, and sufficient heat energy to reach the kindling temperature of the system are the three conditions necessary for burning. The heat evolved from the reaction usually keeps the temperature above the kindling temperature; thus, burnable substances need only be initially ignited.

Oxygen can be prepared in the laboratory by the thermal decomposition of $KClO_3$. $MnO_2$ is usually used to speed up this reaction. In this capacity, $MnO_2$ is a catalyst. A glowing splint can be used as a test for $O_2$.

The soluble oxides of nonmetals form acid solutions when placed in water. The soluble oxides of metals form basic solutions when placed in water. Acid and basic solutions neutralize the effects of one another. The general equation for such a reaction is:

$$acid + base \rightarrow salt + water$$

The triatomic molecular species of oxygen, $O_3$, is prepared by passing an electric discharge through diatomic oxygen. Ozone is an allotropic form of oxygen; it is chemically more active than the diatomic form.

The combining capacity of an element is traditionally called the valence of the element. Knowledge of the valences of the elements is the key to writing correct chemical formulas. Groups of atoms that usually remain together in chemical reactions are called radicals; these groups also have numerical values for their valences. Correct formulas for compounds can be determined by writing the elements of a compound, $X$ and $Y$, with their respective valences, $X^{III}Y^{IV}$, and then crisscrossing these numbers as subscripts to obtain the mole ratio of the elements in the compound—$X_4Y_3$. The names of chemical compounds are derived according to certain rules.

## QUESTIONS AND PROBLEMS

5.1 What properties of "air" did Priestley observe? Why did Priestley believe it was air that was expelled from the red powder?

5.2 Define burning. What three conditions are necessary for burning to take place?

5.3 The term spontaneous combustion is applied to a situation when certain combustible materials suddenly burst into flame. Is this process really spontaneous? Explain.

5.4 Write six equations illustrating the preparation of oxygen by at least four different methods.

5.5 What is a catalyst? Is direct electrical current, D.C., which is required for the electrolysis of water, a catalyst for the reaction? Why?

5.6 Differentiate between a peroxide and a dioxide. What chemical test would you perform to identify a solid as being one or the other?

5.7 Write equations illustrating the oxidation of five different elements to their oxides.

5.8 Write equations illustrating the formation of three different acids from their anhydrides.

5.9 Write equations illustrating the formation of three different bases from their anhydrides.

5.10 Experimentally, what is an acid? a base?

5.11 Write equations illustrating six different acid-base neutralization reactions. Name the salts formed in each case.

5.12 What is allotropy? Give examples of allotropic forms of two different elements.

5.13 If an element is said to have a valence of two, what does this mean?

5.14 Write chemical formulas for the following:

1. sodium nitrate
2. zinc acetate
3. iron(III) sulfate
4. silver arsenate
5. tin(II) bromide
6. potassium nitride
7. mercury(I) chloride
8. magnesium oxalate
9. chromium(III) oxide
10. ferrous phosphate
11. triphosphorus pentanitride
12. arsenic(III) sulfide
13. lithium peroxide
14. ammonium dichromate

15. calcium hydrogen carbonate
16. mercuric iodide
17. disulfur decafluoride
18. aluminum hydroxide
19. dinitrogen tetroxide
20. titanium(III) phosphide
21. ammonium sulfite
22. copper(II) sulfate 5-hydrate
23. iodine trichloride
24. calcium chlorate
25. lead dihydrogen phosphate
26. ammonium sulfate
27. mercurous nitrite
28. tetraiodine enneoxide
29. potassium permanganate
30. cuprous cyanide
31. barium carbonate
32. sodium chromate
33. ferric hydrogen sulfate
34. disulfur heptoxide
35. arsenic acid
36. potassium monohydrogen phosphate
37. dichlorine octoxide
38. sulfurous acid
39. barium peroxide
40. tin(IV) chloride

**5.15** Name the following compounds:

1. $Na_2SO_3$
2. $ZnHPO_4$
3. $FeAsO_4$
4. $AgHSO_4$
5. $SnCrO_4$
6. $K_2CO_3$
7. $P_4S_7$
8. $Hg_2(NO_3)_2$
9. $Mg(CN)_2$
10. $CrCl_3$
11. $FeI_2$
12. $Li_2Cr_2O_7$
13. $HgO$
14. $K_3N$
15. $CuSO_4 \cdot 3H_2O$
16. $I_2O_4$
17. $N_2O_4$
18. $Fe(CH_3COO)_3$
19. $NaNO_2$
20. $Pb(HCO_3)_2$
21. $As_4O_6$
22. $(NH_4)_2SO_4$
23. $P_2I_4$
24. $Ag_2S$
25. $Mg(OH)_2$
26. $Hg(CN)_2$
27. $H_2SO_4$
28. $SbCl_3$
29. $K_2O_2$
30. $CH_3COOH$
31. $H_3PO_4$
32. $Ca(H_2PO_4)_2$
33. $Al_2(C_2O_4)_3$
34. $HOOCCOOH$
35. $Zn(ClO_3)_2$
36. $Br_3O_8$
37. $NH_4F$
38. $Ca(MnO_4)_2$
39. $S_2Cl_2$
40. $SnBr_2$

**5.16** Write chemical equations for each of the following:

a. acetylene$(g)$ + oxygen$(g) \longrightarrow$ carbon dioxide$(g)$ + water$(g)$

b. hydrochloric acid$(aq)$ + aluminum oxide$(s) \longrightarrow$
$\qquad$ aluminum chloride$(aq)$ + water$(l)$

c. ammonium hydroxide$(aq)$ + nitric acid$(aq) \longrightarrow$
$\qquad$ ammonium nitrate$(aq)$ + water$(l)$

d. silver nitrate$(aq)$ + hydrogen sulfide$(aq) \longrightarrow$
$\qquad$ silver sulfide$(s)$ + nitric acid$(aq)$

e. diphosphorus pentasulfide$(s)$ + oxygen$(g) \xrightarrow{\Delta}$
$\qquad$ tetraphosphorus decoxide$(s)$ + sulfur dioxide$(g)$

f. sodium hydroxide$(aq)$ + phosphoric acid$(aq) \longrightarrow$
$\qquad$ sodium dihydrogen phosphate$(aq)$ + water$(l)$

g. mercury(I) nitrate$(aq)$ + iron(III) chloride$(aq) \longrightarrow$
$\qquad$ mercury(I) chloride$(s)$ + iron(III) nitrate$(aq)$

h. sodium hydrogen carbonate$(s) \xrightarrow{\Delta}$
$\qquad$ sodium carbonate$(s)$ + carbon dioxide$(g)$ + water$(g)$

i. ozone$(g) \longrightarrow$ oxygen$(g)$

j. sulfur trioxide($g$) + water($l$) ⟶ sulfuric acid($aq$)

k. tin($s$) + phosphoric acid($aq$) ⟶
$$\text{hydrogen}(g) + \text{tin(II) phosphate}(s)$$

l. chlorine($aq$) + copper(II) bromide($aq$) ⟶
$$\text{copper(II) chloride}(aq) + \text{bromine}(l)$$

m. silver nitrate($aq$) + sodium hydroxide($aq$) ⟶
$$\text{silver oxide}(s) + \text{water}(l) + \text{sodium nitrate}(aq)$$

n. iron($s$) + sulfuric acid($aq$) ⟶
$$\text{hydrogen}(g) + \text{iron(III) sulfate}(aq)$$

o. ammonium acetate($s$) + barium hydroxide($aq$) $\xrightarrow{\Delta}$
$$\text{ammonia}(g) + \text{barium acetate}(aq) + \text{water}(l)$$

p. tin(IV) oxide($s$) + carbon($s$) $\xrightarrow{\Delta}$
$$\text{tin}(s) + \text{carbon monoxide}(g)$$

q. calcium hydrogen carbonate($s$) + acetic acid($aq$) ⟶
$$\text{calcium acetate}(aq) + \text{carbon dioxide}(g) + \text{water}(l)$$

r. barium fluoride($s$) + sulfuric acid($aq$) $\xrightarrow{\Delta}$
$$\text{barium hydrogen sulfate}(aq) + \text{hydrogen fluoride}(g)$$

s. lead(II) sulfite($s$) + hydrochloric acid($aq$) ⟶
$$\text{sulfur dioxide}(g) + \text{water}(l) + \text{lead(II) chloride}(s)$$

t. potassium chromate($aq$) + sulfuric acid($aq$) ⟶
$$\text{potassium dichromate}(aq) + \text{potassium sulfate}(aq) + \text{water}(l)$$

**5.17** A manufacturer bottles oxygen gas at 0.0°C and 20.0 atmospheres of pressure in 22.4 l cylinders. **a.** What weight of $KClO_3$ does he need as a source of oxygen for each cylinder? **b.** What weight of oxygen does each cylinder contain? **c.** What is his likely source of oxygen?

Ans.  **b.** 640 g

**5.18 a.** How many moles of $O_2$ gas at 30.0°C and 750 torrs will be obtained from the reaction of 0.390 g of $Na_2O_2$ with water? **b.** What volume will the oxygen occupy if dry under the given conditions of temperature and pressure?

Ans.  **b.** 63.0 ml

**5.19** $5.20 \times 10^2$ g of acetylene are dissolved in acetone for use in an oxyacetylene torch. What volume of $O_2$ must be stored at 27.0°C and 60.0 atm to react with all the acetylene?

**5.20 a.** If $1.92 \times 10^2$ g of oxygen gas are converted completely to ozone gas at −50.0°C, what weight of ozone gas will result? **b.** If the reaction occurs in a reaction chamber of fixed 50.0 l volume, what will be the pressure within the chamber before and after reaction? **c.** If the ozone is bubbled into a solution of silver nitrate, the unusual, black silver(II) oxide forms according to: $\quad 2AgNO_3(aq) + O_3(g) + H_2O(l) =$
$$2AgO(s) + O_2(g) + 2HNO_3(aq)$$

What weight of AgO is theoretically possible from the amount of ozone produced in part **a** of this problem reacting with an excess of aqueous $AgNO_3$? **d.** What volume of $O_2$, measured at STP, can also be formed?

Ans.   **b.** 2.20 atm before reaction; 1.47 atm after reaction;
     **d.** 89.6 l

**5.21** The four elements $W$, $X$, $Y$, and $Z$ are found to have the following atomic weights relative to the atomic weight of hydrogen being one:

    $W = 8$      $X = 11$      $Y = 15$      $Z = 22$

Compounds of the four elements show the following weight ratios:

| COMPOUND | WEIGHT RATIO |
|---|---|
| 1. $W$ with $X$ | 6:11 |
| 2. $W$ with $Y$ | 4:10 |
| 3. $Z$ with $Y$ | 22:15 |
| 4. $Z$ with $X$ | 2:1 |

   **a.** What are the formulas for compounds 1, 2, 3, and 4?
   **b.** What are the valences of $W$, $X$, $Y$, and $Z$?

# SUGGESTED READINGS

Crosland, M. P. *Historical Studies in the Language of Chemistry.* Harvard University Press, 1962.

Jaffe, Bernard. *Crucibles: The Story of Chemistry* (paperback). Fawcett, 1962. Chapter 3 tells the story of Priestley.

Partington, J. R. *A Short History of Chemistry* (paperback). Harper, 1960.

*For the world was built in*
*order and the atoms march in tune.*

*Ralph Waldo Emerson* (1803–1882)

**CHAPTER 6** | # Liquids and Solids

We saw in Chapter 2 how a model of atoms and an atomic theory were evolved to explain certain behavior of elements in chemical reactions. Dalton's atomic theory can explain the existing experimental fact of the constant chemical composition of compounds formed from elements. Moreover, the theory was extended in Chapters 2 and 3 to apply to the ideal physical behavior of gases. Atoms or molecules in the gaseous state were also pictured as indivisible particles but moving *independently* of each other. This model enabled us to understand why experimental relationships such as Boyle's and Charles's laws might exist. However, no real gas behaves ideally under all conditions of pressure and temperature. All gases deviate from ideal behavior particularly at high pressure and low temperature. The following data and their graphical representation clearly show the behavior of *real* rather than ideal gases. (Fig. 6.1.)

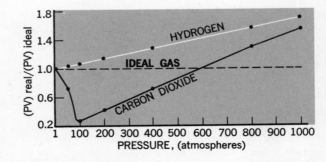

**FIGURE 6.1** Behaviors of different real gases deviate to varying extents from that of an ideal gas.

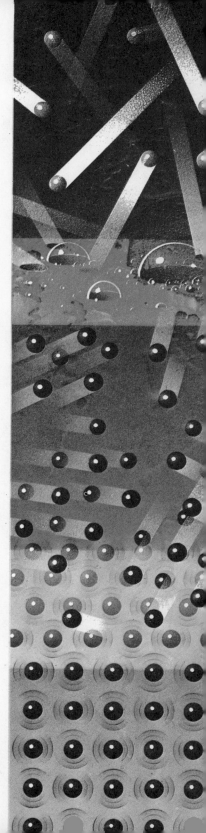

**TABLE 6–1** $P \times V$ Values for $H_2$ and $CO_2$ Relative to the Constant $P \times V$ Value of an Ideal Gas at Different Pressures

| Pressure (atm) | $\dfrac{PV_{H_2}}{PV_{\text{ideal gas}}}$ | $\dfrac{PV_{CO_2}}{PV_{\text{ideal gas}}}$ |
|---|---|---|
| 1.0000 | 1.0000 | 1.0000 |
| 50.000 | 1.0330 | 0.7413 |
| 100.00 | 1.0639 | 0.2695 |
| 200.00 | 1.1336 | 0.4087 |
| 400.00 | 1.2775 | 0.7178 |
| 800.00 | 1.5665 | 1.2990 |
| 1000.0 | 1.7107 | 1.5525 |

The *real* behavior of gases is due to the fact that gaseous atoms or molecules do *not* move independently of each other. They do exert an attraction upon each other. From what does this attraction arise? Our simple model of atoms cannot account for it. Our marble-like model is incomplete.

## THE LIQUID STATE

The fact that substances exist in liquid and solid states clearly indicates the existence of attractive forces between the atoms or molecules that make up those substances. Since gaseous atoms or molecules do deviate from ideal behavior under certain conditions of temperature and pressure, we must alter our model of atoms to account for this fact. We must impart attractive forces to the hard, spherical, indivisible atoms. What the nature of these attractive forces might be must await our attention until later. Now, however, we will consider how the presence of these forces could lead to real rather than ideal gas behavior.

How might we alter our simple model of atoms to give the marbles the ability to attract each other? Let us imagine the marbles with magnets buried within them. We know, experimentally, that the force of attraction between magnets becomes more pronounced as magnets approach each other more closely. We also can determine that as magnets are placed farther and farther apart from each other the force of attraction between them decreases until, in effect, it vanishes. Thus, depending on the distance between them, magnets can attract each other with varying strengths or not at all. So, we propose, do atoms and molecules behave in the gaseous state. We are now ready to consider why gases might deviate from ideal behavior when pressure is increased and temperature is decreased.

### 6.1 A model for real gas behavior

Picture the magnetized marbles rolling along straight-line paths chaotically in some container. If the marbles were moving very fast and if, also, the container was large, the marbles would not stay near each other for very long. Any marble that came close enough to another one to experience a magnetic force of attraction would deviate slightly from its straight-line path but very quickly would be out of range of the attractive force. Under these conditions the observable effect of the magnetic force on the motion of the marbles would be very small. Now, however, let us either decrease the speed of the marbles, or decrease the size of the container. In either event, the marbles will now spend more time near each other, and the attractive forces between them will, therefore, be more pronounced.

The deviation from ideal gas behavior can be understood in the same manner. Lowering the temperature leads to a decrease in molecular motion. Increasing the pressure forces molecules closer to each other. As a result, the gas molecules approach each other and remain close to each other for periods of time that are long enough for *intermolecular* attractive forces to influence the behavior of neighboring molecules. The deviation from ideal gas behavior by real gases, particularly at low temperatures and high pressures, is thus understandable in light of intermolecular attractive forces. If these intermolecular attractive forces are like magnetic forces, the *lack* of deviation from ideality by real gases at high temperatures and low pressures can also be understood.

## 6.2 Condensation of gases

When gas molecules are cooled, they are slowed down. By virtue of their decreased velocity, they remain near each other for greater lengths of time as they move about. As a result, the attractive forces that exist between molecules can take hold. Therefore, at lower temperatures, molecules will cling to each other as if they were magnets. These large collections, or *aggregates*, of gas molecules will move as units. These aggregates will continue to attract single molecules as well as other aggregates. Consequently, they continue to grow in size. A point is reached when these aggregates become so large that they are visible as particles of fog or mist. Another point is reached at which the kinetic energy of the aggregates is insufficient to overcome the *potential energy* of attraction associated with gravitational forces. Then the droplets or particles of fog fall and collect as a *liquid*. The process just described is most simply called *condensation*. The condensation of a liquid from the gaseous state is the most direct evidence for the existence of intermolecular attractive forces.

All gases will condense at low temperatures and elevated pressures. Depending upon the strength of the intermolecular attractive forces of a given gaseous species, a wide variety of temperatures and pressures may be required. At one atmosphere of pressure, for example, water vapor *first* begins to condense at 100°C. Under the same conditions of pressure, neon gas must be cooled to −245.8°C to condense. At higher pressures it would not be necessary to cool the two gases as low to achieve condensation.

## 6.3 The critical temperature of gases

It might seem possible to apply so much pressure to a gas that it would condense regardless of the temperature. Experimentally, this is not realized. There is one temperature for every gas known *above which that gas may not be liquefied no matter how much pressure is applied.* That temperature is called the *critical temperature* of the gas.

In terms of our new model of gases, the critical temperature corresponds to that temperature above which the average kinetic energy of molecules is high enough always to exceed the effect of intermolecular attractive forces, no matter how closely the molecules approach each other. Aggregation can never take place. Liquefaction can never take place.

At the critical temperature, $T_c$, of a gas it is necessary to apply pressures in excess of one atmosphere to achieve liquefaction. The critical pressure, $P_c$, of a gas *is the pressure that must be applied to a gas at its critical temperature in order for liquefaction to occur.* Table 6–2 lists the critical constants of some common gases.

**TABLE 6–2**  CRITICAL CONSTANTS OF SOME COMMON GASES

| Gas | $T_c(°K)$ | $P_c(atm)$ |
|---|---|---|
| Ammonia, $NH_3$ | 405.5 | 111.5 |
| Carbon dioxide, $CO_2$ | 304.1 | 72.9 |
| Chlorine, $Cl_2$ | 417 | 76 |
| Helium, He | 5.1 | 2.26 |
| Hydrogen, $H_2$ | 33.2 | 12.8 |
| Nitrogen, $N_2$ | 126.0 | 33.5 |
| Oxygen, $O_2$ | 154.3 | 49.7 |
| Sulfur dioxide, $SO_2$ | 430.3 | 77.7 |
| Water, $H_2O$ | 647.3 | 218.2 |

### 6.4 Evaporation of liquids

Having considered in some detail the condensation of gases to the liquid state, we turn to the equally familiar reverse change of state, the evaporation of liquids to the vapor state.

In a liquid, molecules still possess kinetic energy. Within the body of the liquid, molecular kinetic energies never become large enough, however, for molecules to move very far apart from one another. On the other hand, surface molecules, which are not subject to attractive force in all dimensions, often do gain sufficient kinetic energy to break away from the surface and enter the gas phase. (Fig. 6.2.) Since kinetic energy increases with temperature, the evaporation process is enhanced at higher temperatures.

### 6.5 Evaporation is a cooling process.

It is a common observation that when a liquid evaporates from the skin, the skin feels cooler. The body's mechanism for cooling in hot weather is the perspiration process. Liquid molecules in contact with the skin absorb heat energy. That heat energy from the skin is converted into the kinetic energy that enables the molecules to break away from each other and into the vapor state.

The heat absorption necessary for evaporation is the key to the refrigeration process. In the usual refrigeration mechanisms, one step involves the very rapid evaporation of a liquid from a high-pressure to a low-pressure state. The heat required for this conversion is absorbed from the surrounding atmosphere, which becomes cooler. In a well-insulated refrigerator system, low temperatures can be reached and maintained indefinitely through a cyclic process that includes the important evaporation step.

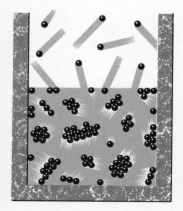

**FIGURE 6.2** Representation of molecular behavior in the liquid state

### 6.6 Liquid air

As we have noted, all gases can be liquefied. Air, which is a mixture of oxygen, nitrogen, argon, and a few other gases in much smaller

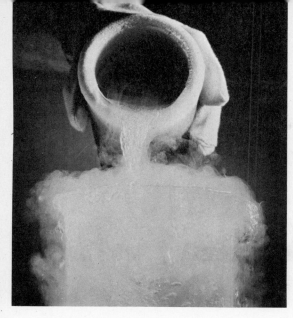

Liquid air

amounts, is no exception. In *Gulliver's Travels* a famous academy was visited, and Jonathan Swift reports how some of its scientists were condensing air and letting the *liquid air* flow like water. Swift believed the liquefaction of air a dream never to be realized. Yet today liquid air is one of our most useful products and thousands of tons of it are manufactured each year.

Liquid air, made from air from which water vapor and carbon dioxide have been removed by absorption, is a pale-blue liquid almost as dense as water. It contains about 21 per cent oxygen and 78 per cent nitrogen, and it begins to boil at −190°C. When liquid air boils, the liquid nitrogen in it boils off first, and the mixture becomes richer and richer in liquid oxygen. Liquid air is used chiefly as a source of oxygen, nitrogen, argon, and the other gases of the atmosphere. These gases are boiled off at different temperatures.

Because of the great tendency of liquid air to evaporate, it is necessary that it be kept in special containers called *Dewar flasks*, which are similar in construction to the familiar *Thermos bottle*. Because of its extremely low temperature, great care should be taken in handling liquid air. The properties of substances change dramatically when immersed in liquid air. Liquid mercury becomes a solid and is hard enough to be used as a hammer head, whereas lead becomes elastic, and rubber turns hard and brittle. Many metals become far better conductors of electricity at liquid air temperatures. The resistance of copper to the passage of an electric current, for example, is decreased 50 times.

## 6.7 Vapor pressure and how it is measured

When a liquid evaporates, the vapor formed exerts a pressure above the liquid. The experimental determination of the vapor pressure of

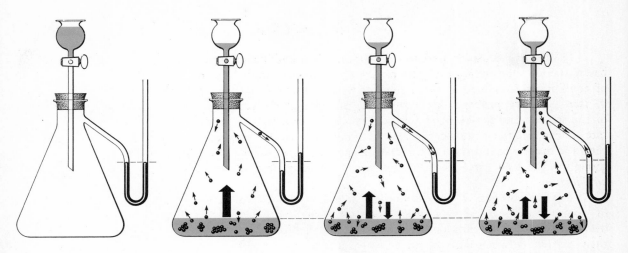

**FIGURE 6.3a–d** The vapor pressure of a liquid is measured in a closed system at constant temperature.

liquids is shown schematically in Figures 6.3a, b, c, d. We note that the vapor pressure is measured in a *closed system* at a constant temperature. (Fig. 6.3a.) Initially, molecules escape, at a *constant rate of evaporation*, from the liquid surface into the vapor phase only. (Fig. 6.3b.) As the concentration of vapor molecules increases, vapor molecules begin, in their random motion, to strike the liquid surface and to condense there. Slowly, the *rate* of condensation increases from its low value. All the while the liquid level slowly drops, and the mercury level of the manometer slowly changes to indicate a rise in pressure *due only to vapor*. (Fig. 6.3c.) In time, a point is reached when the rate of condensation has increased and *exactly equals* the rate of evaporation. At this point there is no further observable drop in liquid level. The atmosphere now holds the maximum amount of vapor it can *at the given temperature*. The atmosphere is said to be *saturated*. The manometer will show a final, steady vapor pressure. (Fig. 6.3d.) This is the *saturated vapor pressure* of the liquid at the given temperature. It is this pressure that is experimentally measured and recorded.

### 6.8 Vapor pressure and equilibrium

The *steady state* that is attained between a liquid and its vapor is an important example of an *equilibrium system*. As observed in the measurement of vapor pressure, an equilibrium state may be defined as *that condition of a system for which no further change in measurable properties of the system is apparent*. In the case of a liquid in equilibrium with its vapor at a constant temperature, there is no observed change in the liquid level or in the vapor pressure. This definition of equilibrium, based on experimental observations, is an *operational definition*.

We may consider a second definition of an equilibrium state, based on our *interpretation* of the experimental observations. A state of equilibrium is defined as *that condition of a system when the rates of two opposing processes are equal.* We interpreted the attainment of the steady state between a liquid and its vapor as being due to the rate of evaporation equaling the rate of condensation. To emphasize the *idea* that at equilibrium two opposing processes *are taking place,* though at the same rate, chemists often speak of the state of *dynamic equilibrium.*

The definition of the equilibrium state based on interpretation of observed facts is called a *conceptual* definition. The relationship between conceptual definitions and operational definitions is the same, then, as that between theory and experiment. Just as a theory must change to fit new experimental facts, so, too, will conceptual definitions change when new experimental facts are discovered.

Symbolically, the chemist indicates the equilibrium state by means of double arrows, ⇌. The equilibrium state we have just considered would be symbolized, therefore, as:

$$\text{liquid} \rightleftharpoons \text{vapor}$$

## 6.9 Vapor pressure and temperature

The vapor pressure of a liquid depends upon the ability of liquid surface molecules to overcome the effect of intermolecular forces of attraction holding them to the surface. If the surface molecules have sufficiently great kinetic energies, those forces will be overcome. Thus, vapor pressure depends on, or is a function of, kinetic energy. Kinetic energy, in turn, is a function of temperature, and therefore, vapor pressure must also be a function of temperature. In Figure 6.4 are shown the vapor pressures of water, acetone, and ethylene glycol.

Close examination of Figure 6.4 shows that the vapor pressure of acetone is higher than that of water, at all temperatures. Accordingly, we generally say that acetone is more *volatile* than water. Ethylene glycol, common *permanent antifreeze,* on the other hand, is less volatile than water.

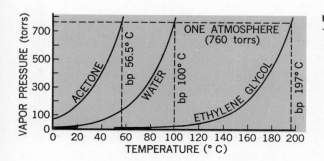

**FIGURE 6.4** Vapor pressure curves for different liquids. The *normal boiling point* is indicated.

### 6.10 Boiling

In Figure 6.4 the pressure of 760 torrs has been singled out, and we see that the temperatures at which the vapor pressures of acetone, water, and ethylene glycol equal 760 torrs are 56.5°C, 100°C, and 197°C, respectively. These temperatures are the *normal boiling points* of the three liquids. The *normal boiling point of a substance is that temperature at which its vapor pressure equals one atmosphere (760 torrs) of pressure.*

Boiling of a liquid, as opposed to simple evaporation, is characterized by the presence of vapor bubbles within the body of the liquid. The vapor pressure within the bubbles exceeds the external pressure on them; consequently, they are able to escape. Unlike evaporation, which is a surface phenomenon, boiling occurs *throughout* a liquid.

### 6.11 The nature of liquids

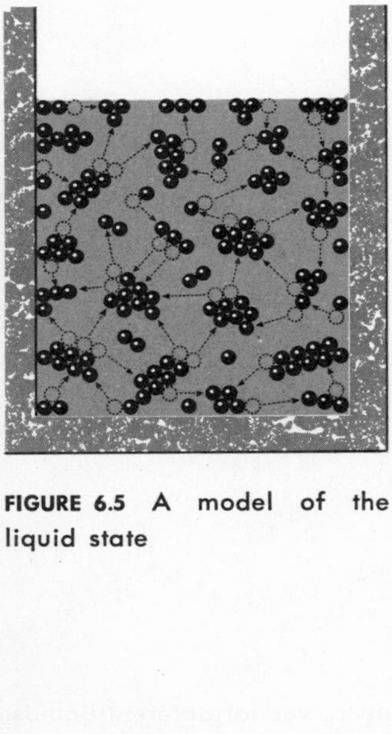

**FIGURE 6.5** A model of the liquid state

Liquids, unlike gases, do not change their volume to any appreciable extent with changes in pressure or temperature. This difference in behavior between a gas and a liquid is explained by the fact that the molecules in a gas have relatively large spaces between them, whereas the molecules in a liquid are packed closely together. Liquids are *fluid,* which indicates that even though the molecules are held together by attractive forces, these forces are not strong enough to hold the molecules rigidly in place. Many different methods of study provide us with a model of liquids wherein there are *clusters,* or *groups, of molecules* and there is a continuous decrease and increase in the size of these clusters from only a few molecules to perhaps as many as 100 molecules. Chemists speak of the *short range order* in liquids. By short range order, they mean that the molecules are grouped in an orderly fashion within these small clusters but that there is no order or regularity that extends over the whole body of the liquid. (Fig. 6.5.) It is in the ultimate of condensed phases, the solid state, that order and regularity appear uniformly. It is to the solid state we now turn.

## THE SOLID STATE

When a liquid freezes, fluidity is lost and the resulting solid is rigid. This rigidity of the solid state would suggest that the kinetic energy of the molecules in a solid is so small that the attractive forces can hold the molecules rigidly in place. Again, the structure of solids has been investigated by a large variety of techniques. The evidence is that *solids have an ordered structure that continues throughout the extent of the solid.* Thus, solids have *long range order.* Liquids may be considered to be composed of very small, solid-like clusters packed to-

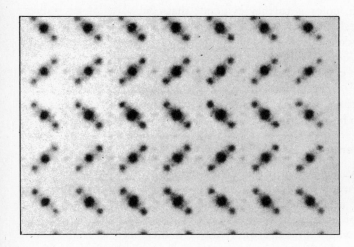

A 44 million diameter magnification of atoms within a crystal of pyrite, $FeS_2$. Crystalline solids have *long range order.*

gether, whereas a solid is a single, large cluster. *Solids that have a repeated pattern of internal order throughout, resulting in well-defined forms, are known as crystals.* The word *crystal* is derived from a Greek word meaning "clear ice." All metals and most solid elements and compounds are capable of assuming a crystalline form, showing sharp edges and flat surfaces.

### 6.12 Water of crystallization

The familiar compound washing soda, a form of sodium carbonate, exists as a crystalline solid. When a crystal of washing soda is heated or even exposed to air, it gives off water and crumbles to a white powder. The weight of water liberated bears a fixed ratio to the weight of the crystal and from this we can conclude that the water is united chemically in the compound of which the crystal is composed. *Water that is thus chemically united with a substance is called water of crystallization,* or *water of hydration.* Such water is often rather loosely held in chemical combination and may be easily expelled. In the symbolism of chemical formulas, the water of crystallization is usually shown separated from the rest of the formula by a centered dot. For washing soda, the formula is $Na_2CO_3 \cdot 10H_2O$. A substance that contains water of crystallization is called a *hydrate.*

Another common hydrate is crystallized copper sulfate. When this blue-colored compound is heated, its water of crystallization is liberated and it, too, crumbles to a white powder.

$$CuSO_4 \cdot 5H_2O(s) \rightarrow CuSO_4(s) + 5H_2O(g)$$

copper sulfate     copper sulfate
5-hydrate     (anhydrous)
(blue)     (white)

This change in color is further evidence that the water of crystallization is chemically united with the copper sulfate. Use is made of the difference in color between white anhydrous copper sulfate and the blue hydrated copper sulfate as a test for water.

Many crystalline substances, such as sugar, $C_{12}H_{22}O_{11}$, do not contain water of crystallization. They are said to be *anhydrous*, meaning *without water*. Crystals that have lost their water of crystallization are also said to be anhydrous.

## 6.13 Efflorescence

Crystallized washing soda is said to be *efflorescent*, which means that *it gives up its water of crystallization on exposure to air*. The molecules of water have a tendency to escape from the crystal. When they do, they exert a pressure that is known as the *vapor pressure* of the solid hydrate. The vapor pressure of hydrates is measured as is the vapor pressure of liquids. Any moisture in the air around the hydrate exerts its own vapor pressure, which acts to prevent the escape of the water in the hydrate. If the vapor pressure of the hydrate is greater than that of the water vapor present in the air, the hydrate loses water and is said to *effloresce*. The drier the air, the faster the loss of water of crystallization.

## 6.14 Deliquescent substances take up water.

Dry calcium chloride when left exposed to air is found to increase in weight due to the absorption of water from the atmosphere. Such a substance is said to be *deliquescent*. Its hydrated form has a vapor pressure that is less than that of the water vapor of the air at ordinary temperatures. The higher the amount of water vapor in the air, the faster the process of deliquescence. Deliquescence ceases when the hydrate formed has a vapor pressure equal to that of the water vapor in the air.

Calcium chloride is often used to sprinkle dry roads, tennis courts, and coal mines. It absorbs moisture from the air and, in this way, helps to keep the dust down. Magnesium chloride, an impurity found in common table salt, is also deliquescent. Removal of the magnesium chloride leads to a pure table salt that remains dry in damp weather, that does not cake, and that pours easily.

Deliquescent substances may be used as *drying*, or *dehydrating*, agents. When used in the laboratory, these drying agents, or *desiccants*, are often placed in the lower compartment of a vessel known as a desiccator; the upper compartment, only partially separated from the lower, contains the substance to be dried. It must be noted, of course, that a substance cannot be dried in a desiccator if it is more deliquescent than the drying agent which is used.

The desiccator is an important laboratory apparatus. How does this apparatus function?

### 6.15 The melting of solids

As heat energy is added to a solid, it is absorbed by the molecules in the rigidly ordered solid state structure. The absorbed energy is converted to molecular kinetic energy. The motion of molecules within a crystal is restricted to vibrations to and fro about an equilibrium position, since intermolecular attractive forces are very strong in crystals. (Figure 6.6.) As energy is added continuously, molecular vibrations increase markedly. This is evident from an increase in the temperature of the solid. Finally, enough heat energy will have been added to the solid so that molecular vibrations are strong enough to overcome the long range forces of order present; the solid structure begins to break down. Individual molecules as well as large aggregates of molecules break apart from each other. The long range order of solids is replaced by the short range order characteristic of liquids. The solid has melted.

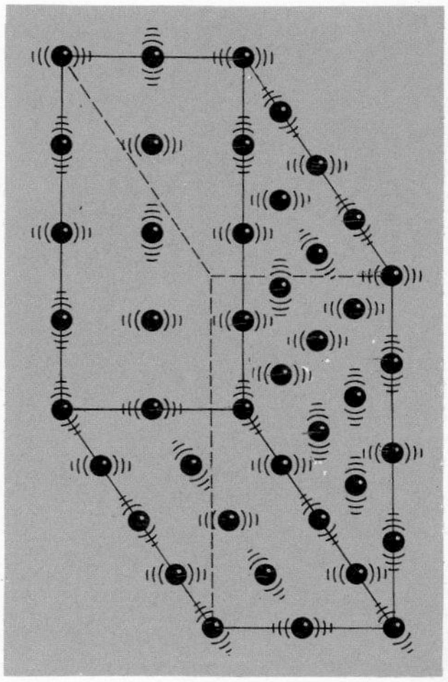

The temperature at which a solid exists *in equilibrium* with its *melt* is called the melting point of the solid. At the melting point solid melts at the same rate liquid freezes:

$$solid \rightleftharpoons liquid$$

If this equilibrium system is thermally isolated from its environment (no heat enters or leaves the system), there will be no apparent change in the amounts of solid and liquid present. On the other hand, if heat energy is added to the system at the melting point, that energy will be absorbed until all the solid melts with *no increase in the temperature.* If heat is removed from the system at its melting point, liquid will freeze until completely converted to solid with *no decrease in the temperature.* (Fig. 6.7.)

**FIGURE 6.6** Vibrational motion within a crystal.

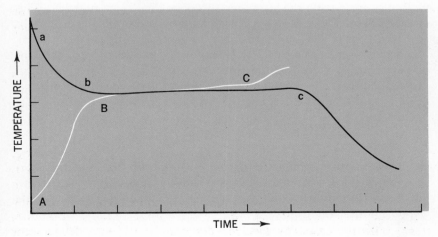

**FIGURE 6.7** A heating curve and a cooling curve for the same pure substance. Describe the physical appearances and transitions of the substance indicated by *curve* ABC and by *curve* abc.

### 6.16  A closer look at the melting of solids

It is important to review carefully and in detail the behavior of a solid on heating. Such a review will help you to understand extremely important facts that are very often confused by people—*heat is a form of energy, and temperature is not*. Recall that we have previously learned that temperature is a measure of the average kinetic energy of molecules. Further, we can say that temperature is a measure of the "hotness" of matter. When the average kinetic energy of the molecules in a piece of matter increases, we can "feel" the piece of matter become hotter—we can measure a rise in temperature.

Heat, though, is a form of energy, and when it is absorbed by matter, heat energy must be conserved by its conversion to other forms of energy. Examine again Figure 6.7. As heat energy is added to a solid at its melting point (point B), the *temperature* of the equilibrium system

$$solid \rightleftharpoons liquid$$

*remains constant* until the solid has completely melted (from point B to point C). Since the temperature remains constant, the average molecular kinetic energy remains constant. Therefore, the heat energy being absorbed during the melting of a solid is *not* being converted into energy of motion. Where does the absorbed heat energy go? When matter absorbs heat energy without an increase in temperature, the heat energy is being converted totally to stored energy, or *potential energy*.

At the melting point of a solid, the long range order holding molecules in a rigid pattern is completely broken down. Energy is required to break that long range order. Energy is required to break molecules apart from the attractive forces holding them together. This energy is stored as a "keeping apart" kind of energy. Under the right conditions, separated molecules can, however, return to their initial, unseparated state. When this happens, the "keeping apart" kind of potential energy stored within them is released in the converted form of heat energy. The amount of this released heat energy is exactly equal to the amount of heat energy that was absorbed during the melting process.

### 6.17  Heat energy and the calorie

We have carefully noted the distinction between heat and temperature. Since the use of temperature scales for measuring temperature differences is familiar to us, we might next consider how to express *amounts* of heat energy.

We must first recognize that energy, by its very nature, cannot be directly measured. In attempting to measure energy we are limited to measuring properties of matter that are determined by the energy content of matter. For example, we are indirectly measuring molecular kinetic energies when we measure the temperature of something. Since heat energy, too, cannot be directly measured, scientists have established an indirect way of measuring such energy. They have arbitrarily defined a unit amount of heat energy in terms of directly measurable properties of matter. This unit amount of energy is called the *calorie*. The calorie is defined as *the amount of heat energy necessary to increase the temperature of one gram of water by 1°C.* Note carefully that the measurable properties of matter (water) that are used in defining the calorie are weight and temperature.

With this definition it is possible to calculate amounts of heat energy absorbed or liberated by matter. For example, if a sample of 1.00 g of water increases in temperature by 10.0°C, that sample, by definition, must have absorbed 10.0 calories of heat energy. That is:

$$\text{Number of calories absorbed} = (1.00 \text{ g}) \left( \frac{1.00 \text{ cal}}{\text{g-deg}} \right)^{\dagger} (10.0 \text{ deg})$$

$$\text{Number of calories absorbed} = 10.0 \text{ cal}$$

## 6.18 Heat absorption and heat capacity

We might next consider the heat absorption properties of different substances. We have just seen that 10.0 calories of heat energy absorbed by 1.00 g of $H_2O$ results in a temperature rise of 10.0°C for the water. Will a similar 10.0°C temperature increase be noted when 1.00 g of copper metal or 1.00 g of crystalline sugar absorbs 10.0 calories of heat energy? When we perform the experiment to determine the answers, we discover that when 1.00 g of copper absorbs 10.0 calories of heat energy, the temperature of the copper rises by almost 55.0°C and not by 10.0°C. The 1.00 gram of sugar (sucrose) increases in temperature by nearly 17.0°C when it absorbs 10.0 calories of heat energy. Clearly, different substances respond differently to the absorption of the same amount of heat energy.

We remember that the heat energy absorbed by matter will be converted into molecular kinetic energy, as indicated by a temperature rise, and also into potential energy. Comparing 1.00 g each of water, copper, and sugar, we can deduce from the temperature effects noted

---

* When dealing with large amounts of heat energies, as is often the case, the chemist prefers to use the larger unit called the *kilocalorie, kcal, which is equal to 1000 calories*. Dietitians and nutritionists, however, prefer to call 1000 calories a "large Calorie, Cal." A 900 Calories diet is, therefore, a 900 kcal, or 900,000 (small) calories, diet.

† $\frac{\text{cal}}{\text{g-deg}}$ is read "calorie(s) per gram for every 1.0°C rise in temperature."

that their conversion of heat energy into molecular kinetic energy is in the order

copper > sugar > water.

Conversely, the conversion of heat energy into potential energy for the 1.00 g samples is in the order

water > sugar > copper.

Since different substances behave differently on the absorption of heat, chemists have defined a property of substances to measure such differences in behavior. That property is called the *heat capacity* of a substance. The heat capacity of a substance *depends upon the amount* of the substance absorbing heat energy. A convenient amount of matter for comparison is the mole. Hence, a conveniently defined quantity for comparison of heat capacities is the *molar heat capacity*. The molar heat capacity of a substance is defined as *the amount of heat energy required to increase the temperature of one mole of a substance by 1°C.*\* By virtue of this definition, the *molar* heat capacity of liquid water (18 g/mole) must be 18 calories/mole-degree (read as "calories per mole for every 1.0°C rise in temperature"). Table 6–3 gives experimental values for the molar heat capacities of some common substances. All the values indicated were experimentally obtained at a *constant pressure* of one atmosphere. $C_p$ is the symbol for the molar heat capacity measured at constant pressure.

### 6.19 Molar heats of fusion and vaporization

What energy is absorbed when one mole of ice (18.0 grams) is heated from −10.0°C to +110.0°C? From Table 6–3, we note that one mole of ice will absorb 8.86 calories for every degree rise in temperature. Thus, heating one mole of ice from −10.0°C to 0.0°C will involve:

$$(1.00 \text{ mole}) \left( 8.86 \frac{\text{cal}}{\text{mole-deg}} \right) (10.0 \text{ deg}) = 88.6 \text{ cal}$$

As heat is added continuously to ice at its melting point, the temperature remains constant until all the ice has melted. Measurement in-

---

\* The heat capacity of any substance *changes slowly with the temperature.* For example, the amount of heat energy required to raise the temperature of water by 1°C depends, in very careful measurements and calculations, upon the temperature region in which the 1°C rise occurs. Thus, it takes less heat energy to increase the temperature of a gram of water from 85°C to 86°C than it does from 5°C to 6°C. Since the calorie has been defined in terms of a 1°C rise in temperature for one gram of water, the need to specify which 1°C rise should be apparent. Accordingly, the calorie is operationally defined as the amount of heat energy required to raise the temperature of one gram of water from 14.5°C to 15.5°C. The calorie thus defined is called the "15° calorie."

dicates that 1440 cal/mole are absorbed during the melting (or fusion) process. Thus, there is an energy change associated with the change in state (or phase) from solid to liquid even though there is no temperature change. *The energy involved in melting one mole of a solid at its melting point is called the molar heat of fusion.* The molar heat of fusion of ice is 1.440 kcal/mole.

Thus far, we have added enough energy to one mole of ice at −10.0°C to bring it to the liquid state at 0.0°C. This energy totals 1529 cal (88.6 cal + 1440 cal). The mole of water may now be heated to 100.0°C. From Table 6–3 we note that one mole of liquid water will absorb 18.00 cal/mole for every degree rise in temperature. Thus, the additional heat required to raise one mole of water from 0.0°C to 100.0°C is:*

$$(1.00 \text{ mole})\left(18.00 \frac{\text{cal}}{\text{mole-deg}}\right)(100.0 \text{ deg}) = 1800 \text{ cal}$$

**TABLE 6–3**    Molar Heat Capacities of Some Common Substances

(Measurements made at 25.0°C unless otherwise noted.)

| Solids | $C_p \left(\frac{cal}{mole\text{-}deg}\right)$ | Liquids | $C_p \left(\frac{cal}{mole\text{-}deg}\right)$ |
|---|---|---|---|
| Aluminum (Al) | 5.82 | Acetic acid ($CH_3COOH$) | 28.2 |
| Carbon as graphite (C) | 2.07 | Ammonia as a liquid at | |
| Copper (Cu) | 5.85 | −77.7°C ($NH_3$) | 19.2 |
| Ice at 0°C ($H_2O$) | 8.86 | Benzene ($C_6H_6$) | 32.0 |
| Iron (Fe) | 6.49 | Ethyl alcohol ($C_2H_5OH$) | 26.7 |
| Iron(III) oxide ($Fe_2O_3$) | 25.0 | Mercury (Hg) | 6.65 |
| Lead (Pb) | 6.41 | Water ($H_2O$) | 17.996 |
| Potassium nitrate ($KNO_3$) | 22.2 | | |
| Sodium carbonate ($Na_2CO_3$) | 26.41 | | |
| Sodium chloride (NaCl) | 11.88 | | |
| Sucrose ($C_{12}H_{22}O_{11}$) | 102.6 | | |
| Sulfur (rhombic form) ($S_8$) | 5.40 | | |

| Gases | $C_p \left(\frac{cal}{mole\text{-}deg}\right)$ |
|---|---|
| Ammonia ($NH_3$) | 8.523 |
| Carbon dioxide ($CO_2$) | 8.874 |
| Hydrogen ($H_2$) | 6.892 |
| Methane ($CH_4$) | 8.536 |
| Nitrogen ($N_2$) | 6.960 |
| Oxygen ($O_2$) | 7.017 |
| Water vapor at 100°C ($H_2O$) | 8.64 |

* For the purposes of this calculation, we will neglect the slight variation in the heat capacity of water with change in temperature.

At 100.0°C, as the water converts from the liquid to the vapor state, it is again experimentally observed that energy is added *at constant temperature* until the phase change is complete. The potential energy required for the vaporization process is much greater than that for the melting process. The *molar heat of vaporization* of water, as measured at its normal boiling point, is 9.720 kcal/mole. To bring one mole of ice from −10.0°C to the vapor state at 100.0°C has required the addition of 13,049 cal (88.6 cal + 1440 cal + 1800 cal + 9720 cal).

Finally, from Table 6–3, we can calculate the energy needed to superheat one mole of steam from 100.0°C to 110.0°C. The molar heat capacity of steam being 8.64 cal/mole-deg, the energy required is:

$$(1.00 \text{ mole})\left(8.64 \frac{\text{cal}}{\text{mole-deg}}\right)(10.0 \text{ deg}) = 86.4 \text{ cal}$$

The over-all change can be represented by the successive steps in this fashion, where $Q$ represents the energy absorbed:

1. Ice (1.00 mole at −10.0°C)      → Ice (1.00 mole at 0.0°C).                    $Q_1 =$     89 cal
2. Ice (1.00 mole at 0.0°C)        → Water (1.00 mole at 0.0°C).                  $Q_2 =$  1,440 cal
3. Water (1.00 mole at 0.0°C)      → Water (1.00 mole at 100.0°C).               $Q_3 =$  1,800 cal
4. Water (1.00 mole at 100.0°C)    → Water Vapor (1.00 mole at 100.0°C).         $Q_4 =$  9,720 cal
5. Water Vapor (1.00 mole at 100.0°C) → Water Vapor (1.00 mole at 110.0°C).      $Q_5 =$     86 cal

Total $Q$ = 13,135 cal

Consequently, the total amount of energy required to change a mole of ice at −10.0°C to a mole of water vapor at 110.0°C is 13,135 calories.

If the Law of the Conservation of Energy is to hold, then the reverse reaction—the change of a mole of water vapor at 110.0°C to a mole of ice at −10.0°C—must release exactly the same energy, or 13,135 calories. Experiment will verify that such, indeed, will occur. Likewise, the reverse process in each individual step releases exactly the same number of calories that the forward process absorbed. To melt a mole of ice required 1440 calories; when a mole of water freezes, 1440 calories are released. To evaporate a mole of water required 9720 calories; when a mole of water vapor condenses, 9720 calories are released.

The heat of fusion represents the amount of potential energy that the molecules of the solid must gain to overcome the long range order imposed by the attractive forces. At the melting point, the long range order is broken up completely and the solid melts into very many small molecular clusters of different sizes. The liquid state with its characteristic short range order results.

The heat of vaporization represents the amount of potential energy that is necessary for molecules in the liquid state to overcome their mutual attraction, to separate into individual molecules, and to expand away from each other in the characteristic manner of gas molecules. This is a more drastic process than melting, and it is not very surprising that the heat of vaporization is greater than the heat of fusion.

## 6.20 The nature of two attractive forces

We have seen that the existence of liquids and solids is direct evidence of the existence of attractive forces in these phases. Two basic types of forces are known that could account for this. The first is *gravitational force*, which is the force of attraction between the masses of any two substances. The earth revolves about the sun because of the gravitational attraction between the two bodies. It is due to the same force that a stone thrown into the air falls back to earth. An astronaut orbits the earth in his capsule for the same reason. However, molecular masses are so small that gravitational force is too weak to account for the strength of molecular attractions in liquids and solids.

The second type of force is electrical in nature. It is known as *coulombic force*. Only two kinds of electrical charge are known; they are designated *plus* and *minus*. It is an experimental fact that if two bodies have opposite kinds of charge, they attract each other, whereas two bodies each with the same kind of electrical charge repel each other. The strength of coulombic attractive force, $F$, depends directly upon (is a function of) the product of the *amount* of opposite electrical charges, $q_1$ and $q_2$. The coulombic force also varies *inversely* with the *square* of the distance, $r$, between the opposite charges. These relationships were first discovered and expressed mathematically by the French scientist Charles Coulomb (sharl COO loam). Coulomb's Law is summarized by the equation

$$F = k \frac{q_1 q_2}{r^2}$$

where $k$ is a constant, the value of which depends upon the units for charge and distance.

The dependence on $\frac{1}{r^2}$ is important, as $F$ has only $\frac{1}{4}$ of its original value when the distance between the charges is doubled; only $\frac{1}{16}$ when it is 4 times as great; and so forth. So the force of attraction very rapidly decreases with increase in the distance of separation.

Coulombic forces are found to be adequate to account for the attraction in liquids and solids, and all present experimental evidence supports the belief that they indeed are the source of the attraction. The decrease in coulombic attractive forces with increase in molecular separation also explains why gases, in general, show very little evidence of attractive forces.

### 6.21 Solids may be classified according to structure.

Careful examination of the heat capacity data for solids recorded in Table 6–3 leads to the fact that metals, in general, all have molar heat capacities of approximately 6 cal/mole-deg. The solid compounds iron(III) oxide, potassium nitrate, sodium carbonate, and sodium chloride, on the other hand, fall into a class of solid compounds having higher molar heat capacities, ranging between 11.88 cal/mole-deg and 26.41 cal/mole-deg. It might seem, then, that solids fall into different classes. Indeed, when a host of different experimental observations on crystalline solids are examined in detail, *four* classes are discovered. These four classes are: metallic crystals, ionic crystals, molecular crystals, and covalent crystals. Table 6–4 gives examples of each of these solid types.

**TABLE 6–4**    EXAMPLES OF FOUR CLASSES OF SOLIDS

| *Metallic Crystals* | *Ionic Crystals* |
|---|---|
| Copper, Cu | Barium chloride, $BaCl_2$ |
| Magnesium, Mg | Calcium nitrate, $Ca(NO_3)_2$ |
| Silver, Ag | Potassium nitrate, $KNO_3$ |
| Tungsten, W | Zinc iodide, $ZnI_2$ |

| *Molecular Crystals* | *Covalent Crystals* |
|---|---|
| Carbon dioxide, $CO_2$ | Carbon (diamond and graphite), C |
| Hydrogen chloride, HCl | Phosphorus (red), P |
| Ice, $H_2O$ | Silicon carbide, SiC |
| Phosphorus (white), $P_4$ | Silicon dioxide (quartz), $SiO_2$ |

In later chapters, we shall consider structural arrangements in the solid state that lead to these four classes. At this point, we want to consider two of the classes briefly.

### 6.22 Ionic and molecular solids

The two most commonly encountered solid types are ionic solids and molecular solids. Table 6–5 lists the eight compounds of these two classes given as examples in Table 6–4, along with their melting points. Quite clearly, the coulombic attractive forces in ionic solids are much greater than those in molecular solids. It takes more energy to melt ionic solids. Why the coulombic forces in ionic solids are far greater than those in molecular solids becomes clearer when another experimental study of these solid types is made.

**TABLE 6–5** THE MELTING POINTS OF SOME IONIC
AND MOLECULAR SOLIDS

| Ionic Solids | Mp (°C) | Molecular Solids | Mp (°C) |
|---|---|---|---|
| $BaCl_2$ | 962 | $CO_2$ | −56.6 |
| $Ca(NO_3)_2$ | 561 | | (under pressure) |
| $KNO_3$ | 334 | HCl | −112 |
| $ZnI_2$ | 446 | $H_2O$ (ice) | 0 |
| | | $P_4$ | 44.1 |
| | | | (no air present) |

### 6.23 The structure of ionic solids

When a *pure* molecular solid melts, the liquid formed *does not con-duct an electric current.* However, the liquids that form when *pure* ionic solids melt *are excellent conductors of electricity.* The electrical conductivity of ionic melts has been shown to be due to the pressure of moving, charged atoms or radicals present in the melt. These charged species are called *ions.* In the solid state, ionic solids are thus composed of ions of opposite charge bound in a rigid and regular structure known as an *ionic crystal lattice.*

Pure ionic solid *melts* are excellent conductors of electricity.

Many different experiments have shown that in ionic compounds *metal ions bear positive charge.* Thus, electrically neutral sodium atoms, Na, in forming ionic compounds become positive sodium ions, $Na^{+1}$. Magnesium atoms, Mg, become magnesium ions bearing a doubly positive charge, $Mg^{+2}$. Other positive ionic species are $Fe^{+2}$, $Fe^{+3}$, $K^{+1}$, $Zn^{+2}$, and $NH_4^{+1}$, the ammonium ion. We note that *the positive charges of metal ions correspond to metal valences.* (We will consider theoretical justification for the amounts of positive charge on metal ions in Chapter 11.)

Since, experimentally, *all* compounds are electrically neutral, the positive metal ion charges in ionic solids are balanced by equal numbers of negative charges. *Negative charges are carried by nonmetal and acid radical ions.* Thus, electrically neutral chlorine atoms, Cl, in forming ionic compounds become negative chloride ions, $Cl^{-1}$. Oxygen atoms, O, become oxygen ions bearing doubly negative charge, $O^{-2}$, the *oxide ion.* Other negative ionic species are $N^{-3}$, $S^{-2}$, $(NO_3)^{-1}$, $(SO_4)^{-2}$, and $(PO_4)^{-3}$. We note that *the negative charges of nonmetal and acid radical ions correspond to nonmetal and acid radical valences.* (We will consider theoretical justification for the amounts of negative charge on nonmetal and acid radical ions in Chapter 11 also.)

Positive ions are simply called *cations* (CAT eye ons). Negative ions are simply called *anions* (AN eye ons). Experiments show that ionic solids consist of orderly arrays of cations and anions in the crystal lattice. (Fig. 6.8.) It is not possible to single out individual molecules in ionic solids. No ion-pair exists independently of other neighboring ions. The ionic crystal lattice is one *giant* molecule. Thus, the formula for an ionic solid can only be considered as the simplest formula for the solid.

Being oppositely charged, cations and anions strongly attract each other. It requires much heat energy to overcome this effect. When that energy is supplied, the crystal lattice comes apart as the solid melts and the ions are freed of each other. The moving ions in the liquid state are responsible, then, for the electrical conductivity of that state. The ionic melt as a whole, it must be understood, *remains electrically neutral.* (Fig. 6.9.)

### 6.24 The structure of molecular solids

Returning to the second broad class of solids, molecular solids, we recall that nonconducting liquids result when such pure solids melt. Molecular solids, then, do not contain ions of opposite charge. How then do electrical forces arise to hold such solids together? Many different experiments have led chemists to propose the following model for such solids.

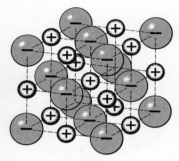

**FIGURE 6.8** Orderly arrangement of cations and anions in an ionic solid crystal lattice

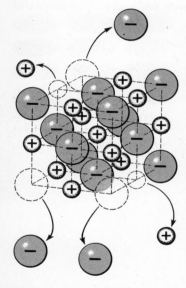

**FIGURE 6.9** A partially melted ionic crystal. The ions in the melt are free to move. (See photo, page 161.) The melt, as a whole, remains electrically neutral.

In molecular solids, *electrically neutral* molecules are present. Within these molecules, however, there is a slightly *unequal* distribution of positive and negative charge. The result is that one part of the molecule is relatively more positive than another part. Therefore, the part that is relatively less positive must, of necessity, be relatively more negative. A simple, though at first glance misleading, way to represent this is to label one "end" of a molecule positive and the other "end" negative, as shown in Figure 6.10. Molecules having such an uneven electrical distribution are called *dipoles*. Molecular solids consist of orderly arrays of molecular dipoles, as shown in Figure 6.11.

The representations in Figures 6.10, and 6.11 can mislead you. The $\delta^+$ and $\delta^-$ signs do not stand for unit amounts of positive and negative electricity. If they did, we would be dealing with ions, which we are not. The Greek small letter delta, $\delta$, is used to stand for the word "partially." The symbols $\delta^+$ and $\delta^-$ represent the relative difference in electrical properties of the different parts of the molecule. The negative end of the molecule is only *partially* negative. It is much less negative than a *unit* negative ion. Similarly, the positive end of the molecule is only *partially* positive. It is much less positive than a *unit* positive ion. Accordingly, the coulombic attraction between opposite ends of dipoles *is less than* that between a unit cation and a unit anion. Dipole-dipole attractive forces are weaker than ionic attractive forces. Accordingly, it takes less heat energy to supply dipoles with sufficient potential energy to overcome attractive forces. Molecular solids then, in general, are low-melting materials.

We have considered briefly qualitative models that satisfactorily help to account for the important differences in melting points and electrical characteristics of ionic and molecular solids. We will return later to all four types of solids mentioned and will consider more detailed models for them based on modern concepts of the structure of atoms and molecules.

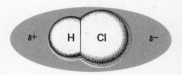

**FIGURE 6.10** A dipolar HCl molecule drawn to scale

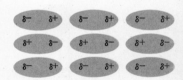

**FIGURE 6.11** Arrangement of molecular dipoles in a solid. How do molecular solids differ from ionic solids?

## SUMMARY

The existence of the liquid and solid states of matter necessitates the postulation of intermolecular attractive forces. Experimentally observed critical temperatures serve to substantiate such a new model for molecules in the gaseous state.

Evaporation of a liquid results when the surface molecules gain sufficient kinetic energy to overcome the intermolecular attractive forces binding them. The molecules in the gaseous state above a liquid surface exert a vapor pressure which is dependent only upon the temperature of the system. At a given temperature and in a closed system, a state of equilibrium exists in which the rates of evaporation and condensation are equal. Boiling, a "whole liquid" phenomenon, occurs at that temperature at which the vapor pressure of the liquid equals the external pressure above the liquid.

Liquids are characterized by short range order; solids by long range order. The temperature at which a solid exists in equilibrium with its melt is called the melting or freezing point of the substance.

When a substance changes state, large amounts of heat energy are absorbed with *no* increase in the temperature and therefore no increase in the kinetic energy of the system. This energy must manifest itself as potential energy, a hidden form of energy, a "keeping apart" kind of energy.

The arbitrary unit for heat energy is the calorie. One calorie of heat energy is needed to increase the temperature of one gram of water by 1°C. The heat capacity of a substance is a measure of its heat absorption properties. The molar heat capacities of substances have low values when compared with molar heats of fusion and vaporization.

## QUESTIONS AND PROBLEMS

6.1  How is the kinetic molecular theory of gases extended to explain the properties of *real gases?* Under what conditions do the properties of real gases approach those of an ideal gas? Why?

6.2  Under what conditions will a gas condense to form a liquid? How is this explained?

6.3  What is the critical temperature of a gas? Give a model to account for its existence.

6.4  Describe a model for evaporation on the molecular level. How does the model account for the experimental fact that the rate of evaporation increases with temperature?

6.5  Define, conceptually and operationally, a state of equilibrium.

6.6  Describe how the macroscopic properties of a beaker of water placed into a closed, dry system change with time. Describe, conceptually, the same changes.

6.7  Refer to Figure 6.4. Why doesn't ethylene glycol normally boil at 100°C? Under what conditions will ethylene glycol boil at 100°C? Under what conditions will water *not* boil at 100°C?

6.8  What is meant by *short range* and *long range* order?

6.9  Describe and explain the macroscopic properties of an efflorescent and of a deliquescent substance. Give examples of each.

6.10  Define the calorie. How many calories are required to increase the temperature of 10.0 g of water by 10.0°C? How many kilocalories is this?

6.11 Define the molar heat capacity of a substance. Refer to Table 6–3. **a.** How many calories are required to raise the temperature of 780 g of benzene, $C_6H_6$, by 10°C? **b.** How many calories are required to raise the temperature of 460 g of ethyl alcohol, $C_2H_5OH$, from 25.0°C to 35.0°C?
 Ans.  **b.** 2670 calories

6.12 When 5.40 g of aluminum metal at 75.0°C cool to 25.0°C, how much heat is evolved?

6.13 Suppose 1.392 kcal are added at constant volume to a 280-g sample of $N_2$ gas at 25.0°C and 740 torrs. **a.** To what temperature will the $N_2$ gas increase? **b.** What will be the new pressure in the constant volume container?
 Ans.  **b.** 790 torrs

6.14 What properties should a gas have to make it suitable as a refrigerant? Explain.

6.15 It is an experimental observation that when a gas *in an isolated system* expands to a region of lower pressure, the temperature of the gas is decreased. Conceptually, how would you account for this so-called Joule-Thomson effect? (Recall that a decrease in temperature indicates a lower average molecular kinetic energy.)

6.16 Account for the observation that when a carbon dioxide fire extinguisher is operating, a fine cloud of $CO_2$ "snow" forms.

## SUGGESTED READINGS

Holden, A. and P. Singer. *Crystals and Crystal Growing* (paperback). Doubleday, 1960.

MacDonald, D. K. C. *Near Zero: The Physics of Low Temperature* (paperback). Doubleday, 1961.

SCIENTIFIC AMERICAN
Bernal, J. D., "The Structure of Liquids." Aug. 1960
Derjaguin, B. V., "The Force Between Molecules." July 1960
Fullman, R. L., "The Growth of Crystals." Mar. 1955
Sproull, R. L., "The Conduction of Heat in Solids." Dec. 1962
Wannier, G. H., "The Nature of Solids." Dec. 1952

*Free access to the edifice of science is*
*allowed not only to those who devised the plan,*
*worked out the drawings, prepared*
*the materials, or piled up the brickwork,*
*but also to all those who are desirous of making*
*a close acquaintance with the plan, and wish*
*to avoid dwelling in its vaults.*

*Dmitri Mendeleev (1834–1907)*

**CHAPTER 7** | # Noble Gases, Salt

Thus far in our studies we have learned of the existence of 104 elements. These relatively few fundamental kinds of matter are found, however, chemically combined in thousands upon thousands of different compounds. It is the study of the elements and their compounds that we call chemisty. If there were no patterns or regularities in the behavior of the elements, the study of chemistry would be unbelievably complex—a hopeless maze of countless separate facts. Scientists, however, have discovered a number of patterns or regularities of behavior among the different chemical elements and have developed theories that account for these patterns. Both the patterns and the theories that explain them help us to understand not only the elements themselves but also the countless compounds that are formed from them.

## PATTERNS OF BEHAVIOR OF FIVE RARE GASES

There are many regularities in behavior and properties that may be observed among the elements. We shall begin our study by considering the most basic chemical property of the elements—chemical activity. Through experiment, scientists have discovered that nearly all of the elements have the property of chemical activity. That is, under certain conditions each of the elements will combine with another element (or with more than one other element) to form a compound. For example, at room temperature, the yellow-green, gaseous element chlorine combines with the element sodium, a soft, silvery solid, to form the compound sodium chloride, which is common table salt. Under other conditions, chlorine combines with hydrogen to form hydrogen chloride gas, which dissolves in water to form hydrochloric acid.

*166*

# Formers, Periodicity

There are, however, six of the 104 elements that either have not shown this property of chemical activity or exhibit it weakly, and we turn first to a study of them.

## 7.1 The rare and noble gases

The six elements that are not chemically active to any significant degree are called the *rare* or *noble* gas elements. These gases are helium, He, neon, Ne, argon, Ar, krypton, Kr, xenon (ZEE non), Xe, and radon, Rn. They are rare, indeed. Except for argon, which is third in abundance among all gases in the atmosphere, the others exist only in minute amounts. (See Table 7–1.) They are termed noble in light of their general chemical inactivity. In fact, for more than seventy years

**TABLE 7–1** COMPOSITION OF DRY AIR

| Substance | Per Cent by Volume |
|---|---|
| $N_2$ | 78 |
| $O_2$ | 21 |
| Ar | 0.93 |
| $CO_2$ | varies—average 0.03 |
| $H_2$ | 0.01 |
| Ne | 0.0018 |
| He | 0.0005 |
| Kr | 0.0001 |
| Xe | 0.00001 |
| Rn | varies—very low |

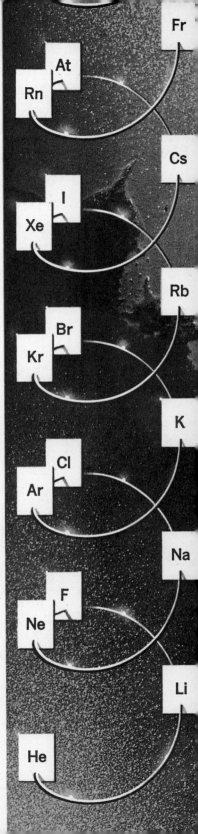

the six gases were most familiarly known as the *inert* gases. During those years no compound of those elements was known. Since 1962, however, a number of stable compounds of some of these elements have been prepared. While this achievement has compelled chemists to take a fresh look at established theories of atomic structure and chemical activity, the fundamental stability of the noble gas elements remains one of the startlingly clear regularities in nature.

The chemical inactivity shared by the noble gases indicates a basic similarity among the six elements. Thus, it is not surprising that they share a number of common properties. The most distinctive property of the group of elements is that at room temperature they are all gases. Careful investigation proves that, unlike any other elemental gas, they exist as monatomic species in the gas phase.

## 7.2 The discovery of the noble gases

Because they are rare, odorless, and colorless, and because they are not chemically active, we can see why the presence of the noble gases was not suspected until fairly recent times. The first clue to their existence was provided by an English scientist, Henry Cavendish, almost two centuries ago.

Among his other scientific work, Cavendish conducted an experiment in which he attempted to change atmospheric nitrogen into nitric acid. He wrote, "Having condensed as much (nitrogen) as I could, *only a small bubble of air* remained. So that if there is any part of the nitrogen of our atmosphere which differs from the rest, we may safely conclude that it is not more than $\frac{1}{120}$th part of the whole."

More than a hundred years passed before two English scientists, John Rayleigh (RAY lee) and William Ramsay, repeated Cavendish's experiment. After isolating a small quantity of the gas that Cavendish had called "a bubble of air," they subjected it to every known test. Finally, in 1894, they concluded that they had discovered a new element, which, unlike any of the known elements, seemed chemically inert. They named this element *argon*, from the Greek word meaning "lazy."

Helium, lightest of the rare gases, was actually identified some years prior to the discovery of argon. It was first found, not on earth, but in the sun. Its presence there was discovered by means of an optical instrument called the *spectroscope*. (See Chapter 9.) Elements when heated emit their own characteristic energies. When viewed through this instrument, these energies appear in part as lines of color.

During a total solar eclipse visible in India in 1868, Pierre Jannsen, a Frenchman, observed with a spectroscope the energy streaming from the inner atmosphere of the sun (chromosphere). Among the lines of color he saw was a yellow one which could not be related to any of the known terrestrial elements. Later that year, Joseph Lockyer, an Englishman, using a specially designed spectroscope that could examine the sun's chromosphere by blocking out the sun itself, verified Jannsen's discovery. Consequently, discovery of a new chemical element was claimed. The element was named *helium* from the Greek word for "sun." Before the end of the nineteenth century, Ramsay found this new element on our planet.

Helium is actually found in significant quantities trapped in the earth. It is found to such a degree because it is often a final product of the disintegration of radioactive elements and, thus, has accumulated over eons of time. Nearly all the helium in the world is recovered from natural gas deposits in the United States, some of which contain as much as eight per cent by volume of helium. Important helium recovery installations are located in the Texas panhandle, northwestern New Mexico, Kansas, and Utah. United States production of helium from natural gas deposits totaled about 250 million cubic feet in 1960.

Ramsay and his co-workers isolated three other rare gases from liquid air samples between 1894 and 1898. These were named *neon*, from the Greek word for "new"; *krypton*, from the Greek word for "hidden"; and *xenon*, from the Greek word for "strange." The last of the rare gases to be discovered was *radon*. It was isolated as one of the radioactive disintegration products of radium, from which it was named. (Radioactivity is discussed more fully in Chapters 8 and 32.)

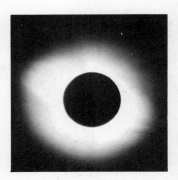

The chromosphere of the sun is visible during a total solar eclipse.

## 7.3 Properties of the noble gases

Some of the physical properties of the rare gases are listed in Table 7–2.

**TABLE 7–2**  SOME PHYSICAL PROPERTIES OF THE RARE GASES

|  | He | Ne | Ar | Kr | Xe | Rn |
|---|---|---|---|---|---|---|
| Atomic weight (amu) | 4.00 | 20.18 | 39.94 | 83.80 | 131.3 | 222 |
| Melting point (°C) | — | −249 | −189 | −157 | −112 | −110 |
| Boiling point (°C) | −269 | −246 | −186 | −153 | −107 | −62 |
| Heat of fusion (kcal/mole) | — | 0.08 | 0.27 | 0.36 | 0.49 | 0.8 |
| Heat of vaporization (kcal/mole) | 0.02 | 0.44 | 1.50 | 2.31 | 3.27 | 3.92 |

Study the table. Can you detect some patterns in the properties of the six elements with increasing atomic weight? Do the boiling points increase, or decrease? the heats of fusion? the heats of vaporization?

Suppose scientists were to discover another inactive element, having an atomic weight greater than that of radon. What conclusions could you draw about the element? Do you think it would be a solid, liquid, or gas at room temperature? How do you think its boiling point would compare with that of radon? How do you think it would compare with radon as far as the other properties listed in the table are concerned?

Figure 7.1 is a graph of the boiling points of the six known noble gas elements as a function of their atomic weights. If another noble gas element, with an atomic weight greater than that of radon, were discovered, it would be possible to predict its boiling point with fair accuracy. This could be done by extrapolating the curve of the graph to a point at which it meets the line corresponding to the atomic weight. Similar predictions could be made for the other properties shown in Table 7–2.

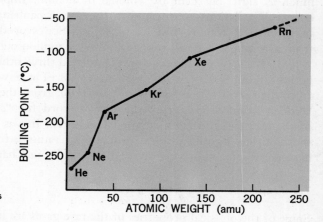

**FIGURE 7.1**   Boiling points of the noble gas elements

## 7.4 Attractive forces and the noble gases

You have already learned that a substance can exist in the liquid or solid state only because there are attractive forces between the atoms or molecules that make up the substance. The heats of fusion and vaporization of substances are measures of the strength of those attractive forces. The values of the heats of fusion and vaporization are very low for all of the noble gas elements. Since little energy is needed to overcome the attractive forces between atoms of these elements in the liquid and solid states, we can conclude that the attractive forces are very weak. Look at Table 7–2 again. Which of the noble gas elements requires the least energy to overcome its attractive forces in the liquid and solid states? Which requires the greatest energy? Does the table show any relation between atomic weight and the strength of the attractive forces within each of the noble gas elements? You can see that the greater the atomic weight of any of these elements, the greater the attractive forces binding the atoms together. For example, the forces that tend to attract helium atoms to one another in the liquid or solid states must be very weak indeed, since it is so easy to overcome them and release helium as a gas. In fact, helium has the lowest boiling point of any known substance and cannot be solidified at any temperature unless high pressures are simultaneously applied. Solid helium can be prepared at 1.1°K at a pressure of 26 atmospheres.

## PATTERNS OF CHEMICAL BEHAVIOR: A VALUABLE TOOL OF SCIENCE

You have now seen that by knowing that a certain pattern exists within a group of elements, it is possible to predict the properties of any member of the group from a knowledge of the properties of any other member. The idea of related groups or families of elements developed very slowly during the history of chemistry. But today, the knowledge that elements fall into related groups is one of the most valuable tools of the chemist.

To appreciate the importance of this tool, it is necessary that the student of chemistry have some knowledge of the significant groups or families that exist among the 104 chemical elements. Two groups in addition to the noble gases are the halogens and the alkali metals. Let us consider these two families to demonstrate further the existence of regularities and similarities among the chemical elements.

### 7.5 The halogens

Four elements strikingly different in their physical and chemical properties from the six noble gases are the diatomic elements fluorine, $F_2$, chlorine, $Cl_2$, bromine, $Br_2$, and iodine, $I_2$. Fluorine is a violently active, pale-yellow gas that can only be prepared and handled safely under strictly controlled conditions. Chlorine is a dense, choking, poisonous, greenish-yellow gas of high chemical activity. Bromine is a red-brown, highly corrosive, volatile liquid at room temperature. Iodine exists as beautiful silver-black crystals of relatively high vapor pressure that yield a violet vapor. Iodine is moderately active chemically.

These four elements have properties that are closely related. Long and careful experimentation studying those properties has clearly indicated that the four elements comprise a chemical family. One of the properties of the family has given the four elements their family name. Each of the elements reacts with metals to form salts. From the Greek words meaning "salt formers" comes the family name *halogens* for these four active nonmetal elements. Salts formed by the halogens are called *halides*.

A fifth halogen exists, the one of highest atomic weight. It is the synthetic element *astatine*, At, which was first made in 1940 by a team of American chemists, Corson, Mackenzie, and Segrè, at the University of California. (See Chapter 32 for a discussion of the modern synthesis of elements.) Astatine is the only halogen that has no stable, nonradioactive form; hence, its name, which is derived from the Greek word meaning "unstable." Little is known of the physical and chemical properties of astatine by direct experimentation. It is, however, possible to predict some of those properties. What do you think is the normal physical state of astatine? What color do you think it might be? What would you predict to be the formula for elemental astatine? What would you predict with respect to the chemical activity of the element?

### 7.6 Laboratory preparation of the halogens

The first halogen to be discovered was chlorine. Scheele obtained it in 1774. Although the gas made his nose and throat sting and almost blinded him, he wrote to a friend: "Oh how happy I am; I seldom think of eating, or drinking, or where I live; I scarcely pay attention to my pharmaceutical business. But to watch new phenomena, this is my consuming interest." The method by which chlorine was first prepared is still the common laboratory method used today. Manganese dioxide, $MnO_2$, and hydrochloric acid, $HCl$, are mixed in a flask and heated, resulting in the liberation of chlorine gas, $Cl_2$. The chlorine gas is heavier than air, and it is normally collected, as shown in Figure 7.2, by displacing air from a second flask. The equation for this reaction is:

$$4HCl(aq) + MnO_2(s) \overset{\Delta}{=} 2H_2O(l) + MnCl_2(aq) + Cl_2(g)$$

**Karl Scheele** (1742–1786, Swedish). As a practicing pharmacist, Scheele made many of his great chemical discoveries in the back rooms of apothecary shops. In addition to his discoveries of oxygen and chlorine, he was a pioneer in the study of other gases, such as arsine, hydrogen sulfide, and hydrogen fluoride. The toxic nature of these compounds led to his early death at age 43.

**FIGURE 7.2** Chlorine generator. Why is chlorine gas collected by displacement of air?

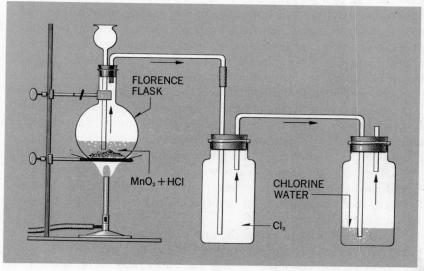

FLORENCE FLASK

$MnO_2 + HCl$

CHLORINE WATER

$Cl_2$

Bromine and iodine are also prepared by the action of $MnO_2$ on water solutions of their acids, hydrobromic, HBr, and hydriodic, HI. Soluble salts (KBr or KI, for example) are first added to another acid, such as dilute sulfuric acid, to obtain the halogen acid needed. The equation for the reaction in which hydrobromic acid is formed is:

$$2KBr(s) + H_2SO_4(aq) = K_2SO_4(aq) + 2HBr(aq)$$

Then the $MnO_2$ is added and the mixture heated. The final equations for the preparation of bromine and iodine are:

$$4HBr(aq) + MnO_2(s) \overset{\Delta}{=} MnBr_2(aq) + 2H_2O(l) + Br_2(g)$$

and

$$4HI(aq) + MnO_2(s) \overset{\Delta}{=} MnI_2(aq) + 2H_2O(l) + I_2(g)$$

Fluorine cannot be prepared in the same way. In fact, fluorine can only be prepared using specialized equipment not commonly found in most laboratories. The gas readily attacks glass and water. Its commercial preparation, as well as that of chlorine, will be considered in Chapter 19.

## 7.7 How bromine and iodine are prepared industrially

Most bromine is extracted commercially from the minute percentage (0.0065%) of bromides present in sea water. Elemental chlorine replaces the bromine of the bromides. Some of our bromine is also obtained from the bromides found in salt wells and salt lakes. The principal chemical reaction may be represented by the equation:

$$MgBr_2(aq) + Cl_2(g) = MgCl_2(aq) + Br_2(l)$$

About 90 per cent of our iodine is obtained from brine that comes up with the oil in California oil fields. This brine contains NaI and $MgI_2$. Chlorine is passed through the brine and replaces the iodine. The equation for this reaction is:

$$MgI_2(aq) + Cl_2(g) = MgCl_2(aq) + I_2(s)$$

These reactions demonstrate an important chemical relationship among the halogens. The halogens can displace (from compounds) the other halogens that have higher atomic weights. Thus, $Cl_2$ displaced bromine and iodine from the magnesium bromide and magnesium iodide. Bromine will displace iodine from iodides:

$$Br_2(l) + 2NaI(aq) = 2NaBr(aq) + I_2(s)$$

Heavier halogens, however, do not displace lighter ones from their compounds. (Displacement reactions are special cases of a general type of reaction known as an *oxidation-reduction* reaction. Oxidation-reduction reactions are first discussed in Chapter 9, and more fully developed in Chapters 18 and 19.)

### 7.8 Some properties of the halogens

Table 7–3 lists some of the properties of fluorine, chlorine, bromine, and iodine.

**TABLE 7–3**  SOME PROPERTIES OF THE HALOGENS

|  | *Fluorine* | *Chlorine* | *Bromine* | *Iodine* |
|---|---|---|---|---|
| Atomic weight (amu) | 19.0 | 35.5 | 79.9 | 127 |
| Boiling point (°C) | −188 | −34 | 58 | 184 |
| Melting point (°C) | −220 | −102 | −7 | 114 |
| Heat of fusion (kcal/mole of $X_2$) | 0.12 | 1.53 | 2.52 | 3.74 |
| Heat of vaporization (kcal/mole) | 1.56 | 4.88 | 7.18 | 9.98 |
| Formula of sodium halide | NaF | NaCl | NaBr | NaI |

Study the table. Do the boiling points increase, or decrease, reading from left to right? How do the melting points and the heats of fusion and vaporization change? At about room temperature (25°C), what is the physical state of each of the halogens? What would you predict for the formula of the sodium compound of astatine?

## THE PERIODIC TABLE: RHYTHM OF THE CHEMICAL ELEMENTS

We have now seen that there are at least two groups of chemical elements in both of which the elements show a regular relationship to each other in their properties. Having considered one family of chemically inactive elements, the rare or noble gases, and one family of chemically active nonmetal elements, the halogens, let us quickly complete our overview with a glance at a family of active metal elements.

### 7.9 The alkali metals

Another group of elements that have been found to be very closely related is composed of lithium, Li, sodium, Na, potassium, K, rubidium, Rb, and cesium, Cs. Francium, Fr, a man-made radioactive element, also is a member of this group. These elements are known as the *alkali metal* family. They are called the alkali metals, since many of their compounds are strong alkalies, or bases. They are prepared as soft, silvery-white metals that are very active chemically. They must be stored either in a dry, inert atmosphere or under oil, since they all react slowly with atmospheric oxygen and violently with water:

$$2\mathrm{Na}(s) + \tfrac{1}{2}\mathrm{O}_2(g) = \mathrm{Na}_2\mathrm{O}(s)$$

$$2\mathrm{K}(s) + 2\mathrm{H}_2\mathrm{O}(l) = 2\mathrm{KOH}(aq) + \mathrm{H}_2(g)$$

The extreme chemical activity of the alkali metals demands that they be handled with extreme care.

The metals will react vigorously with the halogens to form alkali halides such as sodium chloride and cesium fluoride. These metal halides all have a 1 : 1 atomic ratio of alkali to halogen, so that the reaction can be represented generally as:

$$2M(s) + X_2 = 2MX(s)$$

$$\text{where} \quad M = \mathrm{Li, Na, K, Rb, Cs}$$

$$\text{and} \quad X_2 = \mathrm{F}_2, \mathrm{Cl}_2, \mathrm{Br}_2, \mathrm{I}_2$$

In Table 7–4 some properties of the alkali metal elements are listed.

A safe method for *cutting* sodium. What safety equipment may be seen?

**TABLE 7–4** SOME PROPERTIES OF THE ALKALI METALS

| | Lithium | Sodium | Potassium | Rubidium | Cesium |
|---|---|---|---|---|---|
| Atomic weight (amu) | 6.9 | 23.0 | 39.1 | 85.5 | 132.9 |
| Boiling point (°C) | 1331 | 890 | 766 | 701 | 685 |
| Melting point (°C) | 180 | 98 | 63 | 39 | 29 |
| Heat of fusion (kcal/mole) | 0.72 | 0.62 | 0.55 | 0.52 | 0.50 |
| Heat of vaporization (kcal/mole) | 32.2 | 21.3 | 18.5 | 16.5 | 15.8 |
| Density (g/ml) | 0.53 | 0.97 | 0.86 | 1.52 | 1.87 |

Again, as you have done for the noble gases and the halogens using Tables 7–2 and 7–3, respectively, compare the trends in the different properties of the alkali metal elements as evident from this table. The alkali metals will be discussed at greater length in Chapter 21. At the moment, our interest in them lies in their chemical and physical similarity.

### 7.10 Periodicity in the properties of the elements

If we now consider the noble gases, halogens, and alkali metals more carefully, we will discover a pattern of regularity in their behavior.

Let us arrange them in order of increasing atomic weights:

| Element: | He | Li | F | Ne | Na | Cl | Ar | K | Br | Kr | Rb | I | Xe | Cs |
|---|---|---|---|---|---|---|---|---|---|---|---|---|---|---|
| Atomic Weight: | 4.00 | 6.94 | 18.0 | 20.2 | 23.0 | 35.5 | 39.9 | 39.1 | 79.9 | 83.8 | 85.5 | 127 | 131 | 133 |

We see that there is a regular pattern in which a member of any particular group reoccurs every third element. (We note the atomic weight *inversion* between argon and potassium. In view of the regular atomic weight order of the other twelve elements, we will, for the moment, neglect this inversion.) The evidence seems to indicate that there is a recurring pattern in the chemical elements that is related to their atomic weights. The discovery of this rhythm or periodicity has proven to be of inestimable value to the rapid progress of chemistry.

As early as 1829, the German chemist J. W. Dobereiner had made some attempt at a systematization of the elements according to their atomic weights. However, considering that many elements were undiscovered at that time and that the atomic weight scale was still a matter of controversy, chemistry was ill-prepared for much progress in this subject in 1829. In 1869, Dmitri Mendeleev (men deh LAY ef),* a Russian, and Lothar Meyer, a German, independently discovered the principle of the periodicity of the elements. On the basis of the systematic study of the properties of the elements and their compounds then known, a *Periodic Law* could be stated. *The properties of the elements are periodic functions of their atomic weights.* This great achievement provided a new key to the understanding of the elements.

### 7.11 Present basis of the periodic table

The present form of the *periodic table* of the elements is still, in general, based on the table of Mendeleev. However, in 1913 Henry G. J. Moseley, a brilliant young Englishman, experimentally demonstrated a more exact basis for the arrangement of elements in the periodic table.

On the basis of experimentation on the X-ray emission of the elements, Moseley deduced that there exists a *numerical ordering* of the elements. He showed that for proper study the elements should be arranged according to that numerical ordering rather than to the atomic weight ordering of Mendeleev. To emphasize the validity of his results, Moseley endowed each element with an *atomic number* that, for him, corresponded to the element's position in the numerical ordering he deduced. (A more profound significance of atomic numbers will be discussed in the next chapter.)

1915, English). Killed as he was at 28, during the British landing at Gallipoli in World War I, it is hard to say what this young genius might have accomplished had he lived a normal span of life. However, his fame is secure alone through his fundamental discovery of the experimental basis for the ordering of the elements according to atomic numbers.

---

* In transliteration from the Russian spelling, this name also appears in English as Mendeleef, Mendeléjev, Mendeleyev, etc.

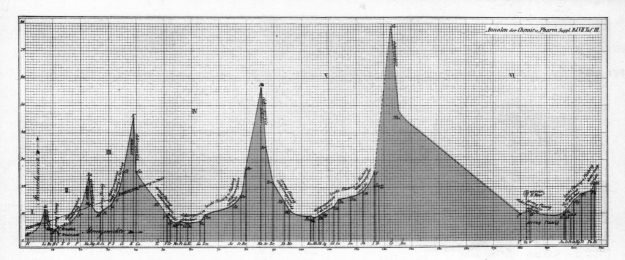

**Ueber die Beziehungen der Eigenschaften zu den Atomgewichten der Elemente.** Von D. Mendelejeff. — Ordnet man Elemente nach zunehmenden Atomgewichten in verticale Reihen so, dass die Horizontal-reihen analoge Elemente enthalten, wieder nach zunehmendem Atomge-wicht geordnet, so erhält man folgende Zusammenstellung, aus der sich einige allgemeinere Folgerungen ableiten lassen.

|  |  | Ti = 50 | Zr = 90 | ? = 180 |
|---|---|---|---|---|
|  |  | V = 51 | Nb = 94 | Ta = 182 |
|  |  | Cr = 52 | Mo = 96 | W = 186 |
|  |  | Mn = 55 | Rh = 104,4 | Pt = 197,4 |
|  |  | Fe = 56 | Ru = 104,4 | Ir = 198 |
|  |  | Ni = Co = 59 | Pd = 106,6 | Os = 199 |
| H = 1 |  | Cu = 63,4 | Ag = 108 | Hg = 200 |
|  | Be = 9,4 | Mg = 24 Zn = 65,2 | Cd = 112 |  |
|  | B = 11 | Al = 27,4 ? = 68 | Ur = 116 | Au = 197? |
|  | C = 12 | Si = 28 ? = 70 | Sn = 118 |  |
|  | N = 14 | P = 31 As = 75 | Sb = 122 | Bi = 210? |
|  | O = 16 | S = 32 Se = 79,4 | Te = 128? |  |
|  | F = 19 | Cl = 35,5 Br = 80 | J = 127 |  |
| Li = 7 | Na = 23 | K = 39 Rb = 85,4 | Cs = 133 | Tl = 204 |
|  |  | Ca = 40 Sr = 87,6 | Ba = 137 | Pb = 207 |
|  |  | ? = 45 Ce = 92 |  |  |
|  |  | ?Er = 56 La = 94 |  |  |
|  |  | ?Yt = 60 !Di = 95 |  |  |
|  |  | ?In = 75,6‖ Th = 118? |  |  |

1. Die nach der Grösse des Atomgewichts geordneten Elemente zeigen eine stufenweise Abänderung in den Eigenschaften.
2. Chemisch-analoge Elemente haben entweder übereinstimmende Atom-gewichte (Pt, Ir, Os), oder letztere nehmen gleichviel zu (K, Rb, Cs).
3. Das Anordnen nach den Atomgewichten entspricht der *Werthigkeit* der Elemente und bis zu einem gewissen Grade der Verschiedenheit im chemischen Verhalten, z. B. Li, Be, B, C, N, O, F.
4. Die in der Natur verbreitetsten Elemente haben *kleine* Atomgewichte

Plot of atomic volume of the elements as a function of atomic weight by Lothar Meyer in *Annalen der Chemie und Pharmacie, Supplementband VII,* (1870). The periodicity of this elemental property, the vol-ume occupied by a mole of solid element, led to Meyer's enunciation of the *Periodic Law.*

Mendeleev's first published periodic table in the *Zeitschrift für Chemie, 12,* p. 405 (1869)

The periodic table based on Moseley's atomic numbers re-moved certain difficulties that arise from a periodic table based on atomic weights. For example, as we have noted, argon has an atomic weight of 39.9 amu and the atomic weight of potassium is 39.1 amu. Argon should, therefore, follow potassium in a table based on atomic weights. But the properties of argon put it in the family of noble gases, preceding potassium. Moseley's research led to an atomic number of 18 for argon and 19 for potassium and thus eliminated the problem of

| Period | Group I | Group II | | | | | | | |
|---|---|---|---|---|---|---|---|---|---|
| 1 | 1   1.0080 **H** Hydrogen | | | | | | | | |
| 2 | 3   6.940 **Li** Lithium | 4   9.013 **Be** Beryllium | | | | | TRANSITION ELEMENTS | | |
| 3 | 11   22.991 **Na** Sodium | 12   24.32 **Mg** Magnesium | | | | | | | |
| 4 | 19   39.100 **K** Potassium | 20   40.08 **Ca** Calcium | 21   44.96 **Sc** Scandium | 22   47.90 **Ti** Titanium | 23   50.95 **V** Vanadium | 24   52.01 **Cr** Chromium | 25   54.94 **Mn** Manganese | 26   55.85 **Fe** Iron | 27   58. **Co** Cobalt |
| 5 | 37   85.48 **Rb** Rubidium | 38   87.63 **Sr** Strontium | 39   88.92 **Y** Yttrium | 40   91.22 **Zr** Zirconium | 41   92.91 **Nb** Niobium | 42   95.95 **Mo** Molybdenum | 43   (99)* **Tc** Technetium | 44   101.1 **Ru** Ruthenium | 45   102. **Rh** Rhodium |
| 6 | 55   132.91 **Cs** Cesium | 56   137.36 **Ba** Barium | 57   138.92 **La** Lanthanum † | 72   178.50 **Hf** Hafnium | 73   180.95 **Ta** Tantalum | 74   183.86 **W** Tungsten | 75   186.22 **Re** Rhenium | 76   190.2 **Os** Osmium | 77   192 **Ir** Iridium |
| 7 | 87   (223)* **Fr** Francium | 88   (226)* **Ra** Radium | 89   (227)* **Ac** Actinium ‡ | 104   (260)* **?** Unnamed | | | | | |

| | | | | | | | | | |
|---|---|---|---|---|---|---|---|---|---|
| † LANTHANIDE SERIES | 58   140.13 **Ce** Cerium | 59   140.92 **Pr** Praseodymium | 60   144.27 **Nd** Neodymium | 61   (145)* **Pm** Promethium | 62   150.35 **Sm** Samarium | 63   152.0 **Eu** Europium | 64   157.26 **Gd** Gadolinium | 65   158.9 **Tb** Terbium |
| ‡ ACTINIDE SERIES | 90   232.05 **Th** Thorium | 91   (231)* **Pa** Protactinium | 92   238.07 **U** Uranium | 93   (237)* **Np** Neptunium | 94   (242)* **Pu** Plutonium | 95   (243)* **Am** Americium | 96   (248)* **Cm** Curium | 97   (247 **Bk** Berkelium |

*Atomic weights appearing in parentheses are those of the most stable known isotop

the atomic weight inversion between these two elements. Similar inversions for cobalt and nickel, and for iodine and tellurium, are similarly eliminated as problems in periodicity. As a result of Moseley's work, the Periodic Law must be restated in modern terms.

**THE PERIODIC LAW.** This fundamental law that summarizes the most valuable regularities observed in the behavior of matter states that *the properties of the elements and their compounds are periodic functions of the atomic number of the elements.*

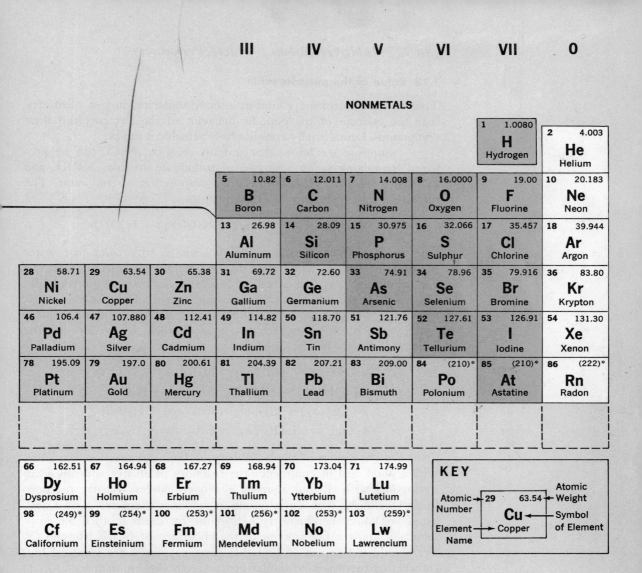

| III | IV | V | VI | VII | 0 |
|---|---|---|---|---|---|

**NONMETALS**

| | | | | | 1  1.0080<br>**H**<br>Hydrogen | 2  4.003<br>**He**<br>Helium |
|---|---|---|---|---|---|---|
| 5  10.82<br>**B**<br>Boron | 6  12.011<br>**C**<br>Carbon | 7  14.008<br>**N**<br>Nitrogen | 8  16.0000<br>**O**<br>Oxygen | 9  19.00<br>**F**<br>Fluorine | 10  20.183<br>**Ne**<br>Neon |
| 13  26.98<br>**Al**<br>Aluminum | 14  28.09<br>**Si**<br>Silicon | 15  30.975<br>**P**<br>Phosphorus | 16  32.066<br>**S**<br>Sulphur | 17  35.457<br>**Cl**<br>Chlorine | 18  39.944<br>**Ar**<br>Argon |

| 28  58.71<br>**Ni**<br>Nickel | 29  63.54<br>**Cu**<br>Copper | 30  65.38<br>**Zn**<br>Zinc | 31  69.72<br>**Ga**<br>Gallium | 32  72.60<br>**Ge**<br>Germanium | 33  74.91<br>**As**<br>Arsenic | 34  78.96<br>**Se**<br>Selenium | 35  79.916<br>**Br**<br>Bromine | 36  83.80<br>**Kr**<br>Krypton |
|---|---|---|---|---|---|---|---|---|
| 46  106.4<br>**Pd**<br>Palladium | 47  107.880<br>**Ag**<br>Silver | 48  112.41<br>**Cd**<br>Cadmium | 49  114.82<br>**In**<br>Indium | 50  118.70<br>**Sn**<br>Tin | 51  121.76<br>**Sb**<br>Antimony | 52  127.61<br>**Te**<br>Tellurium | 53  126.91<br>**I**<br>Iodine | 54  131.30<br>**Xe**<br>Xenon |
| 78  195.09<br>**Pt**<br>Platinum | 79  197.0<br>**Au**<br>Gold | 80  200.61<br>**Hg**<br>Mercury | 81  204.39<br>**Tl**<br>Thallium | 82  207.21<br>**Pb**<br>Lead | 83  209.00<br>**Bi**<br>Bismuth | 84  (210)*<br>**Po**<br>Polonium | 85  (210)*<br>**At**<br>Astatine | 86  (222)*<br>**Rn**<br>Radon |

| 66  162.51<br>**Dy**<br>Dysprosium | 67  164.94<br>**Ho**<br>Holmium | 68  167.27<br>**Er**<br>Erbium | 69  168.94<br>**Tm**<br>Thulium | 70  173.04<br>**Yb**<br>Ytterbium | 71  174.99<br>**Lu**<br>Lutetium |
|---|---|---|---|---|---|
| 98  (249)*<br>**Cf**<br>Californium | 99  (254)*<br>**Es**<br>Einsteinium | 100  (253)*<br>**Fm**<br>Fermium | 101  (256)*<br>**Md**<br>Mendelevium | 102  (253)*<br>**No**<br>Nobelium | 103  (259)*<br>**Lw**<br>Lawrencium |

**KEY**

Atomic Number → 29  63.54 ← Atomic Weight

**Cu** ← Symbol of Element

Element Name → Copper

**FIGURE 7.3**  A modern form of the periodic table of the elements

Figure 7.3 is a representation of one of many forms of a modern periodic table based on atomic numbers. The vertical rows are termed the *Groups*—He, Ne, Ar, Kr, Xe, Rn are the Group 0 elements, while Li, Na, K, Rb, Cs, Fr are in Group I. The horizonal rows are termed the *Periods*. Li, Be, B, C, N, O, F, Ne are in the second period. The reason for the position of hydrogen and many of the other elements will become clear after the next few chapters.

## 7.12 Value of the periodic table

There is no concept more vital to a sound understanding of chemistry than the concept of the periodic behavior of the elements and their compounds. Let us briefly consider how valuable it can be.

Suppose we know that sodium chloride, NaCl, can be prepared by mixing water solutions of sodium hydroxide, NaOH, and hydrogen chloride, HCl, followed by evaporation of the water. The reaction can be represented by the equation:

$$NaOH(aq) + HCl(aq) = NaCl(aq) + H_2O(l)$$

The concept of chemical periodicity leads us to predict that water solutions of LiOH, KOH, RbOH, and CsOH all resemble aqueous NaOH in their chemical behavior. Similarly, aqueous solutions of HF, HBr, and HI should chemically resemble aqueous HCl. Consequently, we can predict that the alkali halides should all be capable of preparation by the reaction between the aqueous alkali hydroxide and the aqueous hydrogen halide. Thus:

$$NaOH(aq) + HBr(aq) = NaBr(aq) + H_2O(l)$$
$$RbOH(aq) + HI(aq) = RbI(aq) + H_2O(l)$$
$$RbOH(aq) + HF(aq) = RbF(aq) + H_2O(l)$$
$$CsOH(aq) + HCl(aq) = CsCl(aq) + H_2O(l), \text{ etc.}$$

From the knowledge of the $NaOH(aq) + HCl(aq)$ reaction, we know with a good deal of confidence the reactions of all five aqueous alkali hydroxides with all four aqueous hydrogen halides—twenty reactions in all. Obviously, such a generalization simplifies chemistry a great deal. So, if we know the chemistry of sodium, for example, then we automatically know a fair amount of the chemistry of Li, K, Rb, and Cs. We should not expect to find that their properties are identical but, rather, that there will be similar properties in varying degrees.

## 7.13 Valence and the periodic table

Another useful generalization we may deduce from the periodic table is the relation between an element's position in the table and the valence of the element. The generalization is most valid for those elements with only one chief valence. Thus, all of the elements of Group I, the alkali metals, have a single valence of 1. Those in Group II have a single valence of 2. All the elements in Group III exhibit the valence of 3. (Indium, In, and thallium, Tl, are more usually found with combining capacities of one.) All the elements of Group IV form oxides of the type $MO_2$, showing a valence of 4. (Tin, Sn, and lead, Pb, are more stably found in compounds where their valence is 2, however.)

Beginning with Group V, valence begins to decrease. The *important* combining capacity for members of Group V is 3, as in $NH_3$, $PCl_3$, $As_2O_3$, etc. For the elements of Group VI, the chief valence of 2 is exhibited in compounds such as $H_2O$, $Na_2S$, $Na_2Te$, etc. The halogens' most stable compounds are the halides, in which they exhibit a valence of 1. It is important to note that the elements of Groups V, VI, and VII are the most chemically versatile of all the elements. They form many stable and useful compounds, in which they are found in valence forms other than the chief ones noted for them. Finally, the noble gases, exhibiting almost no chemical activity as their chief property, have a chief valence of 0.

Disregarding, then, the ten groups of elements labeled the *transition elements*, most of which show variable valences, and the twenty-eight elements that comprise the lanthanide and actinide elements, we have discovered the important periodic relationship for valence:

| Group | I | II | III | IV | V | VI | VII | 0 |
|---|---|---|---|---|---|---|---|---|
| Chief Valence | 1 | 2 | 3 | 4 | 3 | 2 | 1 | 0 |

## 7.14 Mendeleev's predictions

Mendeleev, himself, demonstrated the great value of the periodic classification of the elements. When he first proposed the periodic table, Mendeleev noted that in order to place the elements in their proper chemical family, it was necessary to leave certain gaps. Before Mendeleev's time, it was not possible to predict on any reasonable basis how many elements were still to be discovered and what the properties of these new elements might be. Mendeleev stated that where a gap had to be left in the periodic table, it meant that an undiscovered element fitted there, and its properties could be predicted from its position in the chart. For example, in Mendeleev's time, a gap between the elements silicon and tin had to be left. The element arsenic, which was then known and came closest in atomic weight to filling that gap, had properties resembling those of the elements phosphorus and antimony, but showed no relationship to the elements silicon or tin. Accordingly, Mendeleev predicted the existence of an undiscovered element to fill the gap between silicon and tin. Mendeleev named this missing element *eka-silicon*, meaning "like silicon," and from its position in the chart predicted the properties it should have. In Table 7–5 are listed Mendeleev's predictions for *eka-silicon* and the experimentally determined data for germanium, the element later discovered and placed vertically between the elements silicon and tin. The agreement is truly amazing and exemplary of the predictive power of periodicity.

**Dmitri Ivanovich Mendeleev** (1834–1907, Russian). Mendeleev was the youngest in a family of 17 children. At 35, he announced his Periodic Law of the Elements, which "gave chemistry that prophetic power long regarded as the peculiar dignity of the sister science, astronomy." Though the periodic table of the elements itself is a lasting memorial to his great insight, Mendeleev is further honored by the name of element 101—mendelevium.

**TABLE 7-5**  A Comparison of the Properties
of Eka-Silicon and Germanium

| Property | Eka-Silicon | Germanium |
|---|---|---|
| Atomic weight (amu) | 72 | 72.3 |
| Density of element (g/ml) | 5.5 | 5.36 |
| Formula of oxide | $MO_2$ | $GeO_2$ |
| Density of oxide (g/ml) | 4.7 | 4.70 |
| Formula of chloride | $MCl_4$ | $GeCl_4$ |
| Boiling point of chloride (°C) | <100 | 83 |
| Density of chloride (g/ml) | 1.9 | 1.88 |

On the basis of the concept of chemical periodicity, we can be very confident, now, that there are no undiscovered elements between hydrogen (element 1) and the still unnamed element 104.

### 7.15 Freons, creations from the periodic table

One of the startling demonstrations of the value of the periodic table was the synthesis of a new class of refrigerants. What was urgently needed in the 1920's was a nontoxic, odorless, nonflammable, noncorrosive, and inexpensive compound that could take the place of those refrigerants then in use, all of which had at least some undesirable properties.

How was one to hunt for such an ideal chemical? In 1929, Thomas Midgley, Jr., a young American engineer, went to the periodic table for clues. Midgley, some years earlier, had had enormous success in using the periodic table to help predict properties of compounds yet unknown. That earlier success resulted in his synthesis of tetraethyl lead, $Pb(C_2H_5)_4$, the most widely used *antiknock* additive for gasolines.

For the refrigerant problem, Midgley noticed that the elements at the right of the table were the only ones to form compounds sufficiently volatile for his purpose. Then he noticed that flammability among such compounds decreased from left to right. The toxicity among these compounds, he noticed, decreased from the bottom of the table to the top. These guides seemed to point to compounds of the element fluorine. This was an incredible deduction. "No one," wrote Midgley, "had previously considered it possible that fluorine might be nontoxic in some of its compounds." He then went from the table to his laboratory, and two years later actually came up with the first of a large group of ideal refrigerants that are called the *Freons*. This discovery revolutionized household and commercial refrigeration.

### 7.16 Implications of the periodic table

The discovery of the periodic behavior of the elements posed fundamental questions to scientists. If the elements could be placed in such a regular, ordered arrangement, there must be a basic ordered change in the atoms from one element to the next. Moreover, there must be some common characteristic in the atoms of a family of elements that explains the similarity of their properties. Therefore, there must be a very intimate relationship between the periodic behavior of the elements and the structure of atoms. In the next few chapters we will discuss the experiments and the theories that will unfold the relationship we seek.

## SUPPLEMENT: USES OF THE NOBLE GASES AND THE HALOGENS

The main purpose of this chapter has been to develop the concept of chemical periodicity. In that development, three chemical families were considered—the noble gases, the halogens, and the alkali metals. Since neither the noble gas elements nor the halogens will be covered in any further detail in this book, this supplement is added. In it, some of the wide uses of these two families of elements are covered. That such uses are added in a supplement should not be taken to mean that they are unimportant to chemists, or to you as students of chemistry. The myriad ways in which chemistry is applied to daily life to make that life safer and more healthful and pleasant add immeasurably to what has been aptly called "the romance of chemistry."

### 7.17 Some uses of the noble gases

For many years the noble gases remained chemical curiosities. Helium was the first to be put to use. It has taken the place of hydrogen in inflating blimps and weather observation balloons. Mixed with oxygen, it forms a *synthetic air* that is used under pressure in caissons and is

The disastrous end of the hydrogen-filled dirigible *Hindenburg* at Lakehurst Naval Station on May 6, 1937. What two properties of helium make it a suitable replacement for hydrogen in lighter-than-air craft?

supplied to deep-sea divers to prevent the *bends*. The most widespread modern use of helium involves the liquid form of the element. Liquid helium is an important industrial and laboratory coolant.

Metals such as aluminum and magnesium are arc-welded in an atmosphere of argon or helium to prevent their reaction with the oxygen or nitrogen of the air. Argon is also used as a blanketing gas to prevent discoloration and change of taste during the processing and packaging of certain foods. Electric light bulbs are filled with this gas to retard sublimation of the tungsten filament and to permit the lamp to be operated at higher temperatures.

The noble gases are also widely used in the glowing glass tubes so familiar in advertising signs. When an electric current is sent through a tube from which air has been removed and into which a minute amount of neon gas has been introduced, the gas glows with an orange-red light. The gas is at low pressure, about 12 torrs. Neon and krypton lights are also used to mark airplane routes and to signal pilots.

### 7.18  Uses of chlorine

The chief use of chlorine is in the bleaching, or decolorizing, of textiles, chiefly cotton and linen, and of wood pulp. It cannot be used for bleaching silk or wool because it destroys their fibers.

Chlorine is used as a bleaching agent either in the free state, in chlorine water, or in some unstable chlorine compound such as *bleaching powder*, $CaOCl_2$, tons of which are used annually. Household *laundry bleach*, used extensively today, is made by adding liquid chlorine to a very cold solution of sodium hydroxide. The product of this reaction is sodium hypochlorite, $NaOCl$, a salt of hypochlorous acid, $HOCl$, and an excellent mild bleaching agent:

$$2NaOH(aq) + Cl_2(g) = NaOCl(aq) + NaCl(aq) + H_2O(l)$$

A second very important use of chlorine is in the purification of water. When chlorine is added to water, it reacts with the bacteria present and kills them. Only three pounds of chlorine are used for each million gallons of water. As a result, for example, the death rate from typhoid fever, a disease caused by typhoid bacilli that may be present in drinking water, has been drastically cut. This treatment also kills algae and other low plant and animal life. The use of chlorine as a germicide in public swimming pools may be familiar to you. Chlorine is also used as an antiseptic and disinfectant and finds wide use in the industrial preparation of many diverse and useful compounds.

### 7.19  Some uses of bromine

Most of the bromine produced in the United States is used in the manufacture of ethylene dibromide, $C_2H_4Br_2$. Ethylene dibromide is used along with tetraethyl lead, $Pb(C_2H_5)_4$, and tetramethyl lead, $Pb(CH_3)_4$, two *antiknock* substances, in the *ethyl fluid* additive found in most gasoline mixtures. Antiknock compounds control the rapid rate of combustion of gasoline constituents. This prevents premature explosions (knocking) from occurring in the engine's cylinders. The combustion of the lead compounds in the absence of the ethylene dibromide would lead to the formation of lead oxide:

$$Pb(C_2H_5)_4(g) + 13\tfrac{1}{2}O_2(g) \overset{\Delta}{=} 8CO_2(g) + 10H_2O(g) + PbO(s)$$

The solid oxide would form harmful deposits in the engine cylinders. The ethylene dibromide, however, leads to the formation of the volatile lead bromide, $PbBr_2$, instead:

$$Pb(C_2H_5)_4(g) + C_2H_4Br_2(g) + 16O_2(g)$$
$$= PbBr_2(g) + 10CO_2(g) + 12H_2O(g)$$

The lead bromide vapor escapes from the cylinders through the engine exhaust system.

    Large quantities of bromine are also used in making silver bromide, $AgBr$, the basic light-sensitive component of photographic films. The element is also used in the manufacture of certain dyes and drugs. Bromides act as *depressants* on the central nervous system. Their action is followed by drowsiness and even sleep. Substances of such biochemical activity are called *sedatives*. Bromide sedatives are used in the treatment of insomnia and asthma and are frequently components of headache remedies and sleeping powders.

What is the basic composition of "ethyl fluid" gasoline additives?

## 7.20 Some uses of iodine and fluorine

The chief use of iodine is in the preparation of an excellent antiseptic, *tincture of iodine*. This is a 2 per cent solution of $I_2$ in ethyl alcohol, $C_2H_5OH$, containing also a small amount of sodium iodide.

    Iodine is an important constituent of the human body. There is a definite relation between the presence of iodine in the thyroid gland and the prevalence of certain disorders. The thyroid gland, located in the neck, secretes a compound called thyroxin which helps to regulate the rate of oxidation in the body. Thyroxin contains about 65 per cent iodine.

    When the thyroid gland receives too little iodine, goiter, an enlargement of the thyroid, results, caused apparently by the attempt of the gland to increase its size in order to produce more thyroxin. To offset this deficiency, iodides may be added to drinking water, or about 0.02 per cent of sodium iodide added to so-called *iodized salt*. The normal consumption of seafood or kelp, a giant seaweed, provides the necessary iodine for large segments of the world's population.

Where would this condition be most frequently found?

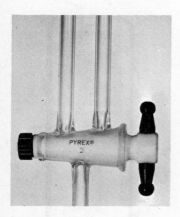

Teflon stopcock plugs are now widely used. These easy-to-clean, chemically inactive plugs require no grease to keep them from "freezing."

An important use of fluorine is in the production of modern refrigerants. A refrigerant, you recall from Chapter 6, is a chemical used to absorb heat as it changes from a liquid to a vapor. The freons, compounds of carbon, chlorine, and fluorine such as dichlorodifluoromethane, $CCl_2F_2$, are excellent refrigerants. The plastic known as *Teflon*, a giant molecular compound of fluorine and carbon, is very resistant to the action of most chemicals and is used widely as an electrical insulator.

Sodium fluoride is added to drinking water in many communities, as the presence of fluoride in water has been shown to reduce considerably the amount of tooth decay in young children. Stannous fluoride, $SnF_2$, is the decay-preventive compound added to so-called fluoride toothpastes.

## SUMMARY

The study of the chemical and physical properties of the elements would be nearly impossible without some kind of organizational framework. The recurrence, or periodicity, of physical and chemical properties allows for the grouping of the elements into chemical families, or groups.

The six members of the "noble gas" family—He, Ne, Ar, Kr, Xe, Rn—are characterized by their general chemical inactivity. Four members of the halogen family—the diatomic elements $F_2$, $Cl_2$, $Br_2$, $I_2$—are the most active nonmetals. A fifth halogen, astatine, $At_2$, has been synthesized, but little is known of its real physical or chemical properties.

Chemically, these elements react with metals to form salts called halides. A halogen of lower atomic weight will replace a halogen of higher atomic weight from its halide. The alkali metals—Li, Na, K, Rb, Cs—are chemically the most active metals. Francium, Fr, a synthetic element, is also a member of this group. They react violently with water to form metal hydroxides, or bases. Hydrogen is liberated during this reaction.

The chemical periodicity of the elements was first discovered as a function of atomic weight. The modern Periodic Law relates chemical periodicity to atomic number. An understanding of chemical periodicity leads to generalizations regarding the physical properties and the chemical reactivity of any member of a group or family of elements. Such generalizations may then be used to predict behavior of new compounds of those elements even before these compounds are synthesized.

## QUESTIONS AND PROBLEMS

**7.1** Using the data in Table 7–2, plot the boiling point (°K) of the noble gases against their molar heats of vaporization. Using the data in Tables 7–3 and 7–4, respectively, repeat the exercise for the halogens and the alkali metals.

**7.2** Compare the three graphs obtained from Problem 7.1. What general statements are you able to make?

**7.3** Find evidence to show that the intermolecular attractive forces in liquid fluorine are of the same relative strength as the interatomic attractive forces in liquid argon.

**7.4** On the basis of your understanding of the kinetic molecular model of real gases, explain the existence of the very small temperature range in which a noble gas exists as a liquid.

**7.5** Using the data in Table 7–3, plot on the same set of axes the melting points and boiling points of the halogens as functions of their atomic weights. On a separate set of axes, plot the molar heats of fusion and of vaporization of the halogens as functions of their atomic weights. From your graphs, predict a value for each of the properties plotted for astatine.

**7.6** Using the data in Table 7–4 repeat the graphing exercise of Problem 7.5. From your graphs of the properties of the alkali metals as functions of their atomic numbers, predict values for the same properties of francium.

**7.7** Write *one* equation for the laboratory preparation of bromine from solid sodium bromide, solid manganese dioxide, and aqueous sulfuric acid.

**7.8** For each of the following pairs of reactants, indicate whether a reaction occurs by writing the equation for that reaction: **a.** $CaCl_2(aq) + Br_2(aq)$; **b.** $Cl_2(g) + KI(aq)$; **c.** $Br_2(l) + CaAt_2(aq)$; **d.** $I_2(s) + NaAt(aq)$; **e.** $Cl_2(g) + NaF(aq)$.

**7.9** Write equations for the reactions that occur between each of the following pairs of reactants: **a.** $Rb(s) + H_2O(l)$; **b.** $Li(s) + O_2(g)$; **c.** $LiOH(aq) + HCl(aq)$; **d.** $NaOH(aq) + HF(aq)$; **e.** $CsOH(aq) + HBr(aq)$; **f.** any alkali metal + water; **g.** any alkali metal + atmospheric oxygen; **h.** any alkali metal base + any hydrohalic acid.

**7.10** Using the Periodic Table only (Fig. 7.3), write formulas for the most probable binary compound that would form between the following elements. The atomic number of each element is given in parentheses to help you locate it in the table.

**a.** calcium(20) selenium(34)      **f.** radium(88) bromine(35)
**b.** potassium(19) nitrogen(7)      **g.** silicon(14) oxygen(8)
**c.** aluminum(13) tellurium(52)     **h.** carbon(6) chlorine(17)
**d.** barium(56) oxygen(8)           **i.** antimony(51) hydrogen(1)
**e.** tin(50) fluorine(9)            **j.** arsenic(33) sulfur(16)

**7.11** Name each of the compounds of Problem 7.10.

**7.12** Which of the uses of the noble gases listed in Section 7.17 do not depend on the chemical inactivity of those gases?

**7.13** a. When fluorine gas is bubbled into water a violent reaction yielding oxygen gas and hydrofluoric acid occurs. Write the equation for that reaction. b. Write the general equation for the reaction that occurs between the other halogens and water. (Sec. 7.18.)

**7.14** Make a list of the different trade names used for tin(II) fluoride (stannous fluoride) in different brands of fluoride toothpastes.

**7.15** Make a list of the trade names for the different liquid laundry bleaches found in a well-stocked supermarket. Record the ingredients and their percentages found in each. What formula would you give to the "inert ingredient" of liquid laundry bleach?

**7.16** During an average day look carefully at the label of every container that you use. Record, by name, every compound that contains an alkali metal or halogen atom in it.

**7.17** a. What volume of $Cl_2$ gas (STP) could be produced from 5.36 g of NaCl? b. What weight of $MnO_2$ would be required in the reaction?

Ans.   b. 3.98 g

**7.18** a. If 4.60 g of sodium are carefully reacted with water, what volume of *dry* hydrogen gas would be formed at 27.0°C and 740 torrs? b. How many moles of base would form?

Ans.   b. 0.200 moles

**7.19** An aqueous solution of hydrochloric acid contains $1.00 \times 10^{-3}$ moles of hydrogen chloride per milliliter of solution. What volume of this solution is required to neutralize exactly 1.50 g of cesium hydroxide?

**7.20** A mixture containing 2.00 moles of xenon and 8.00 moles of fluorine is heated under pressure. Gaseous xenon tetrafluoride forms, which is separated from the unreacted xenon and fluorine. The unreacted gaseous mixture is found to occupy a volume of 100.8 liters at STP. What weight of xenon tetrafluoride was formed in the reaction?

Ans.   379 g

## SUGGESTED READINGS

Cooper, D. G. *The Periodic Table* (paperback). Butterworths, 1960.

Garrett, A. B. *Flash of Genius.* Van Nostrand, 1963. A series of science discoveries, including Freon.

Jaffe, Bernard. *Crucibles: The Story of Chemistry* (paperback). Fawcett, 1961. Chapter 9 tells the story of Mendeleev.

Krotikov, V. A. "The Mendeleev Archives and Museum of the Leningrad University," *Journal of Chemical Education*, December, 1960.

Sanderson, R. T. *Chemical Periodicity*. Reinhold, 1960.

Strong, F. C., III. "The Atomic Form Periodic Table," *Journal of Chemical Education*, July, 1959.

CHEMISTRY

Chernick, C. L., "The Noble Gas Compounds." Jan. 1964

SCIENTIFIC AMERICAN

Lifshitz, E. M., "Superfluidity." June 1958
Selig, H., J. G. Malm, and H. H. Claasen, "The Chemistry of the Noble Gases." May 1964

*To the eyes of the man of imagination,*
*Nature is imagination itself.*

*William Blake* (1757–1827)

# CHAPTER 8

# Electrons, Protons,

Though atomic theory was born of philosophic speculation in the fifth century B.C., it only became a practical, working concept in the early nineteenth century A.D. In Chapter 2 the behavior of gases under changes of pressure, volume, and temperature was considered. It was shown that this behavior was in agreement with a model of a gas consisting of a collection of atoms or molecules. According to this model, the molecules of the gas were relatively far apart and in constant motion. Ideally, they bounced around like marbles colliding with each other and with the walls of their container.

In liquids and solids, the molecules are much closer; and, in general, molecular kinetic energy is much lower in these condensed states. In general, the attraction between molecules is stronger than the tendency to pull apart from each other. In liquids, some molecules still have sufficient kinetic energy to overcome the attraction. They move apart for a short time only, and are quickly attracted to other molecules. This leads to *short range order* or a regular pattern of structure within groups of molecules in the liquid state. These groups are continuously breaking up and reforming. In solids, molecular kinetic energy is so reduced that *long range order* exists. The attraction between molecules (or atoms, or ions) in solids can cause arrangement into a *single group of all the molecules present*. In this manner, the model of atoms and molecules in the gaseous state was extended to explain some of the properties of liquids and solids.

In addition, we have seen that the Laws of Definite Composition and of Multiple Proportions as well as Gay-Lussac's observations on the combining volumes of gases can be interpreted to indicate the

*190*

# Neutrons, and Nuclei

existence of atoms. In compounds and in chemical reactions, elements combined in simple, small whole-number ratios. This was understood to indicate that compounds were formed of small indivisible particles or atoms.

While all these arguments provide a strong case for the existence of atoms, they do not indicate very much about the structure of the atoms themselves. The fact that atoms combine chemically, as well as the existence of interatomic and intermolecular attractive forces, would suggest that atoms must have a structure that can lead to chemical reaction and that can cause attraction. Moreover, the discovery of chemical periodicity indicated that in order to understand the relationships that exist among the elements—both the differences and the similarities—it would be necessary to understand more about the structure of atoms. We shall consider in this chapter the first evidences, all of which are indirect, that led to our present model of the atom. In following chapters, we shall develop in some detail this contemporary model of the atom and discuss how greatly it helps in understanding chemistry.

## THE ELECTRON

Between 1850 and 1900 physicists were studying the effects caused when an electric discharge passes through gases confined in tubes at very low pressures. The glass tubes in which these experiments were carried out were the primitive ancestors of our present-day vacuum tubes and television picture tubes. The phenomenon that interested these physicists may be observed if you look at a vacuum tube in either a radio or a TV set. Notice the glow in the tube between the metal electrodes when the set is turned on. Physicists came to the conclusion that such a glow was caused by rays originating at the negative electrode (the cathode). Consequently, these rays were named *cathode rays.* The exact nature of these rays remained unclear, however, since they could be deflected from their straight-line path by a magnet. Since ordinary light is not affected by a magnet, the rays showed a property of matter rather than of light.

### 8.1 Discovery of the electron

J. J. Thomson, a famous English physicist, undertook to investigate the strange behavior of these cathode rays. In 1897, after 20 years of brilliant research, he announced his results. Thomson showed that the cathode rays were bent from their paths by both electric and magnetic fields. (Fig. 8.1.) Unless these rays were streams of charged particles, they would not have been so affected. Further, positive particles were bent in the opposite direction from negative particles. Thomson could prove from the direction of bending that the cathode rays were negative particles. These negative particles were named *electrons.*

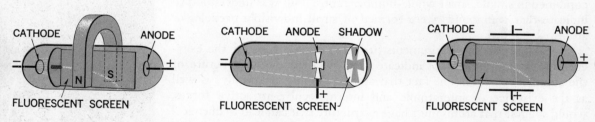

**FIGURE 8.1** Cathode rays, which ordinarily move in straight lines (center), are deflected from their path in a magnetic field (left), and in an electric field (right).

To understand Thomson's experiment, consider how a modern TV picture tube works. In a TV tube, electrons are emitted from the cathode and pass through the tube, striking a fluorescent coating on the screen, where they cause a spot of light to appear.* When the set is first turned on or when it has just been turned off, a single bright spot appears as all the electrons strike the same spot. However, when the set has warmed up, the whole screen glows as a result of electrons striking the whole surface. The electron beam is rapidly being moved back and forth, up and down, across the whole surface of the screen.

---

* Some substances emit a glow when X rays, ultraviolet light, or visible light strike them. If the glow persists for some time after the impinging radiation is cut off, then the substance is said to *phosphoresce*. If the glow ceases at the same moment that the impinging radiation is cut off, then the substance is said to *fluoresce*.

The movement is so rapid that we see only the total glow as though all parts of the surface were being struck simultaneously. This movement of the electron beam results from the fact that moving electrons can be deflected from their straight-line paths by both electric and magnetic fields. When all the electrons in a beam are so deflected, the beam itself appears to curve or bend. In a TV set, small electromagnets cause the electron beam to bend out of a straight-line path. (Fig. 8.2.)

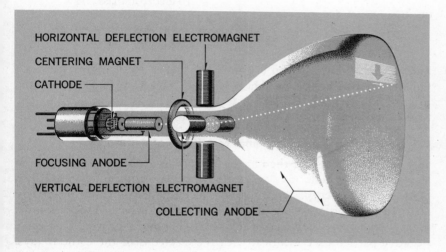

HORIZONTAL DEFLECTION ELECTROMAGNET

CENTERING MAGNET

CATHODE

FOCUSING ANODE

VERTICAL DEFLECTION ELECTROMAGNET

COLLECTING ANODE

**FIGURE 8.2** Television picture tube. The electron beam is deflected by both electric and magnetic fields so that it moves back and forth to activate the atoms in the fluorescent screen.

## 8.2 The charge and mass of the electron

The electric charge carried by the electron is given the arbitrary, relative value of −1; that is, a *unit negative charge.** The halide ions are found to have exactly the same amount and the same type (negative) of charge. The chloride ion is, therefore, represented as $Cl^{-1}$. The alkali metal ions have been found to have the same amount of charge but of opposite type (positive). The positive sodium ion is, therefore, represented as $Na^{+1}$. The charges of ions are always found to be integral multiples, either positive or negative, of the value of the charge of an electron.

The extent to which a charged particle is deflected in a magnetic field is dependent on the ratio between its charge, $e$, and its

---

* The absolute value of the fundamental unit of negative electrical charge, $e$, was first measured by the American physicist Robert Millikan in 1906 in an ingenious experiment. The modern figure for that absolute value is $e = 1.60210 \times 10^{-19}$ coulomb/electron, where a *coulomb* is a basic *amount* of electrical charge. (See page 417.) It is this absolute figure that is represented simply by the symbol −1.

mass, $m$—its $e/m$ ratio. Since it is possible to measure quantitatively the bending of a cathode ray beam in a magnetic field, the ratio $e/m$ can be determined quantitatively. Thomson was the first to do this. If the *measured* absolute value of the unit electronic charge, $e$, is divided by the *measured* value of the ratio of electron charge to electron mass, $e/m$, the *derived* value for the mass of an electron, $m$, is obtained. That is:

$$\text{Calculated electron mass} = \frac{\text{measured electron charge}}{\text{measured ratio of electron charge to electron mass}}$$

or

$$m = \frac{e}{e/m}$$

Such a calculation leads to a value of $9.1091 \times 10^{-28}$ gram/electron.[*] On the relative atomic weight scale based on $O = 16.0000$ amu, the mass of the electron is $5.486 \times 10^{-4}$ amu. This is about $\frac{1}{1850}$ of the mass of the hydrogen atom, lightest of all atoms.

### 8.3 The electron is a fundamental constituent of matter.

Just before the close of the nineteenth century, Thomson turned from the study of cathode rays to another interesting phenomenon. When light of high energy strikes certain metals, such as zinc, negatively charged particles are emitted by the metallic surface. This is known as the *photoelectric effect*. (Fig. 8.3.) Thomson proved that these negative particles are identical with the electrons of the cathode rays. The fact that electrons could be obtained from matter in different ways was very strong indication that electrons are fundamental constituents, or parts, of matter and, consequently, of atoms. As a result of this, the indivisible atom of Dalton could no longer be retained as a useful model.

### 8.4 The Thomson model of the atom

Thomson suggested a new model of the atom, which took into account the existence of electrons. He described it in these words. "We suppose that the atom consists of a number of [electrons] moving about in a sphere of uniform positive electrification. . . . The [electrons] will arrange themselves in a series . . . of concentric shells. The gradual change in the properties of the elements which takes place as we travel along the horizontal rows in [the periodic table] of the elements is also illustrated by the properties possessed by these groups of [electrons]." Thomson's picture might be called the "grapes-in-Jello" model of the atom. (Fig. 8.4.) The electrons correspond to the grapes, while the sphere of positive electricity corresponds to the Jello in which the

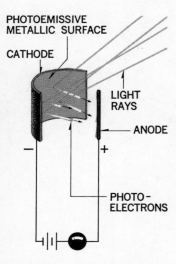

**Joseph John Thomson** (1856–1940, English). Thomson followed Rayleigh as head of the Cavendish Physical Laboratory at Cambridge University. Under his leadership, it became a great center of research on the structure of the atom.

**PHOTOEMISSIVE METALLIC SURFACE**

**CATHODE**

**LIGHT RAYS**

**ANODE**

**PHOTO-ELECTRONS**

**FIGURE 8.3** Photoelectric cell. Light energy is converted into electrical energy via the photoelectric effect.

---

[*] The modern measured value for $e/m$ is $1.758796 \times 10^{11}$ coulombs/kilogram.

grapes are imbedded. Thomson, however, realized the inadequacies of this model. In particular, the assumption of a vague and undefined sphere of positive electricity was unsatisfying. Yet such positive electricity had to be present to neutralize the negative charges of the electrons, since the atom itself is electrically neutral. Nevertheless, the Thomson model of the atom was useful, as it was the first attempt to explain the relationship between electrons and atomic structure. Also, Thomson clearly suggested the dependence of the periodic relation of elemental properties on the electron groups in the atom. This last suggestion is retained in our modern model of the atom.

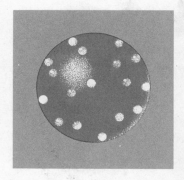

**FIGURE 8.4** Thomson model of the atom

## RADIOACTIVITY: KEY TO ATOMIC STRUCTURE

At the time that Thomson and others were unraveling the mysteries of cathode rays, a French physicist, Henri Becquerel (on REE beck RELL), discovered another phenomenon that exerts a profound influence on our lives today. Becquerel, like his physicist father before him, was interested in studying fluorescence. (See footnote on page 192.) At the time of his momentous discovery, Becquerel was studying the fluorescence of uranium compounds. In one of his experiments he placed crystals of potassium uranyl sulfate, $K_2SO_4 \cdot (UO_2)SO_4 \cdot 2H_2O$, on photographic film that was wrapped in dark paper. The crystals, in place on the wrapped film, were exposed to sunlight. The fluorescent glow emitted by the uranium compound penetrated the dark paper and caused a darkening of the film directly beneath the crystal sample. In a control experiment, sunlight itself caused no darkening of the film, since it could not penetrate the dark paper wrapping. This proved that there was a difference in the energy of the sunlight and that of the fluorescent radiation emitted by the uranium compound. Since it did penetrate the paper wrapping, the fluorescent radiation emitted by the uranium must be of greater energy.

### 8.5 The world of radioactivity is uncovered.

Becquerel, convinced that the film darkening was due to fluorescence, prepared to continue this research. During February 1896 he made ready another similar experiment, but for several days the cloudy winter weather in northern France prevented the sun from shining through and the experiment could not be completed. On March 1, Becquerel decided to use new sets of uranium compounds and photographic film. Fortunately, he developed the earlier films, which had been kept with the crystal samples in a drawer. Becquerel expected at best a faint darkening under the crystals, since exposure to room light did produce some fluorescence. To his amazement, the spots were as dark as though sunlight had been striking the uranium. Becquerel

**Madame Marie Curie** (1867–1934, Polish). Madame Curie and her husband, Pierre, shared the Nobel Prize in physics with Becquerel in 1903 for their researches in radioactivity. In 1911, five years after her husband's accidental death, she accepted another Nobel Prize, this time in chemistry, for their 1902 discovery of radium. Thus, she became the first person ever to win two Nobel Prizes. The remarkable Curie family has a third Nobel Prize to its credit. In 1935, Irène Joliot-Curie and her husband, Frédéric Joliot, the daughter and son-in-law of Marie Curie, received the prize in chemistry for their discovery of induced radioactivity. (See Section 32.5.)

correctly interpreted this to mean that the uranium was spontaneously emitting rays without the stimulation of external light. It was that emission that caused the observed darkening of the photographic plate.

He repeated the experiment with other substances containing uranium, such as *pitchblende*, a mineral ore containing oxides of uranium. Pitchblende, he found, affected a photographic plate even more than other uranium-containing substances did. He suspected some unknown element in the ore to be the cause and asked Madame Marie Sklodowska Curie (sklaw DOFF skah cue REE), a Polish girl working as a science teacher and research assistant in Paris, to undertake the isolation of this unknown element. With her husband, Pierre (pea AIR), Madame Curie began the search for the unknown element that, like uranium, exhibited the phenomenon of spontaneous emission of high energy radiation. She named that phenomenon *radioactivity*.

## 8.6 The discovery of polonium and radium

Proceeding on the hypothesis that the greater radioactivity of some uranium minerals indicated the existence of a substance even more radioactive than uranium in these minerals, Pierre and Marie Curie began an intense chemical separation and analysis of these minerals. The story of this search of the Curies is one of the most interesting and inspiring in all of the history of science. Perseverance, dedication, and intelligence finally brought success, and in 1898 the Curies isolated a new chemical element. It proved to be radioactive. In memory of Poland, Madame Curie's native land, the new element was named *polonium*. Four years later, the Curies isolated from tons of pitchblende a minute amount of yet another new and intensely radioactive element, which was named *radium*.

## 8.7 Alpha, beta, and gamma rays: products of radioactivity

Within a short time, studies with electrical fields showed that three different kinds of "rays" were emitted by radioactive substances. One ray was deflected slightly to one side in an electrical field. It was named an *alpha* (α) *ray*. Another was deflected more strongly, but to the opposite side. It was termed a *beta* (β) *ray*. The third was not deflected at all in an electrical field and was called a *gamma* (γ) *ray*. (Fig. 8.5.)

Becquerel proved that beta rays consisted of negative particles identical in charge and in mass to the electrons that constituted the cathode rays and photoelectric emissions. Ernest Rutherford, a New Zealand-born physicist, demonstrated that alpha rays were positively charged particles with a mass greater than that of the hydrogen atom. Since it was found that helium gas was present in mineral deposits of radioactive substances, Rutherford believed, and it was subsequently proved, that alpha rays were composed of positive *helium ions*. From $e/m$ studies on alpha rays, it was shown that such rays consisted of doubly charged helium ions, $He^{+2}$, each with a relative atomic weight of 4.00 amu. Gamma rays were found to have neither mass nor charge. They are identical in nature to light rays and X rays but of higher energy.

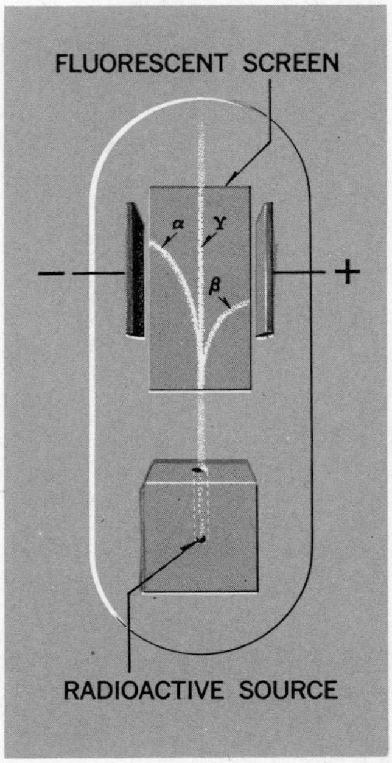

### 8.8  A theory of radioactive disintegration

Rutherford and a co-worker, Frederick Soddy, undertook a detailed study of the radioactivity phenomenon of uranium ores. They considered the nature of the rays emitted by those ores and the existence of new elements in them. These considerations led them to propose a theory of radioactivity in 1902 that was in direct contradiction to the notion of the solid, indivisible atoms proposed by Dalton a century earlier. Their theory stated that when a radioactive substance emits an alpha or a beta particle, it is transformed into a different element with different chemical and physical properties. In other words, when the original radioactive atom "disintegrates," a charged particle is ejected from it and an atom of a new element is formed.

      The existence of the electron and the discovery of radioactivity demanded a new model of the atom in which there were particles as well as positive and negative electrical charges. We have seen how Thomson attempted to account for this in an atomic model that proved inadequate. Rutherford suggested, and interpreted the results of, an experiment that definitely ruled out Thomson's model, and then suggested a much better one.

FIGURE 8.5  Behavior of alpha, beta, and gamma radiation in an electric field. Explain qualitatively the individual curvatures.

## THE NUCLEAR ATOM

In 1907 Rutherford, who had already demonstrated the nature of alpha rays and postulated the theory of radioactivity, became Professor of Physics at the University of Manchester, in England. Here, and then at the Cavendish Laboratory at Cambridge University, he was to plan, direct, and interpret correctly a number of experiments that cleared up much of the mystery of the structure of the atom.

### 8.9  The atom's nucleus is discovered.

In 1909 two of Rutherford's students, Hans Geiger and Ernest Marsden, carefully investigated the passage of alpha particles (from the radioactive element polonium) through a very thin foil of the metal platinum. (Fig. 8.6.) The vast majority of the alpha particles passed straight through the foil. This was as expected. However, about 1 in every 8000 alpha particles was scattered at an angle of 90°, and some even more, from the incident direction. When Rutherford was told of this, he was

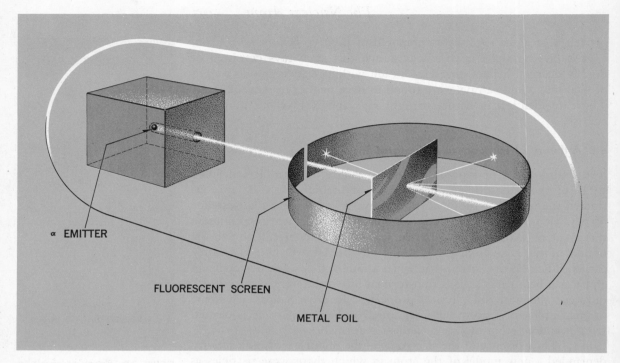

α EMITTER

FLUORESCENT SCREEN

METAL FOIL

**FIGURE 8.6** Alpha particle scattering. This classic experiment led to Rutherford's model of the atom.

astonished. His reaction to the news in his own words was: "It was quite the most incredible event that has ever happened to me in my life. It was almost as incredible as if you fired a 15-inch shell at a piece of tissue paper and it came back and hit you."

Rutherford came first to the conclusion that since most of the alpha particles passed straight through the platinum foil, there had to be a very large amount of empty space in the atoms of platinum. If the atoms were solid little particles, as Dalton suggested, all of the alpha particles would have been deflected. Rutherford then suggested that since only very few alpha particles were deflected very strongly, only a very tiny part of the platinum atom was involved. That tiny piece of the atom had to be very dense and positively charged in order to account for the deflection of positively charged alpha particles. Electrons were both too low in mass and of wrong charge to cause such large deflections. Within two years of the alpha particle scattering experiments, Rutherford postulated the explanation that the atom had a very small central core in which all the positive charge and most of the mass of the atom were concentrated. This small, positively charged, heavy center later became known as *the atomic nucleus*. Rutherford published this momentous theory in the same journal of the Literary and Philosophical Society of Manchester where, a little more than a century before, Dalton had announced his concept of the atom.

## 8.10 Some properties of the nuclear atom

Further research and calculations in Rutherford's laboratory established that the diameter of the nucleus is only about $10^{-12}$ cm, whereas the diameter of the atom, $10^{-8}$ cm, is $10^4$ times greater. This is equivalent to a circular nucleus with a diameter of $\frac{2}{5}$ of an inch located at the center of a circular atom with a diameter the length of a football field. In the Rutherford model, electrons in atoms are distributed in the space outside of the nucleus.

Consider the hydrogen atom, with one electron and an atomic weight of about 1 amu. The Rutherford model of this atom depicts it as a small spherical nucleus that bears a charge of +1 and a weight of 1 amu and outside of which there is a single electron of −1 charge and a weight of $5.5 \times 10^{-4}$ amu. In another case, the Rutherford model depicts the fluorine atom as a nucleus with a charge of +9 and a weight of 19.0 amu, outside of which there are nine electrons.

## 8.11 What is the structure of the nucleus?

Extensive research has since shown that the nucleus is itself primarily composed of particles called neutrons and protons. Protons have a relative weight very close to 1 amu and bear the unit charge of +1.[*]

Neutrons also have a relative weight very close to 1 amu but differ from protons in that they are electrically neutral. Since neutrons and protons are particles found in nuclei, they are called *nucleons*. The number of nucleons in a nucleus is the sum of the number of protons and neutrons. The number for this sum is called the *mass number, A*. The fluorine nucleus consists of 9 protons and 10 neutrons, or 19 nucleons. The mass number of fluorine is, therefore, 19. Notice that the *mass number* of a nucleus must always be a whole number.

You will recall from Chapter 7 that, on the basis of the brilliant research of Moseley, the periodic law relates the recurring properties of the elements to their atomic number. Continuing research into the structure of the atom has led to the discovery that Moseley's arbitrary numerical ordering device, *the atomic number, Z, is equal to the number of protons in an atomic nucleus.*

If the atomic number, Z, equals the number of protons in an atomic nucleus, and the mass number, A, equals the total number of

**Ernest Rutherford** (1871–1937, New Zealand). Himself the student of J. J. Thomson, Rutherford counted among his own famous students Moseley, Chadwick (discoverer of the neutron), Geiger, and Bohr. For his work in radioactivity, Rutherford was awarded the Nobel Prize in 1908. His further discoveries in atomic physics earned him a knighthood in 1914, a peerage in 1931, and the continued accolades of the scientific community. He is buried in Westminster Abbey, near the tombs of Newton and Lord Kelvin.

---

[*] The symbol +1 represents an absolute value of charge equal to $1.60210 \times 10^{-19}$ coulomb. The + sign indicates that this charge moves in the opposite direction from that of an electron in a magnetic or electric field. Obviously, the − and + signs are quite arbitrary in nature.

nucleons, then the difference *A–Z must equal the number of neutrons in the nucleus.*

### 8.12 Nuclei have special symbols.

Nuclear chemists and physicists have agreed on a special way to symbolize nuclei of elements. The representation tells very quickly three fundamental nuclear facts: the element of which the nucleus is a part; how many protons are in it; how many neutrons are in it. The general symbol for any nucleus is $_Z^A X$, where $X$ is the symbol for the atom in which the given nucleus is found, Z is the atomic number, and $A$ is the mass number. Some examples will indicate how the symbols are used and interpreted.

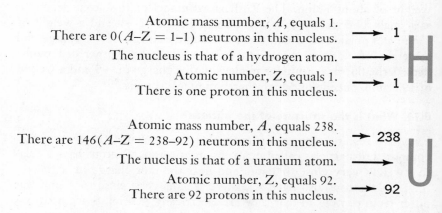

Atomic mass number, $A$, equals 1.
There are $0(A–Z = 1–1)$ neutrons in this nucleus. $\longrightarrow$ 1
The nucleus is that of a hydrogen atom. $\longrightarrow$ H
Atomic number, Z, equals 1.
There is one proton in this nucleus. $\longrightarrow$ 1

Atomic mass number, $A$, equals 238.
There are $146(A–Z = 238–92)$ neutrons in this nucleus. $\longrightarrow$ 238
The nucleus is that of a uranium atom. $\longrightarrow$ U
Atomic number, Z, equals 92.
There are 92 protons in this nucleus. $\longrightarrow$ 92

It is interesting to note that in 1815, soon after Dalton published his atomic theory, William Prout, a London physician, announced the theory that all the chemical elements were made up of groups of hydrogen atoms only. Prout's theory was not taken seriously for 100 years until it became clear that hydrogen nuclei and protons are the same species.

### 8.13 The discovery of isotopes

Since the nucleus of an atom of any element is composed basically of only neutrons and protons, and since each of these has a mass very nearly a whole number, it may have occurred to you that the atomic weights of all the elements ought to be whole numbers. However, the fact that many atomic weights—for example, chlorine (35.457 amu)—are not close to whole numbers does not support this idea.

In 1913, Soddy and T. W. Richards of Harvard University, independently and by different methods, found two different atomic weights for lead obtained from two different sources. In the same year, Thomson separated neon atoms into two different atomic weight species. These were additional startling discoveries that led to the drastic alteration of the Daltonian concept of atomic structure.

The name *isotopes* was given by Soddy to *atoms of the same element, having the same chemical properties but different atomic weights*. Discovery and separation of isotopes of many other elements soon followed. It is now known that while some elements, such as beryllium and fluorine, exist as single *nonradioactive* or *stable* isotopic species, most of the first eighty-three elements exist as more than one. Tin ($Z = 50$) has *ten* known stable isotopic species, each having the same atomic number but a different atomic mass.

## 8.14 The isotopes of oxygen and a new standard for atomic weights

In 1929 two American chemists, William Giauque (gee OKE) and Herrick Johnston, discovered two naturally occurring isotopes of oxygen of weight different from 16.0000 amu. These stable isotopes are $^{17}_8O$ and $^{18}_8O$. Though neither occurs to any great extent in nature, it became recognized that standard definitions of atomic and molecular weights and the mole, based on *all* oxygen atoms being $^{16}_8O$, had to be altered for the most accurate quantitative work. Nuclear chemists and physicists adopted the *oxygen isotope* $^{16}_8O$ for such a standard. Chemists remained content to consider all oxygen atoms to be the same, as they had for more than half a century. For some years, then, two tables of atomic weights existed; one for nuclear chemists and physicists, and one for all other chemists. Though these two tables differed very slightly, their existence was hardly a sign of cooperation among scientists. Accordingly, after considerable debate, a single standard for defining atomic and molecular weights and the mole was agreed upon internationally in 1961. The new definitions are based on the *isotope of carbon* $^{12}_6C$.

RELATIVE ATOMIC WEIGHT.   The relative atomic weight of an element is the weight of one atom of that element relative to the weight of one atom of pure $^{12}_6C$, which, by convention, has the assigned weight of 12.0000 *unified atomic mass units, u.*

RELATIVE MOLECULAR WEIGHTS.   The relative molecular weight of a compound is the weight of one molecule of that compound relative to the weight of one atom of pure $^{12}_6C$, which, by convention, has the assigned weight of 12.0000 unified atomic mass units, u.

THE MOLE.   The mole is the number of atoms contained in *exactly* twelve grams of pure $^{12}_6C$. (Experimentally, this is equal to $6.02252 \times 10^{23}$ atoms.)

It has been pointed out that the new table of atomic weights is significant only in terms of very accurate quantitative work. The relative atomic weights based on O = 16.0000 amu remain sufficiently accurate for our purposes. Those weights, as given in Table 3–1, page 85, differ only slightly from the newly accepted weights based on $^{12}_{6}C$ = 12.0000 u. You may contrast the differences by referring to the table of chemical elements that appears as Appendix I, page 695, and on the front endleaf of this book.

### 8.15 How atomic weights may be calculated

Most elements, then, are really mixtures of isotopes having different atomic weights, each of which is close to, but usually is not exactly, an integer. For example, chlorine gas is really made up of some atoms with a relative atomic weight close to 35 u and other atoms of relative atomic weight close to 37 u. The accepted value for the relative atomic weight of chlorine, 35.457 u, is the *weighted average* of the relative atomic weights of its two naturally occurring, stable isotopes.

To illustrate this more directly, let us consider the calculation for chlorine. In an average sample of 10,000 ($10^4$) atoms of chlorine we should find 75.53 per cent or 7553 of those atoms, each weighing 34.98 u, contributing a weight of:

$$\left(34.98 \frac{u}{atom}\right)(7553 \text{ atoms}) = 26.42 \times 10^4 \text{ u}$$

The remaining 24.47 per cent or 2447 of those 10,000 atoms, each weighing 36.98 u, should contribute a weight of:

$$\left(36.98 \frac{u}{atom}\right)(2447 \text{ atoms}) = 9.049 \times 10^4 \text{ u}$$

The total weight of the 10,000-atom sample is, then:

$$\begin{array}{r} 26.42 \ \times 10^4 \text{ u} \\ + \ 9.049 \times 10^4 \text{ u} \\ \hline 35.47 \ \times 10^4 \text{ u} \end{array}$$

And the *weighted average* relative atomic weight will be:

$$\frac{35.47 \times 10^4 \text{ u}}{10^4 \text{ atom}} = 35.47 \text{ u/atom}$$

To four significant figures this calculated value agrees within better than 0.03 per cent of the experimental value of 35.457 u.

It is important to recognize that the atomic weight just considered is a *calculated* weight derived from two types of experimental data. The latter are the atomic weights of isotopic species and the abundance of such species. It is also important to note that such *calculated* atomic weights of elements agree exactly with *experimental* values of those atomic weights from independent and strictly chemical determinations. This is powerful evidence for the validity of the separate experimental facts, as well as for the existence of isotopes.

## 8.16 Elements redefined

Isotopes exist because of the difference in the number of *neutrons* in the nucleus of each kind of atom. Thus, isotopes of chlorine, $^{35}_{17}Cl$ and $^{37}_{17}Cl$, have 18 and 20 neutrons in their respective nuclei. Both have the same 17 protons in their nuclei. If not, they would no longer be different weight forms of the same element. The isotopes of chlorine behave alike chemically because the chemistry of an element is related to its atomic number, not to its mass number. We can, therefore, redefine the word *element*. *A substance of which all the atoms have the same atomic number is an element.*

Having so redefined an element, let us turn next to a detailed study of the simplest of all the elements, hydrogen; a study that will bring us to the threshold of modern atomic theory.

## SUMMARY

Investigations into the nature of electrical discharges and radioactivity led to a model of the atom that differed significantly from Dalton's indivisible particle. Electrons were found by Thomson to be negatively charged particles, each of which is given the relative assigned value of $-1$. Thomson's work led to a model, admittedly inadequate, of the atom, consisting of discrete negative charges floating in a "sea" of positive charge. The discovery of natural radioactivity—the spontaneous conversion of one element to another by the emission of charged particles—dealt a final, severe blow to Dalton's "indivisible" atom.

Rutherford's interpretation of alpha particle scattering experiments led to a more adequate model of the atom—an infinitesimal, heavy, positively charged nucleus surrounded by electrons dispersed in a relatively vast amount of empty space. Nuclear charge is due to the presence of particles called protons, each of which bears a unit of positive electrical charge. Nuclear mass is the sum of the masses of the protons and of the neutral particles called neutrons that are also part of the nucleus.

All atoms of a given element contain the same number of protons in their nuclei. This number is known as the atomic number, $Z$, of the element. The mass number, $A$, of a nucleus is equal to the total number of nucleons present. Nuclei of the isotopes of an element differ in the number of neutrons present and, consequently, in mass number.

The atomic weight of an element is really the weighted average of its isotopes. The present standard for atomic weights, molecular weights, and the mole is the isotope of carbon $^{12}_{6}C$, which has the assigned weight of 12.0000 unified atomic mass units, u.

## QUESTIONS AND PROBLEMS

8.1 What evidence led to the idea that cathode rays consisted of negatively charged particles?

8.2 a. What is meant by measured and derived quantities? b. Describe an important derived quantity for the electron and how it is obtained from measured quantities.

8.3 a. Name some of the ways in which charged particles may be produced. b. What does this suggest about the fundamental nature of matter?

8.4 a. Briefly describe Thomson's model of the atom. b. In what ways was this model useful? c. What was an inadequacy of this model?

8.5 a. Describe the discovery of natural radioactivity. b. What is meant by natural radioactivity? c. Name two radioactive elements isolated by the Curies from pitchblende.

8.6 a. Briefly describe Rutherford's picture of the atom. b. What evidence led to this model?

8.7 a. List all the information that the atomic number of an element reveals. b. What specific information can be listed about a neutral atom that has 15 electrons?

8.8 List the number and kinds of particles found in a sodium atom having a mass number of 23.

8.9 Could neutral atoms of different elements have the same number of protons? the same number of neutrons? the same mass number? the same number of electrons? Explain your answers.

8.10 Could neutral atoms of the same element have a different number of protons? a different number of neutrons? a different mass number? a different number of electrons? Explain your answers.

8.11 Fill in the blanks for the following table.

| Element | Atomic No. | Protons | Electrons | Neutrons | Mass No. |
|---|---|---|---|---|---|
| Gallium (Ga) | 31 | | | | 70 |
| Magnesium (Mg) | | 12 | | | 24 |
| Nitrogen (N) | | | 7 | 7 | |
| Silicon (Si) | | 14 | | 14 | |
| Chlorine (Cl) | | | 17 | | 35 |
| Prometheum (Pm) | 61 | | | 84 | |

**8.12** What information is conveyed by the symbol $^{15}_{7}N$?

**8.13** The relative atomic weight of the proton is 1.00728 u; that of the neutron is 1.00866 u. **a.** What is the relative weight of one atom of lithium whose mass number is 6? **b.** What is the absolute weight of that atom in grams?

Ans. **b.** $1.005 \times 10^{-23}$ g

**8.14** Calculate the approximate relative atomic weight of lithium atoms consisting of 7.40% isotopes with mass number 6 and the rest with mass number 7.

**8.15** A sample of boron contains atoms with mass numbers of 10 and 11. If the atomic weight of boron is 10.82, calculate the approximate percentage of atoms in the sample that have a mass number of 11.

Ans. 82%

**8.16** **a.** An isotope of element $X$ has 30 protons and 15 neutrons. Write the symbol for its nucleus. What element is it? **b.** An isotope of element $Y$ has a mass number of 131 and contains 77 neutrons. Write the symbol for its nucleus. What element is it? **c.** A neutral isotope of element $Z$ has 19 electrons and a mass number of 40. Write the symbol for its nucleus. What element is it? **d.** An isotope of silver has a mass number of 107. Write the symbol for its nucleus.

**8.17** **a.** When an atom of $^{238}_{92}U$ undergoes natural radioactive transformation, an alpha particle is ejected from its nucleus. What is the nuclear symbol for the atom that is formed? **b.** When an atom of $^{239}_{92}U$ undergoes natural radioactive transformation, a beta particle is ejected from its nucleus. What is the nuclear symbol for the atom that is formed?

# SUGGESTED READINGS

Anderson, David L. *The Discovery of the Electron* (paperback). Van Nostrand, 1964.

Andrade, E. N. da C. *Rutherford and the Nature of the Atom* (paperback). Doubleday, 1964.

Frisch, D. H. and A. M. Thorndike. *Elementary Particles* (paperback). Van Nostrand, 1964.

Romer, Alfred. *The Restless Atom* (paperback). Doubleday, 1960.

CHEMISTRY
Wichers, E., "Why the Carbon-12 Scale." Mar. 1964

SCIENTIFIC AMERICAN
Morrison, P. and E., "The Neutron." Oct. 1951
Nier, A. O. C., "The Mass Spectrometer." Mar. 1952

*Science is a great many things,
... but in the end they all return
to this: science is the acceptance
of what works and the rejection
of what does not. That needs
more courage than we might think.*

*Jacob Bronowski (1908–     )*

---

**CHAPTER 9** | # Hydrogen, Quanta,

Hydrogen is unique among the elements. Structurally, it is the simplest atom, since it consists of merely a one-proton nucleus and one electron. It is the most abundant element in the universe and the primordial matter from which all other matter has come. Finally, from the light it emits when energized has come insight into the basic nature of matter —the structure of atoms.

## HYDROGEN: AN ELEMENT UNTO ITSELF

From astronomical studies, we have learned that most stars consist predominantly of hydrogen gas. Our own sun is approximately 99 per cent hydrogen by weight. The energy of the sun is produced by the conversion of this hydrogen to helium. The temperatures are so high in the sun that hydrogen nuclei fuse together into helium nuclei.* During these nuclear processes, infinitesimal amounts of matter are converted into enormous amounts of energy.

It is now generally believed that all the other elements were built up from hydrogen by fusion reactions in stars. Young stars are almost pure hydrogen, while older stars have converted a significant amount of their hydrogen through the process of fusion. Hydrogen, then, is the basic building block for elemental creation and is the most abundant element in the universe. Astronomers have estimated that more than 90 per cent of all atoms in the universe are hydrogen atoms.

---

\* The temperatures are so high, between 10 and 20 million degrees, that all atoms are *completely* ionized. The sun and all other stars that are evolving through fusion processes must, therefore, consist of great, dense volumes of positive nuclei amidst turbulent clouds of negative electrons—the plasma state.

# and the Bohr Atom

## 9.1 Two theories for the creation of the elements

In one theory of element formation, called the "big bang" theory, the elements now found in the universe are pictured as having been formed in some ancient superstar that exploded. A second theory, called the theory of "continuous creation" indicates that the elements have been formed in all stars over a long period of time. The process of element formation, according to this theory, continues up to the present day.

As a star ages, it goes through several evolutionary stages culminating in its explosive destruction as a supernova. In both the "big bang" and the "continuous creation" theories, such stellar explosions cause ejection of the nuclei of new elements formed through the fusion of hydrogen nuclei, and the remaining hydrogen nuclei into space as gases. These positive nuclei quickly attract free electrons to them and become dense clouds of neutral atoms. Theoretically, the condensation of parts of those clouds becomes the planets of this and other solar systems. During the eons of time necessary for the gas cloud to cool and condense, hydrogen gas would have been rather easily lost into space where large amounts of the gas might eventually recondense to form new stars. Our atmosphere is held close to the earth's surface by gravitational attraction. Since hydrogen has such a low weight, its gravitational attraction is much less than that of other gases and it escapes from the earth more readily, for example, than either oxygen or nitrogen gas.

Considering the atmosphere, the oceans, and the land surface to a ten-mile depth, hydrogen is only third in abundance on earth in the number of atoms. In this crust, 53 per cent of the atoms are oxygen, 16 per cent silicon, and 15 per cent hydrogen. (Compare these data with those in Table 5–1. What accounts for the striking differences in the atom abundance of hydrogen, from 2.70 per cent there to 15 per cent here?) This hydrogen is present almost completely in the form of compounds. Water is 11 per cent hydrogen by weight, and the human body is approximately 10 per cent hydrogen by weight. Plant and animal matter are chiefly compounds of hydrogen with carbon, nitrogen, oxygen, sulfur, and other elements. Petroleum and coal are mixtures of compounds of hydrogen and carbon, known as hydrocarbons.

### 9.2 Deuterium and tritium, isotopes of hydrogen

In 1931 Harold C. Urey (YOU ree), an American chemist, showed that for every 6000 atoms of ordinary hydrogen, in which the nucleus is a single proton, there is one atom of hydrogen in which the nucleus is composed of one proton and one neutron. This isotope of hydrogen was named *deuterium*, $_1^2H$ or $_1^2D$. Water that is composed of deuterium and oxygen is known as *heavy water*, $D_2O$. Both elemental hydrogen and deuterium ordinarily exist as diatomic gases, $H_2$ and $D_2$. The small difference in weight between them causes the elemental isotopes as well as their compounds to have slightly different physical properties. Some of these properties are listed in Tables 9–1 and 9–2.

**TABLE 9–1** SOME PHYSICAL PROPERTIES OF HYDROGEN ISOTOPES

| Property | $H_2$ | $D_2$ |
|---|---|---|
| Molecular weight (amu) | 2.016 | 4.028 |
| Calculated density (g/l at STP) | 0.089 | 0.179 |
| Freezing point (°C) | −259.14 | −254.6 |
| Boiling point (°C) | −252.8 | −249.7 |
| Heat of fusion (cal/mole) | 28 | 47 |
| Heat of vaporization (cal/mole) | 216 | 293 |

**TABLE 9–2** SOME PHYSICAL PROPERTIES OF WATER AND HEAVY WATER

| Property | $H_2O$ | $D_2O$ |
|---|---|---|
| Molecular weight (amu) | 18.016 | 20.029 |
| Freezing point (°C) | 0.0 | 3.8 |
| Boiling point (°C) | 100 | 101.42 |
| Density (g/ml at 20°C) | 0.998 | 1.106 |
| Heat of fusion (kcal/mole) | 1.44 | 1.52 |
| Heat of vaporization (kcal/mole) | 9.72 | 9.96 |
| NaCl solubility (g/1.00 g $H_2O$ at 25°C) | 0.36 | 0.30 |

A third isotope of hydrogen, known as *tritium*, $^3_1H$ or $^3_1T$, has one proton and two neutrons in its nucleus. However, unlike the other hydrogen nuclei, the tritium nucleus is not stable and undergoes radioactive decay. It is present only in minute amounts in nature, but is artificially produced in quantities for research purposes.

### 9.3 Laboratory preparation of hydrogen

Hydrogen is still prepared in the laboratory by the method used by its discoverer, Henry Cavendish. In 1766 Cavendish noticed that a gas was liberated when zinc was dropped into an acid. He collected the gas carefully and made a thorough study of it. He named it "flammable air" because it burned, and believed that he had isolated phlogiston itself. Lavoisier renamed the gas *hydrogen* from the Greek words meaning "water producer."

To prepare hydrogen, zinc is placed in a generator, as shown in Figure 9.1, and dilute hydrochloric or sulfuric acid is poured over it through a thistle tube. The hydrogen is collected in the same way as oxygen; that is, by the *displacement of water*. Why is hydrogen not collected by the displacement of air?

The chemical change that takes place is represented by the following equation:

$$Zn(s) + 2HCl(aq) = ZnCl_2(aq) + H_2(g)$$

In the reaction, zinc takes the place of, or *replaces*, the combined hydrogen of the acid and liberates it as the free diatomic gas. Instead of hydrochloric acid, the salt zinc chloride remains dissolved in the water in the generator.

**Henry Cavendish** (1731–1810, English). This shy, eccentric, and wealthy man, of whom it was said that he "probably uttered fewer words in the course of his life than any man who lived to fourscore years," performed classic experiments on hydrogen, water, and carbon dioxide. In addition, he made original researches in electricity and heat that were never published during his lifetime. The famous Cavendish Physical Laboratory at Cambridge University is named in his honor. The accomplishments of J. J. Thomson, Rutherford, and others who have worked in that Laboratory do even greater honor to him.

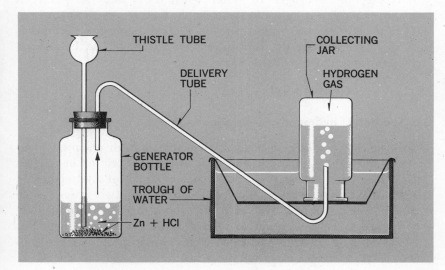

THISTLE TUBE

COLLECTING JAR

DELIVERY TUBE

HYDROGEN GAS

GENERATOR BOTTLE

TROUGH OF WATER

Zn + HCl

**FIGURE 9.1** Laboratory generation of hydrogen. Why should the thistle tube extend below the surface of the liquid in the generator?

All acids that have been discussed so far contain combined hydrogen. That hydrogen may be replaced by certain metals. Hence, to prepare hydrogen, almost any acid and any one of a number of other metals instead of zinc may be used. Other examples are:

$$Ni(s) + H_2SO_4(aq) = NiSO_4(aq) + H_2(g)$$
$$Fe(s) + 2HBr(aq) = FeBr_2(aq) + H_2(g)$$
$$3Pb(s) + 2H_3PO_4(aq) = Pb_3(PO_4)_2(s) + 3H_2(g)$$
$$Mg(s) + H_2CO_3(aq) = MgCO_3(s) + H_2(g)$$

but

$$Cu(s) + H_2SO_4(aq) \rightarrow \text{no reaction}$$
$$Ag(s) + HCl(aq) \rightarrow \text{no reaction}$$

## 9.4  Can hydrogen also be prepared from water?

Perhaps you have been thinking: If the hydrogen of an acid can be replaced by a metal, can the hydrogen of water also be replaced by a metal? The answer is *Yes*. Very active metals, such as sodium, potassium, and calcium, replace the hydrogen of water. A very active evolution of gas and the liberation of heat are noticed when a small piece of sodium, for example, is placed in water. The equation for this reaction is:

$$2Na(s) + 2HOH(l) = 2NaOH(aq) + H_2(g)$$

In the chemical reaction that occurs, sodium replaces half of the hydrogen in water and forms the soluble base sodium hydroxide, NaOH.

Even iron, which is not nearly as chemically active as sodium, will replace the hydrogen of water when the water (as steam) is passed over red-hot iron in a heated tube. In fact, this method has been used to a slight extent commercially to prepare hydrogen. The products of the reaction are the iron oxide known as *magnetite*, $Fe_3O_4$, and hydrogen. The equation for the reaction is:

$$3Fe(s) + 4H_2O(g) \overset{\Delta}{=} Fe_3O_4(s) + 4H_2(g)$$

## 9.5  Reaction of hydrogen and oxygen

Hydrogen can combine with most elements to form chemical compounds. Although pure hydrogen burns quietly in air or in oxygen with a pale-blue, almost colorless, flame, mixtures of hydrogen and oxygen may unite with explosive violence. The two gases, when mixed and kept below a temperature of about 800°C, will not unite; but a spark or a flame will lead to their explosive combination. For this reason, great care must be taken while experimenting with hydrogen to keep all flames away from the generator.

Such reactions as the burning of hydrogen in which energy is spontaneously *liberated* are termed *exothermic reactions*. The reaction may be expressed as a *thermochemical equation* to show the amount of energy liberated.

$$2H_2(g) + O_2(g) = 2H_2O(g) + 116\ kcal$$

Important practical use is made of this high energy yielding reaction. The oxyhydrogen torch produces a temperature of 2400°C and is used to work materials of very high melting points, such as quartz. Liquid hydrogen is used as a fuel in conjunction with liquid oxygen in some of our rocket engines used in space exploration.

The *oxyhydrogen* torch is used in the preparation of special laboratory glassware.

Many chemical reactions *absorb* energy in going from reactants to products. One such reaction involving hydrogen gas is the so-called "water gas" reaction. In this reaction, steam is passed over heated graphite, and a mixture of hydrogen and carbon monoxide gases results. The mixture of product gases is an important industrial fuel known as *water gas*. For the reaction to proceed continuously, heat must be constantly supplied to it.

$$H_2O(g) + C(s) + 31.4\ kcal = H_2(g) + CO(g)$$

Such a reaction is called an *endothermic* reaction. (Thermochemistry will be considered in greater detail in Chapter 13.)

### 9.6 The industrial preparation of hydrogen

When steam is passed over heated graphite in the presence of a catalyst, two reactions occur:

$$C(s) + H_2O(g) = H_2(g) + CO(g)$$

and

$$CO(g) + H_2O(g) \overset{\text{catalyst}}{=} H_2(g) + CO_2(g)$$

The sum of the two reactions,

$$C(s) + 2H_2O(g) \overset{\text{catalyst}}{=} 2H_2(g) + CO_2(g),$$

represents the most important industrial preparation of hydrogen gas. Hydrogen is easily separated from the carbon dioxide gas in the product mixture by bubbling the mixture through a basic solution. Carbon dioxide, an acid anhydride, reacts with basic solutions, but hydrogen does not:

$$CO_2(g) + NaOH(aq) = NaHCO_3(aq)$$

but

$$H_2(g) + NaOH(aq) \rightarrow \text{no reaction}$$

### 9.7 Hydrogen is a powerful reducing agent.

Hydrogen has a very strong attraction for oxygen, and is able to abstract or take oxygen away from some oxides. This chemical property makes hydrogen a *deoxidizing* or *reducing agent*. For example, if pure hydrogen is passed over black copper oxide brought to a red heat, as shown in Figure 9.2, the hydrogen abstracts oxygen from the copper oxide, leaving pure, red copper. This change may be represented by the following equation:

$$CuO(s) + H_2(g) \overset{\Delta}{=} H_2O(g) + Cu(s)$$

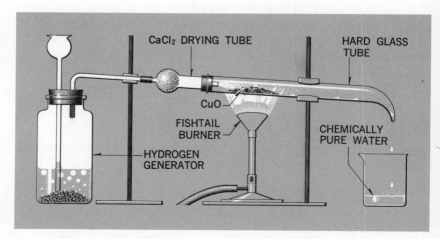

**FIGURE 9.2** *Reduction of copper oxide by hydrogen.* What is the function of the drying tube? Why is the fishtail burner used?

CaCl₂ DRYING TUBE · HARD GLASS TUBE · CuO · FISHTAIL BURNER · CHEMICALLY PURE WATER · HYDROGEN GENERATOR

Other examples of the reduction of metal oxides by reaction with $H_2$ gas at elevated temperatures are:

$$HgO(s) + H_2(g) \overset{\Delta}{=} Hg(l) + H_2O(g)$$

$$2Fe_2O_3(s) + 6H_2(g) \overset{\Delta}{=} 4Fe(s) + 6H_2O(g)$$

$$WO_3(s) + 3H_2(g) \overset{\Delta}{=} W(s) + 3H_2O(g)$$

In the experiment just described, the copper oxide, $CuO$, is *reduced* to copper. At the same time hydrogen, by combining with oxygen, is *oxidized* to water. This illustrates a general principle that whenever one substance is reduced, another is oxidized. Thus, oxidation and reduction always occur in the same (*redox*) reaction. As we noted in Chapter 5, those reactions in which oxygen is a reactant and oxides are products are called *oxidation* reactions. Those reactions wherein oxides lose their combined oxygen, therefore, are called *reduction* reactions. These narrow definitions, which are mainly of historical importance, will be broadened into more useful ones in Chapter 18.

## 9.8 Hydrogen reacts with the halogens.

Hydrogen reacts with fluorine, chlorine, bromine, and iodine to form the gaseous hydrogen halides. The tendency to react with hydrogen decreases through the halogens from $F_2$ to $I_2$. $F_2$ gas reacts with hydrogen violently, even at temperatures as low as $-250°C$.

$$H_2(g) + F_2(g) = 2HF(g)$$

At room temperature, a mixture of $H_2$ and $Cl_2$ reacts slowly in the dark but explosively in sunlight. $Br_2$ reacts with $H_2$ at temperatures above $400°C$ to produce HBr.

The reactions that lead to the formation of HF, HCl, and HBr from the elements are all exothermic:

$$H_2(g) + X_2(g) = 2HX(g) + energy,$$

where $X =$ F, Cl, Br.

The formation of HI from the elements is, however, a slightly endothermic reaction:

$$H_2(g) + I_2(g) + energy = 2HI(g)$$

When the very soluble hydrogen halides are dissolved in water, the resulting solutions are the important *acids*—hydrofluoric, hydrochloric, hydrobromic, and hydriodic acids.

### 9.9 Compounds of hydrogen with metals

Hydrogen is found to react with the most active metals to form compounds called *hydrides*. These reactions are not usually violent and often require high temperatures. For example, sodium hydride, NaH, is formed by bubbling hydrogen gas through molten sodium at about 360°C. The equation for this reaction is:

$$2Na(l) + H_2(g) = 2NaH(s)$$

The metal hydrides are solids at room temperature and react with water to liberate $H_2$. One such reaction is:

$$CaH_2(s) + 2H_2O(l) = Ca(OH)_2(s) + 2H_2(g)$$

Metal hydrides, such as NaH, $CaH_2$, and the more complex lithium aluminum hydride, $LiAlH_4$ are true compounds. Some metals show a more complicated behavior toward hydrogen gas, in which the existence of true compounds is not evident. For example, the metals palladium and platinum when finely divided absorb several hundred times their volumes of hydrogen gas. At room temperature, 1 ml of powdered palladium can absorb 850 ml of hydrogen gas. This phenomenon, known as *occlusion*, is accompanied by such an increase in temperature that the metals actually glow. Upon heating, the metals release the hydrogen. Studies of these metal-hydrogen systems indicate that the hydrogen becomes trapped in the holes that are present throughout the crystal structure of the metal. (Fig. 9.3.)

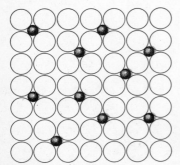

**FIGURE 9.3** *Occlusion.* Small atoms are randomly trapped in the empty spaces between atoms in a metallic crystal.

### 9.10 Some uses of hydrogen

Among the major uses for hydrogen is the conversion of liquid fats and oils into solid shortenings. The long-standing use of lard and butter for cooking purposes in the United States has led to a prejudice against the use of cheaper though equally nutritious cottonseed, corn, and soy bean oils. When *hydrogenated*, these *unsaturated hydrocarbons* (see Chapter 29) form new compounds, having the consistency of lard or butter. Hydrogenation is the basis of the important industry that produces cooking fats (e.g., Crisco, Spry) and oleomargarine.

A second major use for hydrogen is in the catalytic formation of ammonia,

$$3H_2(g) + N_2(g) \overset{\text{catalyst}}{=} 2NH_3(g),$$

in a process described more fully in Chapter 15. Most of the several million tons of ammonia so produced are used as a fertilizer.

From these two vital uses of hydrogen in industry we turn to the vital role that hydrogen has played in unraveling the mysteries of

A truly modern use for hydrogen. This 80-inch *bubble chamber* is used in high-energy nuclear physics research. It has a working volume of 900 liters of liquid hydrogen and operates at 27°K. (See Section 32.4.)

the atom and to the subsequent development of one of the great intellectual achievements of history—the Bohr theory of the atom.

## HYDROGEN: KEY TO MODERN ATOMIC THEORY

As noted before, the hydrogen atom is the simplest in nature. Consequently, it should not seem too surprising that research with hydrogen provided the clues that solved the mysteries of atomic structure. Although a variety of experimental studies led to our present knowledge, one may be singled out as the most important. It was not by measuring such physical properties as boiling point and density, or such chemical properties as reducing power, that the most significant advance was made. Rather, it was the study of the energy of the light emitted by energized hydrogen atoms that proved most fruitful.

### 9.11 The wave model for light

In 1672 Sir Isaac Newton, whose experimental and theoretical contributions in physical science are perhaps unparalleled in history, discovered the now familiar phenomenon of the *refraction* of sunlight and its *dispersion* into a *continuous spectrum* of component colors on passage through a glass prism. (Fig. 9.4.) More than a century later, it was discovered that the resolution of white light into its spectral components could be achieved in another way. If such light is passed through a transparent material upon which thousands of closely spaced parallel lines have been carefully ruled, the visible spectrum is observed. The phenomenon is known as *diffraction*, and the device that causes it is called a *diffraction grating*.

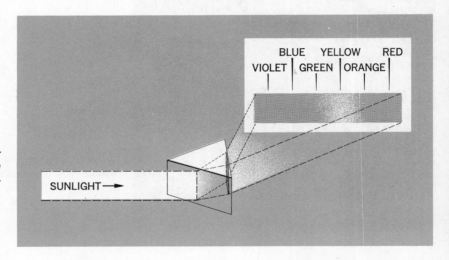

**FIGURE 9.4** Prismatic refraction and dispersion of white light into a continuous spectrum.

    Refraction, diffraction, and a host of other optical phenomena required theoretical explanations. By the late nineteenth century, a wave theory of light served physicists quite adequately as the basis for those explanations. It was also discovered that visible light is but a small part of a vast continuous spectrum of radiation that is electromagnetic in nature. Even this fact could be accommodated by extending the wave theory to all such radiation. Let us briefly examine the fundamental properties of the wave model for visible light and for all other electromagnetic radiations. (The electromagnetic spectrum is discussed in the photographic essay that begins on page 441.)

    The wave theory of electromagnetic radiation pictures it as a continuous wave being generated by some vibrating system. (Fig. 9.5.) Two important properties of the traveling wave are its *velocity* and its *wavelength*. Experimentally, the velocity of all electromagnetic radiation, $c$, is found to be the same—$3 \times 10^8$ meters per second in a vacuum. The wavelength of a particular electromagnetic radiation is denoted by the small Greek letter *lambda*, $\lambda$. It is found to depend on the vibrational properties of the system that is generating it. (Fig. 9.6.)

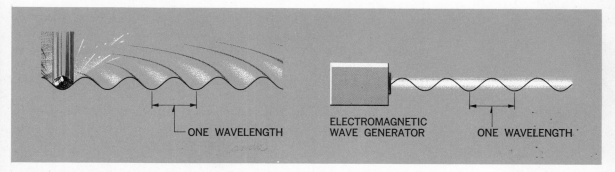

ONE WAVELENGTH

ELECTROMAGNETIC WAVE GENERATOR

ONE WAVELENGTH

**FIGURE 9.5** The wave theory of electromagnetic radiation is derived from considerations of the properties of water waves.

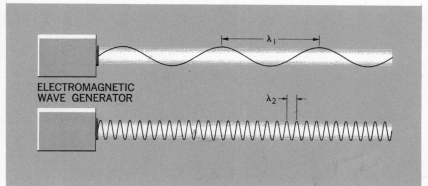

ELECTROMAGNETIC WAVE GENERATOR

**FIGURE 9.6** The wavelength of an electromagnetic radiation depends on the electromagnetic system generating it.

By applying the wave theory of light to careful measurements involving the diffraction of light of different colors, it is possible to calculate wavelengths associated with those colors.

The wavelengths of visible radiations are very short, being of the order of $10^{-5}$ cm. Light that appears blue to the eye has a wavelength of approximately $4 \times 10^{-5}$ cm. The wavelength of red light is approximately $7 \times 10^{-5}$ cm. It has been found convenient in dealing with wavelengths to define a unit length called the *angstrom unit* (ONG strum). One angstrom unit, 1 A, is equal to exactly $1 \times 10^{-8}$ cm. Thus, blue and red light have wavelengths around 4000 A and 7000 A, respectively.*

Examining Figure 9.6 leads us to deduce another fundamental property of electromagnetic waves. Were we to stand at a point equidistant from each wave generator and count the number of waves that pass that point each second, what would we observe? Since both waves are traveling with the same velocity, $c$, more waves of shorter $\lambda$ would

---

* The angstrom unit is named in honor of the nineteenth-century Swedish physicist A. J. Ångström. It is often symbolized by Å. Since, however, Å could be mistaken for °A (absolute temperature), we shall simply use A henceforth.

pass by per second than waves of longer $\lambda$. The number of waves to pass by a given point per second is called the *frequency* of the electromagnetic radiation and is symbolized by the small Greek letter *nu, $\nu$*. The frequency of electromagnetic radiation is determined by the frequency of oscillation of the vibrating system that is generating the radiation.

The important relationship observed between the wavelength, $\lambda$, and the frequency, $\nu$, of all electromagnetic radiation is that they are inversely proportional to each other. That is,

$$\lambda \propto \frac{1}{\nu}$$

or

$$\nu \propto \frac{1}{\lambda}$$

or

$$\lambda\nu = \text{constant}.$$

Since $\lambda$ has the units of cm/wave and $\nu$ has the units of waves/sec, the constant in this last relationship must have the units of velocity:

$$\lambda\nu = \text{constant}$$

$$\left(\frac{\text{cm}}{\text{wave}}\right)\left(\frac{\text{waves}}{\text{sec}}\right) = \frac{\text{cm}}{\text{sec}}.$$

Dealing as we are with electromagnetic radiation that is propagated with velocity $c$, the final and most fundamental relationship of the wave theory of light and all other electromagnetic radiation is:

$$\lambda\nu = c$$

The classical wave theory of electromagnetic radiation, a monumental achievement of intellect, still serves to help us understand a host of phenomena involving electromagnetic radiation. In the wake of startling experimental discoveries of only a short time ago, however, a second theory of electromagnetic radiation has developed and a new scientific age has begun.

## 9.12 The wave theory falters. The quantum theory is born.

The last twenty-five years of the nineteenth century were extraordinary for the fundamental experimental discoveries made. We have already learned of the accomplishments of Thomson, Becquerel, and the Curies in the last years of that century. Others had made contributions equally significant. By the end of that period of time, the sciences of physics and chemistry had experienced such rapid growth that old theoretical models were sorely in need of revision to account for much of what was new. We have already seen that this was the period in which the simple Daltonian model of the atom met its downfall. It also was the time when the wave model of electromagnetic radiation failed to account for significant experimental facts, and physicists sought a new model.

Perhaps the need for a new model of radiation can be most simply seen by examining a phenomenon we considered earlier—the photoelectric effect. This effect, accidentally discovered in 1887 by the outstanding student of electromagnetic phenomena, Heinrich Hertz (HINE rick HURTS), was the object of careful study during the following three decades. We have already noted J. J. Thomson's work that proved it was electrons that were ejected from certain metal surfaces when light shone upon those surfaces. (See Fig. 8.3, page 194.) Other scientists studied carefully the kind of light needed for the ejection of photoelectrons.

It soon became evident that only light of a certain minimum frequency (or wavelength) resulted in the photoelectric effect. (Fig. 9.7.) The wave model of light was totally unable to account for this observation. What, really, was the fundamental meaning of the observation? It was that only light of a certain *minimum energy* would knock electrons from a given metal surface. Somehow the energy of electromagnetic radiation must be related to the fundamental properties of wavelength and frequency.

In 1901, in order to account for another radiation phenomenon that eluded theoretical understanding based on classical wave theory, the German physicist Max Planck postulated a new and revolutionary theory of electromagnetic radiation. The fundamental break Planck made with the classical wave theory was to assume that radiant energy generated by a vibrating system was not continuous in nature but, rather, was emitted in discrete units or *quanta*. In other words, just as matter was atomistic, so, Planck proposed, must energy be considered atomistic *for certain phenomena*. Moreover, Planck was able to deduce that the amount of energy, $E$, carried by a quantum, the smallest unit of energy, was proportional to the frequency of vibration, $\nu$, of the energy-generating system,

$$E \propto \nu;$$

and, thus, he arrived at the basic relationship:

$$E = h\nu$$

where $h$, Planck's constant, is a *universal constant* and has the value $1.5836 \times 10^{-37}$ kcal-sec.*

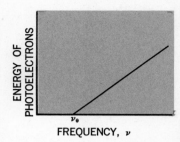

**FIGURE 9.7** The photoelectric effect. Why is $\nu_0$ called the "threshold frequency"?

(Graph axes: vertical—ENERGY OF PHOTOELECTRONS; horizontal—FREQUENCY, $\nu$; marked point $\nu_0$.)

**Max Planck** (1858–1947, German). His quantum theory of radiation, along with Einstein's general theory of relativity, laid the foundations of modern physics and is at the heart of the modern theory of atomic structure. He received the Nobel Prize in 1918, and was an Associate of our own National Academy of Sciences.

---

* Since a wave, *per se*, is not a unit of measurement, the units for frequency, $\nu$, are most usually given as *reciprocal seconds*, sec$^{-1}$ or $\frac{1}{\text{sec}}$, rather than as $\frac{\text{waves}}{\text{second}}$. Thus, you should be able to derive the units of kcal-sec for $h$.

Not only was Planck's *quantum theory of radiation* able to provide a theoretical model for the experimental observations for which it was originally developed, but it soon became the foundation upon which many of the theoretical developments in chemistry and physics since then have been based. In 1905, for example, Einstein applied quantum theory to the photoelectric effect and was able to account in complete theoretical detail for the experimental observations that had eluded a wave model interpretation. There exist, then, two models for the nature of electromagnetic radiation: the continuous wave model of classical physics, and the atomistic particle model of quantum physics. These models do not contradict each other; they complement each other. We turn now to the field in which their complementary application has yielded the most significant results.

### 9.13  Line spectra—fingerprints of the elements

In 1859, six years after his development of the famous laboratory burner that bears his name, Robert Bunsen and his younger colleague Gustav Kirchoff (KEARK hoff) developed an instrument by which the refraction or diffraction of light could be quantitatively studied. Ever since, the study of the light emitted by various elements when they are "excited" by being heated to incandescence has occupied the research efforts of many physicists and chemists. The instrument is known as a *spectroscope*. This study is known as *spectroscopy*. (Fig. 9.8.)

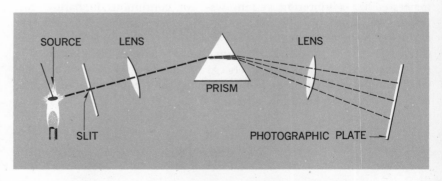

**FIGURE 9.8**  A simple arrangement of parts of a spectroscope

Many important facts were uncovered by spectroscopists. One of the most interesting facts was that the *emission spectrum* of an excited element was not a continuous band of light from red to violet, such as that of the self-luminous sun. Instead, the spectrum of each excited element consisted of a number of separate lines. In addition,

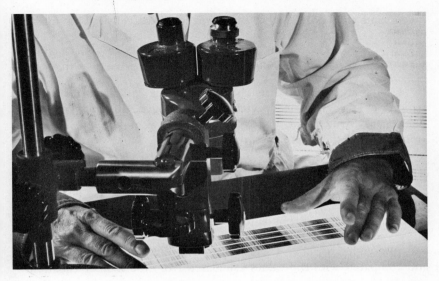

Spectral analysis of elements and compounds is a modern research tool of great value.

no two elements gave identical spectra. Spectral lines could be regarded as the fingerprints of the different elements.

This characteristic of the elements is widely used today as a means of detecting and measuring the nature and amount of different elements in an unknown sample. The total spectrum of the sample is obtained and, from the positions of the lines observed, chemists can easily identify which elements are present. Measurements of the intensity of spectral lines indicate how much of a given element is present. The visible spectra of several elements are shown in color on pages 444–445.

### 9.14 Implication of line spectra

Now let us consider the fact that the light emitted by an energized element gives a series of lines in the spectrum of the element. Each line in the spectrum corresponds to a definite wavelength or frequency. According to the quantum theory of radiation, fixed wavelength or frequency corresponds to a definite fixed energy. Therefore, the line spectra of elements must mean that the atoms are emitting definite amounts of energy. So when atoms are energized or excited on being heated to high temperatures, they get rid of this extra energy that they initially absorbed by sending it out as light radiation, and they return to unexcited states. Atoms of different elements emit certain *fixed amounts of energy* that are characteristic of the particular element. We say that the energy radiated by excited atoms is *quantized*. But it is very important to realize that line spectra are proof that an atom does not emit just *any* size packet of energy. Something about the atom prevents it from emitting quanta of all energies. Atoms of a given kind emit only quanta of given energies. Why? This question perplexed atomic scientists.

### 9.15 The line series of the hydrogen emission spectrum

By 1884 nine lines had been observed in the visible and ultraviolet regions of the emission spectrum of hydrogen. In that year, J. J. Balmer, of Switzerland, discovered that it was possible to relate the frequencies of these nine lines by an equation:

$$\nu = K\left(\frac{1}{2^2} - \frac{1}{b^2}\right)$$

where $K$ is a constant and $b$ has integral values between 3 and 11. Each value of $b$ corresponds to one of the nine spectral lines.

In Table 9–3, some of the experimental lines in the visible and ultraviolet regions of the hydrogen emission spectrum are listed and compared with the values calculated from the Balmer equation.

**TABLE 9–3**   Wavelengths in the Balmer Series of the
Hydrogen Emission Spectrum

| λ Observed | λ Calculated | Value of b |
|---|---|---|
| 6562.79 A | 6562.80 A | 3 |
| 4861.33 | 4861.38 | 4 |
| 4340.47 | 4340.51 | 5 |
| 4101.74 | 4101.78 | 6 |
| 3970.06 | 3970.11 | 7 |
| 3889.00 | 3889.09 | 8 |
| 3835.38 | 3835.43 | 9 |

As spectroscopes were developed that could detect spectral lines in nonvisible regions of the hydrogen emission spectrum, several other spectral series were found. The frequencies of the lines of all of these series were found by the Swedish spectroscopist J. R. Rydberg (1890) to be in agreement with the frequencies *calculated* by a generalized equation:

$$\nu = K\left(\frac{1}{a^2} - \frac{1}{b^2}\right)$$

where $a$ and $b$ are integers.

The existence of discrete spectral emission lines could hardly be explained by any model of the atom in vogue at the end of the nineteenth century. The order and regularity of the appearance of such lines in mathematically describable series was even more enigmatic.

In the first years of the new century, the theoretical problems posed by the quantized emission of energy by excited hydrogen atoms were solved. The solutions were achieved by the bold and courageous application of the quantum theory of radiation.

### 9.16 Bohr's atomic model

Niels Bohr, a young Danish physicist, was spending some time as a mathematical consultant in Rutherford's laboratory in Manchester. While there, in 1913, he suggested an atomic model in accord with the newly discovered nuclear atom of Rutherford. His revolutionary model was also in accord with the Balmer relation and for the first time an atomic model existed that could account for spectra of atoms.

First, Bohr boldly applied the still new quantum theory of radiation and proposed that electrons in atoms existed outside the nucleus only in certain, definite energy levels. That is, electronic energy levels are present in atoms and they are *quantized.*

Secondly, Bohr proposed that as long as electrons stay in certain electronic energy levels or states they neither gain nor lose energy and hence do not radiate energy. These stable energy levels are called *stationary states of the atom.* Bohr stated, however, that electrons may "jump" to a level of higher energy when the atom *absorbs* energy. When an electron drops to a level or state of *lower energy,* the atom *emits* energy. The electron cannot stop in between these levels—these are forbidden zones. Since these jumps can only occur between definite levels, definite amounts of energy are involved. In this way, atoms give definite line spectra of emitted energy. *Every single line in a spectrum represents the transition from one energy state to another.*

It might be easier to understand the implications of the Bohr model by considering a man on a ladder with rungs one foot apart. (Fig. 9.9.) The man cannot be at *any* height above the ground, but only at heights of 1, 2, 3, and so forth, feet. He cannot stay at 1.5 feet, as there is no rung to provide a stable position. The height above the ground is a measure of the potential energy or energy of position of the man. If he is on the bottom rung, he gains considerable potential energy by climbing to the fifth rung. Now he can lose potential energy by jumping to a lower rung. If he does, he can lose one foot $(E \rightarrow D)$, two feet $(E \rightarrow C)$, three feet $(E \rightarrow B)$, four feet $(E \rightarrow A)$ of potential energy. But notice that since he cannot stop between rungs it is not possible to lose 1.50, 1.75, 2.25, and so forth, feet. Therefore, if this potential energy decrease could be registered by a spectroscope, a sharp line spectrum would be observed rather than a *continuous* one.

**FIGURE 9.9** The only stable positions that may be occupied above the ground "state" are well defined.

**Niels Bohr** (1885–1962, Danish). Bohr's monumental contributions to the theory of atomic structure earned him the Nobel prize in 1922. He escaped from Nazi-occupied Denmark to England in 1943. After making great contributions to the development of nuclear weapons in the United States, Bohr returned in 1945 to the Institute of Theoretical Physics in Copenhagen, which he had founded in 1920. In his last years, Bohr's was a strong voice in the call for the peaceful uses of nuclear energy, and he received the first Atoms for Peace Prize in 1957. At his death, Bohr was an articulate philosopher of modern science. The above is a likeness of the stamp issued by the Danish government in honor of the fiftieth anniversary of Bohr's atomic theory.

There being no explanation available by the laws of physics then known for atoms to have such definite energy levels, such levels had to be invented. Bohr was compelled to announce that the usual laws of physics did not apply to things as small as atoms. He suggested, instead, a *quantum theory* of atomic structure.

This was a bold step. The quantum idea was an abstract one with no physical explanation as to why it should be. But it did provide an atomic model that could explain and even predict many experimental observations and, in particular, line spectra. It gained immediate acceptance, and its dramatic successes earned Bohr the Nobel Prize in Physics in 1922.

### 9.17 Energy levels of the hydrogen atom from the Bohr theory

Bohr was able to derive an equation from which the energies of each of the stationary electronic energy states of the hydrogen atom could be calculated. This fundamental equation of the Bohr theory of the atom is:

$$E_n = \frac{-313.6}{n^2} \text{ kcal/mole of electrons}$$

The integer, $n$, which has the values 1, 2, 3, . . . , is called the *principal quantum* number. The existence of such an integer in Bohr's derivation represents the existence of quantized energy levels in his model of the atom. For the energy level of principal quantum number $n = 1$,

$$E_1 = \frac{-313.6}{1^2} \text{ kcal/mole}$$

$$= -313.6 \text{ kcal/mole.}$$

The $E_1$ energy level of the Bohr model is the one closest to the hydrogen nucleus. When a mole of electrons, initially free of the positive attraction of hydrogen nuclei, falls to the level closest to those nuclei, Bohr theory predicts that 313.6 kcal of energy/mole will be released. For any energy level of principal quantum number $n > 1$, less energy is released when a free electron falls into that level. Calculations for the second, fifth, and eighth levels give the following values:

$$E_2 = \frac{-313.6}{2^2} \text{ kcal/mole}$$

$$= -78.4 \text{ kcal/mole}$$

$$E_5 = \frac{-313.6}{5^2} \text{ kcal/mole}$$

$$= -12.5 \text{ kcal/mole}$$

$$E_8 = \frac{-313.6}{8^2} \text{ kcal/mole}$$

$$= -4.9 \text{ kcal/mole}$$

When these values, and others as easily calculated, are plotted as an energy level diagram, Figure 9.10 results.

| ENERGY LEVEL | QUANTUM NUMBER | POTENTIAL ENERGY (kcal/mole) |
|---|---|---|

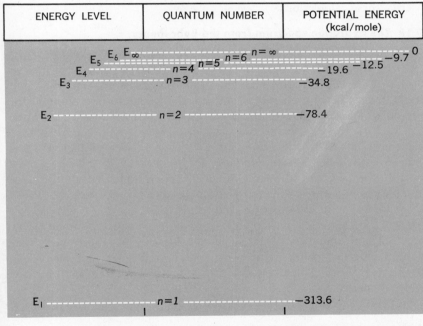

FIGURE 9.10 Energy level diagram calculated for the hydrogen atom

If we consider Figure 9.10 carefully, it becomes clear that the electron in hydrogen at energy level $E_1$ represents a system of minimum potential energy, the lowest rung in the ladder if you like, and thus represents the most stable energy state for the hydrogen atom. The $E_1$ state is called, for this reason, the *ground state* of the hydrogen atom. All higher energy states are called *excited states* of the hydrogen atom.

Another observation of the Bohr model becomes clear on examining Figure 9.10. Unlike ladders with which we are most familiar, the energy level ladder of the Bohr model has rungs that get closer together as the principal quantum number value increases. Thus, it is relatively difficult to raise a mole of electrons from the ground state to the first excited state in hydrogen, the energy for the transition being calculated as:

$$E_{1 \to 2} = E_2 - E_1$$
$$E_{1 \to 2} = (-78.3 \text{ kcal/mole}) - (-313.6 \text{ kcal/mole})$$
$$E_{1 \to 2} = +235.2 \text{ kcal/mole}$$

However, it becomes relatively easier to excite the electrons at higher levels. Energies for some of these higher level transitions are calculated:

$$E_{2 \to 3} = +43.6 \text{ kcal/mole}$$
$$E_{3 \to 4} = +15.2 \text{ kcal/mole}$$
$$E_{4 \to 5} = +\ 7.1 \text{ kcal/mole}$$

Verify these calculations.

### 9.18  The hydrogen spectrum from the Bohr theory

If the energy values *calculated* by Bohr for the stationary states of the hydrogen atom are to have more than theoretical meaning, they must lead to observed experimental facts. Transitions from higher excited states to lower excited states and to the ground state should, for example, release energy that can be related to observed spectral lines.

In the previous section, we calculated energies *absorbed* in the transitions $E_{1 \to 2}$, $E_{2 \to 3}$, $E_{3 \to 4}$, and $E_{4 \to 5}$. The reverse of each of these transitions, which we now symbolize $E_{2 \to 1}$, $E_{3 \to 2}$, $E_{4 \to 3}$, and $E_{5 \to 4}$, *must* result in the *emission* of quanta of specific energies of exactly the same amounts as previously calculated. That this must be can be clearly seen from Figure 9.10. Whether an electron is raised from a lower energy level to a higher one, or drops from that higher one to the lower level, it is only the value of potential energy for each of those levels that determines the amount of absorbed or emitted energy. Thus, as we found for the absorbed energy $E_{1 \to 2}$, so, too, do we find for the emitted energy $E_{2 \to 1}$:

$$E_{2 \to 1} = E_2 - E_1$$

The calculated energy of the emitted quanta can be related to a frequency of radiation by Planck's equation:

$$E_{2 \to 1} = h\nu_{2 \to 1};$$

and then to a calculated wavelength:

$$\lambda_{2 \to 1} = \frac{c}{\nu_{2 \to 1}}$$

Therefore, any *theoretical, calculated* energy emission can be converted to a predicted wavelength or frequency to be compared with an experimentally determined spectrum. It was a monumental achievement of the Bohr theory applied to the hydrogen atom that every experimental spectral line then known for hydrogen agreed with the value calculated for it, and many of those predictable from Bohr theory have since been discovered.

### 9.19 The Rydberg relation and the Bohr theory

By considering in detail *all* electronic transitions from excited states to the ground state, we will discover that Bohr theory adequately explained the order and regularity of the observed hydrogen spectrum empirically described by Rydberg twenty-three years earlier. The amount of energy emitted by any electronic transition from an energy state for which $n > 1$ to the $n = 1$ state is calculated as in the following steps:

$$E_{n \to 1} = E_n - E_1$$

$$E_{n \to 1} = \left(\frac{-313.6}{n^2} \text{ kcal/mole}\right) - \left(\frac{-313.6}{1^2} \text{ kcal/mole}\right)$$

$$E_{n \to 1} = -313.6\left(\frac{1}{n^2} - \frac{1}{1^2}\right) \text{kcal/mole}$$

$$E_{n \to 1} = +313.6\left(\frac{1}{1^2} - \frac{1}{n^2}\right) \text{kcal/mole}$$

This quantum of radiation will have a frequency calculated from Planck's equation:

$$E_{n \to 1} = h\nu_{n \to 1}$$

$$\nu_{n \to 1} = \frac{E_{n \to 1}}{h}$$

Substituting the expression $E_{n \to 1}$ that we previously found, we determine that:

$$\nu_{n \to 1} = \frac{+313.6}{h}\left(\frac{1}{1^2} - \frac{1}{n^2}\right) \text{sec}^{-1}$$

or

$$\nu_{n \to 1} = K\left(\frac{1}{1^2} - \frac{1}{n^2}\right) \text{sec}^{-1}$$

This last relationship is precisely of the form of the Rydberg relation. Recalling the *generalized* Rydberg equation,

$$\nu = K\left(\frac{1}{a^2} - \frac{1}{b^2}\right),$$

it becomes apparent from the Bohr model that $a$ and $b$ are principal quantum numbers for the general energy transition $E_b \to E_a$ where $E_b$ is a state higher in energy than $E_a$. (Fig. 9.11.)

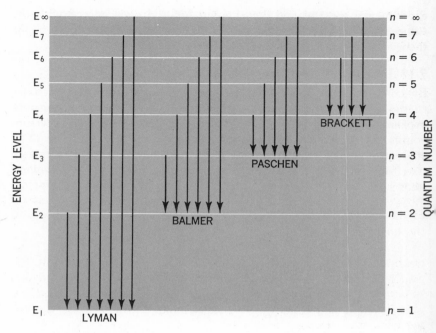

**FIGURE 9.11** Energy level diagram showing electron transitions from excited states to lower energy states in the hydrogen atom. How are such transitions related to the hydrogen emission spectrum?

### 9.20 The Bohr theory fails.

The startling success of the Bohr theory in accounting in almost complete theoretical detail for the experimental facts of the hydrogen spectrum is not repeated for any other element. There are a number of complex reasons why Bohr theory fails in utility beyond the simplest atomic system, hydrogen. Yet even in its failure it serves as a beacon of modern scientific thought. The main legacy of Bohr theory to the very much more complex and abstract atomic theory that followed is the concept of stationary energy states. It is a happy circumstance of modern scientific history that Bohr lived on to help evolve that new theory. In the continuing development of mankind, there are a few great intellects whose genius helps to discover new worlds of thought. Even before his death in 1962, Niels Bohr was considered among these.

## SUMMARY

Hydrogen is the simplest element and the main constituent of the universe. Three isotopes of hydrogen are known: $_1^1H$, $_1^2H$, and $_1^3H$. The element is easily produced in the laboratory by the addition of certain metals to almost any acid. Commercially, the most important production method is by the catalytic reaction of steam with heated graphite. Hydrogen is chemically active at elevated temperatures, forming compounds with both metals and nonmetals. It is also a strong reducing agent.

A study of the light given off by glowing hydrogen gas led to a new theory of the nature of light and the structure of the atom. The classical or wave model for electromagnetic radiation pictures it as continuous waves generated by a vibrating system, all traveling at the same velocity which is equal to the product of the frequency, $\nu$, and the wavelength, $\lambda$. Many optical phenomena are explainable with this model. Because the classical model for light failed to explain the photoelectric effect and the line spectra given off by energized atoms, Planck formulated the quantum theory, which assumes that the energy is given off in discrete packets and is related to the frequency of the radiation by the equation $E = h\nu$. Einstein successfully applied the quantum theory to the photoelectric effect.

Bohr's application of quantum theory to account for the spectral lines of hydrogen resulted in a model that was successful for hydrogen, but failed for all other elements. Bohr's synthesis of the classical and quantum theories of radiation was a significant achievement, which provided the necessary impetus for the development of later theories regarding the electron arrangement of more complex atoms. Bohr's lasting contribution to those later theories was the concept of stationary electron energy states.

## QUESTIONS AND PROBLEMS

9.1 Write equations for the reactions that occur between each of the following pairs of reactants: **a.** $Mg(s) + HCl(aq)$; **b.** $Al(s) + H_2SO_4(aq)$; **c.** $Zn(s) + H_2C_2O_4(aq)$; **d.** $Ni(s) + H_3PO_4(aq)$; **e.** $Fe(s) + CH_3COOH(aq)$; **f.** $K(s) + H_2O(l)$; **g.** $Cs(s) + H_2O(l)$; **h.** $Ca(s) + H_2O(l)$; **i.** $Ba(s) + H_2O(l)$; **j.** $Fe(s) + H_2O(g)$ (at high temperatures).

9.2 In the laboratory preparation of hydrogen, the first bottle of gas collected is usually discarded. Explain.

9.3 What property of hydrogen enables it to be collected by water displacement?

9.4 What are the typical products resulting from the action of a metal and an acid?

9.5 Account for the fact that there is little atmospheric hydrogen near the earth's surface.

9.6 Why could the use of the alkali metals for the preparation of hydrogen be dangerous?

9.7 **a.** Cite evidence for the hypothesis that the planets condensed from material drawn out of our sun by a passing star. **b.** Some astronomers have hypothesized that our sun had a companion star that became a supernova. Is this a more reasonable hypothesis than a for the origin of the planets? Defend your answer.

9.8   How does the kinetic molecular theory account for the raised boiling points of the deuterium isotope equivalents of $H_2$ and $H_2O$?

9.9   a. Write the equation for the "water gas" reaction. b. Describe how this reaction is used for the commercial production of pure hydrogen only.

9.10  Write three equations that illustrate the reducing properties of hydrogen. In each case, point out the oxidizing agent.

9.11  Write equations for the reactions that occur between each of the following pairs of reactants: a. $H_2(g) + Cl_2(g)$; b. $H_2(g) + O_2(g)$; c. $Na(l) + H_2(g)$; d. $Ca(s) + H_2(g)$; e. $LiH(s) + H_2O(l)$.

9.12  What is meant by the term "occlusion"?

9.13  By redefining the terms "oxidation" and "reduction" in terms of hydrogen, show that the catalytic formation of ammonia from nitrogen and hydrogen is an oxidation-reduction reaction.

9.14  a. What is the velocity of light in cm/sec.? b. What is the wavelength in angstrom units of light having a frequency of $7.5 \times 10^{14} \sec^{-1}$?

ANS.  b. $4.0 \times 10^3$ A

9.15  How many kilocalories per quantum are associated with light of: a. $\lambda = 6.00 \times 10^3$ A? b. $\nu = 7.50 \times 10^{14} \sec^{-1}$?

ANS.  b. $1.18 \times 10^{-22}$ kcal

9.16  Contrast the two models for the nature of electromagnetic radiation now in existence.

9.17  Explain why line spectra imply that excited atoms radiate fixed amounts of energy.

9.18  a. Calculate the value of the constant, $K$, in the Rydberg equation. b. Using that value for $K$, show the versatility of the Rydberg equation by calculating wavelengths corresponding to the first three lines of the series produced when $a$ equals 1. (Refer to Balmer's equation to determine what the lowest value of $b$ should be.) c. In what portion of the electromagnetic spectrum are these lines located? d. Calculate the wavelengths corresponding to the first three lines of the series produced when $a$ equals 3. e. In what portion of the electromagnetic spectrum are these lines located?

ANS.  b. $1.22 \times 10^3$ A; $1.03 \times 10^3$ A; 975 A

9.19  a. What is meant by "quantized" energy levels? b. Explain how butter or margarine as purchased in the supermarket can be said to be "quantized"? c. Describe a walk from your home to the store with a companion who can only cover quantized distances, while you must take a continuous path.

**9.20** The energy for the transition of a hydrogen electron is $E_{1 \to 2} = +235.2$ kcal/mole and $E_{4 \to 5} = +7.1$ kcal/mole. Why does it require more energy to activate an electron from the ground state than from an excited state?

**9.21 a.** Calculate the wavelength of light emitted when a hydrogen electron drops from level 3 to level 2 according to Bohr's theory. **b.** Identify the spectral line corresponding to this wavelength. *color*

**9.22** Show that the wavelengths calculated in Problems 9.18b and 9.18d represent energy transitions of the hydrogen electrons given by $E_{2 \to 1}$, $E_{3 \to 1}$, $E_{4 \to 1}$, and $E_{4 \to 3}$, $E_{5 \to 3}$, and $E_{6 \to 3}$ in accordance with Bohr's theory.

**9.23 a.** What volume of dry hydrogen gas could be collected at 27.0°C and 740 torrs when 1.30 g of zinc metal completely react with an excess of hydrochloric acid? **b.** What weight of solid product could be recovered at the end of the reaction?
Ans.   **b.** 2.71 g

**9.24** Cite experimental evidence from this chapter to give meaning to the dual placement of hydrogen in the periodic table given on pages 178–179.

## SUGGESTED READINGS

Bohr, Niels. *Atomic Physics and Human Knowledge* (paperback). John Wiley, 1958.

Bondi, Hermann. *The Universe at Large* (paperback). Doubleday, 1960.

Gamow, George. *The Creation of the Universe* (paperback). Mentor, 1957.

Hoffmann, Banesh. *The Strange Story of the Quantum* (paperback). Dover, 1959.

Lagowski, J. J. *The Structure of Atoms* (paperback). Houghton Mifflin, 1964.

**CHEMISTRY**

Mellor, D. P., "Origin and Evolution of Chemical Elements." Feb. 1964
Mellor, D. P., "Origin and Evolution of Chemical Elements II." Apr. 1964

**SCIENTIFIC AMERICAN**

Fowler, W. A., "The Origin of the Elements." Sept. 1956
Gamow, G., "The Evolutionary Universe." Sept. 1956
Hoyle, F., "The Steady-state Universe." Sept. 1956

*Without speculation there is
no good original observation.*

*Charles Darwin (1809–1882)*

**CHAPTER 10**

# Duality, Uncertainty,

The modern theory of the nature of the atom *is a mathematical one*, and the mathematics is more complex than can be handled at this point in your education. Since that theory is based on a mathematical and *not a physical model* of the atom, it is not possible to provide a rigorously correct physical picture of the atom. Nevertheless, chemists have found it very useful to use physical pictures of atoms, keeping in mind always that these pictures are not exact in all details but are the best physical representation that can be made of mathematical concepts.

After giving a necessary but brief introduction to the basic features of the mathematical model, we shall present the physical model that is used by chemists. Modern atomic theory is without doubt one of the great achievements of the human mind. In studying this chapter, you would do well, then, to regard the treatment both as a story of one of the peaks in man's culture, and as a great unifying principle in chemistry that explains and coordinates millions of experimental observations.

## FOUNDATIONS OF MODERN ATOMIC THEORY

It may seem to you, as you read on in this chapter, that modern atomic theory represents a "quantum jump" in scientific thought. That theory, despite its mathematical complexity, has in reality *evolved* and continues to develop from the continuing quest for understanding that is characteristic of science. The conceptual bases for

232

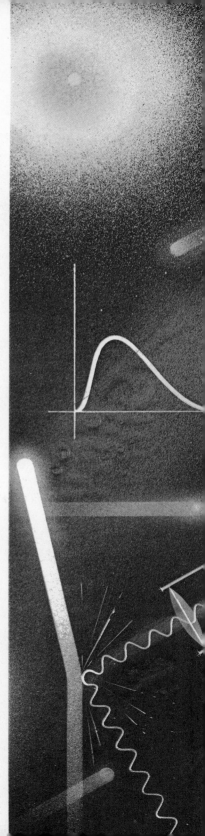

# and Electron Orbitals

modern atomic theory arose especially from the fresh insight into the nature of matter taken by Planck, Einstein, and Bohr in the early years of this century. However, as the contemporary philosopher Karl Popper has aptly stated:

> Theories are nets to catch what we call "the world": to rationalize, to explain, and to master it. We endeavor to make the mesh even finer and finer.

We turn next to consider more recent chapters in the exciting story of man's search for understanding. As we do so, we should recall the "net casters" who came before and who have led us to these better fishing grounds.

## 10.1 Matter has a dual nature.

In 1924 a physicist, Prince Louis de Broglie (d' BROH lee) of France, suggested in his thesis for the Doctor of Philosophy degree in physics that the duality of light is not unique. You will recall that it was confusing but necessary after the discovery of the photoelectric effect to explain the behavior of light as though it had both a wavelike and a particle-like nature. De Broglie in his theoretical studies of atomic structure arrived at the conclusion that dualism may be a general principle. He was able to show that any material particle, in some circumstances, can be treated as though it had a wavelike nature. De Broglie had no small amount of trouble persuading his professors to permit him to publish such a revolutionary idea.

Experiments soon provided support for de Broglie's hypothesis, when it was demonstrated that a beam of electrons could be diffracted in passage through a crystalline solid just as a beam of light is diffracted through a grating. More recently, de Broglie's postulation of the wave nature of matter received further confirmation when beams of neutrons were diffracted on passage through crystals. Diffraction phenomena can best be explained in terms of a wave model and, thus, we see again the unity of nature.

Although it is apparently valid for everything, de Broglie's hypothesis of the dualistic nature of matter is not of importance for objects much larger than atoms and molecules. For understanding those atoms and molecules though, the de Broglie hypothesis serves as one of the three pillars upon which rests modern atomic theory. We have already encountered one other of the conceptual foundations of modern atomic theory, the concept of stationary electron energy states, proposed by Bohr. Now we consider briefly the third fundamental underlying concept of modern atomic theory.

## 10.2 The Uncertainty Principle

How might we go about measuring the position and the velocity of a moving train at the same time? We might measure the *time* it takes for the train to pass between two fixed points. Knowing how far apart the fixed points are (the *distance* between them), we could then calculate the speed of the train as the distance traveled between the two points in the time we measured. Knowledge of the direction in which the train was traveling between the two points allows us to describe the velocity of the train. (The speed of the train could have been, for example, 90 miles per hour. Velocity, however, must include a direction. Thus, the velocity of the train could have been 90 mph south by southeast.)

During our measurement of the train's velocity, what can we say about the train's position? If we think carefully about this, we are led to conclude that the best we can say about the train's position is that it lies somewhere between the two points we fixed to measure velocity. There is, therefore, an element of uncertainty in the simultaneous measurement of the velocity and the position of a moving train. With the development of remarkable timing devices capable of measuring time *intervals* as short as $10^{-9}$ second (a nanosecond, or one *billionth* of a second), the uncertainty becomes too small, itself, to measure and to be of any importance. Having the capability of measuring such small time intervals, we can move the two fixed points so close together that we are essentially able to measure velocity and position at one point in space and time with very little uncertainty. (Fig. 10.1.)

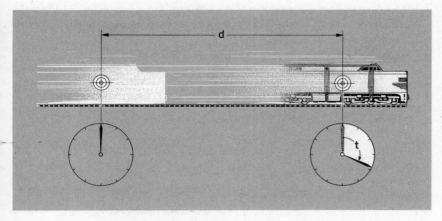

**FIGURE 10.1** The existence of very delicate timing devices permits the fixed distance, *d*, through which a train travels during measurement of its velocity to be made very small. As *d* approaches zero, the recorded time, *t*, will approach zero, and the **simultaneous** measurement of the velocity and position of the moving train can be made with greater certainty.

Basic to our ability to measure simultaneously the velocity and the position of large objects is the fact that such objects are not disturbed to any detectable extent in their motion by the measuring process. Light rays reflecting from large objects and back to a collecting device, which then "sees" the object, have almost no disturbing effect on the motion of the object struck. When the object being measured becomes very small, however, a fundamental uncertainty arises just because relatively large disturbing effects take place.

Objects of atomic size can only be measured with radiation of wavelength comparable to atomic diameters. The principle involved is one that depends upon the reflection process. Just as a water wave will break around and not be greatly reflected by narrow objects, so, too, does light behave. For light to be effectively reflected by an object, the wavelength of the light must be comparable to or less than the width of the object it is shining upon. You might be familiar with the use of sodium vapor lamps with their intense yellow glow for lighting fog-drenched highways. Fog droplets are of such size as to reflect and scatter most of the shorter wavelengths of visible light. This scattering effect prevents safe illumination of roads during fog. The long wavelength yellow light of the sodium vapor lamps, however, is not as effectively scattered by fog droplets. Foggy roads can be safely, albeit eerily, illuminated in this manner.

In the case of extremely small atomic systems, electromagnetic radiation waves in the ultraviolet, X-ray, and gamma ray regions of the spectrum must be used. These correspond to high frequency, high energy radiation. Such high energy radiation when used in the measurement of atomic systems strongly interacts with those systems. When a high energy photon hits a moving electron in an atom, the electron has its energy altered by the impact. (Fig. 10.2.) Unavoidably, then, a fundamental principle at the base of modern atomic

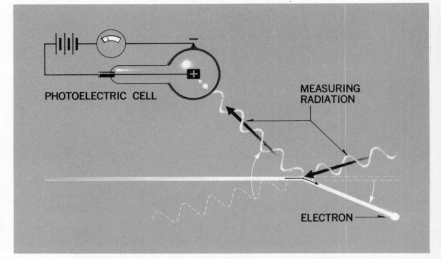

**FIGURE 10.2** Collision of a high energy photon with an electron. This results in a transfer of energy and a change in path of both, leading to uncertainty in knowledge of the energy and position of the electron.

theory reflects the inherent uncertainty in the measurement of atomic systems. This principle was first postulated in 1926 by the German physicist Werner Heisenberg (VER ner HI zen berg), who stated:

> One can never know simultaneously with perfect accuracy both of the two important factors which determine the movement of an electron—its position and its velocity. If we determine experimentally its exact position at any given moment, its movement is disturbed to such a degree by that very experiment that we shall then be unable to find it at all. And conversely, if we are able to measure exactly the velocity of an electron, the picture of its position becomes totally blurred.

The Heisenberg *Uncertainty Principle* can be derived mathematically from considerations of quantum theory. Its importance to us is qualitative, though. We must recognize, for example, that if we cannot measure the exact width of this page to within $10^{-8}$ cm, it does not really matter. If, however, the uncertainty in the measurement of the position of an electron in an atom is $10^{-8}$ cm then a serious problem exists, since an atom itself is about $10^{-8}$ cm wide. With such a large uncertainty, we are led to conclude that it is impossible to state where an electron is in an atom at any particular moment.

### 10.3 Uncertainty and the Bohr model of the atom

From his model of the hydrogen atom, Bohr was able to derive an expression for the radius of the paths, or orbits, of the revolving electron. He found that the radius was calculated as:

$$r = n^2 \cdot a_0$$

where $a_0$ is a constant and $n$ is the principal quantum number. Values for $a_0$ could be calculated, and for hydrogen it has a value of 0.529A. For the ground state of hydrogen where $n = 1$, the radius would be:

$$r = n^2 \cdot 0.529 \text{ A}$$
$$= (1)^2(.529 \text{ A})$$
$$= 0.529 \text{ A}$$

Consequently, according to the Bohr model, the electron in the lowest energy level of hydrogen would rotate about the nucleus at a distance of exactly 0.529A at all times.

Such a precise knowledge of the radius is in conflict with the Uncertainty Principle. If the energy of the first level is well defined, as it must be by Bohr's assumptions about discrete levels of fixed energy, then according to the Uncertainty Principle the radius (i.e., the position) of the electrons in that level cannot be known very precisely. Thus, we have a fundamental conflict between the Bohr model of the atom and the Uncertainty Principle. A better model of the atom would seem to be one that would allow accurate prediction of the energy of the electron levels but would, at the same time, indicate an inability to be precise about the position of electrons.

## PRINCIPLES OF MODERN ATOMIC THEORY

By 1926 physicists and chemists were faced with complex theoretical problems in their attempts to deduce a model for the atom. At the heart of their problems was the need to reconcile the abstract mathematics of their theories with the physical realities of nature. A model for the atom must lead to stationary electron energy states; that is, the model must account for line spectra. A model for the atom must account for the periodic behavior of the elements. Finally, a model for the atom must not violate the Uncertainty Principle. In 1926 the beginnings of such a model were announced.

### 10.4 The Schrödinger wave equation

The Austrian physicist-mathematician Erwin Schrödinger (SHRAY ding er), having pondered over Bohr's and de Broglie's ideas, sought and found a model in which both could be used. Schrödinger set up a mathematical equation that treated the electron in terms of wave behavior. Solutions of the "wave equation" were obtained only for certain values of the electron energy term used in the equation. In other words, an inevitable consequence of the mathematical model that Schrödinger employed was that stationary electron energy states must exist in atoms.

**Erwin Schrödinger** (1887–1961, Austrian). Working from de Broglie's particle-wave theory of matter, Schrödinger developed a wave mechanics model of the atom. That model remains the basis of modern concepts of atomic structure. In 1933 he shared the Nobel Prize in Physics with Dirac for their independent development of wave mechanics.

When the wave equation was solved for the one-electron hydrogen atom, the calculated energy states agreed extremely well with observed spectral energy levels. Perhaps you can imagine the excitement that must have gripped scientists when they learned that the energy levels of atoms could be calculated from an equation for waves. That excitement of the first view of a new and strange scientific "continent" must resemble closely the type of exhilaration that Christopher Columbus, Admiral Peary, and Yuri Gagarin felt.

A more detailed consideration of the form and means of solution of Schrödinger's wave equation awaits you who will pursue science and mathematics in future years. For the present, we will consider some of the *results* of the Schrödinger treatment of atomic theory, and some of the *features* of the model of the atom developed from that theory. Since the theory arises from considerations of quantum physics, the model is known as the *quantum mechanical model* of the atom.

### 10.5 The wave equation and electron position in the atom

The use of the wave equation as an atomic model not only leads to values for stationary electron energy states; it also provides information on the position in space of electrons in those states. However, it does not, as Bohr's model does, describe the position exactly. Instead, it gives a description that fits in well with the Uncertainty Principle. It is not possible to say exactly where in the atom an electron is at a specific time. Instead, the *probability* of finding an electron at a certain point at a specific time can be determined.

Suppose that you have a pet dog in your yard. There will be certain places the dog likes to be more than others—for example, in his dog house or under a shade tree on hot afternoons. If you are asked at 2:30 P.M., May 15, where your dog is, you could say "in the yard" with confidence. But when you are asked to be more specific about his location, you could only say that he is probably either under the tree or in his house. Perhaps you have watched him enough (made enough experiments) to say that the chances of finding him under the tree are 4 in 10 (40 per cent probability), in his house 5 in 10 (50 per cent probability), and elsewhere the chance is only 1 in 10 (10 per cent probability).

In similar fashion, solutions of the wave equation predict the probabilities of the electron being at certain distances from the nucleus at any time. A graph of the probable radial distribution of the electron in the ground state of the hydrogen atom is shown in Figure 10.3. The maximum in the curve occurs at the same distance from the nucleus that Bohr had predicted for the ground state radius. However,

Bohr's theory places the ground state electron *always* at that distance. The quantum mechanical model of the atom derived from the wave equation leads to this only as the *most probable* of distances. The mathematical model clearly indicates that both shorter and longer distances also have some probability.

## 10.6 Electron behavior and quantum numbers

In reaching satisfactory solutions of the Schrödinger wave equation, four numbers related to electron behavior become necessary to such solutions. These numbers are symbolized by the letters $n$, $l$, $m$, and $s$. They are called *quantum numbers* and are found to have values dependent on each other.

Quantum numbers were not new to theoretical interpretations of atomic structure. We recall that the theory first proposed by Bohr included the quantum number $n$. Extensions of Bohr's theory had necessitated three additional quantum numbers, $l$, $m$, and $s$. Thus, solution of the Schrödinger equation *necessarily* led to the existence of quantum numbers, which had been brilliantly, though artificially, introduced in earlier theories.

The quantum mechanical model of the atom relates the four quantum numbers to a complete description of the behavior of electrons in atoms. The $n$ and $l$ quantum numbers are related to a description of the energy state of an electron in an atom.

For a given energy state there is only one value for $n$. This value for $n$ can be any integer greater than zero; that is, $n$ may have the values:

$$n = 1, 2, 3, 4, 5, 6, \ldots$$

In a given energy state there can be more than one value for $l$. In fact, whatever the value of $n$ is for the energy state will determine the number of $l$ values. If $n = 1$, there will be *one* value of $l$. If $n = 2$, there will be *two* values of $l$. In general, for a given value of $n$ there are $n$ values of $l$ associated with it. These $n$ values of $l$ are the $n$ integers from *zero* to $(n-1)$. For example, for $n = 5$, $l$ has the *five* values:

$$l = 0, 1, 2, 3, 4$$

For all energy states except that for which $n = 1$, the existence of more than one value of $l$ has an important physical interpretation. That interpretation is that all energy states described by $n$, except that for which $n = 1$, are actually combinations of two or more energy states described by a combination of $n$ and $l$. Thus, we may pictorially represent the major electron energy level for which $n = 5$

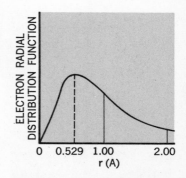

**FIGURE 10.3** Radial distribution probability for the ground state hydrogen electron

*n = distance from nucleus*

*l = angular momentum shape of orbit*

in terms of five contributing levels of energy, each of which has its own description in terms of $n = 5$ and a related $l$ value:

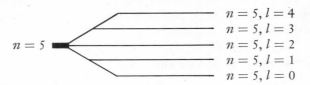

$$n = 5 \quad \begin{cases} n = 5, l = 4 \\ n = 5, l = 3 \\ n = 5, l = 2 \\ n = 5, l = 1 \\ n = 5, l = 0 \end{cases}$$

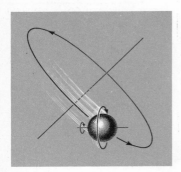

**FIGURE 10.4** *Revolution and rotation of an electron in an atom*

Each contributing electron energy level that is described by a combination of $n$ and $l$ is called an *orbital*. From the diagram given, the implication exists that the orbitals that comprise a given major energy level have slightly differing energies. As we shall see, except for the one-electron hydrogen atom, this implication becomes a theoretical keystone to modern concepts of atomic structure.

How many electrons in an atom may be at the same energy level—may occupy the same orbital—is determined by the magnetic properties of the electron. The quantum numbers $m$ and $s$ are related to the magnetic properties that electrons possess by virtue of being moving charges. There are two electron motions to consider: revolution around the nucleus and self-rotation. (Fig. 10.4.) Each of these motions leads to magnetic states of the electron in a given energy state or orbital.

The quantum number $m$ is related to the magnetic states of the electron that arise from its revolutionary motion. The number of $m$ values, or magnetic states in a given orbital, is found to be determined by the $l$ value for the given orbital. Corresponding to each value of $l$ there are $(2l + 1)$ values of $m$. Thus, for $l = 0$, there will be $(2 \times 0 + 1)$ or 1 value of $m$. For $l = 1$, there will be $(2 \times 1 + 1)$ or 3 values of $m$. For $l = 2$, there will be $(2 \times 2 + 1)$ or 5 values of $m$, and so on. The $(2l + 1)$ numerical values for $m$ are the $(2l + 1)$ integers between $-l$ and $+l$, inclusive. For example, the 5 values of $m$ that are derived from the value $l = 2$ are:

$$m = -2, -1, 0, +1, +2$$

The physical interpretation that we give to the existence of $(2l + 1)$ values for $m$ in a given orbital is that there are $(2l + 1)$ magnetic states possible for a single energy state. The orientation of an electron in space will be determined by its magnetic state. The existence of $(2l + 1)$ quantized magnetic states in a given orbital implies then the existence of $(2l + 1)$ *quantized* spatial orientations for that orbital. If we again consider the major energy level for which $n = 5$, we may pictorially represent the physical interpretation for the existence of $(2l + 1)$ values of $m$ as follows:

| | | | | | | | | | $l = 4$ |
|---|---|---|---|---|---|---|---|---|---|
| $m = -4$ | $m = -3$ | $m = -2$ | $m = -1$ | $m = 0$ | $m = +1$ | $m = +2$ | $m = +3$ | $m = +4$ | |

$m = -3$ $\quad$ $m = -2$ $\quad$ $m = -1$ $\quad$ $m = 0$ $\quad$ $m = +1$ $\quad$ $m = +2$ $\quad$ $m = +3$ $\quad$ $l = 3$

$n = 5$

$m = -2$ $\quad$ $m = -1$ $\quad$ $m = 0$ $\quad$ $m = +1$ $\quad$ $m = +2$ $\quad$ $l = 2$

$m = -1$ $\quad$ $m = 0$ $\quad$ $m = +1$ $\quad$ $l = 1$

$m = 0$ $\quad$ $l = 0$

In other words, instead of there being only one orbital defined by the combination $n = 5$ and $l = 1$, there are $(2l + 1)$ or $(2 \times 1 + 1)$ or 3 such orbitals. These three orbitals are of equivalent energy value but correspond to three different electron spatial orientations.

Finally, a complete description of an electron is provided by consideration of the fourth quantum number, $s$. This so-called "spin" quantum number reflects the magnetic state of an electron caused by its own rotation. Experimentally it is observed, and theoretically it is shown, that *electron spin is quantized, there being only two modes of spin, of equal speed but in opposite directions.* Accordingly, there are only two possible values for the spin quantum number $s$. These values are usually symbolized

$$ s = -\tfrac{1}{2}, +\tfrac{1}{2} $$

where the $-$ and $+$ signs indicate opposite spin directions. The value, of $\tfrac{1}{2}$, is related to the amount of spin involved.

How do we include electron spin in our physical interpretation of the total description of an electron in an atom? We merely indicate that for each magnetic state that is due to the electron's revolutionary motion ($m$ values), there are two possible magnetic states that are due to spin ($s$ values). In other words, we superimpose upon each of the $(2l + 1)$ quantized electron spatial orientations two possible electron spin orientations. That is, two electrons may have identical energies and spatial orientations and differ simply in direction of spin.

### 10.7 A principle to prevent chaos

How can we use the information we have learned thus far to answer the following question: How can we use the quantum mechanical model to describe the eighteen electrons in the argon atom? Considering that our model with its infinite number of major energy states ($n$ values) allows each electron to have an infinite number of descriptions, where do we begin? Unless some ordering rule exists for electrons in orbitals, theoretical chaos results. An ordering rule does exist. It was first stated by the German physicist Wolfgang Pauli (VULF gong POW lee) and is known as the Pauli Exclusion Principle.

**THE PAULI EXCLUSION PRINCIPLE.** This theoretical principle, which brings order to the quantum mechanical model of the atom, states that *it is not possible for any two electrons in the same atom to be described by the same set of four quantum numbers.*

Following this principle, Table 10–1 has been prepared showing possible *allowed* quantum mechanical descriptions of the eighteen electrons in argon.

**TABLE 10–1**  POSSIBLE ALLOWED QUANTUM MECHANICAL DESCRIPTIONS OF THE ELECTRONS IN ARGON

| Electron | $n$ | $l$ | $m$ | $s$ |
|---|---|---|---|---|
| 1 | 1 | 0 | 0 | $-\frac{1}{2}$ |
| 2 | 1 | 0 | 0 | $+\frac{1}{2}$ |
| 3 | 2 | 0 | 0 | $-\frac{1}{2}$ |
| 4 | 2 | 0 | 0 | $+\frac{1}{2}$ |
| 5 | 2 | 1 | $-1$ | $-\frac{1}{2}$ |
| 6 | 2 | 1 | $-1$ | $+\frac{1}{2}$ |
| 7 | 2 | 1 | 0 | $-\frac{1}{2}$ |
| 8 | 2 | 1 | 0 | $+\frac{1}{2}$ |
| 9 | 2 | 1 | 1 | $-\frac{1}{2}$ |
| 10 | 2 | 1 | 1 | $+\frac{1}{2}$ |
| 11 | 3 | 0 | 0 | $-\frac{1}{2}$ |
| 12 | 3 | 0 | 0 | $+\frac{1}{2}$ |

| | | | | |
|---|---|---|---|---|
| 13 | 3 | 1 | $-1$ | $-\frac{1}{2}$ |
| 14 | 3 | 1 | $-1$ | $+\frac{1}{2}$ |
| 15 | 3 | 1 | 0 | $-\frac{1}{2}$ |
| 16 | 3 | 1 | 0 | $+\frac{1}{2}$ |
| 17 | 3 | 1 | 1 | $-\frac{1}{2}$ |
| 18 | 3 | 1 | 1 | $+\frac{1}{2}$ |

In Table 10–1, orbitals having the same $n$, $l$, and $m$ values have been set off from each other. Note then that in any orbital *a maximum of two electrons* may be present. The maximum number of orbital electrons will be present only if the two are spinning in opposite directions.

Examine Table 10–1 carefully. Are all the orbitals having a value of $n = 1$ described? Are all those for which $n = 2$ described? What about all those for which $n = 3$? What are the total number of electrons in one atom that can have a value of $n = 1$? $n = 2$? $n = 3$? $n = 4$? Can you deduce the mathematical relationship between $n$ and the total electron population in orbitals having a given value of $n$?

In examining Table 10–1, the question on the choice of $n$ values may be logically raised. Why was $n = 1$, then $n = 2$, then $n = 3$ chosen, until eighteen electrons were fully described? Is it not true that any electron in the argon atom has an infinite number of $n$ values (energy states) available to it? More than just the natural tendency to begin at the beginning ($n = 1$ rather than $n = 7$, for example), the choice of $n$ values to describe the orbitals occupied in argon was based on energy considerations. As $n$ increases in value from its lowest value of 1, the potential energy value of the major energy level described by $n$ increases. The stability of an electron in an atom increases as the electron occupies lower potential energy levels. Thus, it is logical to begin describing the electrons in any unexcited atom in terms of the lowest potential energy levels available to them. It is just such a consideration of energy that will lead us finally to relate the quantum mechanical model of the atom to the periodic classification of the elements.

## 10.8 Orbitals have shorthand designations.

At the outset, let us first become familiar with the shorthand description of orbitals used by chemists. Four *kinds* of orbitals, or electron energy states, have been found capable of adequately describing the electronic structures of all known atoms in their ground states, as well as explaining much of the chemical bonding between atoms. What *kind* of an orbital one is dealing with is determined by the value of the $l$ quantum number for the orbital. What is meant by orbital *kind* or *type* will be more fully discussed in Chapter 20. For the moment, it is only important to know that there are four types. Depending on the value of $l$, the orbital type is designated as $s$,* $p$, $d$, or $f$ type by chemists. The definition of type is:

| *l value* | *orbital type* |
|:---------:|:--------------:|
| 0 | *s* |
| 1 | *p* |
| 2 | *d* |
| 3 | *f* |

Chemists further designate orbitals in terms of the $n$ value for the orbital. The value of $n$ precedes the letter designating the orbital type. Thus, when a chemist speaks of a $1s$ orbital, he is referring to the electron energy state defined by the quantum numbers $n = 1$, $l = 0$. A $4f$ orbital would have the characteristic values $n = 4$, $l = 3$. Table 10–2 sums up the shorthand designations of orbitals that are used to describe the electronic structure of atoms. The table also includes the *number* of orbitals of a given type as determined by the *number* of $m$ values for a given $l$ value.

**TABLE 10–2** SUMMATION OF ORBITAL TYPES AND NUMBERS AS DETERMINED BY THE QUANTUM NUMBERS $n$, $l$, AND $m$

| $n$ | $l$ | $m$ | *Orbital Type* (from $n$ and $l$) | *Number of Orbitals* (from *number* of $m$ values) |
|:---:|:---:|:---:|:---:|:---:|
| 1 | 0 | 0 | $1s$ | 1 |
| 2 | 0 | 0 | $2s$ | 1 |
| 2 | 1 | $+1, 0, -1$ | $2p$ | 3 |
| 3 | 0 | 0 | $3s$ | 1 |
| 3 | 1 | $+1, 0, -1$ | $3p$ | 3 |
| 3 | 2 | $+2, +1, 0, -1, -2$ | $3d$ | 5 |
| 4 | 0 | 0 | $4s$ | 1 |
| 4 | 1 | $+1, 0, -1$ | $4p$ | 3 |
| 4 | 2 | $+2, +1, 0, -1, -2$ | $4d$ | 5 |
| 4 | 3 | $+3, +2, +1, 0, -1, -2, -3$ | $4f$ | 7 |

* Unfortunately, this is the same symbol as that used for the spin quantum number. These should not be confused. It should be realized that orbital types $g$, $h$, $i$, $j$, etc., corresponding to $l$ values 4, 5, 6, 7, etc., exist.

In Table 10–2, orbitals of the same *n* value have been set off from each other. Again, can you relate *total* electron population of orbitals having the same value of *n*?

## MODERN ATOMIC THEORY AND CHEMICAL PERIODICITY

We have indicated that more careful consideration of the actual energy values for electron orbitals will relate the quantum mechanical model of the atom to the periodic classification of the elements. Let us examine the *experimentally* observed energy levels of atoms and super-impose upon them the orbitals of the quantum mechanical model to which they *theoretically* correspond.

### 10.9 Orbital patterns for hydrogen

The simplest atomic system to examine is that of hydrogen, a one-electron atom. Figure 10.5 is the experimental energy level diagram for hydrogen corresponding to the calculated diagram of Figure 9.10. However, each quantum energy level has been associated with corresponding electron orbitals *calculated* from the quantum mechanical model of the atom. For hydrogen, we note the same excellent agree-

**FIGURE 10.5** Electron orbital pattern for hydrogen: a one-electron atom

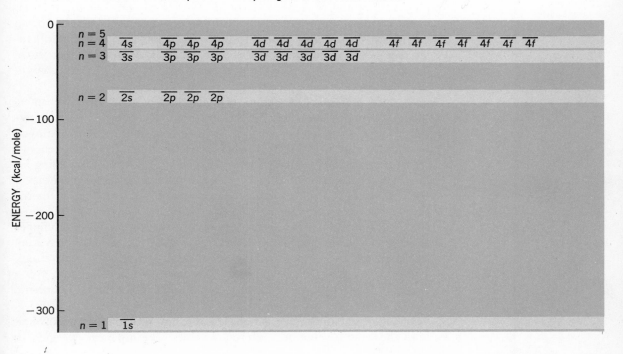

ment between model and experiment that we did for the Bohr model of the atom. We also observe the same direct relationship between the quantum number $n$ and the energy level value that was found in the Bohr theory. As the $n$ value increases, the potential energy level value increases. The electron in hydrogen is in its energetically most stable state when in the $1s$ orbital, the ground state.

One final important observation is that for the hydrogen electron all orbitals *of the same n value* have the same energy. Thus, when the hydrogen electron is excited from the ground state to the third excited state ($n = 4$), there are sixteen orbitals having the same energy in that state. Any one of those orbitals can be occupied by the excited electron without any experimentally observable difference. As we turn now to atoms of elements beyond hydrogen, elements with many electrons, the experimental and theoretical interpretation of their structure becomes more complex.

### 10.10  Orbital patterns for a many-electron atom

The relatively simple emission spectrum of hydrogen, and the excellent agreement of the calculated energy levels with that spectrum, are due to the electrical simplicity of this system with one electron and one proton. As soon as more than one electron is present in an atom, the observed emission spectrum of such an atom is more complex. Accordingly, as we proceed through the periodic table, we find that the complexity of atomic emission spectra increases as the number of electrons in the emitting atoms increases. With many electrons in an atom being excited to emit energy, there results a very intricate and difficult-to-interpret overlapping of spectral emission lines. Moreover, theoretical considerations of many-electron atoms become greatly more complicated.

In the wave equation leading to the quantum mechanical model, there appears an electrical potential energy term. For the hydrogen atom with its one electron and one proton, that term is known. For atoms with many electrons and many protons, the potential energy term can only be approximated. Current scientific understanding of how electrons and protons *in large numbers* interact with each other is not able to lead to the complex counterpart of Coulomb's Law for the interaction of one electron and one proton.

Using approximations, then, in the solution of the Schrödinger wave equation for many-electron atoms, theoretical scientists have determined the best approximations of orbital patterns for such atoms. Figure 10.6 qualitatively shows the *calculated* orbital pattern for a many-electron atom based on the quantum mechanical treatment. When compared to the orbital pattern for hydrogen in Figure 10.5, a very important difference is noted. For many-electron atoms, orbitals with the same $n$ value but different $l$ values *have different energies*. In

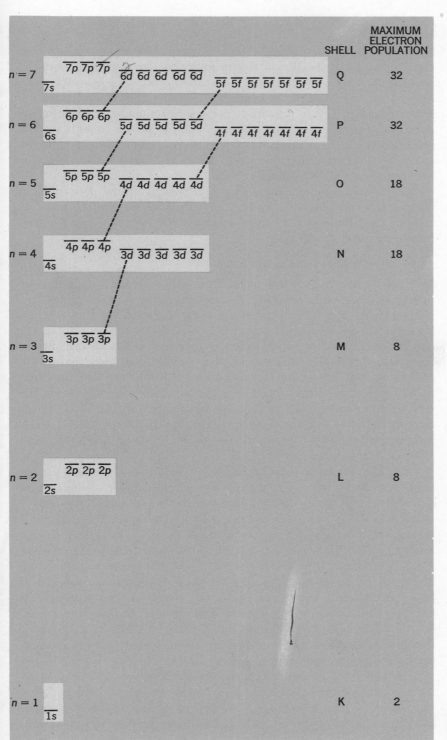

| | SHELL | MAXIMUM ELECTRON POPULATION |
|---|---|---|
| $n = 7$ | Q | 32 |
| $n = 6$ | P | 32 |
| $n = 5$ | O | 18 |
| $n = 4$ | N | 18 |
| $n = 3$ | M | 8 |
| $n = 2$ | L | 8 |
| $n = 1$ | K | 2 |

**FIGURE 10.6** Electron orbital pattern for a many-electron atom

hydrogen, the 3*s*, 3*p*, and 3*d* orbitals were equal in energy. Figure 10.6 clearly shows that the 3*s* orbital is of lower energy than the 3*p* orbital, which, in turn, is of lower energy than the 3*d* orbital in a many-electron atom. This separation of the orbitals of a major energy level into sub-levels of energy is due primarily to the interactions among the many electrons. You will note that the separation is severe enough so that orbitals of different *n* values overlap in energy value. For example, the 4*s* orbital lies between the 3*p* and 3*d* orbitals, and the 6*s* orbital lies between the 5*p* and 4*f* orbitals.

Continued examination of the calculated orbital pattern for a many-electron atom will finally lead us to one of the triumphs of modern atomic theory—theoretical justification for the periodic classification of the elements.

### 10.11 Electron shells and magic numbers

Figure 10.6 clearly indicates a pattern in which groups of orbitals of similar but not equal energies are separated from other groups by larger energy gaps. It can be seen that there is one orbital, the 1*s*, at the lowest energy. Then, after a gap in energy, the 2*s* and 2*p* orbitals are close in energy. After another energy gap, the 3*s* and 3*p* orbitals are found close together. There is another energy gap, then the 4*s*, 4*p*, and 3*d* orbitals have similar energies, and so on. Note that the large energy gaps occur after groups of orbitals that do not always have the same value of *n*. We shall speak of these orbital groups as being "electron shells." The first, or *K shell*, is the 1*s* orbital; the second, or *L shell*, is the 2*s* and 2*p* orbitals; the fourth, or *N shell*, is the 4*s*, 3*d*, and 4*p* orbitals; and so on.

The definition of electron shells in terms of orbital groups lying in a narrow energy zone regardless of the *n* value of each group differs from that which you will find in many other books. On the basis of historical development from Bohr theory to the quantum mechanical theory of the atom, it is more usual to see the term electron shell referring to all the orbitals described by the same quantum number *n*. Thus, for example, the *M* electron shell would be defined as consisting of the 3*s*, 3*p*, and 3*d* orbitals. The *M* electron shell as defined in this book includes only the 3*s* and 3*p* orbitals, based on their proximity in energy value. Similarly, whereas tradition would consider the 4*s*, 4*p*, 4*d*, and 4*f* orbitals as comprising the *N* electron shell, on the basis of energy considerations we consider the 4*s*, 3*d*, and 4*p* orbitals as comprising the *N* electron shell.

It is the maximum electron population of the electron shells as *we* have defined them that leads us to a series of "magic numbers." It is that series of "magic numbers," which, at last, tie together complex modern atomic theory with the chemists' most significant fact—chemical periodicity.

Recalling that each orbital can accommodate two electrons of opposite spin, the electron population of each shell is given in Table 10–3.

**TABLE 10–3**  ELECTRON SHELL POPULATIONS

| Shell | Orbital Types | Number of Orbitals | Maximum Number of Electrons |
|-------|---------------|--------------------|-----------------------------|
| K | 1s | 1 | 2 |
| L | 2s,2p | 1 + 3 = 4 | 8 |
| M | 3s,3p | 1 + 3 = 4 | 8 |
| N | 4s,3d,4p | 1 + 5 + 3 = 9 | 18 |
| O | 5s,4d,5p | 1 + 5 + 3 = 9 | 18 |
| P | 6s,4f,5d,6p | 1 + 7 + 5 + 3 = 16 | 32 |
| Q | 7s,5f,6d,7p | 1 + 7 + 5 + 3 = 16 | 32 |

The magic numbers 2, 8, 8, 18, 18, 32, 32 immediately call to mind the periodic classification of the elements. In that classification, the number of elements in the different periods has the same order:

| PERIOD NUMBER | 1 | 2 | 3 | 4 | 5 | 6 |
|---------------|---|---|---|---|---|---|
| ELEMENTS | H-He | Li-Ne | Na-Ar | K-Kr | Rb-Xe | Cs-Rn |
| NUMBER OF ELEMENTS | 2 | 8 | 8 | 18 | 18 | 32 |

The orbital pattern derived from the mathematical quantum mechanical model of the atom can, then, account for the structural pattern of the periodic classification of the elements. Even more so, theory and fact continue to correspond as we examine the details of periodicity.

## 10.12  Orbital patterns, the structures of atoms, and chemical periodicity

Figure 10.6 serves as the basis for describing electrons in orbitals in atoms. Such descriptions of electron energy states in atoms is what is commonly meant by the *atomic structure* of an element. In assigning orbitals to electrons in atoms, modern atomic theory takes into account a very old experimental observation. In somewhat modern language, that observation is that the most energetically stable systems are those possessing a minimum of potential energy. Thus, the atomic structures of the elements are built up, so to speak, from the ground floor. That is, all orbitals of lower potential energy must be occupied before those of higher energy content can be filled. You may recall that this principle lay behind the construction of Table 10–1.

Hydrogen has its only electron in the 1s orbital when the atom is in its lowest energy state. Chemists depict the atomic structure of hydrogen simply as $1s^1$. This symbolism is also known as the *electron configuration* of hydrogen. Chemists often use a pictorial representation for the electron configuration of the elements. Such a representation for hydrogen atom is

$$\frac{\uparrow}{1s},$$

where the dash represents an electron orbital, the $1s$ indicates which orbital, and the $\uparrow$ stands for a single spinning electron in the orbital and is symbolic of one of the two allowed directions of electron spin.

The next element, helium ($Z = 2$), has two electrons, and these are both in the $1s$ orbital. The electron configuration of He is $1s^2$ and the $K$ electron shell is complete. Pictorially, the electron configuration of He is

$$\frac{\uparrow\downarrow}{1s}.$$

The arrows facing in opposite directions indicate that the two electrons are spinning in opposite directions.

The next element, lithium ($Z = 3$), which begins Period 2 of the periodic classification of the elements, has three electrons in each of its atoms. Since only two electrons can be in the $1s$ energy state (remember the Pauli Exclusion Principle), the third electron in Li must be in the $2s$ orbital. The electron configuration for a lithium atom is then, $1s^2 2s^1$. Pictorially, this is represented as

$$\frac{\uparrow\downarrow}{1s}\bigg|\frac{\uparrow}{2s},$$

where the dividing line indicates that there exists a difference in energy between the two orbitals depicted. The choice of an arrow pointing *upward* for the single $2s$ electron is quite arbitrary. The actual direction of electron spin is not possible to determine. The important point is that there are only two directions of electron spin and they are opposite from each other. We shall use arrows pointing upward and downward to indicate opposite spin.

Beryllium atoms ($Z = 4$) have four electrons, so their electron configuration will be $1s^2 2s^2$, or

$$\frac{\uparrow\downarrow}{1s}\bigg|\frac{\uparrow\downarrow}{2s}.$$

Since the $L$ electron shell consists of $2s$ and $2p$ orbitals, boron ($Z = 5$) has the electron configuration $1s^2 2s^2 2p^1$, or

$$\frac{\uparrow\downarrow}{1s}\bigg|\frac{\uparrow\downarrow}{2s}\bigg|\frac{\uparrow}{2p}\ \frac{}{2p}\ \frac{}{2p}.$$

Carbon $(Z = 6)$ is described as $1s^2 2s^2 2p^2$. With the electron configuration of carbon, a question arises. It was earlier indicated that a given electron orbital can accommodate two electrons of opposite spin. Are then the two $2p$ electrons in the carbon atom in the same orbital spinning in opposite directions, or are they in each of two orbitals spinning in the same direction? Let us ask that question pictorially. Which of the following pictorial representations better depicts the electron orbital population of the carbon atom?

$$\frac{\uparrow\downarrow}{1s}\left|\frac{\uparrow\downarrow}{2s}\right|\frac{\uparrow\downarrow}{2p}\ \frac{\ }{2p}\ \frac{\ }{2p} \qquad \text{or} \qquad \frac{\uparrow\downarrow}{1s}\left|\frac{\uparrow\downarrow}{2s}\right|\frac{\uparrow}{2p}\ \frac{\uparrow}{2p}\ \frac{\ }{2p}$$

It is both an experimental fact* and theoretically calculable that the second representation is the correct pictorial interpretation of the electron orbital occupancy in the carbon atom. In fact, a general principle of the quantum mechanical theory of the atom is that *electrons will fill orbitals of the same energy value one at a time before coupling of electrons in the same orbital occurs*. This principle is known as the *principle of maximum multiplicity*. It is a principle that makes good sense. If each of the $2p$ orbitals has the same energy value, then it seems sensible for two electrons of similar charge to distribute themselves between the two orbitals rather than to assume the same orbital occupancy wherein repulsive forces must be overcome.

In considering the next element of Period 2, nitrogen $(Z = 7)$, the principle of maximum multiplicity is demonstrated to its fullest extent for $p$ orbitals:

$$_7N \quad 1s^2 2s^2 2p^3 \quad \text{or} \quad \frac{\uparrow\downarrow}{1s}\left|\frac{\uparrow\downarrow}{2s}\right|\frac{\uparrow}{2p}\ \frac{\uparrow}{2p}\ \frac{\uparrow}{2p}$$

It is with neon $(Z = 10)$ that Period 2 is completed and the $L$ electron shell is filled. Table 10–4 summarizes the electron configurations for the first ten elements of nature, those of Periods 1 and 2.

Using Figure 10.6 as a guide, prepare a table similar to Table 10–4 for the elements of Period 3, sodium (Na, $Z = 11$) through argon (Ar, $Z = 18$). As a clue to whether your electron configurations are correct, at least so far as numbers of electrons in a given atom are concerned, add up the superscripts following the orbital symbols. This sum must equal the atomic number for the element if you are considering electrically neutral atoms.

If you have interpreted Figure 10.6 correctly, you will have arrived at the following configuration for argon:

$$_{18}Ar \quad 1s^2 2s^2 2p^6 3s^2 3p^6 \quad \text{or} \quad \frac{\uparrow\downarrow}{1s}\left|\frac{\uparrow\downarrow}{2s}\right|\frac{\uparrow\downarrow}{2p}\ \frac{\uparrow\downarrow}{2p}\ \frac{\uparrow\downarrow}{2p}\left|\frac{\uparrow\downarrow}{3s}\right|\frac{\uparrow\downarrow}{3p}\ \frac{\uparrow\downarrow}{3p}\ \frac{\uparrow\downarrow}{3p}$$

---

* The kind of experiment that leads to this fact is discussed in Chapter 24.

**TABLE 10–4** Electron Configurations for the Elements
of Periods 1 and 2

| Element | Electron Configuration | Pictorially |
|---------|------------------------|-------------|
| $_1$H | $1s^1$ | ↑ <br> $1s$ |
| $_2$He | $1s^2$ | ↑↓ <br> $1s$ |
| $_3$Li | $1s^2 2s^1$ | ↑↓ \| ↑ <br> $1s$ $2s$ |
| $_4$Be | $1s^2 2s^2$ | ↑↓ \| ↑↓ <br> $1s$ $2s$ |
| $_5$B | $1s^2 2s^2 2p^1$ | ↑↓ \| ↑↓ \| ↑  __  __ <br> $1s$ $2s$ $2p$ $2p$ $2p$ |
| $_6$C | $1s^2 2s^2 2p^2$ | ↑↓ \| ↑↓ \| ↑  ↑  __ <br> $1s$ $2s$ $2p$ $2p$ $2p$ |
| $_7$N | $1s^2 2s^2 2p^3$ | ↑↓ \| ↑↓ \| ↑  ↑  ↑ <br> $1s$ $2s$ $2p$ $2p$ $2p$ |
| $_8$O | $1s^2 2s^2 2p^4$ | ↑↓ \| ↑↓ \| ↑↓  ↑  ↑ <br> $1s$ $2s$ $2p$ $2p$ $2p$ |
| $_9$F | $1s^2 2s^2 2p^5$ | ↑↓ \| ↑↓ \| ↑↓  ↑↓  ↑ <br> $1s$ $2s$ $2p$ $2p$ $2p$ |
| $_{10}$Ne | $1s^2 2s^2 2p^6$ | ↑↓ \| ↑↓ \| ↑↓  ↑↓  ↑↓ <br> $1s$ $2s$ $2p$ $2p$ $2p$ |

Note that the $M$ electron shell is now filled, and a relatively large
energy gap exists before the start of the $N$ electron shell. The elements
whose electron configurations involve orbitals of the $N$ electron shell
are those of Period 4, potassium (K, $Z = 19$) through krypton (Kr,
$Z = 36$).

Continued interpretation of Figure 10.6 leads us to the following electron configurations for the first two elements of Period 4, in
which $(Ar)$ symbolizes the pictorial electron configuration of argon
given at the bottom of page 251:

$$_{19}K \quad 1s^2 2s^2 2p^6 3s^2 3p^6 4s^1 \quad \text{or} \quad (Ar)\Big|\frac{\uparrow}{4s}$$

$$_{20}Ca \quad 1s^2 2s^2 2p^6 3s^2 3p^6 4s^2 \quad \text{or} \quad (Ar)\Big|\frac{\uparrow\downarrow}{4s}$$

When we reach scandium (Sc, $Z = 21$), we place the twenty-first
electron in a $3d$ orbital, the next available orbital of higher energy:

$$_{21}Sc \quad 1s^2 2s^2 2p^6 3s^2 3p^6 4s^2 3d^1 \quad \text{or} \quad (Ar)\Big|\frac{\uparrow\downarrow}{4s}\Big|\frac{\uparrow}{3d} \ \overline{3d} \ \overline{3d} \ \overline{3d} \ \overline{3d}$$

Moreover, since there are five $3d$ orbitals that can contain a total of ten electrons, scandium must be the first of a series of ten elements in nature, unlike the twenty that precede it. These first twenty elements involved $s$ orbitals or $p$ orbitals only. Indeed, the periodic classification of the elements segregates the ten elements between calcium and gallium in Period 4 as *transition elements*. Table 10–5 summarizes the electron configuration of the transition elements of Period 4. The

**TABLE 10–5.** ELECTRON CONFIGURATIONS FOR THE TRANSITION ELEMENTS OF PERIOD 4

| Element | Electron Configuration* | Pictorially* |
|---------|-------------------------|--------------|
| $_{21}$Sc | $1s^2 2s^2 2p^6 3s^2 3p^6 4s^2 3d^1$ | $(Ar) \; \frac{\uparrow\downarrow}{4s} \left| \frac{\uparrow}{3d} \; \frac{\,}{3d} \; \frac{\,}{3d} \; \frac{\,}{3d} \; \frac{\,}{3d} \right.$ |
| $_{22}$Ti | $1s^2 2s^2 2p^6 3s^2 3p^6 4s^2 3d^2$ | $(Ar) \; \frac{\uparrow\downarrow}{4s} \left| \frac{\uparrow}{3d} \; \frac{\uparrow}{3d} \; \frac{\,}{3d} \; \frac{\,}{3d} \; \frac{\,}{3d} \right.$ |
| $_{23}$V | $1s^2 2s^2 2p^6 3s^2 3p^6 4s^2 3d^3$ | $(Ar) \; \frac{\uparrow\downarrow}{4s} \left| \frac{\uparrow}{3d} \; \frac{\uparrow}{3d} \; \frac{\uparrow}{3d} \; \frac{\,}{3d} \; \frac{\,}{3d} \right.$ |
| $_{24}$Cr | $1s^2 2s^2 2p^6 3s^2 3p^6 4s^2 3d^4$ | $(Ar) \; \frac{\uparrow\downarrow}{4s} \left| \frac{\uparrow}{3d} \; \frac{\uparrow}{3d} \; \frac{\uparrow}{3d} \; \frac{\uparrow}{3d} \; \frac{\,}{3d} \right.$ |
| $_{25}$Mn | $1s^2 2s^2 2p^6 3s^2 3p^6 4s^2 3d^5$ | $(Ar) \; \frac{\uparrow\downarrow}{4s} \left| \frac{\uparrow}{3d} \; \frac{\uparrow}{3d} \; \frac{\uparrow}{3d} \; \frac{\uparrow}{3d} \; \frac{\uparrow}{3d} \right.$ |
| $_{26}$Fe | $1s^2 2s^2 2p^6 3s^2 3p^6 4s^2 3d^6$ | $(Ar) \; \frac{\uparrow\downarrow}{4s} \left| \frac{\uparrow\downarrow}{3d} \; \frac{\uparrow}{3d} \; \frac{\uparrow}{3d} \; \frac{\uparrow}{3d} \; \frac{\uparrow}{3d} \right.$ |
| $_{27}$Co | $1s^2 2s^2 2p^6 3s^2 3p^6 4s^2 3d^7$ | $(Ar) \; \frac{\uparrow\downarrow}{4s} \left| \frac{\uparrow\downarrow}{3d} \; \frac{\uparrow\downarrow}{3d} \; \frac{\uparrow}{3d} \; \frac{\uparrow}{3d} \; \frac{\uparrow}{3d} \right.$ |
| $_{28}$Ni | $1s^2 2s^2 2p^6 3s^2 3p^6 4s^2 3d^8$ | $(Ar) \; \frac{\uparrow\downarrow}{4s} \left| \frac{\uparrow\downarrow}{3d} \; \frac{\uparrow\downarrow}{3d} \; \frac{\uparrow\downarrow}{3d} \; \frac{\uparrow}{3d} \; \frac{\uparrow}{3d} \right.$ |
| $_{29}$Cu | $1s^2 2s^2 2p^6 3s^2 3p^6 4s^2 3d^9$ | $(Ar) \; \frac{\uparrow\downarrow}{4s} \left| \frac{\uparrow\downarrow}{3d} \; \frac{\uparrow\downarrow}{3d} \; \frac{\uparrow\downarrow}{3d} \; \frac{\uparrow\downarrow}{3d} \; \frac{\uparrow}{3d} \right.$ |
| $_{30}$Zn | $1s^2 2s^2 2p^6 3s^2 3p^6 4s^2 3d^{10}$ | $(Ar) \; \frac{\uparrow\downarrow}{4s} \left| \frac{\uparrow\downarrow}{3d} \; \frac{\uparrow\downarrow}{3d} \; \frac{\uparrow\downarrow}{3d} \; \frac{\uparrow\downarrow}{3d} \; \frac{\uparrow\downarrow}{3d} \right.$ |

---

\* These configurations are based on a strict adherence to the theoretical model of orbital patterns shown in Figure 10.6. In reality, experimentally measured properties of some elements clearly indicate that a variation from the theoretical pattern occurs. The electron configurations of Cr and Cu that are more correct in terms of experimental knowledge are, for example:

$_{24}$Cr   $1s^2 2s^2 2p^6 3s^2 3p^6 4s^1 3d^5$

$_{29}$Cu   $1s^2 2s^2 2p^6 3s^2 3p^6 4s^1 3d^{10}$

Variations of these types need be of no concern to us now.

principle of maximum multiplicity operates during the occupancy of *d* orbitals. Note that the pictorial representations of the transition elements emphasize that fact.

The electron configuration of zinc does not represent the completion of the *N* electron shell. The three 4*p* orbitals that can accommodate six electrons are yet to be filled. Accordingly, the remaining six elements of the fourth period, from gallium (Ga, $Z = 31$) to krypton (Kr, $Z = 36$), will involve electrons of the *N* electron shell. Tabulate the electron configurations of those six elements. Further, using Figure 10.6 as a guide, prepare a table of electron configurations for the eighteen elements of the fifth period, from rubidium (Rb, $Z = 37$) to xenon (Xe, $Z = 54$).

We see then how successful the quantum mechanical model of the atom has been in predicting the *form* of the periodic table. Groups I and II consist of elements in which *s* electron orbitals are being occupied. Groups III—0 are those for which electrons fill in *p* electron orbitals of atoms. The transition elements we may call *d* electron orbital elements. The lanthanides and the actinides, as you might predict, consist of elements in which seven *f* electron orbitals are being filled.

Careful consideration of the electron configurations we have worked out will lead us to another important success of modern atomic theory.

### 10.13 Electron configurations and chemical families

In Chapter 7, we learned that families of elements of similar chemical properties exist. Let us consider the electron configuration for the members of the three families of elements studied in Chapter 7—the noble gases, the halogens, and the alkali metals. Table 10–6 summarizes those configurations.

Table 10–6 provides us with the fundamental relationship between the quantum mechanical model of the atom and chemical change. **The chemical behavior of the elements is a periodic function of their electron configuration.** This statement is another assertion of the Periodic Law.

Table 10–6 provides us with a clue to the "why" of chemical reactions, also. The noble gases, unique among all the elements for their chemical stability or general lack of chemical activity, have unique electron configurations. The noble gases, alone among the elements, have completely filled electron shells. It would be reasonable to conclude that this theoretical fact is connected with the experimental fact of their general chemical inactivity. It might also be reasonable to assume that herein lies a possible theoretical clue to the chemical activity of the other elements.

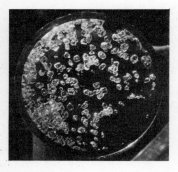

A "noble" gas compound: xenon tetrafluoride, $XeF_4$, crystals

**TABLE 10–6**  ELECTRON CONFIGURATIONS OF THE NOBLE GASES, HALOGENS, AND ALKALI METALS

| | Element | Electron Configuration | | | |
|---|---|---|---|---|---|
| Noble gases | $_2$He | $1s^2$ | | | |
| | $_{10}$Ne | $1s^2$ | $2s^22p^6$ | | |
| | $_{18}$Ar | $1s^2$ | $2s^22p^6$ | $3s^23p^6$ | |
| | $_{36}$Kr | $1s^2$ | $2s^22p^6$ | $3s^23p^6$ | $4s^23d^{10}4p^6$ |
| | $_{54}$Xe | $1s^2$ | $2s^22p^6$ | $3s^23p^6$ | $4s^23d^{10}4p^6$  $5s^24d^{10}5p^6$ |
| Halogens | $_9$F | $1s^2$ | $2s^22p^5$ | | |
| | $_{17}$Cl | $1s^2$ | $2s^22p^6$ | $3s^23p^5$ | |
| | $_{35}$Br | $1s^2$ | $2s^22p^6$ | $3s^23p^6$ | $4s^23d^{10}4p^5$ |
| | $_{53}$I | $1s^2$ | $2s^22p^6$ | $3s^23p^6$ | $4s^23d^{10}4p^6$  $5s^24d^{10}5p^5$ |
| Alkali metals | $_3$Li | $1s^2$ | $2s^1$ | | |
| | $_{11}$Na | $1s^2$ | $2s^22p^6$ | $3s^1$ | |
| | $_{19}$K | $1s^2$ | $2s^22p^6$ | $3s^23p^6$ | $4s^1$ |
| | $_{37}$Rb | $1s^2$ | $2s^22p^6$ | $3s^23p^6$ | $4s^23d^{10}4p^6$  $5s^1$ |
| | $_{55}$Cs | $1s^2$ | $2s^22p^6$ | $3s^23p^6$ | $4s^23d^{10}4p^6$  $5s^24d^{10}5p^6$  $6s^1$ |

# SUMMARY

The modern, or quantum mechanical, theory of atomic structure is derived from three fundamental concepts: stationary electron energy states; the dual, or wave-particle, nature of matter; and the inherent uncertainty in measurements involving atomic systems. The complex mathematical theory built on those concepts leads to a description of electrons in atoms in terms of four quantum numbers—$n$, $l$, $m$, $s$.

The $n$ value of a major stationary energy state determines the number of $l$ values, or contributing energy levels, present. Each contributing energy level consists of a number of energetically equivalent but differently oriented electron energy states known as orbitals. The $l$ value for an orbital determines its type—$s$, $p$, $d$, or $f$—and $(2l + 1)$ equals the number of orbitals of a given type, as well as the number of $m$ values for the contributing energy level. There can be two electrons of opposite spin in the same orbital, a fact reflected by the double-valued $s$ quantum number.

Experimentally, the potential energy pattern for orbitals in many-electron atoms is:

$$1s < 2s < 2p < 3s < 3p < 4s < 3d < 4p < 5s$$
$$< 4d < 5p < 6s < 4f < 5d < 6p < 7s < 5f < 6d$$

Consideration of this fact, in conjunction with

(1)  the Pauli Exclusion Principle,
(2)  the principle that natural processes occur in a way that minimizes energy, and
(3)  the principle of maximum multiplicity,
     leads to the modern theoretical justification for chemical periodicity, and a possible rationale for chemical reaction.

## QUESTIONS AND PROBLEMS

**10.1**  Briefly outline three fundamental concepts of modern atomic theory.

**10.2**  Cite experimental evidence for the dual, or wave-particle, nature of electrons.

**10.3**  De Broglie derived an equation that treats material particles as though they had a wavelike nature:

$$\lambda = \frac{h}{mv}$$

where $\lambda$ is the particle wavelength, $h$ is Planck's constant, $m$ is the mass of the particle, and $v$ is its velocity. Which would show a greater wavelength: **a.** a slow moving electron or a fast moving electron? **b.** an electron moving at $10^6$ meters/second or a rocket moving at this same velocity?

**10.4**  State in your own words what is meant by the Heisenberg Uncertainty Principle.

**10.5**  **a.** Why was it necessary that the Bohr model of the *hydrogen atom* be modified? **b.** What are the main differences between the Bohr and Schrödinger models of the hydrogen atom?

**10.6**  To what does each of the four quantum numbers relate?

**10.7**  **a.** Show the relationship between the $n$ and $l$ quantum numbers by giving all the values of $l$ when $n$ equals 3. **b.** Similarly, give all the values of $m$ when $l$ equals 3. **c.** What are all the values of $m$ when $n$ equals 3?

**10.8**  Relate mathematically: **a.** the number of $l$ values that are possible for any particular $n$ value; **b.** the number of $m$ values associated with any particular $n$ value; **c.** the number of orbitals associated with any particular $n$ value; **d.** the maximum number of electrons associated with any particular $n$ value.

**10.9**  Give the symbol of the orbital type designated by an $l$ value of **a.** 0; **b.** 2; **c.** 5.

**10.10**  What $n$ value allows for: **a.** only the $s$ orbital type? **b.** only the $s$, $p$, and $d$ orbital types? **c.** the $s$, $p$, $d$, and $f$ orbital types?

**10.11** Describe the following orbitals in terms of their corresponding $n$ and $l$ values: **a.** $3s$; **b.** $4d$; **c.** $5p$; **d.** $6f$; **e.** $5g$.

**10.12** What is the maximum number of orbitals of each of the types given in Problem 10.11?

**10.13 a.** State the Pauli Exclusion Principle in your own words. **b.** How does this principle allow the prediction of the maximum number of electrons that can be present for a corresponding $n$ value?

**10.14** Write the electron configuration for oxygen ($Z = 8$). Show pictorially that the principle of maximum multiplicity is obeyed.

**10.15** From the following electron configurations, pick the elements that belong to the same chemical family:

    **a.** $1s^2 2s^2 2p^6 3s^2 3p^6$
    **b.** $1s^2 2s^2 2p^4$
    **c.** $1s^2 2s^1$
    **d.** $1s^2 2s^2 2p^6 3s^2 3p^4$

**10.16 a.** Write the electron configuration for the elements with atomic numbers 65 and 83. **b.** For each element indicate the number of shells that are completely filled and pictorially represent *the unfilled shells*.

## SUGGESTED READINGS

Broglie, Louis de. *Matter and Light* (paperback). Dover, 1939. Reprint.

Hecht, Selig. *Explaining the Atom* (paperback). Viking Press, 1960.

Hochstrasser, Robin M. *Behavior of Electrons in Atoms* (paperback). W. A. Benjamin, 1964.

Sisler, Harry H. *Electronic Structure, Properties, and the Periodic Law* (paperback). Reinhold, 1963.

SCIENTIFIC AMERICAN

Darrow, K. K., "The Quantum Theory." Mar. 1952

Furth, R., "The Limits of Measurement." July 1950

Gamow, G., "The Exclusion Principle." July 1959

Gamow, G., "The Principle of Uncertainty." Jan. 1958

Schrödinger, E., "What Is Matter?" Sept. 1953

*The abiding impulse in every
human being is to seek order
and harmony behind the manifold
and the changing in the existing world.*

*Niels Bohr* (1885–1962)

# CHAPTER 11

# Chemical Bonding

In earlier chapters, chemical compounds were discussed in terms of their physical and chemical properties. It is now appropriate to ask the most fundamental question—*why do chemical compounds form?* What forces cause individual atoms to group into molecules? Are these forces the same for all molecules?

The forces holding atoms together in compounds are called *chemical bonds*. It would seem logical to seek the answers about the nature of chemical bonds in the theory of atomic structure described in the preceding chapter.

## THE IONIC BOND

Just as chemists have come to recognize the existence of different types of compounds, so they now realize the necessity for postulating the existence of more than one type of chemical bond.

You will recall from Chapter 6 that the two most commonly encountered solid types are ionic and molecular solids. Indeed, regardless of physical state, ionic and molecular compounds are the most common ones that exist. The type of chemical bond that is involved in the formation of *ionic* compounds is called the *electrovalent* or *ionic bond*. When *molecular* compounds form, chemists speak of *covalent* bonds as being involved in such compounds.

Ionic and covalent bonds represent extremes in bond types within compounds. The chemical and physical properties of many

# and Molecular Shape

compounds indicate that the bonds within those compounds are neither purely ionic nor purely covalent. In fact, as we shall see later, most chemical bonds between different atoms are best described as being partially ionic and partially covalent.

## 11.1 What are ionic compounds?

The reaction between sodium and chlorine yields sodium chloride:

$$2Na(s) + Cl_2(g) = 2NaCl(s)$$

However, the study of a crystal of sodium chloride shows that there are no molecules of NaCl in it. Instead, a regular network pattern is found in which sodium cations, with a +1 charge, and chloride anions, with a −1 charge, are present in alternating layers. (See Fig. 6.8.) The cations and anions are held together in a crystal lattice by the electrical attraction between the net positive and negative charges on the ions. *The chemical bonds between the ions are then the result of coulombic attraction and are known as electrovalent or ionic bonds.*

To show that the atoms do not form distinct molecules but form ions of opposite charge, which are attracted to each other, the reaction for sodium and chlorine is written as:

$$2Na(s) + Cl_2(g) = 2Na^{+1}Cl^{-1}(s)$$

Na represents the *atomic metal* sodium. $Cl_2$ represents the *molecular gas* chlorine. $Na^{+1}Cl^{-1}$ represents the *ionic solid* sodium chloride in

259

which there are neither uncharged atoms of sodium or chlorine *nor* molecules of NaCl but only $Na^{+1}$ and $Cl^{-1}$ ions.

For neutral sodium atoms, $Na^0$, to form unipositive sodium ions, $Na^{+1}$, each sodium atom must *lose one electron:*

$$Na^0 \rightarrow Na^{+1} + 1e^-$$

For neutral chlorine atoms, $Cl^0$, to form uninegative chloride ions, $Cl^{-1}$, each chlorine atom must *gain one electron:*

$$Cl^0 + 1e^- \rightarrow Cl^{-1}$$

It is logical to assume that in the reaction between sodium and chlorine to form ionic sodium chloride, $Na^{+1}Cl^{-1}$, there is a *transfer of electrons* from neutral sodium atoms to neutral chlorine atoms—one electron from each one sodium atom transferring to each one chlorine atom.

*Most simply, an ionic bond forms as a result of the transfer of electrons from metal atoms to nonmetal atoms during a chemical reaction.*

## 11.2  Relation of $Na^{+1}$ to the electron orbitals of $Na^0$

Now the question arises as to why, in the formation of $Na^{+1}Cl^{-1}$, sodium forms $Na^{+1}$. That is, what causes a sodium atom to lose an electron to a chlorine atom? A further question is why should sodium ($Na^0$) lose only one electron ($Na^{+1}$) and not two ($Na^{+2}$) or three ($Na^{+3}$)? For the answer to these questions, we return to the suggestion made in the last section of Chapter 10. There, you will recall, it was suggested that the relative chemical inactivity of He, Ne, Ar, Kr, Xe, and Rn is due to the fact that these elements have *filled electron shells.* What was suggested is that *filled electron shells are relatively stable electron configurations.*

Now consider the sodium atom, which has a $1s^2 2s^2 2p^6 3s^1$ electron configuration. A sodium atom can achieve a filled electron shell configuration most simply in two ways. It *can lose one electron,* achieving a $1s^2 2s^2 2p^6$ electron configuration (filled $K$ and $L$ shells), and become the $Na^{+1}$ ion. Alternatively, a sodium atom *might gain seven electrons,* achieving a $1s^2 2s^2 2p^6 3s^2 3p^6$ electron configuration (filled $K$, $L$, and $M$ shells), and become the $Na^{-7}$ ion. As was pointed out in Chapter 7, it is an experimental fact that one of the major chemical characteristics of sodium and the other alkali metals is the formation of $+1$ ions. We are led to conclude that the sodium atom loses the single $3s$ electron of its electron configuration to achieve a filled electron shell configuration. Our model would predict similar behavior on the part of the other alkali metal atoms; this behavior is summarized thus:

*Atom*

| | | | *Ion* | |
|---|---|---|---|---|
| Li | $1s^2 2s^1$ | | $Li^{+1}$ | $1s^2$ (like He atom) |
| Na | $1s^2 2s^2 2p^6 3s^1$ | | $Na^{+1}$ | $1s^2 2s^2 2p^6$ (like Ne atom) |
| K | $1s^2 2s^2 2p^6 3s^2 3p^6 4s^1$ | | $K^{+1}$ | $1s^2 2s^2 2p^6 3s^2 3p^6$ (like Ar atom) |
| Rb | $1s^2 2s^2 2p^6 3s^2 3p^6 4s^2 3d^{10} 4p^6 5s^1$ | | $Rb^{+1}$ | $1s^2 2s^2 2p^6 3s^2 3p^6 4s^2 3d^{10} 4p^6$ (like Kr atom) |
| Cs | $1s^2 2s^2 2p^6 3s^2 3p^6 4s^2 3d^{10} 4p^6 5s^2 4d^{10} 5p^6 6s^1$ | | $Cs^{+1}$ | $1s^2 2s^2 2p^6 3s^2 3p^6 4s^2 3d^{10} 4p^6 5s^2 4d^{10} 5p^6$ (like Xe atom) |

We see, therefore, that the model in which filled electron shells are favored electron configurations is a useful one. This model can be used to explain both the relative inactivity of the noble gases and the chemical reactivity of the alkali metals to form +1 cations.

Since the chemistry of the alkali metals is basically a function of the single *s* electron found in the highest energy level of the atoms of those metals, that *s* electron is commonly called a *valence electron*. As electron energy shells have been defined in this book, the valence electrons of an element are those that are present in the highest electron energy shell that is being occupied in that element. That shell is called, therefore, the *valence shell*.

## 11.3 Relation of $Cl^{-1}$ to the electron orbitals of $Cl^0$

Now let us consider the electron change when chlorine atoms form chloride ions. As was pointed out in Chapter 7, one of the outstanding chemical characteristics of the halogen elements is the formation of negative ions, with a −1 charge. To form such anions, the neutral atom must gain an electron.

The electron configuration of the chlorine atom is $1s^2 2s^2 2p^6$-$3s^2 3p^5$. To form the chloride ion, $Cl^{-1}$, it seems quite logical to assume that the chlorine atom gains an electron that becomes the sixth $3p$ electron, required for a filled electron shell configuration. Our model would predict similar behavior for all the halogen atoms and such is summarized thus:

*Atom*

| | | | *Ion* | |
|---|---|---|---|---|
| F | $1s^2 2s^2 2p^5$ | | $F^{-1}$ | $1s^2 2s^2 2p^6$ (like Ne atom) |
| Cl | $1s^2 2s^2 2p^6 3s^2 3p^5$ | | $Cl^{-1}$ | $1s^2 2s^2 2p^6 3s^2 3p^6$ (like Ar atom) |
| Br | $1s^2 2s^2 2p^6 3s^2 3p^6 4s^2 3d^{10} 4p^5$ | | $Br^{-1}$ | $1s^2 2s^2 2p^6 3s^2 3p^6 4s^2 3d^{10} 4p^6$ (like Kr atom) |
| I | $1s^2 2s^2 2p^6 3s^2 3p^6 4s^2 3d^{10} 4p^6 5s^2 4d^{10} 5p^5$ | | $I^{-1}$ | $1s^2 2s^2 2p^6 3s^2 3p^6 4s^2 3d^{10} 4p^6 5s^2 4d^{10} 5p^6$ (like Xe atom) |

We note that for the halogen elements, the valence shells do not contain the same number of valence electrons. Fluorine and chlorine have *seven* valence electrons in the *L* and *M* valence shells, respectively. Bromine and iodine, on the other hand, have *seventeen* valence electrons in the *N* and *O* valence shells, respectively. The significant feature remains that each of those shells requires one more electron in a *p* orbital for completion.

## 11.4 Ionization energies

Another test of the idea that the stability of filled electron shells can be used to explain the formation of ions can be made by comparing the *ionization energies* of different elements. *The ionization energy is the amount of energy necessary to remove the electron in the highest energy level from a gaseous atom or ion.* When an electron is removed from an atom, the latter is ionized; i.e., it becomes a *positive ion.* Table 11–1 lists some experimental ionization energies.

**TABLE 11–1** IONIZATION ENERGIES OF SOME ELEMENTS (KCAL/MOLE)

| Atomic Number | Element | $(I.E.)_1$ | $(I.E.)_2$ | $(I.E.)_3$ | $(I.E.)_4$ |
|---|---|---|---|---|---|
| 1 | H | 313 | — | — | — |
| 2 | He | 567 | 1254 | — | — |
| 3 | Li | 124 | 1744 | 2823 | — |
| 4 | Be | 215 | 420 | 3548 | 5020 |
| 5 | B | 191 | 580 | 874 | 5980 |
| 6 | C | 260 | 562 | 1104 | 1487 |
| 7 | N | 335 | 683 | 1094 | 1786 |
| 8 | O | 314 | 811 | 1267 | 1785 |
| 9 | F | 402 | 807 | 1445 | 2012 |
| 10 | Ne | 497 | 947 | 1500 | 2241 |
| 11 | Na | 118 | 1091 | 1652 | 2280 |
| 12 | Mg | 176 | 347 | 1848 | 2521 |
| 13 | Al | 138 | 434 | 656 | 2766 |
| 14 | Si | 188 | 377 | 772 | 1040 |
| 15 | P | 254 | 453 | 695 | 1184 |
| 16 | S | 239 | 540 | 808 | 1090 |
| 17 | Cl | 300 | 549 | 920 | 1230 |
| 18 | Ar | 363 | 637 | 943 | 1379 |
| 19 | K | 100 | 734 | 1100 | 1405 |
| 20 | Ca | 141 | 274 | 1180 | 1550 |
| 35 | Br | 273 | 498 | 828 | 1154 |
| 36 | Kr | 323 | 566 | 851 | — |
| 37 | Rb | 96 | 634 | 920 | — |
| 38 | Sr | 131 | 254 | — | — |
| 53 | I | 241 | 440 | 723 | — |
| 54 | Xe | 280 | 489 | 740 | — |
| 55 | Cs | 90 | 579 | — | — |
| 56 | Ba | 120 | 231 | — | — |
| 86 | Rn | 248 | — | — | — |

The *first ionization energy*, $(I.E.)_1$, is the energy required for the reaction

gaseous atom + energy → gaseous unipositive ion + electron

or

$$M^0(g) + (I.E.)_1 \rightarrow \qquad M^{+1}(g) \qquad + e^-(g)$$

where $M^0(g)$ stands for an atom of any element in the gaseous state. The *second ionization energy*, $(I.E.)_2$, is the energy required for the process

gaseous unipositive ion + energy → gaseous dipositive ion + electron

or

$$M^{+1}(g) + (I.E.)_2 \rightarrow \qquad M^{+2}(g) \qquad + e^-(g).$$

The third, fourth, and higher ionization energies are similarly defined.

### 11.5 The ionization energies of lithium

Let us consider the ionization energies of lithium $(Z = 3)$. From Table 11–1 we see that 124 kcal/mole are required for the ionization of the first electron in the reaction

$$Li^0(g) + (I.E.)_1 \rightarrow Li^{+1}(g) + e^-(g)$$
$$1s^2 2s^1 \xrightarrow{\hspace{2cm}} 1s^2 \text{ (like He atom)}.$$

However, ionization of the next electron in the reaction

$$Li^{+1}(g) + (I.E.)_2 \rightarrow Li^{+2}(g) + e^-(g)$$
$$1s^2 \xrightarrow{\hspace{2cm}} 1s^1$$

requires almost fifteen times as much energy—1744 kcal. These experimental results are consistent with our theory that filled electron shells are particularly stable ones. The first ionization resulted in an ion with a filled electron shell and as such required relatively little energy. But the second ionization requires going from a filled electron shell configuration to an unfilled one. A great deal of energy is required to bring about such a change, which clearly indicates that this change is not a favored one.

### 11.6 Why magnesium forms a +2 ion

Magnesium $(Z = 12)$ has a first ionization energy of 176 kcal/mole, a second ionization energy of 347 kcal/mole, and a third ionization energy of 1848 kcal/mole. It is not too difficult, therefore, to remove two electrons from atomic magnesium, but it is *very* difficult to remove a third electron. According to the electron orbital pattern, magnesium atoms should have a configuration of $1s^2 2s^2 2p^6 3s^2$. The ionization reactions would be:

**FIRST IONIZATION**

$$Mg^0(g) + (I.E.)_1 \rightarrow Mg^{+1}(g) + e^-(g)$$
$$1s^2 2s^2 2p^6 3s^2 \longrightarrow 1s^2 2s^2 2p^6 3s^1$$

**SECOND IONIZATION**

$$Mg^{+1}(g) + (I.E.)_2 \rightarrow Mg^{+2}(g) + e^-(g)$$
$$1s^2 2s^2 2p^6 3s^1 \longrightarrow 1s^2 2s^2 2p^6 \text{ (like Ne atom)}$$

**THIRD IONIZATION**

$$Mg^{+2}(g) + (I.E.)_3 \rightarrow Mg^{+3}(g) + e^-(g)$$
$$1s^2 2s^2 2p^6 \longrightarrow 1s^2 2s^2 2p^5$$

We see that the loss of the first two electrons results in the formation of a $Mg^{+2}$ ion with filled electron shells. The formation of $Mg^{+3}$ ion in a third ionization requires going from a filled electron shell configuration to one that is unfilled. Again, the fact that such a change requires so much energy, more than a million calories per mole, indicates that it is not a favored change. Ionization energies support the experimental fact that magnesium forms +2 ions rather than +1 or +3 ions.

Notice that the second ionization energy for magnesium is about twice as high as the first. This is easy to understand. In the first ionization of the neutral atom, one of twelve electrons is removed from around a nucleus with a +12 charge. In the resulting $Mg^{+1}$ ion, the 12-proton nucleus attracts each of the eleven remaining electrons more than it did each of the twelve electrons in the neutral atom. Therefore, in the formation of $Mg^{+2}$ ion from $Mg^{+1}$ ion during the second ionization, additional energy is required to overcome this increased attraction.

## 11.7 Observed trends in ionization energies

In Figure 11.1 the first ionization energies for the first twenty elements are plotted. As expected, we see that the largest amounts of energy are required to remove an electron from the noble gases He, Ne, and Ar. Notice, however, that the ionization energy is less for Ar than for Ne and, in turn, less for Ne than for He. Removal of an electron from Ar occurs from a $3p$ orbital (which is higher in energy in the electron orbital pattern than a $2p$ orbital). It is from a $2p$ orbital that an electron is removed in the ionization of neon. *The higher in energy an electron orbital is, the smaller the amount of added energy needed for ionization of an electron from that orbital.* Look at the order of ionization energies for Li, Na, and K. Can they be explained in the same way? Using Table 11–1, check other series of related elements, such as F, Cl, Br, and I, and Be, Mg, Ca, Sr, and Ba.

Several more regularities become apparent from Figure 11.1. Notice, for example, that there is a general increase in the first ionization energies from Li to Ne, followed by a sharp decrease. Another general increase is observed from Na to Ar, followed again by a sharp decrease. These observations can be explained in terms of nuclear charge and electron shell energies.

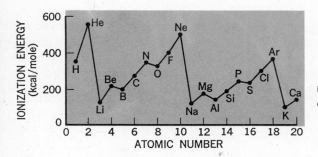

**FIGURE 11.1** First ionization energies, $(I.E.)_1$, of some elements of low atomic number

In considering the first ionizations for the elements Li through Ne, we are dealing in each case with electrons in the same $L$ electron shell. All other things being equal, it should require approximately the same energy to ionize the first electron from each of those elements. However, in going from Li to Ne, nuclear charge increases from $+3$ to $+10$. As we would expect, *as the nuclear charge increases, the coulombic attractive force between the nucleus and the extranuclear electrons is greater.* Thus, more ionization energy is required for each succeeding element from Li to Ne.

When we consider the next element in order, Na, we are now dealing with an element whose highest energy electron is found in the $M$ electron shell. The $M$ electron shell is much higher in energy than the $L$ electron shell. All other things being equal, it therefore requires less ionization energy to remove an electron from the $M$ electron shell than from the $L$ electron shell. Thus, the sharp decrease in ionization energy from Ne to Na is explained.

A repeat of the arguments just presented will serve to account for the observed increase in ionization energy from Na to Ar, followed by the sharp decrease when the $N$ electron shell element potassium, K, is reached.

## THE COVALENT BOND

It is easy to understand why sodium ions and chloride ions would be attracted to one another in a crystal of the ionic compound sodium chloride. Their opposite ionic charges attract each other just as the opposite poles of two magnets do. Much more difficult to understand is what holds atoms together in nonionic molecular compounds. What is the type of attractive force between the two atoms in the molecular gas hydrogen chloride, HCl, for example? Further, we might ask, what is the type of attractive force that exists between atoms and molecules in the liquid and solid states? These questions are basic ones that should be answered by any acceptable model for chemical bond formation.

In 1916, Gilbert N. Lewis, one of America's greatest chemists, published a famous paper, "The Atom and the Molecule," in which he suggested that nonionic molecular compounds arose from the *sharing of electrons among atoms*. More specifically, he proposed that a chemical bond formed in the formation of a molecular compound involves the sharing of a pair of electrons by two atoms. We call such a bond, as Lewis did, a *covalent bond*.

### 11.8 Electron pairs and the covalent bond

Recalling that molecular compounds tend to be formed when nonmetals react with each other (Chap. 6, Sec. 6.22, p. 161), we can state that, *most simply, a covalent bond forms as a result of the sharing of electrons between nonmetals during a chemical reaction.*

We may now consider, in detail, the covalent chemical bond formed between atoms of hydrogen and chlorine in the molecular gas hydrogen chloride, HCl. The hydrogen atom has the electron configuration

$$_1\text{H} \quad \boxed{1s^1} \quad \text{or} \quad \boxed{\uparrow}_{1s} \; .$$

The chlorine atom has the electron configuration

$$_{17}\text{Cl} \quad 1s^2 2s^2 2p^6 3s^2 3p^5 \quad \text{or} \quad \boxed{\uparrow\downarrow}_{1s} \boxed{\uparrow\downarrow}_{2s} \boxed{\uparrow\downarrow}_{2p} \boxed{\uparrow\downarrow}_{2p} \boxed{\uparrow\downarrow}_{2p} \boxed{\uparrow\downarrow}_{3s} \boxed{\uparrow\downarrow}_{3p} \boxed{\uparrow\downarrow}_{3p} \boxed{\uparrow}_{3p}$$

We will represent these situations symbolically as follows:

$$\text{H} \cdot \quad \text{and} \quad {}^{\times\times}_{\times} \text{Cl} {}^{\times}_{\times\times}$$

The H represents the hydrogen nucleus and the • represents the one valence electron outside that nucleus. The Cl represents the chlorine nucleus *and* the filled $K$ ($1s^2$) and $L$ ($2s^2 2p^6$) electron shells outside that nucleus. The seven valence electrons of the $M$ electron shell in chlorine ($3s^2 3p^5$) are represented by the seven x marks. The pairing of six of those electrons in three orbitals—the $3s$ orbital and two of the $3p$ orbitals are filled—is shown by three pairs of x marks.

To have a complete $K$ valence electron shell, the hydrogen atom requires one more electron. Similarly, one more electron would result in a complete $M$ valence electron shell for chlorine. Modern

**Gilbert Newton Lewis** (1875–1946, American). Lewis' research on the significance of electron pairs in molecular structure led to modern theories of chemical bonding. He also made valuable contributions to our concepts of acids and bases and to our understanding of fluorescence and phosphorescence. An important part of his career was spent in the study and teaching of thermodynamics—energy relationships in chemical reactions. His textbook on the subject remains a classic in the field. The roll of students who studied with him at the University of California contains the names of many great contemporary chemists.

atomic theory indicates that these requirements are met when hydrogen and chlorine atoms combine to form hydrogen chloride molecules and mutually share a pair of electrons. We represent this situation symbolically in terms of a *Lewis "electron dot" structure* as:

$$H \overset{\times \times}{\underset{\times \times}{\times} Cl \overset{\times}{\underset{\times}{}}}$$

The $\overset{\times}{\times}$ represents the *simple covalent bond* formed between hydrogen and chlorine in hydrogen chloride. In HCl, the pair of electrons of the covalent bond is *simultaneously* a part of the electron configuration of the hydrogen atom and of the chlorine. Simultaneously, then, the valence electron shells of both hydrogen and chlorine are filled in the covalent molecular compound hydrogen chloride.

The symbols chosen to represent the valence electrons of hydrogen and chlorine, respectively, were made different merely for convenience. There is no way experimentally to distinguish which electron of a covalent bonding pair is being contributed by either of the atoms being bonded. Accordingly, chemists most often simplify Lewis structures and show only the covalent bonds of such structures, using a simple *dash* between atoms to represent the bonding electron pair. For hydrogen chloride this simplified representation is

$$H - Cl$$

The covalent bond structure for HCl represents a satisfactory theoretical interpretation of much experimental data known for this molecular gas. For example, the single covalent bond between the hydrogen and chlorine atoms represents well the experimental fact that the combining capacities or valences for each of these elements is one. Such good correlation between theory and experiment basically exists for covalent compounds of a number of nonmetals—H, F, Cl, O, N, S, and P, in particular. However, the correlation collapses in one very important case and the theory *must be modified*.

### 11.9 The case of carbon and orbital hybridization

If we consider the electron configuration of carbon,

$$_6C \quad 1s^2 2s^2 2p^2 \quad \text{or} \quad \frac{\uparrow\downarrow}{1s}\frac{\uparrow\downarrow}{2s}\left|\frac{\uparrow}{2p}\frac{\uparrow}{2p}\frac{}{2p}\right. \quad \text{or} \quad \overset{\times \times}{\underset{\times}{C}} \times \quad ,$$

we are led to conclude that carbon should form two covalent bonds in its compounds, since only two of its four valence electrons are available for sharing. Experimentally, our prediction is a total failure. There is no stable compound of carbon known in which two covalent bonds can theoretically account for the properties of such a compound. Indeed, the experimental fact is that for the nearly two million molecular compounds in which carbon is the basic constituent,* the properties of such compounds can only be interpreted if carbon forms *four* covalent bonds. For example, the simplest stable molecular compound of carbon and hydrogen known is the gas methane, which has the true molecular formula $CH_4$ and not $CH_2$. Moreover, all experimental evidence indicates that each C—H bond in $CH_4$ is identical. That is, for example, when methane reacts with chlorine according to the equation

$$CH_4(g) + Cl_2(g) = CH_3Cl(g) + HCl(g),$$

no one of the four hydrogen atoms in $CH_4$ can be experimentally determined to be more weakly bonded to carbon than the other three and, therefore, more easily substituted for by a chlorine atom. These experimental facts require modification of the quantum mechanical theory of the atom in order that they be explained.

The modified theory still retains the electron configuration for an *unbonded carbon atom* in its lowest energy state as $1s^2 2s^2 2p^2$, or

$$\underset{1s}{\uparrow\downarrow}\;\underset{2s}{\uparrow\downarrow}\;\underset{2p}{\uparrow}\;\underset{2p}{\uparrow}\;\underset{2p}{\phantom{\uparrow}} \quad.$$

This electron configuration is modified in terms of the *reacting carbon atom*. In that case, the theory proposes that one of the 2s electrons is *promoted* to a higher energy 2p orbital in an *energy-consuming step:*

$$\underset{1s}{\uparrow\downarrow}\;\underset{2s}{\uparrow\downarrow}\;\underset{2p}{\uparrow}\;\underset{2p}{\uparrow}\;\underset{2p}{\phantom{\uparrow}}$$

The modified theory further proposes that *four new electron energy states of identical energy value are formed* in place of the original 2s and 2p electron energy states:

$$\underset{1s}{\uparrow\downarrow}\;\underset{2s}{\uparrow\downarrow}\;\underset{2p}{\uparrow}\;\underset{2p}{\uparrow}\;\underset{2p}{\phantom{\uparrow}} \quad\rightarrow\quad \underset{1s}{\uparrow\downarrow}\;\underset{}{\uparrow}\;\underset{}{\uparrow}\;\underset{}{\uparrow}\;\underset{}{\uparrow}$$

The energy value for each of the new orbitals can be calculated in a complicated way that essentially involves the mathematical mixing of the original properties of the *one 2s* and the *three 2p* orbitals. To indicate that the properties of an orbital have resulted from such a mixing, the chemist has borrowed a term from the biologist and calls such an orbital a *hybrid orbital*. Each of the four *identical* hybrid orbitals calculated from the mathematical mixing of one s and three p orbitals

---

* This enormous number of compounds of the single element carbon constitutes the subject matter in the study known as *organic chemistry*. Some of the principles, practices, and achievements of that study are covered in Chapters 29, 30, and 31.

is labeled an $sp^3$ orbital. For the case of a reacting carbon atom, the modified theory proposes the electron configuration:

$$1s^2 2(sp^3)^4 \quad \text{or} \quad \frac{\uparrow\downarrow}{1s} \left| \frac{\uparrow}{2(sp^3)} \quad \frac{\uparrow}{2(sp^3)} \quad \frac{\uparrow}{2(sp^3)} \quad \frac{\uparrow}{2(sp^3)} \right| \quad \text{or} \quad \overset{\times}{\underset{\times}{\times}} \overset{}{C} \overset{}{\times}$$

The hybridized electron configuration of carbon readily accounts qualitatively for the four covalent bonds of identical nature in methane:

$$\begin{array}{c} \text{H} \\ \overset{\times\bullet}{} \\ \text{H} \overset{\times}{:} \text{C} \overset{\bullet}{:} \text{H} \\ \overset{\bullet\times}{} \\ \text{H} \end{array} \qquad \text{or} \qquad \begin{array}{c} \text{H} \\ | \\ \text{H}-\text{C}-\text{H} \\ | \\ \text{H} \end{array}$$

Further, energy calculations indicate that the increase in stability gained when carbon atoms form four covalent bonds in compound formation more than counterbalances the instability involved in promoting the $2s$ electron to a $2p$ orbital and the subsequent formation of the four $sp^3$ hybrid orbitals.

Orbital hybridization will be discussed again in more detail in Chapters 20 and 25. For the present, this vital theoretical modification has been considered so that Lewis structures for covalent compounds of carbon can be derived that make theoretical, as well as experimental, sense. Before we proceed to such Lewis structures, let us turn to a consideration of the shape of covalent molecules.

## 11.10 Electron sites and the shape of covalent molecules

At first glance, the Lewis structure for methane implies that the molecule is flat:

$$\begin{array}{c} \text{H} \\ \overset{\times\bullet}{} \\ \text{H} \overset{\times}{:} \text{C} \overset{\bullet}{:} \text{H} \\ \overset{\bullet\times}{} \\ \text{H} \end{array}$$

The four pairs of bonding electrons depicted cannot, however, lie in the same plane. This is a result we can determine by considering the electrical repulsions involved. The four pairs of bonding electrons tend to repel each other. The most stable configuration in space for those four electron pairs will be the one in which they are as far apart from each other as possible, though, of course, still localized in chemical bonds. The flat Lewis structure for $CH_4$ implies that the four electron pairs in the molecule are as far apart from each other as are the four corners of a square:

This configuration in space is not the one, however, in which the four electron pairs are as far apart from each other as they can be. It can be experimentally shown that the most energetically stable state for the four pairs of electrons results when the electron pairs assume a *regular tetrahedral orientation* in space with respect to each other:

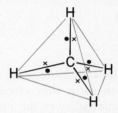

The tetrahedral geometry of the methane molecule predicted from the simple coulombic repulsions of four electron pairs implies that each of the four H—C—H bond angles should have the tetrahedral bond angle value of 109.5°. Experimentally, these bond angles are *exactly* verified.

In addition to the tetrahedral orientation brought about by ($sp^3$) hybridization, the same orientation will be assumed by four separated $s$ and $p$ valence electron pairs that are not involved in hybridization. Four such separated electron pairs will be tetrahedrally oriented whether they are bonding pairs or not. Figure 11.2 a–d depicts how this fact will determine the geometry of covalent molecules in which four separated $s$ and $p$ valence electron pairs are present.

**FIGURE 11.2** Molecular shapes determined by *four* electron sites: a. *one* site involved in bonding; b. *two* sites involved in bonding; c. *three* sites involved in bonding; d. all *four* sites involved in bonding

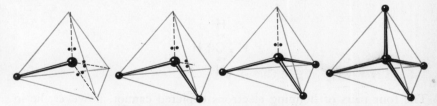

As we continue to learn more of the facts of chemistry, we shall come across molecular compounds in which electron pairs are localized in three rather than four separate positions in space. Other covalent molecules are characterized by two positions of electron localization. Figures 11.3 and 11.4 indicate the kinds of geometries we should predict for such molecules.

With this introduction to theoretical considerations of simple covalent bonding, hybrid bonding orbitals, and predicted molecular geometries, we can proceed to analyze the bonding and structural characteristics of a number of common molecular compounds.

### 11.11 Rules for deriving Lewis structures

In attempting to deduce the Lewis electron dot structure for a molecule, it is wise to follow a set of rules that is consistent with theory and experiment. Such a set of rules follows.

1. Represent only the valence electrons of an element. There may be either $2(K$ shell$)$, $8(L$ and $\bar{M}$ shells$)$, $18(N$ and $O$ shells$)$, or $32(P$ shell$)$ valence electrons in a filled valence shell as such electrons and shells have been defined *in this book*. Quite obviously, Lewis structures could become as cumbersome as Daltonian symbols if some limit were not set as to which valence electrons should be shown. Most generally, it is only $s$ and $p$ electrons that are involved in covalent bonding between nonmetals. Accordingly, it will only be the $s$ and $p$ valence electrons that will be depicted in Lewis structures. Thus, we limit ourselves to a maximum of eight valence electrons. Choose some appropriate symbol (a · or an x or some other mark is usual) for these electrons, regardless of their $s$ or $p$ type, and let the symbol for the element represent all other electrons and the nucleus of the element. For example, the Lewis structures for the noble gas atoms could be:

He:,  : Ne :,  : Ar :,  : Kr :,  : Xe :,  : Rn :

Where two or more atoms are involved in a Lewis structure, different marks may be conveniently used for different atoms. In addition to the Lewis structures for HCl and $CH_4$, given before, other structures illustrating this rule are:

H ⁚ H for $H_2$,   ⁑ Cl ⁚ Cl : for $Cl_2$, and   ⁑ Cl ⁚ C ⁚ Cl ⁑ for $CCl_4$

2. In most cases, the representation of the valence electrons should correspond to the valence $s$ and $p$ orbital electron configuration of the element. Where such a configuration indicates a *pair of electrons* in a given valence orbital, this is represented by a *pair of marks*. If a given valence $s$ or $p$ orbital is occupied by a *single electron*, this is represented by a *single* mark. Some examples follow.

**FIGURE 11.3** *Three separate bonding electron sites lead to a planar, triangular molecular structure.*

**FIGURE 11.4** *Two separate bonding electron sites lead to a linear molecular structure.*

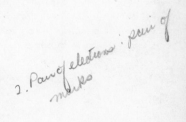

| Element | Electron Configuration | Pictorial Representation | Lewis Structure |
|---|---|---|---|
| $_7N$ | $1s^2 2s^2 2p^3$ | $\uparrow\downarrow$ $\mid$ $\uparrow\downarrow$ $\mid$ $\uparrow$ $\uparrow$ $\uparrow$   $1s$ $2s$ $2p$ $2p$ $2p$ | $\cdot\ddot{N}\cdot$ |
| $_8O$ | $1s^2 2s^2 2p^4$ | $\uparrow\downarrow$ $\mid$ $\uparrow\downarrow$ $\mid$ $\uparrow\downarrow$ $\uparrow$ $\uparrow$   $1s$ $2s$ $2p$ $2p$ $2p$ | $\cdot\ddot{O}:$ |
| $_9F$ | $1s^2 2s^2 2p^5$ | $\uparrow\downarrow$ $\mid$ $\uparrow\downarrow$ $\mid$ $\uparrow\downarrow$ $\uparrow\downarrow$ $\uparrow$   $1s$ $2s$ $2p$ $2p$ $2p$ | $:\ddot{F}:$ |

3. In a case where the valence $s$ and $p$ electron configuration of an element does not lead to the experimentally observed covalent bonding characteristics of that element, then a *hybrid bonding* configuration must be deduced. In Section 11.9, the case of carbon was covered. At this point, carbon compounds will be the only ones in which orbital hybridization will be a factor. Recall that the electron orbital configuration of the *neutral carbon atom,*

$$1s^2 2s^2 2p^2 \quad \text{or} \quad \frac{\uparrow\downarrow}{1s} \left| \frac{\uparrow\downarrow}{2s} \right| \frac{\uparrow}{2p} \frac{\uparrow}{2p} \frac{}{2p} \quad \text{or} \quad \ddot{C}\cdot \;,$$

becomes *in a bonding situation*

$$1s^2 2(sp^3)^4 \quad \text{or} \quad \frac{\uparrow\downarrow}{1s} \left| \frac{\uparrow}{2(sp^3)} \frac{\uparrow}{2(sp^3)} \frac{\uparrow}{2(sp^3)} \frac{\uparrow}{2(sp^3)} \right. \quad \text{or} \quad \cdot\dot{\underset{\cdot}{C}}\cdot \;.$$

4. Except for H and He, the maximum number of valence $s$ and $p$ electrons that can be present in a free atom is eight. Lewis structures for simple covalent bonding are based on the theoretical first principle that nonmetals share electrons in such bonding to achieve an $s^2 p^6$ valence electron configuration. This principle is appropriately called the *octet rule*.

    In addition to applying each of the above four rules in the determination of Lewis structures for molecules, it will be expected that you recall that molecules have shape. Where the spatial orientations of $s$ and $p$ valence electron sites as described in Section 11.10 apply, they should be used.

    We turn next to the application of the rules for deriving Lewis structures and depicting molecular shapes as they fit three broad types of molecular compounds.

### 11.12 Molecules having single covalent bonds only

The bonding characteristics of great numbers of molecular substances are simply satisfied by the presence of *single* covalent bonds between the atoms comprising such substances. The simple diatomic fluorine molecule can serve as a first example. The fluorine atom has the electron configuration

$$_9F \quad 1s^2 2s^2 2p^5 \quad \text{or} \quad \boxed{\uparrow\downarrow}\,\boxed{\uparrow\downarrow}\,\boxed{\uparrow\downarrow}\,\boxed{\uparrow\downarrow}\,\boxed{\uparrow} \atop 1s\;\;2s\;\;2p\;\;2p\;\;2p \quad \text{or} \quad :\!\overset{\cdot\cdot}{\underset{\cdot}{F}}\!:$$

Therefore,

$$F_2 \text{ is} \quad :\!\overset{\cdot\cdot}{\underset{\cdot\cdot}{F}}\!\overset{\times\times}{\underset{\times\times}{F}}\!\overset{\times}{\times} \quad \text{or} \quad F\!-\!F \;.$$

The shape of the $F_2$ molecule, as of all diatomic molecules, is of geometric necessity *linear*.

Let us consider next the cases of water, $H_2O$, and ammonia, $NH_3$, two of the most commonly encountered molecular substances. For water, we begin by considering the electron configuration of oxygen:

$$_8O \quad 1s^2 2s^2 2p^4 \quad \text{or} \quad \boxed{\uparrow\downarrow}\,\boxed{\uparrow\downarrow}\,\boxed{\uparrow\downarrow}\,\boxed{\uparrow}\,\boxed{\uparrow} \atop 1s\;\;2s\;\;2p\;\;2p\;\;2p \quad \text{or} \quad :\!\overset{\cdot\cdot}{\underset{\cdot}{O}}\!\cdot$$

Therefore, water has the simple Lewis structure

$$\overset{\cdot\cdot}{\underset{\times\,\cdot}{:O:}}\!H \quad \text{or} \quad :\!\overset{\cdot\cdot}{O}\!-\!H$$
$$\quad\;\; H \qquad\qquad\qquad\quad H$$

and a predicted *bent* shape. (Fig. 11.5a.)

For ammonia, we begin by considering the electron configuration of nitrogen:

$$_7N \quad 1s^2 2s^2 2p^3 \quad \text{or} \quad \boxed{\uparrow\downarrow}\,\boxed{\uparrow\downarrow}\,\boxed{\uparrow}\,\boxed{\uparrow}\,\boxed{\uparrow} \atop 1s\;\;2s\;\;2p\;\;2p\;\;2p \quad \text{or} \quad \cdot\!\overset{\cdot\cdot}{N}\!\cdot$$

Therefore, ammonia has the simple Lewis structure

$$H\overset{\cdot\cdot}{\underset{\cdot\times}{:N:}}H \quad \text{or} \quad H\!\overset{\overset{\cdot\cdot}{N}}{\diagup\;|\;\diagdown}\!H$$
$$\quad H \qquad\qquad\qquad\quad H$$

and a predicted *pyramidal* shape. (Fig. 11.5b.)

Finally, let us attempt the Lewis structure for a hydrocarbon more complex than methane. In all molecular hydrocarbons, carbon atoms are covalently bonded to each other, and any remaining bonding electrons of carbon are covalently bonded to hydrogen atoms. Two gases, ethane, $C_2H_6$, and propane, $C_3H_8$, have the following Lewis structures,

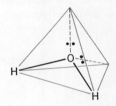

**FIGURE 11.5** a. The molecular structure of water

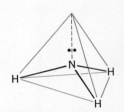

**FIGURE 11.5** b. The molecular structure of ammonia

ethane

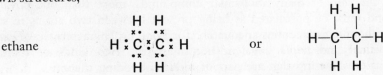

and

propane

$$\underset{\substack{\cdot x \ \ \ x \cdot \ \ \cdot x}}{\overset{\substack{H \ \ H \ \ H \\ x \cdot \ \ \cdot x \ \ x \cdot}}{H \overset{|}{\underset{|}{C}} \overset{|}{\underset{|}{C}} \overset{|}{\underset{|}{C}} H}}$$   or   $$H - \overset{\overset{\textstyle H}{|}}{\underset{\underset{\textstyle H}{|}}{C}} - \overset{\overset{\textstyle H}{|}}{\underset{\underset{\textstyle H}{|}}{C}} - \overset{\overset{\textstyle H}{|}}{\underset{\underset{\textstyle H}{|}}{C}} - H$$ ,

and shapes as predicted from the tetrahedral orientation of the hybridized carbon atoms present. (Fig. 11.6.)

**FIGURE 11.6** The molecular structure of propane. Is the carbon chain in hydrocarbons linear (180°)?

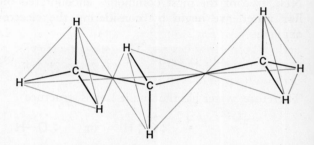

Hydrocarbons in which hydrogen atoms are replaced by other nonmetal atoms or groups are called *substituted hydrocarbons.* Lewis structures for substituted hydrocarbons are derived from the structure of the parent hydrocarbon:

Chloroethane, $C_2H_5Cl$

$$\underset{\substack{\cdot x \ \ \ x \cdot}}{\overset{\substack{H \ \ H \\ x \cdot \ \ \cdot x}}{H \overset{|}{\underset{|}{C}} \overset{|}{\underset{|}{C}} \overset{\cdot\cdot}{\underset{\cdot\cdot}{Cl}} :}}$$   or   $$H - \overset{\overset{\textstyle H}{|}}{\underset{\underset{\textstyle H}{|}}{C}} - \overset{\overset{\textstyle H}{|}}{\underset{\underset{\textstyle H}{|}}{C}} - Cl$$

**EXERCISE**

Write Lewis structures and give predicted shapes for the following molecules, each of which contains single covalent bonds only.

| | |
|---|---|
| 1. $I_2$ | 5. $C_2H_5I$ |
| 2. HBr | 6. $H_2S$ |
| 3. $PH_3$ | 7. ICl |
| 4. $CH_2Cl_2$ | 8. $C_4H_{10}$ |

## 11.13  Molecules having multiple covalent bonds

In the case of many molecular compounds, more than one covalent bond must be postulated as being present between two atoms in such compounds to account adequately for bonding characteristics. *Double* covalent and *triple* covalent bonds are the two kinds of multiple covalent bonding that are part of modern bonding theory.

Let us consider molecular carbon dioxide, $CO_2$, as our first example. From the Lewis structures of carbon and oxygen,

$$\cdot \overset{\cdot}{\underset{\cdot}{C}} \cdot \quad \text{and} \quad \overset{\times\times}{\underset{\times}{\times}} O \overset{\cdot}{\underset{\times}{\times}}$$

we would begin the Lewis structure for $CO_2$* as

$$\underset{\times\times}{\overset{\times}{\times}} O \overset{\cdot}{\underset{\cdot}{\times}} C \underset{\cdot}{\overset{\cdot}{\times}} \overset{\times\times}{\underset{\times}{O}} \times \quad \text{or} \quad \underset{\times\times}{\overset{\times}{\times}} O \overset{\cdot}{\underset{\cdot}{\phantom{}}} - C - \overset{\times\times}{\underset{}{O}} \times$$

We note, however, that the octet rule is not satisfied for any of the three atoms. Each oxygen atom has seven valence electrons; the carbon atom now has six. The octet rule can be most simply satisfied for all three atoms if a *second* covalent bond forms between the carbon atom and each oxygen atom:

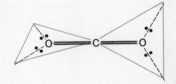

FIGURE 11.7  The molecular structure of $CO_2$. Refer back to Figure 11.4 and interpret fully the orientation of *all* the electron sites in $CO_2$.

$$\underset{\times\times}{\overset{\times}{\times}} O \overset{\curvearrowright}{-} C \overset{\cdot}{\underset{\cdot}{\curvearrowleft}} \overset{\times\times}{\underset{}{O}} \times \quad \text{or} \quad \underset{\times\times}{\overset{}{\times}} O \overset{\times\cdot}{=} C \underset{\cdot\times}{} \overset{}{O} \times \quad \text{or} \quad \underset{\times\times}{\overset{}{\times}} O = C = \overset{\times\times}{\underset{}{O}} \times$$

or, most simply,

$$O = C = O$$

Now each atom in the molecule has eight valence electrons.

Recalling Figure 11.4, the localization of the electrons in *two* positions around the carbon atom in $CO_2$ leads us to predict that the molecule would be *linear*. (Fig. 11.7.)

As a second example of multiple covalent bonding, we next consider the simple $N_2$ molecule. As before, the Lewis structure for the nitrogen atom is:

$$\cdot \overset{\cdot\cdot}{\underset{\cdot}{N}} \cdot$$

We begin the Lewis structure for $N_2$ as

$$\cdot \overset{\times}{\underset{\cdot\cdot}{N}} \overset{}{\underset{\times\times}{N}} \times \quad \text{or} \quad \cdot \overset{}{\underset{\cdot\cdot}{N}} - \overset{}{\underset{\times\times}{N}} \times$$

and note that each atom now has six valence electrons. Formation of a second covalent bond between the two nitrogen atoms

$$\cdot \overset{\frown\times}{\underset{\cdot\cdot}{N}} \overset{}{\underset{\times\times}{N}} \times \quad \text{or} \quad \cdot \overset{\cdot\times}{\underset{\cdot\cdot}{N}} \overset{}{\underset{\times\times}{N}} \times \quad \text{or} \quad \cdot \overset{}{\underset{\cdot\cdot}{N}} = \overset{}{\underset{\times\times}{N}} \times$$

* Though carbon dioxide is written as $CO_2$, the two oxygen atoms in the molecule are *both* bonded to the carbon atom and not to each other, that is, as OCO. Only in *peroxides* are oxygen atoms bonded to each other. Fig. 5.3, p. 122.

leads to seven valence electrons for each. The octet rule is satisfied only with the formation of a third covalent bond in the molecule,

$$\cdot N{=}N\times \qquad \text{or} \qquad N{=}N \qquad \text{or} \qquad N{\equiv}N$$

or, more simply,

$$N{\equiv}N$$

As an example of a compound in which both single and multiple covalent bonds are present, we will consider ethene (ethylene), $C_2H_4$, an *unsaturated* hydrocarbon. We begin the structure

$$H{:}C{:}C{:}H \qquad \text{or} \qquad H{-}C{-}C{-}H$$

and note that while each hydrogen atom now has a filled valence electron shell (two electrons), each carbon atom has seven valence electrons. The octet rule for the carbon atoms is satisfied with the formation of a second covalent bond between them:

$$H{-}C{=}C{-}H \qquad \text{or} \qquad H{-}C{:}C{-}H \qquad \text{or} \qquad H{-}C{=}C{-}H$$

Each carbon atom in ethene is surrounded by *three* electron sites, hence, recalling Figure 11.3, the geometry predicted for the molecule involves triangular orientation of atoms in the same plane. (Fig. 11.8.)

**EXERCISE**

Write Lewis structures and give predicted shapes for the following molecules in which multiple covalent bonds will be required.

1. $CS_2$     3. $C_3H_6$
2. $HCN$     4. $H_2CO$

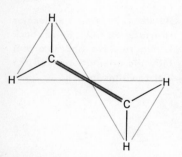

**FIGURE 11.8** The molecular structure of ethene. Interpret fully the orientation of *all* the electron sites in this molecule.

## 11.14 The coordinate covalent bond

A too common chemical reaction that occurs in most high school and college chemistry laboratories is the following:

$$NH_3(g) + HCl(g) = NH_4Cl(s)$$

The reaction takes place each time an open bottle of hydrochloric acid is placed near an open bottle of ammonium hydroxide. The solid white smoke that forms settles in time on windows, laboratory bench tops, and so on, as a fine white powder.

The reaction is a very interesting one in that two molecular gases, $NH_3$ and $HCl$, in which covalent bonds only are present, combine in the gas phase to form an *ionic* solid, $(NH_4)^{+1}Cl^{-1}$; that is, we may rewrite the reaction as:

$$NH_3(g) + HCl(g) = (NH_4)^{+1}Cl^{-1}(s)$$

Recalling the Lewis structure for the $NH_3$ and $HCl$ molecules,

$$
\begin{array}{c}
H \\
\overset{\bullet\times}{H:N:} \\
\overset{\times\bullet}{H}
\end{array}
\quad \text{and} \quad
H\overset{\bullet\bullet}{:}\overset{\bullet\bullet}{Cl}\overset{\bullet\bullet}{:} \;,
$$

we are led to a Lewis structure for $NH_4Cl$ as

$$
\begin{array}{c}
H \\
\overset{\bullet\times}{\phantom{H}} \\
H:N:H:Cl: \cdot \\
\overset{\times\bullet}{\phantom{H}} \\
H
\end{array}
$$

Since experimentally $NH_4Cl$ is ionic and contains $(NH_4)^{+1}$ and $Cl^{-1}$ ions, we conclude that the Lewis structures for those ions are

$$
\left[
\begin{array}{c}
H \\
\overset{\bullet\times}{\phantom{H}} \\
H:N:H \\
\overset{\times\bullet}{\phantom{H}} \\
H
\end{array}
\right]^{+1}
\quad \text{and} \quad
\left[
:\overset{\bullet\bullet}{\underset{\bullet\bullet}{Cl}}:
\right]^{-1} \cdot
$$

The positive charge on the $(NH_4)^{+1}$ ion results from the extra proton $(H^{+1})$ that separated from the chlorine atom and is now bonded to the ammonia molecule. The negative charge on the $Cl^{-1}$ ion results from the electron left behind by the hydrogen nucleus as it separated from the chlorine atom.

If we examine the Lewis structure of the tetrahedral $(NH_4)^{+1}$ ion carefully, we observe that the octet rule is satisfied for the nitrogen atom and that each of the four hydrogen atoms has a complete two-electron valence shell. In one case, however, the two-electron covalent bond between the nitrogen atom and a hydrogen atom has come about only because the nitrogen atom has contributed both electrons of the electron pair. A covalent bond in which one atom contributes both electrons of the bond is called a *coordinate covalent bond*.

While, theoretically, the mechanism of formation of a coordinate covalent bond is different from that of a simple covalent bond, the final bonds cannot be distinguished from each other. (Fig. 11.9.)

All acid radical *negative* ions will have Lewis structures involving coordinate covalent bonds. In deriving such Lewis structures,

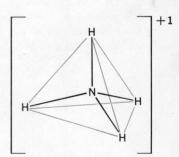

**FIGURE 11.9** The structure of the ammonium ion. Which bond is the coordinate covalent bond? Explain.

you must not forget that extra electrons are present that account for the negative charge. We may consider the sulfate ion, $(SO_4)^{-2}$, as an example.

The electron configuration for sulfur is:

$$_{16}S \quad 1s^2 2s^2 2p^6 3s^2 3p^4 \quad \text{or} \quad \boxed{\uparrow\downarrow}\boxed{\uparrow\downarrow}\boxed{\uparrow\downarrow}\;\boxed{\uparrow\downarrow}\;\boxed{\uparrow\downarrow}\boxed{\uparrow\downarrow}\boxed{\uparrow}\;\boxed{\uparrow} \quad \text{or} \quad {}^{\times}_{\times}\overset{\times}{\underset{\times}{S}}{}^{\times}$$
$$\phantom{xxxxxxxxxx} 1s\;2s\;2p\;2p\;2p\;3s\;3p\;3p\;3p$$

In the $(SO_4)^{-2}$ *radical*, a central sulfur atom, lacking two electrons for a complete valence shell, is tetrahedrally surrounded by four oxygen atoms, each of which also requires two more electrons for a complete valence shell. With two additional electrons present in the $(SO_4)^{-2}$ ion, a number of "different" Lewis structures may be derived involving coordinate covalent bonding. Three examples follow, in which the two additional electrons that impart the $-2$ charge are indicated by minus signs:

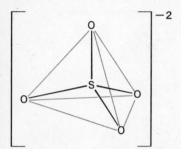

**FIGURE 11.10** The structure of the sulfate ion. Can the coordinate covalent bonds be distinguished?

Again, though symbolically the three Lewis structures for the $(SO_4)^{-2}$ ion *look* different, the bonds in the ion are experimentally identical to each other. (Fig. 11.10.)

**EXERCISE**

Write Lewis structures and give predicted shapes for the following ions in which coordinate covalent bonds will be required.

1. $(PH_4)^{+1}$     3. $(ClO_4)^{-1}$
2. $(SO_3)^{-2}$     4. $(NO_3)^{-1}$

## 11.15 The nature of the covalent bond

To state that a covalent bond is formed by two atoms sharing an electron pair does not tell us why atoms would share electrons. It is necessary to delve deeper into the nature of covalent bonds in order to learn why they are formed and why, once formed, they hold atoms together in molecules.

For purposes of discussing the nature of the covalent bond, let us consider two hydrogen atoms colliding and forming a covalent molecule of $H_2$. Each hydrogen atom consists of a one-proton nucleus and a single $1s$ orbital electron. To minimize confusion, we shall speak of nucleus $A$ and electron $A$ of one atom and of nucleus $B$ and electron $B$ of the other atom. As the two atoms approach each other, in addition to the coulombic attractive force between each nucleus and its own electron, new coulombic attractive forces begin operating between nucleus $A$ and electron $B$ and between nucleus $B$ and electron $A$. Furthermore, coulombic repulsive forces are also experienced between the two electrons and between the two nuclei. (Fig. 11.11.) Let us follow the course of formation of a hydrogen molecule in terms of the energy involved.

Two separated hydrogen atoms possess electrical potential energy. As the two atoms approach each other, they begin to feel the effects of coulombic attraction. There is a conversion of electrical potential energy into kinetic energy. As the distance between the atoms decreases, the conversion is more rapid. An inter-nuclear distance is finally reached, at which the potential energy of the two-atom system reaches a minimum. At this distance, as attractive forces have become balanced by repulsive forces, the stable diatomic molecule has formed. Should the inter-nuclear distance become smaller, the repulsive forces would predominate. (Fig. 11.12.)

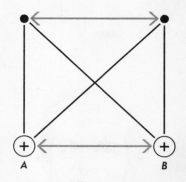

**FIGURE 11.11** The coulombic forces of attraction and repulsion between two one-electron atoms

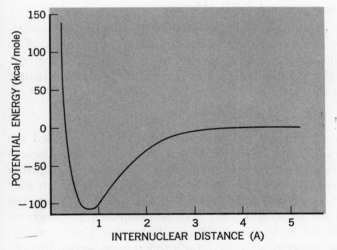

**FIGURE 11.12** The electrical potential energy between two hydrogen atoms. To what does the distance 0.74 A correspond?

Let us now summarize our picture of a covalent bond between any two nuclei. The charges of the two nuclei and their orbital electrons create both attractive and repulsive forces. At a certain distance between the nuclei, these forces are balanced exactly, and a stable molecule results. In this stable molecule, each nucleus exerts an attractive force on its own bonding electron as well as on the bonding electron of the other atom. Consequently, the two electrons of the covalent bond are shared by the two atoms. When this process is treated mathematically by means of quantum mechanics, we find that there is a very high probability for finding the pair of electrons of the bond between the two atoms. The higher the probability of finding the electrons between the two atoms rather than elsewhere, the stronger is the bond (i.e., the greater is the energy required to break it).

So, the force of attraction in a covalent bond is still *electrostatic*—the two positive nuclei are held together by the high concentration of negative charge between them. The greater the concentration of this negative charge (the higher the probability), the stronger the bonding.

## INTERMEDIATE CHEMICAL BONDS

Chemists have long recognized that there are very few compounds whose bonding characteristics can be treated simply in terms of pure ionic bonding or pure covalent bonding. For the most part, compounds show experimental behavior that is best explained by the presence of chemical bonds having partial ionic and partial covalent character. How can the chemist describe such behavior?

### 11.16 Electronegativity and chemical bonds

We recall that it is experimentally possible to measure the ionization energies required to remove electrons from gaseous atoms. With much more difficulty, it is also possible to measure the energy released when a gaseous atom accepts an electron to become a negative ion. That is, for the reaction

$$F(g) + e^-(g) \rightarrow F^{-1}(g),$$

energy is released and can be measured. That energy is called the *electron affinity* of fluorine atom. Ionization energies and electron affinities are measures of the electron-holding or -attracting properties of atoms, but only for the very special conditions under which they are measured. To study the characteristics of a chemical bond between atoms, the chemist must have some way of comparing the electron-attracting powers of atoms already chemically bonded. Unfortunately, it is not possible as yet to measure those properties of atoms directly. Consequently, chemists have developed an indirect means for comparing the electron-attracting powers of atoms *in chemical bonds.*

Under the strong influence of the American chemist Linus Pauling, an important calculated property of atoms has been derived. This calculated property is called the *electronegativity* of an atom. The electronegativity of an atom is a *relative measure of the electron-attracting power of an atom when it is in a chemical bond.* It might be pointed out that different chemists calculate electronegativities of atoms in different ways, so that different electronegativity scales are in existence. The arbitrary electronegativity values of Pauling are

**Linus Carl Pauling** (1901– American). Awarded his doctorate from the California Institute of Technology in 1925, he has continued there to investigate the arrangement of atoms in crystals and the interatomic forces that bind these atoms together. This work led to an understanding of the structure of proteins, for which Dr. Pauling was awarded the 1954 Nobel Prize in Chemistry. He has made significant contributions to the quantum mechanical theory of chemical bonding and is particularly renowned for his concept of electronegativity. Dr. Pauling's persistent effort in the movement to ban nuclear weapons and to end nuclear weapons testing led to his becoming the first American to win a second Nobel prize—the 1962 Nobel Peace Prize.

listed in Table 11–2. Metals such as sodium and calcium have low values of the electronegativity, whereas nonmetals such as oxygen and chlorine have large values. The electronegativity value of 4.0 for fluorine is the highest of any element, indicating that the strongest electron-attracting atom *in compounds* is fluorine.

**TABLE 11–2**   TABLE OF ELECTRONEGATIVITIES OF SOME ELEMENTS (ON THE ARBITRARY PAULING SCALE)

| H | | | | | | |
|------|------|------|------|------|------|------|
| 2.1 | | | | | | |
| Li | Be | B | C | N | O | F |
| 1.0 | 1.5 | 2.0 | 2.5 | 3.0 | 3.5 | 4.0 |
| Na | Mg | Al | Si | P | S | Cl |
| 0.9 | 1.2 | 1.5 | 1.8 | 2.1 | 2.5 | 3.0 |
| K | Ca | Ga | Ge | As | Se | Br |
| 0.8 | 1.0 | 1.6 | 1.7 | 2.0 | 2.4 | 2.8 |
| Rb | Sr | | | | | I |
| 0.8 | 1.0 | | | | | 2.4 |
| Cs | Ba | | | | | |
| 0.7 | 0.9 | | | | | |

## 11.17 Usefulness of electronegativity

The larger the difference in electronegativity between two atoms, the more likely will electrons be transferred from one to the other. From Table 11–2, cesium, Cs, and fluorine, F, have the greatest difference in electronegativity:

$$4.0 - 0.7 = 3.3$$
$$\text{F} \qquad \text{Cs}$$

Cesium fluoride, CsF, as expected, is essentially a purely ionic compound. When we compare sodium, Na, and chlorine, Cl, the difference in their electronegativities is rather large:

$$3.0 - 0.9 = 2.1$$
$$\text{Cl} \qquad \text{Na}$$

As might be anticipated from this, sodium loses its electron to chlorine to form ionic sodium chloride, NaCl. The bonds in NaCl, though, are not as purely ionic as those in CsF.

Phosphorus and hydrogen react to form phosphorus trihydride, $PH_3$. Since phosphorus and hydrogen have the same electronegativity value, namely 2.1, neither can take electrons from the other. The expected result of pure covalent bond formation in $PH_3$ is confirmed experimentally. What are the experimental observations chemists seek out?

Ionic compounds have high melting points and usually very high boiling points. They normally dissolve in water but not in such solvents as benzene or ether. An electric current easily passes through solutions of ionic compounds.

Covalent compounds, on the other hand, have lower melting and boiling points. They frequently are more soluble in benzene or ether than in water. Nonaqueous solutions of covalent compounds do not conduct electric currents.

From electronegativity differences between atoms in a compound, it is possible to predict with a fair degree of certainty whether a compound is essentially ionic or essentially covalent. Once we have predicted this, it is then possible to make good guesses at some of the properties of the compound. For example, the electronegativity difference between Ca and Cl is 2.0. This would lead us to expect $CaCl_2$ to be an ionic compound and consequently to have a high melting point. The melting point is 772°C. It should dissolve in water, and, indeed, its solubility is high. About 100 g of the solid dissolves per 100 ml of water. This solution should conduct an electric current, and it does.

Carbon and chlorine have an electronegativity difference of only 0.5, so $CCl_4$ should exhibit the properties of a covalent compound. As expected, $CCl_4$ has a low melting point ($-22.8$°C), very low solubility in water (0.08 g per 100 ml $H_2O$), but is completely soluble in benzene. The benzene solution does not conduct electric current.

## 11.18 Electronegativity and inorganic nomenclature

At the end of Chapter 5, the question was raised as to why the formulas of binary compounds between nonmetals were written as they appear. Why do we write $S_4N_4$ rather than $N_4S_4$, or ICl rather than ClI? Since the advent of the concept of electronegativity, chemists have agreed to write the formulas for, and name binary compounds of, nonmetals as though the compounds were derivatives of the more electronegative nonmetal atom. Thus, in addition to $S_4N_4$ and ICl as examples of this convention, we have $OF_2$, oxygen difluoride, but also $Cl_2O$, dichlorine monoxide. Since electronegativity is a relatively modern concept, historical usage still prevails in the formulas and names of a number of binary compounds that predate the concept and the convention based on it. The most notable example of an exception to that convention is $NH_3$, ammonia, instead of $H_3N$, trihydrogen nitride.

## 11.19 Intermediate bonds and per cent ionic character

Let us now consider the compound formed by the union of hydrogen and chlorine—i.e., hydrogen chloride. Hydrogen has an electronegativity value of 2.1, and chlorine of 3.0. The difference of 0.9 is much less than that between sodium and chlorine in an essentially ionic bond but more than that between phosphorus and hydrogen in an essentially covalent bond. This could suggest to us that although there is a difference in the relative attraction for electrons between hydrogen and chlorine, it is not great enough for chlorine to take the electron completely away from hydrogen. The result might be *intermediate bonding—a compromise between ionic and covalent bonding. Electrons are still shared between the two atoms but not equally.* Although the chlorine atom in hydrogen chloride is not a true anion, it is more negative than the hydrogen due to this unequal sharing.

The three cases we have discussed may be represented in this fashion:

$$\underset{\textit{Ionic}}{Na^{+1} \, Cl^{-1}} \qquad \underset{\textit{Intermediate}}{\overset{\delta+ \quad \delta-}{H-Cl}} \qquad \underset{\textit{Covalent}}{\overset{\textstyle H}{\underset{}{\overset{|}{H-P-H}}}}$$

where, as before (Chapter 6, p. 163), the $\delta^+$ indicates that the hydrogen atom in a hydrogen chloride molecule is *not* a positive ion but, relatively speaking, is less negative, therefore more positive, than the chlorine atom. The $\delta^+$ is read as "partially positive." Similarly, the $\delta^-$ indicates that, relatively speaking, the chlorine atom is more negative than the hydrogen atom. The $\delta^-$ is read as "partially negative."

Unless the atoms in a covalent chemical bond have the same electronegativity value, as in $Cl_2$ or $PH_3$, there is an unequal sharing of electrons, and the bond cannot be purely covalent. The degree of inequality in the electron sharing increases as the difference in electronegativities increases. Chemists indicate the amount of deviation from the equal sharing in a true covalent bond by referring to the *per cent ionic character* of the covalent bond. The per cent ionic character of an intermediate bond can be calculated. In Table 11–3, the per cent ionic character of the bonds in the hydrogen halides is listed.

**TABLE 11–3** THE PER CENT IONIC CHARACTER AND RELATIVE POLARITY OF THE HYDROGEN HALIDES

| Gaseous Molecule | Electronegativity Difference | Per Cent Ionic Character | Dipole Moment (in Debye* units) |
|---|---|---|---|
| HF | 1.9 | 60 | 1.91 |
| HCl | 0.9 | 19 | 1.03 |
| HBr | 0.7 | 11 | 0.80 |
| HI | 0.3 | 4 | 0.42 |

---

* Debye units were named in honor of P. J. W. Debye (1884–   ), whose brilliant investigations into the electrical polarity of molecules led to the development of the dipole theory. For related investigations into molecular structure, he was awarded the 1936 Nobel Prize in Chemistry.

### 11.20 The meaning and importance of dipoles

In Chapter 6, when the subject of molecular and ionic crystals was introduced, it was pointed out that molecules such as water are electrically neutral but may be *dipoles*—that is, *they may have an unequal distribution charge within them*. Such molecules are said to be *polar*. Now we can see that this unequal distribution of charge can arise from the unequal sharing of electrons in *intermediate* bonds. Covalent bonds, themselves, may be *polar*.

The *dipole moment* of a molecule is *the experimental measure of the net unequal distribution of charge in such a molecule*. If our explanation of the origin of the dipole nature of molecules is correct, then the dipole moment of the molecules in a related series of *diatomic* molecules should increase as the difference in electronegativities between the atoms increases. From Table 11–3 we can see that this is indeed the case for the hydrogen halides.

In the case of a polyatomic molecule, bond polarity alone may not account qualitatively for the net polarity of the molecule. The spatial orientation of the bonds within the molecule must also be considered. In the next chapter we shall see how important this is in the case of water. Finally, the presence and orientation of nonbonded valence electrons will have an effect on the net polarity of a molecule. For example, though each P—H bond in $PH_3$ is nonpolar, since the electronegativities of P and H are the same, the presence of one pair of nonbonded valence electrons on the phosphorus atom leads to a small dipole moment for the molecule as a whole. (Fig. 11.13.)

You may have been wondering why you should be bothered with what seems like rather abstract and minor details—as, for example, the fact that most chemical compounds have bonds that are neither completely covalent nor completely ionic. The answer is that it is often these "minor and abstract" details which, in fact, make our physical universe what it is. If chemical bonds were only completely ionic or completely covalent, molecules would not form dipoles. Without their dipolar nature, many compounds would not exist in the liquid and solid states except under extreme conditions such as required for the noble gases.

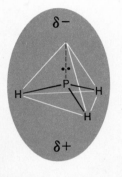

**FIGURE 11.13** $PH_3$ has a small dipole moment, which is due to the unbonded electron pair.

## SUMMARY

Electrovalent, or ionic, bonds form when a metallic atom loses an electron to a nonmetallic atom. Oppositely charged ions form, which are held together by electrostatic attraction. The ions usually have filled electron shell configurations. The ionization energies needed for the removal of electrons from gaseous atoms or ions correlate well with the theory that filled electron shell configurations are extremely stable ones. Variations of ionization energies of the elements in a period or in a group can be understood in terms of nuclear charge and electron orbital energy variations.

When nonmetals react, covalent bonds are formed through the mutual sharing of electrons. The "electron dot" representation, or Lewis structure, of covalently bonded molecules is widely used and should be well understood. The model of covalent bonding is modified to include orbital hybridization in order to explain the bonding properties of carbon.

The geometry of covalent compounds may be deduced from the consideration that the bonding electron pairs will tend to be as far apart from each other as possible.

The atoms in molecular compounds may be held together by single, double, or triple covalent bonds, or a combination of these. Coordinate covalent bonds represent a shared electron pair, both members of which are donated by one atom.

Both pure ionic and pure covalent bonding are rare. Most chemical bonds have properties lying between these extremes. The concept of electronegativity is useful in attempting to understand how intermediate bond types arise and lead to various molecular properties.

## QUESTIONS AND PROBLEMS

11.1  For the reaction between lithium metal and fluorine gas: **a.** write the chemical equation; **b.** give the electron configurations of all species; **c.** describe some of the properties of the product and explain them in terms of the chemical bonds present.

11.2  **a.** Give electron configurations for each of the following *ions:* $H^{-1}$, $Ca^{+2}$, $N^{-3}$, $Sc^{+3}$, $Se^{-2}$, $Fe^{+2}$, $Fe^{+3}$, $Cu^{+1}$, $Cu^{+2}$, $Zn^{+2}$.
**b.** What basic difference is there in the electron configurations of the first five ions and those of the last five?

11.3  **a.** Define the second ionization energy for an element $M$.
**b.** Using data from Table 11–1, plot the second ionization energies of the elements Li–Ca as a function of atomic number. Compare your graph with Figure 11.1.

11.4  Describe and explain how ionization energies vary within a period and within a group of elements.

11.5  **a.** Using Table 11–1, explain why aluminum forms a +3 ion.
**b.** Explain the increases from $(I.E.)_1$ to $(I.E.)_2$ to $(I.E.)_3$ to $(I.E.)_4$ for aluminum.

**11.6**  Describe and analyze the nature of the covalent bond in diatomic hydrogen molecules.

**11.7**  Identify each bond in each of the following as to its type:

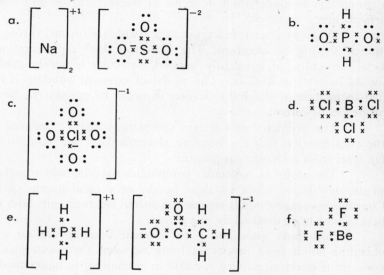

**11.8**  For *each specie* in Problem 11.7 that contains covalent bonds, redraw the specie to show the correct spatial orientations of the bonds. Use a single dash to represent each covalent bond.

**11.9**  Write Lewis structures and give predicted shapes for the following. The central atom in polyatomic species appears in boldface.

a. HI
b. HCCH
c. $H_2\textbf{Se}$
d. $(O\textbf{Cl})^{-1}$

e. O**Cl**(OH)
f. Br**Cl**
g. $(\textbf{P}Cl_4)^{+1}$
h. O**P**(OH)$_3$

i. $O_2\textbf{N}(OH)$
j. HC**O**(OH)
k. C**O**
l. $(O\textbf{N}O)^{-1}$

**11.10**  Give the electron configuration of carbon in methane, $CH_4$.

**11.11**  a. Write the Lewis structure and give the predicted shape for the $NH_3$ molecule. b. What factors lead to the inherently high polarity of the molecule?

**11.12**  Using Table 11–2, what properties would you expect the following to have: a. $Rb_2O$; b. $Cl_2O$; c. $Cs_4C$; d. $H_4C$?

**11.13**  Using Table 11–2, arrange the following molecules in order of *decreasing* ionic character: $PH_3$, $NH_3$, $AlBr_3$, $RbCl$, $CaS$, $MgO$, $GaSe$, $KCl$, $NaI$, $ICl$.

**11.14**  What are each of the following a measure of: a. first ionization energy; b. electronegativity; c. dipole moment?

## SUGGESTED READINGS

Barrow, G. M. *The Structure of Molecules* (paperback). W. A. Benjamin, 1963.

Debye, P. *Polar Molecules* (paperback). Dover, 1945.

Ryschkewitsch, G. E. *Chemical Bonding and the Geometry of Molecules* (paperback). Reinhold, 1963.

CHEMISTRY

King, L. C., "Molecular Architecture." Feb. 1964

*Water is the mother of the vine,*
*The nurse and fountain of fecundity,*
*The adorner and refresher of the world.*

*Charles Mackay (1814–1889)*

**CHAPTER 12** | # Water

In earlier chapters, the properties of hydrogen and oxygen were studied. We now turn to consider the properties of their principal compound, water. Water is such a common substance in our lives that we are apt to take it for granted as just another chemical. Water is everywhere. It covers some three quarters of the surface of the earth. Its vapor permeates the atmosphere. Water is the "universal solvent" to such an extent that we tend to consider nonaqueous solvents as unusual. There is much experimental evidence that life began in an aqueous medium, and present-day living cells consist largely of water.

## THE MOLECULAR STRUCTURE OF WATER AND ICE

Water is a very exciting example of the complexity and the simplicity of nature. For water is far more complex in its behavior than would seem probable from its simple molecular formula. Yet at the same time it is that simple formula which provides the key to understanding the complex behavior of water and aqueous solutions.

### 12.1 The dipole nature of water

Recalling the electron configuration of hydrogen,

$$_1\text{H} \quad 1s^1 \quad \text{or} \quad \underset{1s}{\uparrow} \quad \text{or} \quad {}^\times\text{H} \,,$$

and of oxygen,

$$_8\text{O} \quad 1s^2 2s^2 2p^4 \quad \text{or} \quad \boxed{\uparrow\downarrow}\boxed{\uparrow\downarrow}\boxed{\uparrow\downarrow}\boxed{\uparrow}\boxed{\uparrow} \atop 1s \;\; 2s \;\; 2p \;\; 2p \;\; 2p \quad \text{or} \quad :\!\overset{\cdot\cdot}{\text{O}}\!\cdot \;,$$

water has, as we have seen before, the simple Lewis structure:

$$\ddot{\ddot{O}}_{\times}^{\cdot\cdot}H \quad \text{or} \quad O{-}H$$
$$H \qquad\qquad H$$

As before, also, the four electron sites around the oxygen atom being tetrahedrally oriented, water, itself, must be a bent molecule:

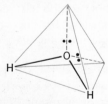

The experimentally determined bond angle of 105° in water is less than the expected tetrahedral angle of 109°. It can be calculated that the repulsive interaction of the *lone pairs* of electrons on the *bonded pairs* of electrons will account for the small closing of the bond angle. (Fig. 12.1.)

There are a number of experimental techniques available to verify the bent molecular structure of water. One of the simpler and more conclusive techniques involves determination of the polarity of the water molecule. According to the electronegativity data given in Chapter 11, hydrogen has a value of 2.1 and oxygen a value of 3.5.

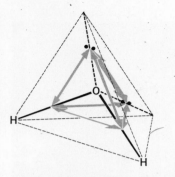

FIGURE 12.1    Lone-pair–bond-pair electron interaction: a model for water

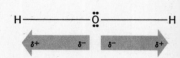

FIGURE 12.2    A linear water molecule: an experimentally invalid model

It would seem possible to predict, therefore, that any covalent bond between hydrogen and oxygen should have a fair degree of ionic character. Thus, we would expect the bonds to be polar. If the hydrogen atoms were exactly opposite each other on the oxygen atom so that the angle between the two oxygen-hydrogen bonds was exactly 180°, the polarity of the bonds would be equal but in opposed directions. The net effect would be a canceling of the polarities and, consequently, the water molecule as a whole would have no dipole nature. (Fig. 12.2.)

However, dipole moment experiments show that the water molecule does have a dipole nature. So we must conclude that the angle between the bonds must be different from 180° in order that the polarities of these bonds not completely cancel each other. From the measured degree of dipolarity for the water molecule, it can be calculated that the bond angle must be 105°.

## 12.2  Relation of $H_2O$ to $H_2S$, $H_2Se$ and $H_2Te$

In Chapter 7 it was pointed out that the periodic table is of great help in correlating the properties of different compounds. The properties of a compound should be related in a regular fashion to those of similar compounds of the other elements in the same chemical group. Thus, we should expect the properties of oxygen compounds to be related to the properties of similar compounds of sulfur, selenium, and tellurium. If this relationship does not emerge, then it becomes necessary to search for a reason for the discrepancy. Let us consider $H_2O$, $H_2S$, $H_2Se$, and $H_2Te$ to discover any pattern in their properties. The boiling points of these compounds are plotted in Figure 12.3.

The boiling points rise steadily from $H_2S$ to $H_2Te$. This means that the force of attraction that holds the molecules in the liquid state must also increase from $H_2S$ to $H_2Te$. From the relative electronega-

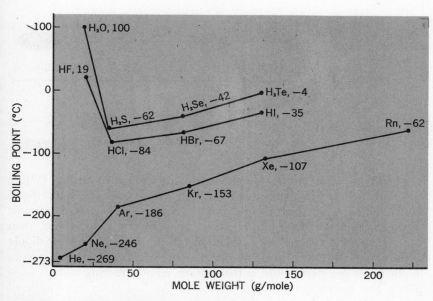

**FIGURE 12.3**   Some boiling point relationships

tivities, $H = 2.1$, $S = 2.5$, $Se = 2.4$, $Te = 2.11$, we expect the dipole moments to *decrease* from $H_2S$ to $H_2Te$, so the increased force of intermolecular attraction must *not* be due to the normal dipole character of the molecules. Furthermore, as can also be seen in Figure 12.3, an increase in boiling point with increasing molecular weight is a general trend and is even found in nonpolar substances such as the noble gases.

## 12.3  Van der Waals forces and boiling points

From both the experimental and theoretical viewpoint, any intermolecular forces to help account for the observed increase in boiling point with increasing molecular weight must be strong enough to hold molecules together in the liquid state but far too weak to lead to chemical bonding. Modern bonding theory has led to an appropriate kind of intermolecular force that well meets the restrictions noted. It is called the van der Waals force, named in honor of the Dutch physicist J. D. van der Waals (VAHN der wall), whose late-nineteenth-century studies of the properties of real gases led to an understanding of the existence of such a force.

Van der Waals forces are the result of the mutual interaction of the electrons and nuclei of electrically neutral atoms or molecules that are extremely close together. In all matter, nuclei and electrons are not at rest but are in ceaseless motion. In any given instant of time, this motion will produce a slight *imbalance* in the normal distribution

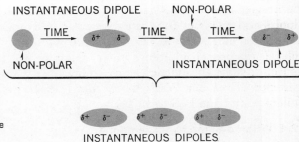

FIGURE 12.4 Instantaneous dipole—instantaneous dipole
attraction: a model for van der Waals forces

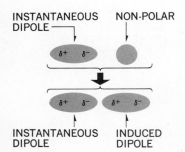

FIGURE 12.5 Instantaneous dipole—induced dipole attraction: a model for van der
Waals forces

of charge of an electrically neutral atomic or molecular species. Where
the normal distribution of charge is such that the species is normally
nonpolar, as is the case of the noble gas atoms, then *instantaneous
dipoles* will arise. Two neighboring instantaneous dipoles will then
experience what can be called instantaneous dipole-instantaneous dipole
attraction. (Fig. 12.4.) It may also be that an instantaneous dipole occurs
in one noble gas atom while, at that instant, its neighboring atom is nonpolar. The instantaneous dipole nature of the first atom can "induce"
(that is, cause to appear) a dipole in the second atom. The two atoms
will then experience what can be called an instantaneous dipole-induced
dipole attraction. (Fig. 12.5.) No matter what the initial source of the
weak momentary dipoles is, as the electrons in the first atom oscillate
to the other side of the atom, the electrons in the second atom will
follow suit. If the atoms are close enough and their kinetic energies are
low, they will remain attracted by the repetition of the *temporary
dipoles*. Such, we think, is the nature of van der Waals forces between
noble gas atoms, which are normally nonpolar.

In the case of molecules that exist naturally as dipoles, van der
Waals forces enhance the permanent dipole-dipole attractive forces that
normally exist between the molecules. (Fig. 12.6.) As the atomic number

FIGURE 12.6 Enhanced dipole—dipole attraction:
a model for van der Waals forces

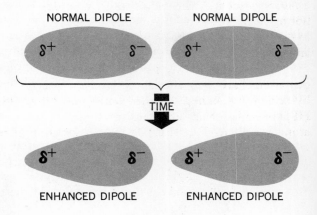

of the atoms in molecules increases, there are more electrons present in the heavier molecules. As a result, the strength of the van der Waals dipoles also increases for these molecules. This increase in strength of the dipoles increases the van der Waals attraction between the molecules. It requires an additional input of energy, therefore, to give heavy molecules sufficient kinetic energy to break away from each other. The existence of van der Waals forces thus helps to explain the increase in boiling point from $H_2S$ to $H_2Te$.

## 12.4 Water and the hydrogen bond

From the upward trend in the boiling points of $H_2S$, $H_2Se$, and $H_2Te$, the boiling point for $H_2O$ might be expected to be about $-70°C$ rather than the $+100°C$ that it actually is. This is a very large difference, indicating the presence of some important attractive force not present in $H_2S$, $H_2Se$, or $H_2Te$. The boiling points for the hydrogen halides are also shown in Figure 12.3. Again the expected increase in boiling point due to increasing van der Waals attraction is observable from HCl to HI. However, like $H_2O$, HF has a much higher boiling point than anticipated.

The anomalous behavior of water and hydrogen fluoride can be explained by a special type of bonding that is a part of modern bonding theory. Under certain conditions, a hydrogen atom that is *covalently* bound to a *highly electronegative* atom in one molecule will be strongly attracted to a similar atom of a neighboring molecule. The neighboring molecules, therefore, will be *more* strongly attracted to each other through the electrical influence of the hydrogen atom. The nature of this attraction is strong enough for chemists to speak of the formation of a *hydrogen bond* between the molecules.

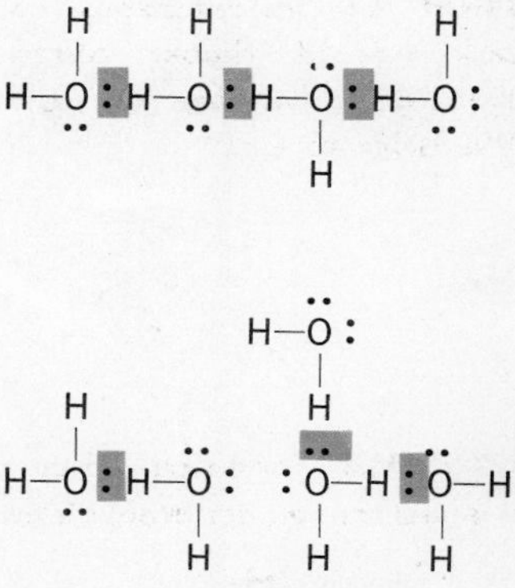

Hydrogen bonding is exhibited only with the most electronegative atoms—N, O, F. Presumably, these atoms are so electronegative that the hydrogen atom has only a very small share of the electron pair of the covalent bond. In such a case, the hydrogen will resemble a *bare proton* and, hence, will exert considerable attraction on neighboring negative atoms. It is important to note that the small size of the hydrogen atom prohibits crowding more than two atoms around it in any bonding situation.

In water, one oxygen atom is covalently bonded to two hydrogen atoms (protons) and, also, may have one or two hydrogen bonds by which it is linked to other water molecules. (Fig. 12.7.) In liquid HF, molecular chains of HF exist with hydrogen atoms linking fluorine atoms together. (Fig. 12.8.) It is the association of molecules of water

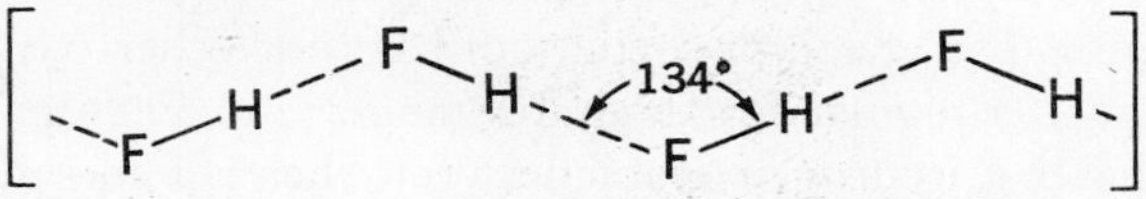

**FIGURE 12.7** Hydrogen bonding between water molecules: a model to explain anomalies

**FIGURE 12.8** A model of hydrogen bonding in liquid hydrogen fluoride

and hydrogen fluoride into clusters of large "super" molecules via hydrogen bonding that explains the anomalous boiling points of those compounds. Since fluorine is the most electronegative of the elements, hydrogen bonding in HF is particularly strong. It is so strong that when liquid HF vaporizes, such species as $H_2F_2$, $H_4F_4$, and even $H_6F_6$ exist at moderate temperatures. Water, on the other hand, vaporizes as a monomolecular species.

What may seem a minor aspect of chemistry is often in reality of greatest importance. If hydrogen bonding did not exist, water would be a gas at ordinary temperatures and there would be no animal or vegetable life as we know it. The structure and properties of proteins and nucleic acids—essential molecules of living matter—depend on hydrogen bonding. We shall consider this further in Chapter 31. Truly, then, we are held together by hydrogen bonding.

## 12.5  The structure of ice

By measuring the angles with which a beam of X rays is deflected by ice crystals, scientists have been able to ascertain the structure of ice.

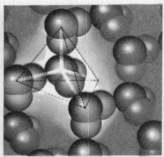

**FIGURE 12.9** The structure of ice and the theoretical role of the hydrogen bond

The X-ray diffraction pattern from a single ice crystal

In ice, the two hydrogen atoms of a water molecule form hydrogen bonds with oxygen atoms of two other water molecules. The result is a network of O—H—O bonds extending in all three directions as shown in Figure 12.9. Each oxygen atom has four other oxygen atoms surrounding it in a regular tetrahedral arrangement. Each pair of oxygen atoms shares a hydrogen atom between them. The result of this bonding is that ice has an open, porous structure. As a result of hydrogen bonding, small holes are present throughout the structure of ice, which leads to ice having a relatively low density. If the hydrogen bonds were weaker and did not impose such an open structure, ice might well be denser than water. Were such the case, ice would have sunk as it formed on the oceans during the past history of the earth. Below the oceans' waters, ice would have been insulated from warming conditions. The eventual result would have been a gradual decrease in the temperature of the oceans and a frozen world.

## 12.6 A model of liquid water

As you know, pure water is an odorless, tasteless liquid that is colorless except in thick layers, when it appears blue. We see from Table 12–1 that liquid water is slightly more dense than ice and that its density is greatest at 4°C. From these data and many other types of measurements of the properties of water, it has been possible to postulate a model for the structure of liquid water.

**TABLE 12–1**    THE DENSITY OF ICE AND LIQUID WATER

| State | Temperature | Density (g/ml) |
|---|---|---|
| Ice | 0°C | 0.917 |
| Liquid | 0°C | 0.9998 |
| Liquid | 4°C | 1.0000 |
| Liquid | 10°C | 0.9997 |
| Liquid | 25°C | 0.9971 |
| Liquid | 100°C | 0.9584 |

FIGURE 12.10 Ice to water: a collapsing structure

FIGURE 12.11 Water as an expanding liquid

When ice melts, some hydrogen bonds are broken, enough to cause a partial collapse of the open ice structure. Unlike a crystal of ice, which is essentially one giant hydrogen-bonded molecule, the liquid consists of smaller icelike groups of water molecules as well as single molecules. Some of the larger icelike groups of molecules may contain several hundred hydrogen-bonded individual water molecules.

As a result of the partial collapse of the open ice structure, the molecules in the liquid state can pack in somewhat closer than in ice, and the density of the liquid is greater. (Fig. 12.10.) However, as the temperature is raised, more hydrogen bonds break, and the icelike groups in the liquid break down further. At the same time, small groups and single molecules increase in kinetic energy. The increased molecular motion causes the liquid to expand. (Fig. 12.11.)

Between 0°C and 4°C, the collapsing of the rigid ice structure is the more important effect, and the density of water increases between those temperatures. Above 4°C, the increased molecular motion effect

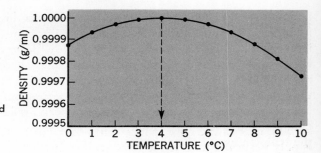

**FIGURE 12.12** The density of water between 0°C and 10°C

predominates and the liquid continues to expand in volume, thereby decreasing in density. At 4°C, where neither effect predominates, water exhibits its maximum density of 1.0000 g/ml. (Fig. 12.12.)

## PROPERTIES OF WATER

Since water is such a common substance, its physical and chemical properties have been studied in great detail. To catalog these properties would require a volume at least equal in size to this one. We will end our specific study of the substance water, therefore, with the consideration of a few of its properties and uses. As you continue to read on in this book, however, you will note how frequently water appears as a solvent, a chemical reactant, or a product. As you live each day, you should become aware of the countless ways water serves man in every facet of complex modern society.

### 12.7 Water has a high specific heat

We learned in Chapter 6 that all substances have a measurable *heat capacity*. We defined the *molar* heat capacity as the amount of heat energy required to raise the temperature of one mole of a substance by 1°C. When the molar heat capacities of different substances are compared (see Table 6–3, page 157), the value of 17.996 cal/mole-deg for liquid water does not seem very high, relative, for example, to the value of 6.65 cal/mole-deg for liquid mercury. In comparison with benzene ($C_p = 32.0$ cal/mole-deg), the molar heat capacity of water might even seem to have a low, or at least a medium, value. The comparisons just made involved the same number of molecules (atoms in the case of mercury) of each of the three substances water, mercury, and benzene—an Avogadro number. If, on the other hand, we compare the heat absorption properties of the same three substances on a weight basis, then water is found to have the highest heat capacity.

The heat absorption properties of substances on a weight basis are measured in terms of the *specific heat* of those substances. The specific heat (sp. ht.) is defined as the amount of heat energy required to raise the temperature of 1.00 g of a substance by 1°C. The relation-ship between specific heat and molar heat capacity is, simply:

Molar Heat Capacity = Specific Heat × Mole Weight

$$C_{p_{5,85}} = \text{sp.ht.} \times M$$

Since, as you recall, water is used to define the calorie, by definition the specific heat of water is 1.00 cal/g-deg at 15°C. By contrast, the specific heat of mercury is only 0.033 cal/g-deg, and that for benzene is only 0.41 cal/g-deg at the same temperature.

Gram for gram, then, it is found that liquid water has a higher heat absorption capacity than most other substances. This is consistent with our model for the structure of water. As heat energy is absorbed by liquid water, instead of most of that energy being converted into molecular kinetic energy (increasing temperature), it is converted into what we called "keeping apart" energy in Chapter 6. In other words, a large part of the heat energy is absorbed by the water molecules to overcome the van der Waals forces, the dipole-dipole forces, and, for water especially, the hydrogen-bonding forces that impose a relatively ordered structure to the liquid. This absorbed potential energy (no temperature increase) then keeps the separated molecules apart. (Re-read Section 6.18, page 155.)

The fact that on a gram-for-gram basis water absorbs more heat energy per degree than most other substances has led to its ex-tensive use as the coolant in automobile engines. For the same reason, we find it in wide use in hot water heating systems for homes.

## 12.8 Some chemical properties of water

Water is a *stable compound;* that is, it cannot be decomposed easily because of the stability of the covalent bond between the O and H atoms. It does not even begin to decompose thermally into hydrogen and oxygen until a temperature of 1000°C is reached. Even at 2500°C, only two per cent of water is decomposed. However, it can be decom-posed into $H_2$ and $O_2$ at room temperature by passing a direct electric current (D.C.) through it. (See Fig. 1.1, page 5.)

$$2H_2O(l) \overset{\text{D.C.}}{=\!=} 2H_2(g) + O_2(g)$$

At ordinary temperatures, water reacts violently with the more chemically *active metals,* such as sodium and potassium, to liberate hydrogen gas.

$$Na(s) + H_2O(l) = NaOH(aq) + \tfrac{1}{2}H_2(g)$$

At higher temperatures, less active metals, such as zinc, will react with steam to liberate $H_2$ gas. In such cases, the oxide of the metal is formed.

$$Zn(s) + H_2O(g) \overset{\Delta}{=\!=} ZnO(s) + H_2(g)$$

The oxygen of water may be chemically liberated by reaction with very active nonmetals. Fluorine gas will violently react with water to liberate $O_2$ gas.

$$F_2(g) + H_2O(l) = H_2F_2(aq) + \tfrac{1}{2}O_2(g)$$

Chlorine gas will react similarly, as would be expected from its periodic relationship to fluorine. That same relationship would lead us to expect that the reaction would not be as violent, and it is not. After the principles of electrochemistry are studied in Chapter 18, it will be possible for you to predict which elements and compounds when added to water should, in theory, lead to liberation of $H_2$ or $O_2$ from it.

### 12.9  The purification of water

The purest form of water in nature is rain water. However, even rain water is not pure water, for it is mixed with the gases of the atmosphere and with small amounts of dust and other impurities that it has washed out of the air.

Surface water that flows over the ground collects fine particles of undissolved solid material. Ground water that soaks into the earth carries almost no such load, since the soil acts as a filter and holds back the solid particles. But ground water is still not pure water no matter how clear and sparkling it may be, for it contains minerals that have been dissolved out of the soil.

Today water used for drinking purposes is put through one or more of the following processes of purification, depending upon the nature of the impurities it contains: 1. *Aeration*, which consists of spraying water into the air or letting it flow down a series of steps in thin sheets so that sunlight and oxygen may kill most bacteria present; 2. *Filtration*, which consists of straining water through a suitable sieve (filter), thus separating substances both in suspension and afloat (Sand filtration dates back to 1829, when London purified its drinking water by passing the water through beds of fine sand.); 3. Chemical purification, including *chlorination* (Chapter 7) and *ozonation* (Chapter 5), which consists of adding chemicals that kill harmful organisms in water; 4. *Coagulation*, which consists of adding alum or other chemicals that form jelly-like masses enmeshing the suspended fine matter in water; 5. *Demineralization*, which consists of passing water through tanks of synthetic resins in which *ion exchange* takes place (see page 562); 6. *Distillation*, which consists of the evaporation and subsequent condensation of water, leaving any dissolved solid impurities behind.

### 12.10  The desalinization program: water for tomorrow

It has been stated with accuracy that it is possible to "write the story of man's growth in terms of his epic concerns with water." Early civi-

The *Pont du Gard*, great Roman aqueduct at Nîmes, France, was built A.D. 14 and stands 155 feet high.

lizations sprang up along valleys fertilized by great rivers such as the Nile. Among the remaining monuments to the civilization of the Roman Empire are great aqueducts such as the *Pont du Gard* in southern France.

Today's technology requires ever more water—about 300 billion gallons a day in the United States alone, a seven-fold increase in sixty years. At present, more than 100 billion gallons of water are used daily for irrigation, and another 75 billion gallons for industry. About 15 tons of water are required to grow a bushel of corn, approximately 18 tons to produce a pound of beef. Twenty-five thousand gallons of water are used in the production of one ton of steel. Either directly or indirectly, water enters into the production of almost every natural and manufactured product.

With an ever growing demand for more and more water, it is easy to forecast severe future shortages in many areas of the world. Even today North Africa and coastal Australia are two areas in immediate proximity to unlimited sea water but severely impeded in their growth by a shortage of pure water.

In acknowledgment of the need for ever expanding water supplies, the United States and many other nations have initiated research into economical methods of obtaining fresh water from *saline* (sea or brackish) water. Water that is suitable for human consumption or irrigation must contain less than 1000 parts per million (ppm) of dissolved salts. Brackish water contains more than 1000 ppm but less than sea water, which contains about 35,000 ppm.

The production of drinking water from sea water is very old, dating back at least to the time of Aristotle, about 350 B.C. Today, ships of nearly all kinds obtain drinking water and water for use in boilers by

A desalinization plant: complex engineering to slake the thirst of man

Chambers for growing algae in heavy water: research for foods to satisfy man's hunger

distilling sea water under reduced pressure. While this process can be used to produce small amounts of water for special purposes, the cost of production is still too high to allow its use for purification of the billions of gallons daily that will be needed for agriculture and industry. And so today various processes for the desalinization of water, among them distillation, flash evaporation, controlled freezing, and demineralization by ion-exchange resins, are being tried, while research to uncover new processes goes on.

### 12.11 Heavy water

When water is formed from oxygen and either of the two heavier isotopes of light hydrogen, the molecular weight will be greater than 18, the molecular weight of ordinary water. Such water is called "heavy water." There being three hydrogen isotopes, $^1_1H$, $^2_1H(D)$, and $^3_1H(T)$, and three oxygen isotopes, $^{16}_8O$, $^{17}_8O$, and $^{18}_8O$, with which the chemist can conveniently work, a whole variety of heavy waters can be synthesized. Most commonly used and known as *heavy water*, however, is deuterium oxide, $D_2^{16}O$.

Deuterium oxide is present in ordinary water to the extent of about 1 part in 6000. It can be separated from ordinary water by electrolysis or distillation. As we saw in Table 9–2 (page 208), $D_2O$ has slightly higher melting and boiling points as well as a somewhat higher density than $H_2O$. The maximum density of liquid $D_2O$ occurs at 11.6°C, rather than at 4°C as for liquid $H_2O$. All this reflects the fact that the covalent bond between O and D is slightly more polar than between O and H, which leads to the observed enhanced intermolecular attractive forces. This greater polarity suggests that the D—O bond is slightly stronger than the H—O bond, a fact that is borne out by experiment.

$D_2O$ arrests the growth of seedlings, and it is toxic to animals. Heavy water is used mainly in nuclear reactors of the swimming pool type as a neutron moderator (page 688), and in modern scientific research.

### 12.12 Hydrogen peroxide: some properties and structure

In 1818, Louis Thenard (tay NAR), a French teacher of chemistry, discovered a compound that could be decomposed into equal volumes of oxygen and hydrogen. This compound is hydrogen peroxide, $H_2O_2$. Hydrogen peroxide is an oily liquid with a pale blue color, almost one and one half times as dense as water. It is odorless and is soluble in all proportions in water, alcohol, and ether. The high polarity of liquid $H_2O_2$, comparable to that of water, clearly precludes a simple linear arrangement of atoms in the molecule. Moreover, spectroscopic measurements indicate that, unlike $H_2O$, $H_2O_2$ is a nonplanar molecule. (Fig. 12.13.) Like water, $H_2O_2$ is extensively hydrogen bonded in the solid and liquid states which accounts for its high melting and boiling points of $-0.9°C$ and $151°C$, respectively.

**FIGURE 12.13** A model of a hydrogen peroxide molecule

### 12.13 Some uses of hydrogen peroxide

Hydrogen peroxide is valuable because it is unstable. It spontaneously decomposes into water and oxygen:

$$H_2O_2(l) = H_2O(l) + \tfrac{1}{2}O_2(g)$$

The rate of this reaction is rapidly increased by heat or light or, as we have seen previously, by a catalyst such as $MnO_2$.

Some colored compounds lose their color when they are oxidized. Fibers containing compounds that give them their color can be bleached by exposing them to oxygen. Hydrogen peroxide is used as an oxidizing agent to bleach, or decolorize, cotton goods, wool, wood pulp, some wood used for furniture, as well as silk, hair, feathers, glue, and other animal substances.

Some bacteria are killed when exposed to oxygen. Hydrogen peroxide is therefore used as a household antiseptic. The household product actually is mainly water with a small amount (usually 3 per cent) of hydrogen peroxide dissolved in it. It also contains some *inhibitor*, which retards the decomposition of the hydrogen peroxide.

### 12.14 The preparation of hydrogen peroxide

$H_2O_2$ may be prepared by treating barium peroxide with dilute sulfuric acid at a temperature below $15°C$:

$$H_2SO_4(aq) + BaO_2(s) = H_2O_2(aq) + BaSO_4(s)$$

Most of the hydrogen peroxide produced commercially is made by gently heating persulfuric acid, $H_2S_2O_8$, which reacts with water according to the equation:

$$H_2S_2O_8(l) + 2H_2O(l) = 2H_2SO_4(aq) + H_2O_2(aq)$$

In this process the hydrogen peroxide is distilled out under reduced pressure and decomposition losses can be held to as low as 5 per cent. Commercially, $H_2O_2$ is sold as *superoxol*, which is a 30 per cent $H_2O_2$ solution. A 90 per cent $H_2O_2$ solution is used as an oxidizer in rocket engine research. In these concentrated forms, $H_2O_2$ is a very dangerous material to handle.

## SUMMARY

Water is a simple, yet complex, substance, whose study has led to greater understanding of natural phenomena. By studying the boiling points of compounds related to water, greater insight into the nature of intermolecular attractive forces is obtained. The van der Waals force and especially the hydrogen bond are used to explain some of the unique properties of water. An open-structure model for ice and a molecular-cluster model for liquid water, both based on hydrogen bonding, seem to account well for the volume-temperature behavior of water in its condensed states—behavior that has permitted life to exist on earth.

Though chemically a relatively unreactive compound, water is almost a universal solvent. Processes for purifying water are, therefore, vital and in widespread use. The desalinization of sea water holds the promise of an unlimited future water supply.

The preparation and properties of, and some uses for, hydrogen peroxide were considered. The oxidizing properties of this compound were seen to make it a valuable one.

## QUESTIONS AND PROBLEMS

12.1   Give the Lewis structure for water. Describe a model to explain why the experimental shape of the water molecule differs from the predicted one.

12.2   Describe experimental evidences that the water molecule is not linear.

12.3   Why would $(H_2O)_x$ be an acceptable formula for water in its condensed states?

12.4   Describe three intermolecular attractive forces present in liquid water. To what extent are these forces present in ice? To what extent are they present in water vapor?

12.5   Describe a model for water in its condensed states that explains the change in volume of water as the temperature changes from $-1.0°C$ to $25.0°C$.

12.6   Describe on a molecular basis the changes that occur in a small pond as it freezes over.

12.7   Predict the boiling point of a compound $H_2X$, where $X$ is a newly found element of Group VI with atomic number 116.

12.8   Describe the heat absorption properties of water on the basis of its structure. To what practical use are those properties put?

12.9   Using Table 6–3, page 157, calculate the specific heats of: aluminum, graphite, sucrose, ethyl alcohol, and methane.
ANS.   graphite, 0.17 cal/g-deg; ethyl alcohol, 0.58 cal/g-deg

12.10  Write equations for the reaction of lithium metal and of calcium metal with water.

12.11  Write equations for the reaction of iron metal and of nickel metal with steam. $Fe_3O_4$ and $NiO$ are the solids that form.

12.12  Describe four methods for purifying water.

12.13  Determine and describe the methods for purifying water that are used in your community.

12.14  What makes desalinization different from ordinary water purification methods? Of what importance is desalinization?

12.15  Describe experimental evidence for greater polarity of the D-O bond than of the H-O bond.

12.16  In what ways are hydrogen peroxide and water structurally similar? In what ways are they structurally different?

12.17  Write equations for the preparation and decomposition of hydrogen peroxide.

12.18  Show how the formulas for water and hydrogen peroxide illustrate the law of multiple proportions.

## SUGGESTED READINGS

Davis, K. S. and J. A. Day. *Water: The Mirror of Science* (paperback). Doubleday, 1961.

CHEMISTRY
Choppin, G. R., "Water, $H_2O$ or $H_{180}O_{90}$?" Mar. 1965

SCIENTIFIC AMERICAN
Buswell, A. M. and W. H. Rodebush, "Water." Apr. 1956

*The energy of the universe is constant.*
*The entropy of the universe strives for a maximum.*

*Rudolf Clausius* (1822–1888)

**CHAPTER 13**

# Chemical Energy

Energy is all-important to civilization. Some regions of the world have abundant sources of energy, which can supply power for home and industry at a low cost. These regions often enjoy a relatively high standard of living. Conversely, areas of the world in which energy resources are meager often have a much lower standard of living. In the not too distant future, it is hoped that nuclear energy will provide cheap power to all the peoples of the world. Until that day dawns, chemical processes will continue to be the most important energy source at our disposal.

It is the energy released in the oxidation of carbon in fuels such as coal, petroleum, and natural gas that warms our homes, cooks our food, runs our automobiles, and moves the wheels of our factories. It is the energy from chemical reactions that sustains life and moves civilization. We turn now to a brief study of chemical energy.

## 13.1 Heats of chemical reaction

We have learned previously that there are two fundamental types of energy—kinetic energy and potential energy. We might examine a familiar chemical reaction in light of these two energy types to determine the *energy profile* of the reaction.

If a spark or a flame is applied to a contained mixture of hydrogen and oxygen gases, a violent explosion occurs. The reaction is described by the equation:

$$2H_2(g) + O_2(g) = 2H_2O(g)$$

The explosion, we realize, could only come about with a sudden and large increase of pressure within the container. Analyzing the equation for the reaction, we see that the reaction itself leads to a *decrease* in the number of moles of gas in the system. This, of course, cannot produce a pressure increase. But the facts are clear. There was an explosion. We must logically deduce that another product of the reaction was the large amount of heat energy that led to the sudden increase in gas pressure in the confined system. The energy produced by the chemical reaction appeared as kinetic energy (a large temperature change is our clue to this), but from where did this energy come?

Since the Law of the Conservation of Energy must be satisfied, we must conclude that before the hydrogen and oxygen gases reacted, they contained an amount of stored energy. Part of this *chemical potential energy* was converted to, and released as, heat energy during the reaction. It is logical to conclude that the product gas, water vapor, also contains chemical potential energy equal to the difference between that of the original system and that which was released. *It is the difference between the chemical potential energies of products and reactants that appears as the heat of a chemical reaction.*

## 13.2 Heats of reaction are measured in calorimeters.

As is to be expected, the chemist is not only interested in whether a chemical reaction yields energy. He also wants to know *how much* energy is released. Heats of chemical reaction are measured accurately through the use of the calorimeter.

The calorimeter is a container that is insulated from its surroundings by an outer layer of liquid or solid, or by a vacuum. A first experiment is run to determine the heat input necessary to cause a 1°C rise in temperature of the calorimeter. The heat energy needed is

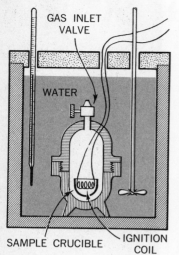

GAS INLET VALVE

WATER

SAMPLE CRUCIBLE — IGNITION COIL

**FIGURE 13.1** A calorimeter used to determine heats of reaction. The sample and a pressurized gas, usually oxygen, are placed in the inner chamber.

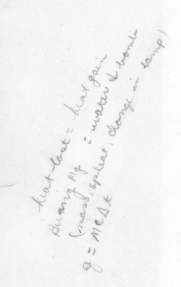

called the *calorimeter constant*. Then the reactants are placed in the calorimeter, one, in known amount, usually 0.01 to 0.1 mole, the other, usually a gas, in excess. Reaction is initiated by electrically heating the sample slightly or by a spark. The reaction releases heat energy, which, after a short time, is evenly distributed throughout the calorimeter. By considering the previously measured calorimeter constant and by measuring the temperature rise in the calorimeter, it is a simple matter to calculate the number of calories released in the reaction. From the known reactant weight used, the energy released per mole of that reactant or per mole of product can be calculated.

A common type of calorimeter includes a known weight of water as part of the heat absorbing system. (Fig. 13.1.) For this case, the reaction heat becomes evenly distributed within the inner metal container and the surrounding water. From a knowledge of the heat capacities (or specific heats) of the metal container and of the water, it is possible to calculate from the total temperature rise the number of calories released in the reaction.

**EXAMPLE**

A calorimeter consists of an aluminum bomb weighing 1.080 kg immersed in $9.700 \times 10^2$ g of water, all contained in a well-insulated system at an initial temperature of 24.92°C. A 0.4800-g sample of pure magnesium ribbon is added to the bomb, which is then charged with pure oxygen gas under pressure and then sealed. A surge of current is sent through the magnesium ribbon, which ignites and undergoes rapid, complete combustion. After heat transfer occurs through the walls of the aluminum bomb, a steady temperature of 27.35°C is finally recorded. Calculate the molar heat of combustion of magnesium. (Sp.ht. of Al = 0.216 cal/g-deg.)

**SOLUTION**

1. The total energy released is first calculated from the measured temperature *rise* in the known weights of the aluminum bomb and the water.

   a) The temperature rise is calculated.
   $$(27.35 - 24.92)°C = 2.43°C$$

   b) The energy increase in the bomb is calculated.
   $$(1.080 \times 10^3 \text{ g}) \left(0.216 \frac{\text{cal}}{\text{g-deg}}\right)(2.43°) = 5.66 \times 10^2 \text{ cal}$$

   c) The energy increase in the water is calculated.
   $$(9.700 \times 10^2 \text{ g}) \left(1.00 \frac{\text{cal}}{\text{g-deg}}\right)(2.43°) = 23.6 \times 10^2 \text{ cal}$$

   d) The total energy increase or energy released is calculated.
   $$(5.66 \times 10^2 \text{ cal}) + (23.6 \times 10^2 \text{ cal}) = 29.3 \times 10^2 \text{ cal}$$

2. The heat of combustion is then calculated from the number of moles of magnesium that reacted.

a) The number of moles of magnesium is calculated.

$$\frac{0.4800 \, g}{24.0 \, g/mole} = 2.00 \times 10^{-2} \text{ mole}$$

b) The molar heat of combustion is calculated.

$$\frac{29.3 \times 10^2 \text{ cal}}{2.00 \times 10^{-2} \text{ mole}} = 1.46 \times 10^5 \text{ cal/mole}$$

Thus:

$$Mg(s) + \tfrac{1}{2}O_2(g) = MgO(s) + 146 \text{ kcal/mole}$$

## 13.3 Exothermicity and heat of reaction

When the reaction between hydrogen and oxygen gases is studied calorimetrically, the measured heat for the reaction is 57.82 kcal per mole of steam produced. The heat of a chemical reaction is symbolized by $\Delta H$ (read as "delta $H$"). It must be carefully understood that this reaction heat is a measure of the *difference* between the chemical potential energy, or *heat content*, $H$, of products and of reactants. That is, for the general case of an exothermic reaction:

$$\text{Reactants} \rightarrow \text{Products} + \text{Energy}$$

$$\Delta H_{\text{reaction}} = H_{\text{products}} - H_{\text{reactants}}$$

Since, for an exothermic reaction, energy is released, the heat content of the products of such a reaction *must be less than* the heat content of the reactants. That is:

$$H_{\text{products}} < H_{\text{reactants}}$$

Therefore, $\Delta H_{\text{reaction}} < 0$ (i.e., negative), for exothermic reactions. (Fig. 13.2.) Thus, the specific exothermic reaction we have been considering is represented by the complete equation:

$$\tfrac{1}{2}H_2(g) + \tfrac{1}{2}O_2(g) = H_2O(g) \qquad \Delta H = -57.82 \text{ kcal/mole}$$

## 13.4 Endothermicity and heat of reaction

At moderate temperatures, the reaction between hydrogen gas and iodine vapor to form gaseous hydrogen iodide requires a continual input of energy. Experimentally, 6.20 kcal per mole of HI is required for the endothermic reaction:

$$\tfrac{1}{2}H_2(g) + \tfrac{1}{2}I_2(g) = HI(g)$$

For the general case of an endothermic reaction:

$$\text{Reactants} + \text{Energy} \rightarrow \text{Products}$$

Thus, it is evident that the products of the reaction have a higher heat content than the reactants. (Fig. 13.3.) That is:

$$H_{\text{products}} > H_{\text{reactants}}$$

Since, for *any* reaction,

$$\Delta H_{\text{reaction}} = H_{\text{products}} - H_{\text{reactants}},$$

then, for endothermic reactions, $\Delta H_{\text{reaction}} > 0$ (i.e., positive). Thus, the specific endothermic reaction we have been considering is represented by the complete equation:

$$\tfrac{1}{2}H_2(g) + \tfrac{1}{2}I_2(g) = HI(g) \qquad \Delta H = +6.20 \text{ kcal/mole}$$

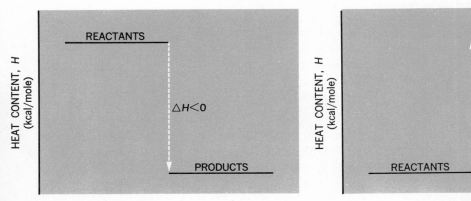

**FIGURE 13.2** Energy content relationship for an exothermic reaction system

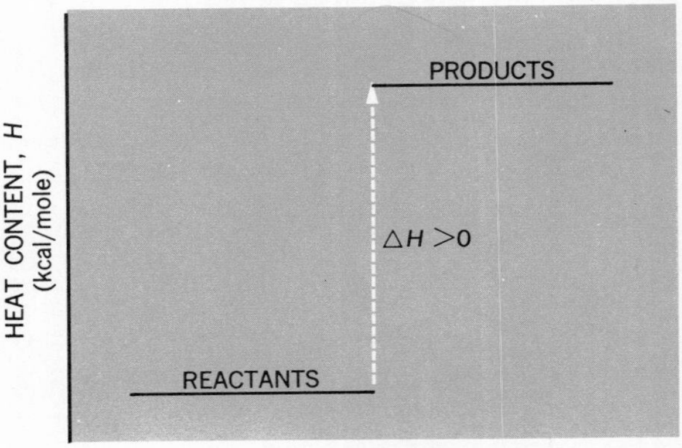

**FIGURE 13.3** Energy content relationship for an endothermic reaction system

## 13.5  Heats of formation

The heats of reaction measured when hydrogen and oxygen react and when hydrogen and iodine react may conveniently be considered to be the measured *heats of formation* of steam and of hydrogen iodide. As we shall see, knowledge of the heat of formation of a compound from its elements is particularly useful to the chemist. Accordingly, in compilations of calorimetric data, tables of heats of formation are common. The heats of formation, symbolized $\Delta H_f$, of a number of important compounds are given in Table 13–1.

## 13.6  The relation between heat content and chemical bonds

The heat of formation is a measure of the attraction between atoms combined in a molecule. *Most of the energy involved in chemical reactions comes from the breaking or the forming of chemical bonds.* In the formation of water, H—H bonds and O—O bonds must be

**TABLE 13–1** HEATS OF FORMATION (25°C; 1 atm)

| Compound | $\Delta H_f$ (kcal/mole) | Compound | $\Delta H_f$ (kcal/mole) |
|---|---|---|---|
| $H_2O(g)$ | −57.8 | $CO_2(g)$ | −94.0 |
| $H_2O(l)$ | −68.3 | $CS_2(l)$ | +21.0 |
| $H_2O_2(l)$ | −44.5 | $CH_3OH(l)$ | −57.0 |
| $HF(g)$ | −64.2 | $NaF(s)$ | −136.0 |
| $HCl(g)$ | −22.1 | $NaCl(s)$ | −98.2 |
| $HBr(g)$ | −8.6 | $NaBr(s)$ | −86.0 |
| $HI(g)$ | +6.2 | $NaI(s)$ | −68.8 |
| $SO_2(g)$ | −71.0 | $MgCl_2(s)$ | −153.4 |
| $SO_3(g)$ | −94.4 | $CaCl_2(s)$ | −190.0 |
| $NO(g)$ | +21.6 | $SrCl_2(s)$ | −198.0 |
| $NO_2(g)$ | +8.1 | $BaCl_2(s)$ | −205.6 |
| $NH_3(g)$ | −11.0 | $CuO(s)$ | −37.1 |
| $CO(g)$ | −26.4 | $Cu_2O(s)$ | −39.8 |

broken and H—O bonds are formed. To break the H—H bonds and the O—O bonds requires energy, whereas formation of the H—O bonds releases energy. However, we know that the net reaction is exothermic. It can be concluded, therefore, that more energy is released in the formation of the H—O bonds than is absorbed in breaking the H—H bonds and the O—O bonds.

Let us take another example—hydrogen iodide. Since the formation of HI is endothermic, it can be concluded that the energy released in forming H—I bonds is less than that absorbed in breaking H—H bonds and the I—I bonds. In conclusion, the heat of formation of a compound is not just a simple measure of the strength of the bonding in that compound, but involves *differences between bond-breaking energies and bond-forming energies.*

## 13.7 Hess's Law of Constant Heat Summation

Most chemical reactions occur between molecules that are more complex than those involved in compound formation from elements. An example is the oxidation of nitrogen monoxide, NO, to nitrogen dioxide, $NO_2$. When this reaction, which is involved in the formation of smog, is studied in a calorimeter, the following is found:

(1) $NO(g) + \frac{1}{2}O_2(g) = NO_2(g)$ $\quad \Delta H = -13.5$ kcal/mole

From Table 13–1, it can be seen that:

(2) $\frac{1}{2}N_2(g) + \frac{1}{2}O_2(g) = NO(g)$ $\quad \Delta H_f = +21.6$ kcal/mole

and

(3) $\frac{1}{2}N_2(g) + O_2(g) = NO_2(g)$ $\quad \Delta H_f = +8.1$ kcal/mole

It might be reasonable to assume that reaction (3) takes place in two steps:

$$\text{Step 1:}\quad N_2 \rightarrow NO$$
$$\text{Step 2:}\quad NO \rightarrow NO_2$$

In that case, reaction (2) corresponds to the first step, and reaction (1) to the second step. If reactions (2) and (1) are added algebraically, the result is:

(2) $\frac{1}{2}N_2(g) + \frac{1}{2}O_2(g) = NO(g)$     $\Delta H_f = +21.6$ kcal/mole

(1) $NO(g) + \frac{1}{2}O_2(g) = NO_2(g)$     $\Delta H = -13.5$ kcal/mole

$$\frac{1}{2}N_2(g) + O_2(g) = NO_2(g) \qquad \Delta H = +8.1 \text{ kcal/mole}$$

This final reaction is identical to reaction (3). The value of $\Delta H$ for this reaction is identical to the $\Delta H$ of reaction (3). Since the sum of the reactions (2) and (1) is identical to reaction (3), the Law of the Conservation of Energy *requires* that the sum of the $\Delta H$'s of reactions (2) and (1) be identical to the $\Delta H$ of reaction (3). This principle was discovered by the Swiss-born, Russian chemist G. H. Hess in 1840.

**HESS'S LAW OF CONSTANT HEAT SUMMATION.** Yet another expression of the Law of the Conservation of Energy, this law states that *the heat evolved or absorbed in any chemical reaction is constant, and is independent of whether the reaction takes place in one or many steps.*

### 13.8 Hess's law and the calculation of heats of reaction

The value of Hess's law and of heats of formation data lies in their joint use to predict heats of reaction. For example, let us attempt to predict the heat liberated in the following reaction:

$$\text{(1)} \quad CS_2(l) + 3O_2(g) = CO_2(g) + 2SO_2(g)$$

Again we will assume that the reaction may be analyzed in a stepwise fashion. *The stepwise analysis must involve separate reactions involving each of the reactants and products.* For reaction (1), whose $\Delta H$ we wish to predict, we go to Table 13–1 to find related reactions involving only $CS_2(l)$, $CO_2(g)$, and $SO_2(g)$. The reactions are:

(2) $C(s) + 2S(s) = CS_2(l)$     $\Delta H_2 = +21.0$ kcal/mole

(3) $C(s) + O_2(g) = CO_2(g)$     $\Delta H_3 = -94.0$ kcal/mole

(4) $S(s) + O_2(g) = SO_2(g)$     $\Delta H_4 = -71.0$ kcal/mole

How can we algebraically manipulate reactions (2), (3), and (4) to obtain reaction (1)? With thought, the following scheme arises:

$$(3)\ \cancel{C(s)} + O_2(g) = CO_2(g) \qquad\qquad \Delta H_3$$
$$(4)\ \cancel{S(s)} + O_2(g) = SO_2(g) \qquad\qquad \Delta H_4$$
$$(4)\ \cancel{S(s)} + O_2(g) = SO_2(g) \qquad\qquad \Delta H_4$$
$$-(2) \qquad\quad CS_2(l) = \cancel{C(s)} + \cancel{2S(s)} \qquad -\Delta H_2$$

$$(1)\ CS_2(l) + 3O_2(g) = CO_2(g) + 2SO_2(g) \qquad \Delta H_1$$

From Hess's law, therefore:

$$\Delta H_1 = \Delta H_3 + 2(\Delta H_4) - \Delta H_2$$
$$\Delta H_1 = (-94.0\ \text{kcal/mole}) + 2(-71.0\ \text{kcal/mole}) - (+21.0\ \text{kcal/mole})$$
$$\Delta H_1 = -257.0\ \text{kcal/mole of } CS_2 \text{ oxidized.}$$

When reaction (1) is run in a calorimeter, the heat of the reaction is determined to be $\Delta H = -257.0$ kcal per mole of $CS_2$ oxidized, in agreement with our prediction.

In order to use Table 13–1 in the predictive manner just illustrated, it is necessary that the heat of formation of every *compound* in the reaction under study be listed. It is important to realize that the stepwise reaction sequence used in such calculations is a figment of the imagination. Chemists usually do not know in what steps, or in how many steps, a reaction actually takes place. Only the *total energy change* between initial reactants and final products is known. The power of Hess's Law of Constant Heat Summation is precisely that this total energy change is completely independent of the kind and number of steps between initial reactants and final products. The chemist and you, therefore, are free to use any sequence of reactions that will algebraically result in the net reaction under study.

## 13.9 Entropy: another property of matter

In our considerations of the energy profile for a chemical reaction system, we have treated only one of the two effects that *determine whether a spontaneous reaction will take place*. The first of these effects is most clearly seen from the energy profile for exothermic reactions. On the basis of much experimental evidence, as well as on theoretical grounds, *chemical reactions tend to occur spontaneously in that direction leading to a decrease in potential energy*. As we have seen in Figure 13.2, all exothermic reactions involve such a potential energy decrease.

Since for all endothermic reactions there is always an increase in potential energy when reactants form products, as we saw in Figure 13.3, we might assume from the principle just enunciated that endothermic reactions should not occur spontaneously. For many years in the history of chemistry this assumption was held to be true. It became evident in time, on the basis of many experiments, that potential energy effects alone are not the only ones that determine the spontaneity of chemical reactions. For example, when sugar is added to water it dissolves readily to form a solution. It can be experimentally determined that this process is accompanied *by an absorption of heat*:

$$C_{12}H_{22}O_{11}(s) \xrightarrow{\text{H}_2\text{O}(l)} C_{12}H_{22}O_{11}(aq) \qquad \Delta H = +1.32 \text{ kcal/mole}$$

Clearly, the dissolution of sugar is an endothermic process that proceeds *spontaneously* from a state of lower potential energy to one of higher potential energy.

Consider the chemical reaction:

$$C(s) + H_2O(g) = CO(g) + H_2(g) \qquad \Delta H = +31.4 \text{ kcal/mole}$$

If energy is provided for this system, reactants will *spontaneously* form products though the energy profile for the system as a whole shows an increase in potential energy.

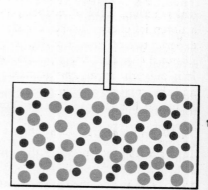
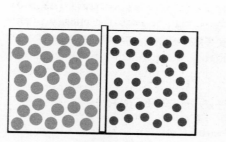

**FIGURE 13.4** When helium and neon mix, there is no measurable energy change. Would an input of energy be required to restore the gases to their original distribution?

We may finally consider another process that proceeds spontaneously *without any change in energy content.* (Fig. 13.4.) On carefully examining the dissolution of sugar, the reduction of steam by carbon, and the mixing of two nonreacting gases, what characteristic do we observe that is common to each process? Analyzing each system carefully, we note that the *degree of orderliness* has decreased from initial to final state. Thus, solid sugar contains the great degree of order that is common to molecular crystal solids. Water, as for most liquids, is in a relatively disordered state. After the solution process, the final system of sugar plus water is quite disordered. The sugar is now randomly distributed in a disordered liquid environment.

In the reaction system involving solid carbon and steam there is, prior to reaction, some degree of order in light of the ordered crystal structure of the solid carbon. The steam molecules, of course, are in the great disorder characteristic of the gaseous state. After reaction, however, with only gaseous CO and $H_2$ present, there is only disorder.

Finally, the compartmentalization of the barrier-separated helium and neon gases represents order of a type. When the barrier between the two gases is removed, a random distribution of the gaseous atoms spontaneously takes place with no observed energy required or expended. Clearly, such a random distribution is a much more probable state after the barrier is removed than if the two gases were to remain unmixed. This more probable, more random state is also one of more disorder.

All matter has an inherent property that is a measure of its state of order, randomness, or probability. That property of matter is called its *entropy*, S. Whenever matter undergoes a physical or chemical change, that change is accompanied by an entropy change —a change in the order, randomness, or probability of the reaction system. This entropy change, $\Delta S$, is independent of the potential energy changes that may occur simultaneously.

Just as it is a fundamental, experiential observation that chemical reactions *tend* to occur spontaneously in the direction leading to a potential energy decrease ($\Delta H < 0$), so it is an equally fundamental, experiential observation that *chemical reactions tend to occur spon­taneously in the direction leading to an entropy increase* ($\Delta S > 0$). It is only through *experimental* knowledge of *both* the energy profile and the entropy profile that the spontaneity or lack of spontaneity for a chemical reaction can be predicted.

## 13.10 Free energy: yet another property of matter

It is possible to measure the change in energy accompanying many chemical reactions in two ways. In particular, reactions in which electron transfer occurs among the reactants can very often be studied both calorimetrically and in an electric cell. In the latter case, as the reaction proceeds, measurable electrical energy is produced. This electrical energy represents the *maximum useful work* obtainable from the energy released during the reaction. When this maximum available energy, or *free energy*, is compared with the calorimetrically determined energy release, $\Delta H$, for the same electron transfer reaction, under the same conditions of temperature and pressure, the two figures do not agree. In some cases the free energy is greater than $\Delta H$. In other cases it is less than $\Delta H$. Immediately, we may be concerned that the Law of the Conservation of Energy is being denied. Earlier we noted that no matter how the total-energy release in a chemical reaction came about, it had a constant value, dependent only on the heat content of initial reactants and final products. What is the answer to our dilemma?

Since we have also observed that there is an entropy change accompanying every chemical reaction, let us look to that change for our solution. Consider an exothermic reaction in which the products are more ordered than the reactants, that is a change for which $\Delta S < 0$. Many spontaneous precipitation reactions fit such a description. For example:

$$AgNO_3(aq) + HCl(aq) = AgCl(s) + HNO_3(aq) \quad \Delta H = -15.7 \text{ kcal/mole}$$

When the free energy released for this reaction is determined, it is found to be 13.2 kcal/mole. Thus, while the total potential energy change accompanying the reaction appears as a release of 15.7 kcal of heat energy per mole, only 13.2 kcal/mole is available for work. Where did the remaining 2.5 kcal/mole disappear to? It is logical to assume that the system itself "siphoned off" the 2.5 kcal/mole as the energy needed *to organize* the AgCl crystal lattice. The free energy released in this reaction is the difference between the total energy released, through the breaking and forming of bonds, $\Delta H$, and the *organization energy* required to bring about the greater orderliness of the products.

The data given for the reaction under study were for a temperature of 298°A. How do you think these data would change at a higher temperature? In many cases the $\Delta H$ of a reaction changes little with temperature. But what about the organization energy? Is it not logical that at higher temperatures more energy will be required to organize systems that have higher kinetic energies at those higher temperatures? Indeed, such is the experimental observation. The organization energy is a product of two factors: the magnitude of the change in the order of the system, that is, the entropy change, $\Delta S$; and the absolute temperature, $T$, at which the change in order takes place. That is:

$$\text{Organization energy} = T\Delta S$$

The free energy change accompanying any chemical reaction at constant pressure and constant temperature is, then, the difference between the total energy change, $\Delta H$, and the organizational energy change, $T\Delta S$, for the reaction. That is:

$$\text{Free energy change} = \Delta H - T\Delta S$$

The free energy change is given the symbol $\Delta G$. Thus,

$$\Delta G = \Delta H - T\Delta S$$

is a fundamental relationship for *any* chemical reaction. It indicates that the potential energy and entropy changes at a given temperature determine the free energy, or maximum work potential, for the reaction at constant pressure and the given temperature.

The symbol for free energy, $G$, was chosen in honor of Josiah Willard Gibbs, perhaps this nation's greatest scientific intellect to date, who, in the nineteenth century, laid the foundations of a powerful theory that underlies the fuller understanding of the dynamics of chemical reactions.

## 13.11 Chemical thermodynamics: the broad highway

The relationship

$$\Delta G = \Delta H - T\Delta S$$

is a fundamental derivation of a great intellectual structure that is called *chemical thermodynamics*. Underlying all the consequences of chemical thermodynamics are two fundamental, experiential laws of nature. These, the first two laws of chemical thermodynamics, are succinctly stated in the quotation that opens this chapter.

Along with that other magnificent intellectual creation, atomic theory, chemical thermodynamics provides the theoretical mortar that binds myriad facts of nature into a great edifice—chemistry. By virtue of its predictive nature, chemical thermodynamics provides more:

> "The fascination of a growing science lies in the work of the pioneers at the very borderland of the unknown, but to reach this frontier one must pass over well-traveled roads; of these one of the safest and surest is the broad highway of thermodynamics."

From *Thermodynamics and the Free Energy of Chemical Substances* by G. N. Lewis and M. Randall. (McGraw-Hill, 1923), p. *v*.

## SUMMARY

Since the energy of the universe is constant, we can investigate chemical and physical events as series of energy exchanges. The energy released or absorbed as a result of a chemical change is due to differences between the heat content, or chemical potential energy, of products and reactants. Of particular importance is the difference in heat content between a compound and the elements comprising the compound—the heat of formation of the compound. Ultimately, most of the heat of a chemical reaction can be ascribed to bond breaking and bond forming.

Hess's Law of Constant Heat Summation, summarizes the fact that any complex reaction may be analyzed sequentially and algebraically in terms of energy changes. This permits the calculation of energy changes, which may then be subjected to experimental verification.

Josiah Willard Gibbs (1839–1903, American). After graduating from Yale University in 1858, Gibbs continued his studies in Europe over the following eleven years and then returned to Yale and received his doctorate in 1863. From 1869 until his death, this unassuming genius was professor of mathematical physics at his alma mater. During those years he published a great number of theoretical papers, many in the obscure *Transactions of the Connecticut Academy of Sciences*. In fact, it was only when his most important paper, "On the Equilibrium of Heterogeneous Substances," first published in 1876, was translated into German *twenty-three years later* that Gibbs's accomplishments became internationally recognized.

A second thermodynamic property of matter is entropy, a measure of internal disorder or state of probability. The change in entropy, $\Delta S$, and the change in heat content, $\Delta H$, that accompany a chemical reaction, and the temperature at which such reaction occurs, determine the spontaneity of the reaction. At constant pressure, the fundamental relationship involved is $\Delta G = \Delta H - T\Delta S$, where $\Delta G$ is the Gibbs free energy change, and the product $T\Delta S$ has been called the organization energy.

## QUESTIONS AND PROBLEMS

**13.1**    Name as many different forms of energy as you can.

**13.2**    What relationship is there between the thermal stability of compounds and their heats of formation?

**13.3**    The calorimeter constant for a particular experimental setup is 1.69 kcal/deg. When 2.00 g of calcium are made to react with excess chlorine gas in this measuring system, the observed temperature rise is 5.60°C. What is the molar heat of formation of calcium chloride?

**13.4**    Chlorine gas is pumped into a bomb calorimeter of 2.24 l capacity until the pressure is 24.0 atm at 27.0°C. An excess of hydrogen is pumped into the calorimeter and the mixture is ignited. The observed temperature rise is 0.480°C. Assuming complete reaction of the chlorine, what is the molar heat of formation of hydrogen chloride gas if the calorimeter constant is 0.422 kcal/deg?
Ans.    —22.1 kcal/mole

**13.5**    If 0.450 g of ethane is ignited in an atmosphere of excess oxygen using the same equipment described in the example on page 306, and the observed temperature rise is 4.64°C, what is the molar heat of combustion for ethane?
Ans.    —373 kcal/mole

**13.6**    Using data from Table 13–1, calculate the heat of reaction *per mole of the first reactant* given in each of the following:
a. $SO_2(g) + \frac{1}{2}O_2(g) = SO_3(g)$
b. $4NH_3(g) + 5O_2(g) = 4NO(g) + 6H_2O(g)$
c. $2CH_3OH(l) + 3O_2(g) = 2CO_2(g) + 4H_2O(g)$
d. $2CO(g) + O_2(g) = 2CO_2(g)$
Ans. b. —54.1 kcal/mole; d. —67.6 kcal/mole

**13.7**    The heat of formation for $CO_2(g)$ listed in Table 13–1 was determined for the reaction:
$$C(graphite) + O_2(g) = CO_2(g)$$

The combustion of the second allotropic form of carbon may be written:

$$C(diamond) + O_2(g) = CO_2(g) + 94.5 \text{ kcal/mole}$$

What is $\Delta H$ for the following reaction?

$$C(graphite) = C(diamond)$$

**13.8** Diamond has a more compact and ordered structure than graphite. **a.** In the industrial conversion of graphite to diamond, is the entropy change greater, or less, than zero? **b.** Is the Gibbs free energy change greater, or less, than zero? **c.** Under the conditions of the process, is the change in heat content greater, or less, than zero? **d.** Under ordinary conditions, the change in heat content approximates the value calculated in Problem 13.7. Under these conditions, compare the thermodynamic stability of the allotropes of carbon.

**13.9** Using data from Table 13–1, calculate the molar heat of vaporization of water. Compare your answer with the value of 9.720 kcal/mole given on page 158. Explain the difference between the two values and suggest a reason for this difference in terms of structure.

Ans. 10.5 kcal/mole

**13.10** Qualitatively describe the heat content, entropy, and free energy changes that occur when water spontaneously evaporates, and give reasons for these changes.

**13.11** Qualitatively describe the heat content, entropy, and free energy changes that occur when the temperature of water is lowered to 0°C, and give reasons for these changes.

## SUGGESTED READINGS

Jaffe, Bernard. *Men of Science in America.* Simon and Schuster, 1958. Chapter 13 discusses the life and chemical contributions of Josiah Willard Gibbs.

Mahan, B. H. *Chemical Thermodynamics* (paperback). W. A. Benjamin, 1963.

Nash, L. K. *Elements of Chemical Thermodynamics* (paperback). Addison-Wesley Publishing Co., 1962.

Strong, L. E., and W. J. Stratton. *Chemical Energy* (paperback). Reinhold, 1964.

Wilson, Mitchell, and the Editors of LIFE. *Energy* (LIFE Science Library). Time Inc., 1963.

SCIENTIFIC AMERICAN

McChesney, Malcolm, "Shock Waves and High Temperatures." Feb. 1963

Schurr, Sam H., "Energy." Sept. 1963

*Time hath a taming hand.*

*John Henry Cardinal Newman* (1801–1890)

**CHAPTER 14** | # Chemical Kinetics

As we have just seen, it is obvious that knowledge of the thermal energy released in a chemical reaction, such as the burning of coal, is important. It is frequently of equal importance to know whether that energy will be released immediately, or over a period of minutes or, perhaps, of days or months. In other words, it is necessary to know how fast a chemical reaction occurs. *The study of the rates of chemical reactions is known as chemical kinetics.* The measurement of these rates of reaction, understanding how the rate may be changed, and development of a theory of reaction rates are important aspects of modern chemical research.

## 14.1  Chemical kinetics and chemical thermodynamics

A fundamental principle of chemical thermodynamics that we learned was that the energy change between initial reactants and final products of a reaction is independent of how many, and what, steps are involved. Implicit in this principle is a corollary. *The energy changes in a chemical reaction are independent of time.* Thus, the same amount of energy is released (or absorbed) regardless of whether a reaction occurs in one one-thousandth of a second or in a thousand years. Knowledge of the thermodynamic properties of a reaction system tells only part of the history of that system. Knowledge of the chemical kinetics helps to complete the history.

For example, knowledge of the thermodynamic properties of hydrogen gas, oxygen gas, and steam allows the chemist to predict that hydrogen and oxygen gas will react spontaneously to form steam with the evolution of energy. However, when hydrogen gas and oxygen gas are mixed at ordinary temperatures, the rate of their reaction is infinitesimally slow. The need for an input of reaction-initiating energy comes from a knowledge of the kinetic properties of the system. Thus, knowledge of the thermodynamic and kinetic properties of a chemical reaction together give a more complete story.

## 14.2 Some chemical reactions are instantaneous.

Many reactions between inorganic compounds in aqueous solutions are instantaneous. For example, a white precipitate of silver chloride forms simultaneously with the addition of a solution of silver nitrate to a solution of hydrochloric acid:

$$AgNO_3(aq) + HCl(aq) = AgCl(s) + HNO_3(aq)$$

When a solution of sodium hydroxide and one of iron(III) chloride are mixed, a reddish, gelatinous precipitate of iron(III) hydroxide forms as rapidly as the two solutions are mixed:

$$FeCl_3(aq) + 3NaOH(aq) = Fe(OH)_3(s) + 3NaCl(aq)$$

The neutralization reaction between solutions of acids and bases is also instantaneous:

$$H_2SO_4(aq) + 2KOH(aq) = K_2SO_4(aq) + 2HOH(l)$$

Only recently, with the advent of remarkable experimental techniques, has it been possible to measure the rates of such very rapid reactions. The science of chemical kinetics, for the most part, has been limited to slower reactions.

### 14.3 Slower reactions and the measurement of reaction rates

When a piece of iron is placed in a solution of hydrochloric acid, a slow evolution of bubbles of hydrogen gas is evidence of a reaction:

$$Fe(s) + 2HCl(aq) = H_2(g) + FeCl_2(aq)$$

A piece of zinc, added to hydrochloric acid, leads to an even more rapid evolution of hydrogen gas. A piece of gold, on the other hand, shows no evidence of reaction. Obviously, then, the rate of a chemical reaction is first *determined by the nature of the reacting substances*.

Many experimental techniques have been developed for determining reaction rates. All involve the measurement of the change in concentration of one of the components of the reaction—for a reactant, a decrease in concentration; for a product, an increase in concentration. In one such technique, the reactants are mixed and, periodically, a small sample of the reaction mixture is withdrawn and the concentrations analyzed. In many cases, upon withdrawal, the small sample is rapidly cooled to stop further reaction before analysis, since, as we shall see, the rate of a reaction is temperature dependent.

In many cases, it is possible to measure some property that reflects the concentration without withdrawing samples. For example, if there is a color change accompanying the reaction, the change in color intensity can be measured and related to a change in concentration of the colored species. Thus, when chlorine is added to a bromide solution,

$$Cl_2(aq) + 2NaBr(aq) = Br_2(aq) + 2NaCl(aq),$$

the increase in intensity of the red-brown color of bromine is directly proportional to its increasing concentration. When a zinc bar is immersed in a solution of copper sulfate, the gradual decrease in intensity of the blue color of the copper sulfate can be directly related to its decreasing concentration.

In the case of reactions between gases, pressure changes as the reactions proceed may be used to determine the reaction rates. For example, in the high temperature reaction between hydrogen gas and nitrogen monoxide gas,

$$2H_2(g) + 2NO(g) = N_2(g) + 2H_2O(g),$$

four moles of gaseous reactants convert to three moles of gaseous products. As the reaction proceeds, there is, therefore, a decrease in pressure. Appropriate gas law calculations can convert the decrease in pressure per unit of time into a decrease in quantity of reactants per unit of time. That is, the measured pressure changes can be converted into calculated reaction rates.

## 14.4 Reactions usually involve several steps.

For most reactions that have measurably slow rates, it has been found that the over-all reaction occurs not in one but in several steps. For example, an over-all net chemical reaction may be represented by the equation:

$$2A + 2B + C \rightarrow D + F$$

Such a reaction, however, may actually be the result of three sequential reactions, such as:

| | | |
|---|---|---|
| (1) | $A + B \rightarrow C$ | (fast) |
| (2) | $2C + B \rightarrow D + E$ | (slow) |
| (3) | $A + E \rightarrow F$ | (fast) |

Net: $2A + 2B + C \rightarrow D + F$

In such a case, we recall that the net heat of reaction is the difference in heat content between $(2A + 2B + C)$ and $(D + F)$ and is independent of the steps involved. However, since intermediate reaction (2) is much slower than reactions (1) and (3), the net rate of reaction for the production of $(D + F)$ from $(2A + 2B + C)$ is determined by the rate of the slow reaction (2).

*The rate of a chemical reaction is determined by the rate of the slowest step in the reaction sequence.* This is a more or less obvious conclusion based on common observation. Consider, for example, a line of cars moving on a narrow highway. Suppose the first car is being driven at only 40 mph; then even if the cars behind can be driven at 100 mph, they are limited to the same speed as that of the slow car, that is, 40 mph.

## 14.5 Reactions occur when collisions occur.

In order for a chemical reaction to occur, it has been proposed that reacting molecules must collide with each other. During the moment of collision, energy transfer occurs, chemical bonds break, new ones form, and reactants are converted to products. For the general reaction considered in Section 14.4, three separate collisions must occur for the sequence of intermediate reactions to lead to the net conversion of reactants to products. The two fast reaction steps,

(1) $A + B \rightarrow C$

and (3) $A + E \rightarrow F$,

involve *bimolecular* collisions; that is, only two atoms are needed for collision and reaction. For the slow reaction,

(2) $2C + B \rightarrow D + E$,

it is seen that a *trimolecular* collision is needed.

When some marbles are put in a transparent box and shaken, careful observation reveals many collisions between two marbles but only very few among three marbles. We can say, then, that *two-body collisions are much more probable than three-body collisions*. Simultaneous collisions between four or more bodies are so rare as to be negligible. Since a chemical reaction must involve collisions, it is to be expected that reactions requiring trimolecular collisions would be slower than those requiring only bimolecular collisions, all other conditions being the same. We can now understand why intermediate reaction (2) should be slow and, therefore, rate-determining.

### 14.6 Determination of the mechanism of a reaction

The sequence of steps involved in the over-all reaction is known as the *reaction mechanism*. Frequently, it is extremely difficult to determine the correct reaction mechanism. From measurement of the change in reaction rate as changes in the concentration of the various reactants occur, it may be possible to decide the slow, rate-determining step. If only a few steps are involved in the total reaction mechanism, knowledge of the slow step in turn may allow the experienced researcher to suggest the other steps. The determination of reaction mechanisms still presents a great challenge to the researcher and requires experience and careful, logical thought.

One of the exciting facets of the study of reaction mechanisms is our present inability to predict with much accuracy the mechanism from the net reaction equation. In fact, reactions whose net

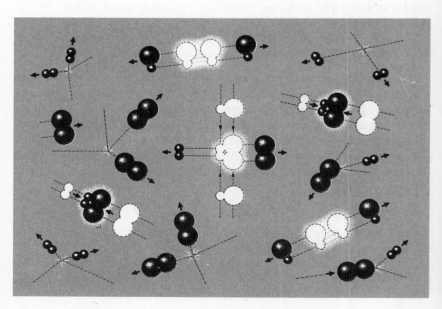

**FIGURE 14.1** The $H_2$-$I_2$-HI reaction system

equations are quite similar may have different mechanisms. In Chapter 7, we studied the chemical relationships of the halogens. In the gas phase, chlorine and iodine each reacts with hydrogen:

$$H_2(g) + Cl_2(g) = 2HCl(g)$$
$$H_2(g) + I_2(g) = 2HI(g)$$

The second reaction has been studied and is known to proceed by a simple mechanism involving bimolecular collisions between hydrogen and iodine molecules. (Fig. 14.1.) It would seem probable that the first reaction should occur by the same mechanism. However, careful research has shown that the mechanism is actually different and quite complex.

The hydrogen and chlorine gases react via a *chain* mechanism. The *chain-initiating step* involves the dissociation of chlorine molecules into chlorine atoms upon the absorption of radiant energy:

$$(1) \quad Cl_2 + h\nu \rightarrow 2Cl$$

The energetic chlorine atoms, known as *free radicals*, become involved in *chain-propagating steps* upon collision with hydrogen molecules:

$$(2) \quad Cl + H_2 \rightarrow HCl + H$$
$$(3) \quad H + Cl_2 \rightarrow HCl + Cl$$

As long as there are atomic chlorine and atomic hydrogen free radicals present, a chain reaction proceeds with the continuous formation of hydrogen chloride molecules. There are, however, reactions that can occur which eliminate the energetic free radicals from the system. Such *chain-breaking steps* are:

$$(4) \quad Cl + Cl \rightarrow Cl_2$$
$$(5) \quad H + H \rightarrow H_2$$
$$(6) \quad H + Cl \rightarrow HCl$$

Thus, whereas the formation of HI from $H_2$ and $I_2$ in the gas state occurs simply in a one-step bimolecular collision reaction, we may hypothesize the following complex, four-step, chain reaction mechanism for the formation of HCl from $H_2$ and $Cl_2$ in the gas state:

$$(1) \quad Cl_2 + h\nu \rightarrow 2Cl$$
$$(2) \quad Cl + H_2 \rightarrow HCl + H$$
$$(3) \quad H + Cl_2 \rightarrow HCl + Cl$$
$$(4) \quad Cl + Cl \rightarrow Cl_2$$

$$\text{Net: } Cl_2 + H_2 \overset{h\nu}{\rightarrow} 2HCl$$

Thus, it is *not possible* to deduce the reaction mechanism for a reaction from the net chemical change that occurs. The reaction mechanism must be experimentally determined.

### 14.7 Bond rupture and reaction rate

We saw earlier that many reactions occurring in solutions are often instantaneous. However, do not interpret this to mean that *all* such reactions are instantaneous. In many cases, the reaction rate is quite slow. An example of such a reaction is the precipitation of $MgNH_4PO_4$ from solutions of $MgCl_2$, $NH_3$, and $Na_2HPO_4$:

$$MgCl_2(aq) + NH_3(aq) + Na_2HPO_4(aq) = MgNH_4PO_4(s) + 2NaCl(aq)$$

*Thus, if the reaction mechanism is not a simple, one-step combination, the likelihood of a slow rate is much greater.*

One of the reactions that you will study in the laboratory, or have demonstrated to you, is known as the iodine "clock reaction." When aqueous solutions of potassium iodate and of sodium bisulfite are mixed together, they react:

$$4KIO_3(aq) + 10NaHSO_3(aq) = 2I_2(aq) + 5Na_2SO_4(aq)$$
$$+ 2K_2SO_4(aq) + 3H_2SO_4(aq) + 2H_2O(l)$$

The appearance of the iodine some time after the reactants are mixed suggests at least a two-step mechanism. It is more likely that several steps are involved. At least one of those steps will involve the breaking of the *covalent* I—O bonds in the $(IO_3)^{-1}$ ion. The study of many different reaction mechanisms has led chemists to understand that the breaking of bonds is very often the slowest step. This leads to another general principle of chemical kinetics: *When chemical bonds are not broken, the reaction is usually rapid, whereas when chemical bonds are broken, the reaction is usually slow.*

### 14.8 Effect of concentration on reaction rate: rate laws

To this point, we have learned that both the number of molecules that must collide simultaneously and the breaking of chemical bonds determine the over-all reaction rate. Two other factors that can greatly affect the reaction rate are the concentration and the temperature of the reactants.

In 1867 Cato Guldberg and Peter Waage (VAH geh), professors of mathematics and chemistry at the University of Oslo, Norway, demonstrated that the rate of a chemical reaction is *proportional to the product of the concentration of the reactants*. If the concentration of either or both reactants involved in a reaction increases, the rate of the reaction will increase. Thus, combustions that occur slowly in air will occur very much more rapidly in pure oxygen.

We may consider the quantitative dependence of reaction rates by returning to the reaction between $H_2$ and $I_2$ in the gas phase. Experimentally, it is found that a mixture of $H_2$ and $I_2$, *each* at a partial pressure of 0.5 atm, reacts at a certain rate. If, in another mixture of $H_2$ and $I_2$, the $H_2$ is at a partial pressure of 1 atm, while the $I_2$ remains at 0.5 atm, the measured reaction rate is found to be twice as fast as that of the first mixture. You will recall that the partial pressure of a gas is, in effect, a measure of its concentration. (Sec. 2.14.) So doubling the partial pressure, or the concentration, of $H_2$ has doubled the reaction rate. Thus, the reaction rate is proportional to the concentration of $H_2$:

$$\text{Rate} \propto [H_2]*$$

If a third mixture is studied in which the partial pressure of $H_2$ is held at 0.5 atm but the partial pressure of $I_2$ is 1.0 atm, the rate is again found to be double that of the first mixture. Therefore,

$$\text{Rate} \propto [I_2].$$

Combining results, we determine that the rate of the reaction between $H_2$ and $I_2$ in the gas phase is proportional to the product of the concentrations of both gases:

$$\text{Rate} \propto [H_2][I_2]$$

or

$$\text{Rate} = k[H_2][I_2]$$

where $k$, the proportionality constant, is known as the *reaction rate constant*. The entire expression is known as the *reaction rate law. It is an experimentally derived expression.*

Recalling the very different mechanisms for the net reactions between $H_2$ and $I_2$, and $H_2$ and $Cl_2$, it might be expected that the form of the rate laws for the reactions would be different. Experimentally, however, they are the same. Thus, for the reaction

$$H_2(g) + Cl_2(g) \xrightarrow{h\nu} 2HCl(g),$$

the experimental rate law is:

$$\text{Rate} = k[H_2][Cl_2]$$

When the $H_2$–$Br_2$ gas phase reaction is studied, a free radical chain reaction mechanism similar to that of the $H_2$–$Cl_2$ reaction is deduced. Yet for the simple stoichiometric reaction,

$$H_2(g) + Br_2(g) \xrightarrow{h\nu} 2HBr(g),$$

the experimental rate law is found to be no less complex than:

$$\text{Rate} = \frac{k[H_2][Br_2]^{\frac{1}{2}}}{k' + \dfrac{[HBr]}{[Br_2]}}$$

---

* The square bracket will henceforth symbolize the concentration of a substance expressed in moles per liter.

The point being stressed is that it is not possible to consider the stoichiometric equation for a reaction and thereby deduce the kinetic properties of the reaction. *The kinetic properties of a reaction system cannot be predicted. They must be experimentally determined.*

The increase in reaction rate with increase in concentration of reactants is easily understood by the theory that molecules must collide to react. Increasing the number of molecules in a certain volume increases the *frequency of collision* and, thus, increases the rate of reaction.

### 14.9 The effect of temperature on reaction rate

It is a common observation that increasing the temperature of a reaction system increases the reaction rate. A rough rule of thumb is that *the reaction rate doubles with every 10°C increase in temperature.*

Let us consider this relationship more closely. Again, if we use the model that molecules must collide to react, then the explanation would seem quite direct. As the temperature increases, the translational kinetic energy of a molecule increases. This results in molecules colliding more frequently, as was explained in Chapter 3. So the reaction rate increases because *the frequency of collision increases with increasing temperature* as it does with increasing concentration.

### 14.10 Not every collision causes a reaction.

For the decomposition of hydrogen iodide,

$$2HI(g) \rightarrow H_2(g) + I_2(g),$$

the experimental rate law is

$$\text{Rate} = k(HI)^2;$$

and it is found that a simple bimolecular collision mechanism completes the kinetic description of the system. For one mole of HI gas at room temperature and a pressure of 1 atm, it can be calculated that approximately $10^{28}$ molecular collisions occur each second in each milliliter of gas volume. Since under these conditions there are less than $10^{20}$ molecules in each milliliter of gas, we might expect that all of the molecules would collide, and hence react, in less than one-millionth of a second (a microsecond). Experimentally, however, the reaction is not a rapid one. This forces us to reconsider our fundamental concept in the collision model of reactions. *We must conclude that not every collision causes a reaction.* In fact, as in the case of HI, only a very small percentage of the total number of collisions lead to a reaction. In most of the collisions, the two HI molecules bump each other and bounce apart without a chemical reaction taking place.

We must consider modifying our collision model of reaction. We must take into account the energy of collision. It is not sufficient that molecules merely collide for reaction. They must collide with sufficient energy to bring about bond breaking. *The threshold energy required to initiate a chemical reaction is called the activation energy.*

Recalling the discussion in Section 3.6 of molecular kinetic energies as a function of temperature, we are able to explain why relatively few molecular collisions lead to reaction. We will simplify our discussion by considering that one of the molecules in a bimolecular collision is stationary (zero kinetic energy). The collision energy, then, will simply be the kinetic energy of the molecule that collides with the stationary one. Recall that a whole distribution of kinetic or collision energies exists at a given temperature. If the activation energy is high, then, only a few collisions have energies to bring about reaction. (Fig. 14.2.)

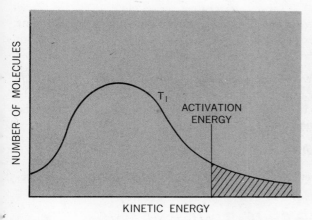

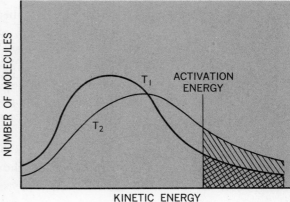

**FIGURE 14.2** Experimentally, all molecules of the same mass, at the same temperature, do not have the minimum energy required for reaction.

**FIGURE 14.3** An increase in temperature results in more molecules having the minimum energy required for reaction.

We can test this model, which requires an activation energy to be surpassed for a collision to cause reaction, by considering the temperature effect on the distribution of collision energies. Again, assuming that one molecule in a bimolecular collision is stationary, we see that at a higher temperature there are more molecules having the minimum collision energy required for reaction than there are at a lower temperature. (Fig. 14.3.) In other words, the reaction rate increases with an increase in temperature, precisely a result verified by experiment.

To sum up, *the rate of reaction is dependent on the frequency of collision (concentration and temperature effect) and on the energy of the molecules in the collision (temperature effect).*

### 14.11  The theory of the activated complex

The proposal that a certain amount of kinetic energy must be possessed by molecules for a reaction to take place would seem to ignore exothermic reactions. Why should such energy-releasing reactions require the presence of extra energy before they can take place? That is, why should exothermic reactions require activation energy? We know that they do, since many exothermic reactions are rather slow. Indeed, we now see why it is necessary to spark a hydrogen-oxygen mixture before reaction will occur. Since the collision model of reactions seems to answer so many other questions, it is logical to try to fit exothermic reactions into the same framework.

Consider the general reaction

$$A + B \rightarrow C + D \qquad \Delta H_R < 0$$

Let us suppose when $A$ and $B$ collide, they momentarily form a new species:

$$A + B \rightarrow (AB) \qquad \Delta H_a > 0,$$

where $(AB)$, the new species, is called an *activated complex*, and $\Delta H_a$ is the energy of activation that we have previously considered. Shortly after its formation, the activated complex decomposes to form the products of the reaction:

$$(AB) \rightarrow C + D \qquad \Delta H_d < 0,$$

with $\Delta H_d$ being the energy released in the decomposition. The net reaction is, therefore:

$$A + B \rightarrow C + D \qquad \Delta H_R = \Delta H_a + \Delta H_d$$

This model of an intermediate activated complex is quite possible. We have indicated that when molecules collide there must be a rearrangement of atoms to form new chemical bonds if products are to form from reactants. Such rearrangements could occur in an activated complex. Refer back to Figure 14.1. Can you identify $H_2$–$I_2$ activated complexes? Since the activated complex was first suggested, many of these complexes have been observed. In most reactions, however, their existence can only be guessed at, since the short time of their existence has not made direct observation possible.

With the concept of the activated complex, we can relate the thermodynamic and kinetic properties of a reaction system. The key to such a relationship is that the energy of activation, $\Delta H_a$, *is always endothermic*, while the heat of decomposition of the activated complex, $\Delta H_d$, *is always exothermic*. The net heat of the reaction, $\Delta H_R$, is determined, therefore, by the difference between $\Delta H_a$ and $\Delta H_d$ as shown in Figures 14.4 and 14.5.

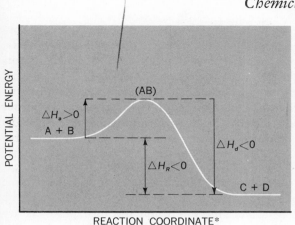

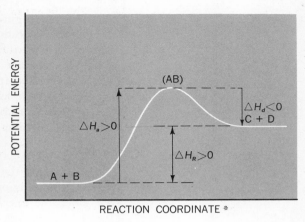

**FIGURE 14.4** Energy profile for an exothermic reaction. How does this profile differ from Figure 13.2?

**FIGURE 14.5** Energy profile for an endothermic reaction. How does this profile differ from Figure 13.3?

## 14.12 How catalysis may be explained

The model of the activated complex has been successful in explaining the process of catalysis. It is assumed that a catalyst leads to the formation of a new activated complex, which forms with a lower heat of activation than does the activated complex for the uncatalyzed reaction. Accordingly, more collisions are now effective in bringing about reaction. Hence, the reaction rate is increased. (Fig. 14.6.)

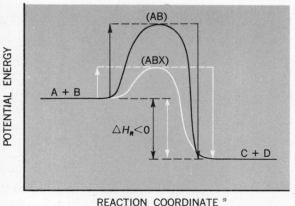

**FIGURE 14.6** Energy profile for an exothermic reaction —catalyzed and uncatalyzed

---

* The reaction coordinate is, in essence, an indication of the progress of the reaction. Moving along the coordinate parallels molecular reactant approach, collision, formation of activated complex, separation, and divergence of molecular products.

From Figure 14.6 we see that the uncatalyzed reaction between $A$ and $B$ leads to the formation of the activated complex $(AB)$. With a catalyst, the activated complex is $(ABX)$. $(AB)$ decomposes to $C + D$, *whereas* $(ABX)$ decomposes to $C + D + X$. This satisfies the requirement that a catalyst must be in the same state at the initiation and the completion of a reaction. $\Delta H_a'$ (with catalyst) is smaller than $\Delta H_a$ (no catalyst), so the catalyzed reaction is faster. $\Delta H_d$ (no catalyst) is greater than $\Delta H_d'$ (with catalyst). More importantly:

$$\Delta H_a' + \Delta H_d' = \Delta H_a + \Delta H_d$$

This means that the heat of reaction for the net reaction is the same whether the reaction is run with or without catalyst. This must be true, since the initial reactants are $A + B$ and the final products are $C + D$ in both cases. Therefore, in accordance with Hess's law, the same heat of reaction is required.

### 14.13 Heterogeneous and homogeneous catalysis

We have seen that solid manganese dioxide catalyzes the decomposition of aqueous hydrogen peroxide:

$$H_2O_2(aq) \xrightarrow{MnO_2(s)} H_2O(l) + \tfrac{1}{2}O_2(g)$$

Many gas phase reactions are catalyzed by solids. One industrial method for the manufacture of sulfuric acid involves the oxidation of sulfur dioxide to sulfur trioxide, using solid vanadium pentoxide as a catalyst:

$$2SO_2(g) + O_2(g) \xrightarrow{V_2O_5(s)} 2SO_3(g)$$

A catalyst that is not in the same physical state as the reactants is called a *heterogeneous catalyst*. It is believed that when a heterogeneous catalyst is used, one of the reactants is held by weak chemical bonds to the surface of this catalyst by a process known as *chemisorption*. This allows the reactants to react with a lower activation energy.

If the catalyst is in the same physical form as the reactants, it is termed a *homogeneous catalyst*. In the lead chamber process, a second industrial method for the manufacture of sulfuric acid, the oxidation of $SO_2$ gas to $SO_3$ is catalyzed by nitrogen dioxide gas, $NO_2$:

$$2SO_2(g) + O_2(g) \xrightarrow{NO_2(g)} 2SO_3(g)$$

The reaction between solutions of thallium(I) chloride and cerium(IV) chloride is catalyzed by a small amount of aqueous manganese(II) chloride:

$$TlCl(aq) + 2CeCl_4(aq) \xrightarrow{MnCl_2(aq)} TlCl_3(aq) + 2CeCl_3(aq)$$

In both of these homogeneously catalyzed reactions, it is probable that the catalyst becomes involved in a sequence of steps involving bimolecular collisions only, while the uncatalyzed reactions might involve trimolecular steps in their reaction mechanisms.

While catalysts are now found in wide industrial use, there is still much to be learned about catalytic mechanisms. To a large extent, the selection of a catalyst appropriate to a given reaction involves guesswork. Unraveling catalytic mechanisms is important not merely in an industrial sense but more so to life itself. It is now realized that almost all reactions that occur within living cells are catalyzed by substances known as *enzymes*. Thus, research in catalysis stands out as one of the vital activities at today's chemical frontiers.

## SUMMARY

While it is possible from a knowledge of thermodynamic properties to predict whether a certain reaction should occur, it is only through *experiment* that the rate of the reaction can be learned. A whole spectrum of reaction rates exists—from essentially instantaneous rates to infinitesimally slow rates. These rates are found to depend upon the nature of the reacting substances, the temperature, and the concentration of reactants and, sometimes, products.

Experimental measurement of the rate of a chemical reaction leads to a reaction rate law relating that rate to the concentration of substances in the reaction system. Often this rate law leads to the deduction of the reaction mechanism. It is not possible to predict reaction rate laws or reaction mechanisms from reaction stoichiometries.

A theory of reaction rates has been developed that is based on bimolecular collisions of reacting species. When such collisions occur with energies equal to, or in excess of, the activation energy needed for reaction at a given temperature, products will form from reactants. If the energy profile of a reaction system is drawn, there is a maximum energy state found that corresponds to a transition state between reactants and products. Often it is experimentally possible to determine the nature of the activated complex that briefly exists only in this transition state. The theory of reaction rates accounts well for the concentration and temperature dependencies of reaction rates, as well as for the phenomenon of catalysis.

## QUESTIONS AND PROBLEMS

14.1    **a.** What is meant by the rate of a chemical reaction? **b.** In what ways could the rate of the following reaction be expressed?

$$N_2(g) + 3H_2(g) = 2NH_3(g)$$

**14.2**   Suggest which measurable property in each of the following reaction systems could be used in determining the reaction rate:

  **a.** $Cl_2(aq) + 2KBr(aq) = Br_2(aq) + 2KCl(aq)$

  **b.** $Cu(s) + 2AgNO_3(aq) = Cu(NO_3)_2(aq) + 2Ag(s)$

  **c.** $CH_3COOH(aq) + NaHCO_3(aq)$
$$= CO_2(g) + NaOOCCH_3(aq) + H_2O(l)$$

  **d.** $C(s) + H_2O(g) = H_2(g) + CO(g)$

**14.3**   The concentration of a reactant $A$ changes from 0.0500 moles/liter to 0.0250 moles/liter in 30.0 minutes. Calculate the average reaction rate during this time interval.

**14.4**   What is the rate law for the following reaction?

$$A + 2B = C + D$$

**14.5**   If the mechanism for the reaction in Question 14.4 is

$$\begin{aligned} A + \quad B &= AB \quad \text{slow} \\ AB + \quad B &= C + D \quad \text{fast} \end{aligned}$$

$$\text{Net:} \quad A + 2B = C + D,$$

  what is the rate law for the reaction?

**14.6**   Which of the following reactions do you think would proceed at the more rapid rate?

  **a.** $Na_2CO_3(aq) + 2HCl(aq) = 2NaCl(aq) + CO_2(g) + H_2O(aq)$

  **b.** $Na_2CO_3(aq) + MgCl_2(aq) = 2NaCl(aq) + MgCO_3(s)$

  Explain your answer.

**14.7**   Which of the following reactions do you think would proceed at the more rapid rate? Explain your answer.

  **a.** $2Na(s) + I_2(s) = 2NaI(s)$

  **b.** $2Cs(s) + I_2(s) = 2CsI(s)$

**14.8**   A lump of coal burns at a moderate rate in air. Coal dust burns explosively. Liquid bromine reacts more slowly than bromine vapor. Explain these facts on the basis of collision theory.

**14.9**   Which system in each of the following reaction system pairs do you think has the more rapid reaction rate? Explain your answers.

  **a.** $N_2(10 \text{ atm}) + 3H_2(10 \text{ atm}) = 2NH_3(g)$
$N_2(5 \text{ atm}) + 3H_2(5 \text{ atm}) = 2NH_3(g)$

  **b.** $C(s) + 2H_2O(g) = 2H_2(g) + CO_2(g)$
$C(s) + 2H_2O(g) \overset{\text{catalyst}}{=} 2H_2(g) + CO_2(g)$

  **c.** $C(s) + \frac{1}{2}O_2(g) \overset{500°C}{=} CO(g)$
$C(s) + \frac{1}{2}O_2(g) \overset{1500°C}{=} CO(g)$

  **d.** $Na(s) + I_2(s) = 2NaI(s)$
$Na(s) + I_2(g) = 2NaI(s)$

**14.10** **a.** Draw a reaction energy profile for the reaction:
$$A + B = C + D \qquad \Delta H > 0$$
**b.** Using that profile, describe the behavior of molecules of *A* and *B* that collide with energy less than the energy of activation. **c.** Using that profile, describe the behavior of molecules of *A* and *B* that collide with energy greater than the energy of activation.

**14.11** **a.** Draw a reaction energy profile for the *reverse* of the reaction in Problem 14.10. **b.** Draw a reaction energy profile for this system with a catalyst present.

**14.12** From the thermodynamic properties of the graphite-diamond system at 25°C and one atmosphere (Prob. 13.7, p. 316), explain the apparent stable existence of diamonds under ordinary conditions.

**14.13** What does each of the following terms mean?

| | |
|---|---|
| **a.** chemical kinetics | **f.** enzyme |
| **b.** reaction mechanism | **g.** chemisorption |
| **c.** stoichiometry | **h.** homogeneous catalysis |
| **d.** chain reaction | **i.** activated complex |
| **e.** activation energy | **j.** reaction rate law |

## SUGGESTED READINGS

Eyring, Henry and Edward M. *Modern Chemical Kinetics* (paperback). Reinhold, 1963.

King, Edward L. *How Chemical Reactions Occur* (paperback). W. A. Benjamin, 1963.

Latham, J. L. *Elementary Reaction Kinetics* (paperback). Butterworth, 1962.

Prettre, M. *Catalysis and Catalysts* (paperback). Dover, 1963.

SCIENTIFIC AMERICAN
Bunker, D. L., "Computer Experiments in Chemistry." July 1964

*Observe how system into system runs....*

*Alexander Pope* (1688–1744)

**CHAPTER 15** | # Chemical Equilibrium

In order to describe chemical reaction systems more fully, we must add to our considerations of chemical energy and chemical kinetics yet a third aspect of almost all such systems. From an experimental point of view it has long been recognized that chemical reactions can occur in two directions. Lavoisier's classic twelve-day experiment, you will recall, involved first the formation of mercuric oxide,

$$Hg(l) + \tfrac{1}{2}O_2(g) = HgO(s),$$

and then its decomposition,

$$HgO(s) = Hg(l) + \tfrac{1}{2}O_2(g).$$

The *reversibility* of chemical reactions and the principles associated with such reversibility become our next consideration in the full description of a chemical reaction system.

### 15.1 Reversible reactions and chemical equilibrium

Let us consider two experiments involving the reversible reaction between hydrogen gas and iodine vapor to form colorless, gaseous hydrogen iodide. In the first experiment, 1.00 mole each of $H_2$ and $I_2$ are added to a 1.00-liter reaction vessel at 445°C. As time passes, the intense purple color of the iodine vapor diminishes. This is our experimental observation that the reaction

$$H_2(g) + I_2(g) = 2HI(g)$$

is taking place. An instant is reached when a constant intensity of color is observed that no longer changes with the passing of time provided that the temperature remains constant. It would *appear* that

334

the reaction has stopped. From the color intensity, we are able to calculate the final concentrations of product HI formed and reactant $H_2$ and $I_2$ left. They are $[HI] = 1.60$ moles/liter, $[H_2] = 0.20$ moles/liter, and $[I_2] = 0.20$ moles/liter.

We now perform our second experiment. We add 2.00 moles of HI to a 1.00-liter reaction vessel at 445°C. As time passes, a purple color appears in the vessel. This is our experimental observation that the reaction

$$2HI(g) = H_2(g) + I_2(g)$$

is taking place. As more time passes, the intensity of the color increases until a point in time is reached when no further color change occurs provided that the temperature remains constant. It *appears* that the reaction has stopped. Again we determine the final concentrations of all species present and, exactly as at the conclusion of our first experiment, we find $[HI] = 1.60$ moles/liter, $[H_2] = 0.20$ moles/liter, and $[I_2] = 0.20$ moles/liter. We have reached the same state for a reaction system from opposite directions under the same conditions.

From all observations of the constant macroscopic properties of the system in the final state reached, we might conclude that all reaction has ceased. The total reaction system, however, is composed of two competing reaction systems. We recall that two competing physical processes, such as the evaporation of a liquid and the condensation of its vapor, could lead to a final *steady state* in a closed system in which *no further change in measurable properties of the system is apparent*. The attainment of such a steady state became our operational definition for a *state of equilibrium*. It is quite logical,

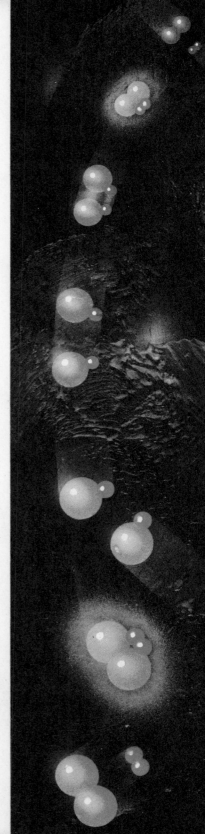

therefore, to assume that the steady state achieved from two directions in the closed gaseous system $H_2$-$I_2$-HI, at constant temperature, is a state of *chemical* equilibrium. We describe this state as:

$$H_2(g) + I_2(g) \rightleftharpoons 2HI(g)$$

### 15.2 Chemical equilibrium is a dynamic equilibrium.

When we went beyond the operational level to interpret the state of *physical equilibrium*, we arrived at a *conceptual definition* for that state. We conceived of the equilibrium state between a liquid and its vapor to be that state in which the *rates* of the opposing physical processes, evaporation and condensation, were equal. From our understanding of principles of chemical kinetics, we logically arrive at a similar conceptual definition for *chemical equilibrium*. A state of chemical equilibrium is reached in the $H_2$-$I_2$-HI system when the rate of formation of hydrogen iodide from hydrogen and iodine exactly equals the rate of decomposition of hydrogen iodide into hydrogen and iodine. Since at equilibrium two opposing chemical reactions are taking place, albeit at the same rate, *the state of chemical equilibrium is a state of dynamic equilibrium.*

### 15.3 The kinetic approach to the Law of Chemical Equilibrium

From our two experiments on the $H_2$-$I_2$-HI equilibrium system, we arrive at two vital conclusions. We have already seen that the first of these conclusions is that *the equilibrium state may be reached from either direction.* Secondly, if we were to examine the equilibrium concentrations of hydrogen, iodine, and hydrogen iodide at the same temperature, *regardless of initial nonequilibrium conditions*, we would discover that they bear a constant mathematical relationship to each other. From our kinetic interpretation of dynamic chemical equilibrium, and from our experimental knowledge of the kinetics of the opposing reactions that lead to the equilibrium state, we can deduce what that relationship must be.

Experimentally, as we have seen, the rate law for the formation of hydrogen iodide from hydrogen and iodine is:

$$R_f = k_f[H_2][I_2]$$

where $R_f$ and $k_f$ symbolize the experimental rate and the rate law constant for the *forward* ($f$) direction in the reaction

$$H_2(g) + I_2(g) \underset{r}{\overset{f}{\rightleftharpoons}} 2HI(g).$$

We have also learned that the experimental rate law for the *reverse* ($r$) reaction, the decomposition of hydrogen iodide, is:

$$R_r = k_r[HI]^2$$

*At equilibrium the rates of the forward and reverse reactions are equal:*

$$R_f = R_r$$

Substituting for $R_f$ and $R_r$, we find:

$$k_f[H_2][I_2] = k_r[HI]^2$$

On rearrangement, we have:

$$\frac{k_f}{k_r} = \frac{[HI]^2}{[H_2][I_2]}$$

Since $k_f$ and $k_r$ are constants, the division of one by the other leads to a constant, and we have finally:

$$K = \frac{[HI]^2}{[H_2][I_2]}$$

This expression is known as the *law of chemical equilibrium* for the reaction

$$H_2 + I_2 \rightleftharpoons 2HI,$$

and $K$ is called the *equilibrium constant*. Thus, through a consideration of the kinetic properties of the system, we have arrived at a quantitative expression for the constant mathematical relationship that describes the composition of a system at chemical equilibrium. This expression, the law of chemical equilibrium, is, however, more dependent on the fundamental properties than on the kinetic properties of a reaction system.

## 15.4 Chemical thermodynamics and the Law of Chemical Equilibrium

Though it is not possible to derive within the scope of this book, the law of chemical equilibrium is one of the great theoretical outcomes of chemical thermodynamics. For the general reaction

$$aA + bB \rightleftharpoons cC + dD,$$

chemical thermodynamics leads to the general *Law of Chemical Equilibrium:*

$$K = \frac{[C]^c[D]^d}{[A]^a[B]^b}$$

The *numerator* of the expression is the product of the *equilibrium concentrations* of the products, each raised to a power equal to its stoichiometric coefficient in the chemical equation for the reaction. The *denominator* is the product of the *equilibrium concentrations* of the reactants, each raised to a power equal to its stoichiometric coefficient in the chemical equation for the reaction.

Some examples of equilibrium law expressions are given in Table 15–1. Observe that where a pure solid or pure liquid appears

**TABLE 15–1**   Equilibrium Law Expressions

| System | K |
|---|---|
| $2NO_2(g) \rightleftharpoons N_2O_4(g)$ | $\dfrac{[N_2O_4]}{[NO_2]^2}$ |
| $N_2(g) + 3H_2(g) \rightleftharpoons 2NH_3(g)$ | $\dfrac{[NH_3]^2}{[N_2][H_2]^3}$ |
| $C(s) + H_2O(g) \rightleftharpoons CO(g) + H_2(g)$ | $\dfrac{[CO][H_2]}{[H_2O]}$ |
| $H_2(g) + S(l) \rightleftharpoons H_2S(g)$ | $\dfrac{[H_2S]}{[H_2]}$ |
| $Fe_3O_4(s) + 4H_2(g) \rightleftharpoons 4H_2O(g) + 3Fe(s)$ | $\dfrac{[H_2O]^4}{[H_2]^4}$ |
| $NaF(aq) + H_2O(l) \rightleftharpoons HF(aq) + NaOH(aq)$ | $\dfrac{[HF][NaOH]}{[NaF]}$ |

as a reactant or a product in an equilibrium system *its concentration does not appear in the equilibrium law expression.* This comes about by virtue of the essential constancy of concentration of a substance in a condensed state. If you like, you may think of the constant concentration of a pure solid or pure liquid as being incorporated in the final equilibrium constant, $K$.

## 15.5 Calculations involving the equilibrium constant

The law of chemical equilibrium for a given equilibrium system is independent of all external conditions. Thermodynamically, it is determined by the free energy content of reactants and products. *The value of $K$, however, is determined by the temperature of the system.* The value of $K$ is a measure of the degree to which the equilibrium system favors reactants or products. At one temperature, it may be that relatively low equilibrium concentrations of products are present. At a second and higher temperature, it may be that the equilibrium concentrations of products are now higher than those of the reactants. These observations would be reflected by the fact that $K$ at the higher temperature would be greater than $K$ at the lower temperature. Values for $K$ are calculated from *measured* equilibrium concentrations of products and reactants.

**EXAMPLE**

Calculate the equilibrium constant for the $H_2$-$I_2$-HI equilibrium system at 445°C.

**SOLUTION**

We use the data for this system given in Section 15.1.

$$H_2(g) + I_2(g) \rightleftharpoons 2HI(g)$$

At equilibrium:    0.20 m/l    0.20 m/l    1.60 m/l

$$K = \frac{[HI]^2}{[H_2][I_2]}$$

$$K = \frac{(1.60 \text{ m/l})^2}{(0.20 \text{ m/l})(0.20 \text{ m/l})}$$

$$K = \frac{2.56 \ \text{m}^2/l^2}{0.040 \ \text{m}^2/l^2}$$

$$K = 64$$

As a result of the form of the equilibrium law *for this system*, the equilibrium constant has no units associated with it. For the general case $K = \frac{[C]^c[D]^d}{[A]^a[B]^b}$, $K$ will have the units $\frac{(\text{moles/liter})^{c+d}}{(\text{moles/liter})^{a+b}}$. By convention, chemists do not include units for $K$ values in tabulations or calculations. In calculating equilibrium concentrations, however, it is important to add a concentration unit to the calculated answer.

We may use the value of $K$ calculated in the previous example for determining the equilibrium concentrations in any $H_2$-$I_2$-HI system *at 445°C.*

**EXAMPLE**

At 445°C an equilibrium mixture contains 0.80 m/l of HI and 0.40 m/l of $I_2$. What is the equilibrium concentration of $H_2$?

**SOLUTION**

$$H_2(g) + I_2(g) \rightleftharpoons 2HI(g)$$

At equilibrium:    X m/l    0.40 m/l    0.80 m/l

$$K = \frac{[HI]^2}{[H_2][I_2]}$$

At 445°C, $K = 64$:    $$64 = \frac{(0.80)^2}{[H_2](0.40)}$$

$$[H_2] = \frac{(0.80)^2}{(64)(0.40)}$$

$$[H_2] = 2.5 \times 10^{-2} \text{ m/l}$$

## 15.6 Stoichiometry, kinetics, and equilibrium

It must be emphasized that the law of chemical equilibrium is a necessary outcome of the thermodynamic properties of a reaction system.

The equilibrium constant expression corresponding to that law is, as we have seen, simply related to the stoichiometry of the reaction system. Though we first arrived at the law of chemical equilibrium through a consideration of the kinetic properties of the $H_2$-$I_2$-HI system, it is only fortuitous that the experimental rate laws led directly and simply to the same law of chemical equilibrium that results from chemical thermodynamics. The point being re-emphasized is that *rate laws for the forward and reverse reactions occurring in an equilibrium system must be experimentally determined*. Though we may look at the stoichiometric relationship,

$$H_2(g) + Br_2(g) \rightleftharpoons 2HBr(g),$$

and, *with certainty*, write the law of chemical equilibrium in terms of that relationship,

$$K = \frac{[HBr]^2}{[H_2][Br_2]},$$

we cannot deduce either forward or reverse rate laws from that relationship. Thus, while we may be tempted to write

$$R_f = k_f[H_2][Br_2]$$

as the rate law for the forward reaction in the $H_2$-$Br_2$-HBr equilibrium system, we find our guess to be grossly incorrect. Recall that *the experimental rate law* in this case is:

$$R_f = \frac{k[H_2][Br_2]^{\frac{1}{2}}}{k' + \dfrac{[HBr]}{[Br_2]}}$$

### 15.7 Factors affecting chemical equilibria: Le Chatelier's Principle

If we hold the temperature of an equilibrium system constant, then the value of the equilibrium constant remains the same. Under these conditions it is possible, nonetheless, to affect the equilibrium concentrations by changing other conditions. For example, in the gas phase equilibrium system,

$$2NO_2(g) \rightleftharpoons N_2O_4(g),$$

when, at constant temperature, the pressure on the system is increased, it is observed that the brownish color that is due to the $NO_2$ present *diminishes* in intensity until a new constant intensity is observed. Why might this be?

When the pressure on the equilibrium system is increased, the gaseous constituents are forced to occupy a smaller volume than they did previously. The total number of moles per unit volume becomes greater than it was under the original conditions of equilibrium. This imposed concentration change, as well as the pressure change that brought it about, could be made less pronounced if a reduction in the total number of gaseous moles could occur. When $NO_2$ combines to form $N_2O_4$, such a reduction does, indeed, occur. The new equilibrium concentrations of $NO_2$ and $N_2O_4$ yield the $K$ value for the given temperature.

On the other hand, when a pressure increase is imposed on the $H_2$-$I_2$-HI equilibrium system at constant temperature, no change in the equilibrium concentrations of the gaseous species is observed. Inspection of the equation for the equilibrium reaction,

$$H_2(g) + I_2(g) \rightleftharpoons 2HI(g),$$

shows that a chemical change in either direction does not lead to a change in the number of gaseous moles, hence no change occurs in response to an imposed pressure change.

If additional sulfuric acid is added to the aqueous solution equilibrium system

$$2K_2CrO_4(aq) + H_2SO_4(aq) \rightleftharpoons K_2Cr_2O_7(aq) + K_2SO_4(aq) + H_2O(l),$$

the equilibrium is momentarily unbalanced. When equilibrium is restored *at the same temperature*, an increased intensity of orange color indicates that yellow $K_2CrO_4$ has been converted to orange $K_2Cr_2O_7$. Before and after the addition of the $H_2SO_4$, the law of chemical equilibrium for the system has to be satisfied:

$$K = \frac{[K_2Cr_2O_7][K_2SO_4]}{[K_2CrO_4]^2[H_2SO_4]}$$

If, on adding the $H_2SO_4$, no chemical change takes place, then the concentration of the $H_2SO_4$ alone would change. It would increase and $K$ would decrease. Since $K$ does not change if the temperature remains unchanged, then when $H_2SO_4$ is added, some of the acid must react with the $K_2CrO_4$ to form products. The new equilibrium concentrations must be such as to lead to the same value of $K$.

Observations concerning the effect of external conditions on chemical equilibria were summarized into a generalization by the nineteenth-century French chemist Henry Le Chatelier (luh shah tell YAY).

**LE CHATELIER'S PRINCIPLE.** Allowing us to predict the direction of shift in equilibrium concentrations, this principle states that *when a change in condition is imposed upon a system at equilibrium, the equilibrium concentrations will shift in a way to counteract partially the imposed change.*

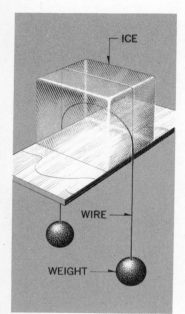

**FIGURE 15.1** Regelation: Le Chatelier's principle in action. Describe the phenomenon illustrated.

This principle is also useful in considering physical equilibria. For example, when pressure is applied to the equilibrium system,

$$\text{ice} \rightleftharpoons \text{water},$$

Le Chatelier's principle allows us to predict that there will be a shift to a smaller volume to counteract partially the increased pressure. Since ice has a greater volume than water, we would predict that ice melts when pressure is applied to it. This prediction is verified by experiment. (Fig. 15.1.)

We might wonder what change in an uncatalyzed equilibrium system would be brought about by the addition of a catalyst. Since the presence of a catalyst in a reaction system merely lowers the activation energy for both the forward and the reverse reactions, chemical equilibrium is attained more quickly in the presence of a catalyst. *The presence of a catalyst, therefore, has no effect on the equilibrium concentrations of the substances in the system.*

### 15.8 Temperature changes and changes in the equilibrium state

Le Chatelier's principle is useful in helping to predict how the equilibrium will change with temperature. If we consider the endothermic reaction,

$$\tfrac{1}{2}H_2(g) + \tfrac{1}{2}I_2(g) \rightleftharpoons HI(g) \qquad \Delta H = +6.20 \text{ kcal/mole},$$

then Le Chatelier's principle allows us to predict that at higher temperatures the *equilibrium state* should shift in favor of product. We arrive at this result by reasoning that at higher temperatures more heat energy is present. Since the reaction is endothermic and absorbs energy in the formation of product, higher temperatures mean greater absorption of heat and greater production of product. Thus, we predict that $K$ values for endothermic reactions should increase with temperature. Experimentally, they do. Conversely, for the exothermic reaction,

$$\tfrac{1}{2}H_2(g) + \tfrac{1}{2}Br_2(g) \rightleftharpoons HBr(g) \qquad \Delta H = -8.65 \text{ kcal/mole},$$

we predict that at higher temperatures the equilibrium state should shift in favor of reactants, since the decomposition of HBr is the heat absorption process. Experiment bears out our prediction and leads to the general conclusion that $K$ *values for exothermic reactions decrease with increasing temperature.*

### 15.9 Thermodynamics, kinetics, equilibrium, and industry

The full understanding of the thermodynamic, kinetic, and equilibrium properties of a reaction system underlies the economic exploitation of such a system. For example, let us consider in detail the $N_2$-$H_2$-$NH_3$ gas system:

$$\tfrac{1}{2}N_2(g) + \tfrac{3}{2}H_2(g) \rightleftharpoons NH_3(g) \qquad \Delta H = -11.04 \text{ kcal/mole}$$

Under ordinary conditions the reaction is infinitesimally slow, there being a very high energy of activation required for relatively inert nitrogen gas to react with hydrogen gas. Thus, at the outset, the economic production of ammonia from elemental hydrogen and nitrogen depends on a kinetic factor. To overcome this factor that hinders the progress of the reaction, the reaction should be run under catalytic conditions.

Next we observe that the reaction leads to a reduction in moles, from a total of two moles of reactants to one mole of products. Once equilibrium is attained, therefore, we predict on the basis of Le Chatelier's principle that if the system were under pressure, more ammonia would be produced. Subject to the economics of building and maintaining high pressure equipment, the reaction should be run at high pressures.

Finally, we observe that the reaction is exothermic. Accordingly, low temperatures would favor the production of ammonia. Low temperatures, however, reduce reaction rates and lead to too slow a production of ammonia to be economical. Balancing kinetic and thermodynamic factors, then, the reaction should be run at moderate temperatures. In 1906, on the basis of reasoning such as the above, Fritz Haber, in Germany, conceived the process for converting inert atmospheric nitrogen into vital, chemically reactive ammonia. Reasoning such as Haber's, in which thermodynamic, kinetic, and equilibrium factors are balanced with cost and time factors, is the basis of applied chemistry, or chemical engineering. You need but look about you to see the technological fruits of such application and engineering, and to realize the practical significance of understanding the principles of chemical thermodynamics, chemical kinetics, and chemical equilibrium.

## SUMMARY

Chemical equilibrium is a dynamic state in which, at a given temperature, the rates of the forward and the reverse reactions are equal. At equilibrium, the concentrations of reactant and product species bear a constant mathematical relationship to each other. That relationship, the law of chemical equilibrium, is derived from chemical thermodynamics. For the general reaction

$$aA + bB \rightleftharpoons cC + dD,$$

the law is of the form

$$K = \frac{[C]^c[D]^d}{[A]^a[B]^b}.$$

At a given temperature, the value for the equilibrium constant, $K$, for an equilibrium system will not change. Therefore, we are able to predict how equilibrium concentrations will be affected by imposed changes on equilibrium systems at a given temperature. Le Chatelier's principle summarizes the effects and, further, enables us to understand temperature effects on chemical equilibria. Along with thermodynamic and kinetic considerations, knowledge of the equilibrium properties of chemical systems is essential for their economic exploitation.

## QUESTIONS AND PROBLEMS

**15.1** Describe molecular behavior that could explain the observed macroscopic changes with time when 1.00 mole each of hydrogen and iodine are added to a 1.00 l reaction vessel at 445°C.

**15.2** For the reaction system

$$mM + nN \rightleftharpoons qQ + rR,$$

**a.** give the chemical kinetic definition of the equilibrium state;
**b.** give the thermodynamic definition of the equilibrium state.

**15.3** Write the law of chemical equilibrium for each of these:

**a.** $PCl_5(g) \rightleftharpoons PCl_3(g) + Cl_2(g)$
**b.** $H_2O(g) + CO(g) \rightleftharpoons H_2(g) + CO_2(g)$
**c.** $HgO(s) \rightleftharpoons Hg(l) + \frac{1}{2}O_2(g)$
**d.** $4NH_3(g) + 5O_2(g) \rightleftharpoons 4NO(g) + 6H_2O(g)$
**e.** $N_2O_5(g) \rightleftharpoons 2NO_2(g) + \frac{1}{2}O_2(g)$
**f.** $CaCO_3(s) \rightleftharpoons CaO(s) + CO_2(g)$
**g.** $NH_3(aq) + HF(aq) \rightleftharpoons NH_4F(aq)$
**h.** $COCl_2(g) \rightleftharpoons CO(g) + Cl_2(g)$

**15.4** Colorless dinitrogen tetroxide gas decomposes endothermically to form brown nitrogen dioxide gas. At 55.0°C, a 1.00 l vessel is found to contain 1.15 moles of $N_2O_4$ gas in equilibrium with 2.00 moles of $NO_2$ gas. Calculate the value of the equilibrium constant for the decomposition of $N_2O_4$ at 55.0°C.

**15.5** How will the equilibrium concentration of the $N_2O_4$ of the system described in Problem 15.4 be affected **a.** by an increase in the pressure on the system? **b.** by an increase in the temperature of the system to 100°C? **c.** by addition of a catalyst to the system? **d.** Which macroscopic properties of the system could be used to study the change in concentration of $N_2O_4$?

**15.6** At 445°C, an equilibrium mixture contains 0.20 m/l each of hydrogen and iodine. What is the equilibrium concentration of hydogen iodide?  ($K = 64$ when HI is considered as the product.)
Ans.   1.6 m/l

15.7   **a.** For the reaction system

$$CO_2(g) + H_2(g) \rightleftharpoons CO(g) + H_2O(g),$$

it is found that the equilibrium concentrations at 900°C are: $[CO_2] = 0.310$ m/l; $[H_2] = 0.310$ m/l; $[CO] = 0.190$ m/l; $[H_2O] = 0.690$ m/l. Calculate the value of the equilibrium constant. **b.** If, at 900°C, an equilibrium mixture contains $[CO_2] = 0.650$ m/l, $[CO] = 0.350$ m/l, and $[H_2O] = 0.350$ m/l, what is the equilibrium concentration of $H_2$?

Ans.   **b.** 0.138 m/l

15.8   An important industrial process involves the oxidation of ammonia gas to nitrogen monoxide gas as the first step in the ultimate synthesis of nitric acid:

$$4NH_3(g) + 5O_2(g) \rightleftharpoons 4NO(g) + 6H_2O(g) \quad \Delta H = -54 \text{ kcal/mole } NH_3$$

Predict the technical conditions under which you would expect a maximum yield of NO gas. Compare your predictions with the details of the Ostwald process considered on page 574, and explain any differences.

15.9   How does an increase in pressure affect each of the equilibrium systems listed in Table 15–1?

15.10  A 1.00 l container at 1000°C contains 0.102 mole of ammonia, 1.03 moles of nitrogen, and 1.62 moles of hydrogen. Calculate $K$ at 1000°C for the equilibrium system $N_2(g) + 3H_2(g) \rightleftharpoons 2NH_3(g)$.

15.11  For the equilibrium system $2NO(g) + O_2(g) \rightleftharpoons 2NO_2(g)$, $K$ is $6.45 \times 10^5$ at 200°C. How many moles of nitrogen monoxide will exist in equilibrium with 0.190 mole of nitrogen dioxide and 0.606 mole of oxygen in a 1.00 l reaction vessel at 200°C?

Ans.   $3.04 \times 10^{-4}$ moles

15.12  For the equilibrium system $H_2(g) + CO_2(g) \rightleftharpoons H_2O(g) + CO(g)$, $K$ has the value of 4.40 at 1700°C. If a 20.0 l reaction vessel contains 12.0 moles of hydrogen, 8.00 moles of carbon dioxide, and 10.0 moles of water vapor at 1700°C, how many moles of carbon monoxide must also be present?

## SUGGESTED READINGS

Carnell, P. H., and R. N. Reusch. *Molecular Equilibrium* (paperback). W. B. Saunders Co., 1963. A programmed manual.

Denbigh, Kenneth. *The Principles of Chemical Equilibrium* (paperback). Cambridge University Press, 1961.

Sienko, M. J. *Equilibrium: Freshman Chemistry Problems and How to Solve Them, Part 2* (paperback). W. A. Benjamin, 1964.

*Solutions fill the oceans,*
*solutions are running in our veins ....*

*Svante Arrhenius* (1859–1927)

# CHAPTER 16

# Solubility

From your experiences in the chemistry laboratory, and from your observations of common, daily occurrences, it should be evident that much of the chemistry of the elements involves water solutions of compounds of those elements. Having considered the properties of pure water in some detail in Chapter 12, it is fitting to turn to a detailed study of how those properties change when substances are dissolved in water. In this study, we will find that energy effects, kinetic effects, and equilibrium effects all play important roles.

## 16.1 General energy considerations favoring solubility

Three energy terms arise in considering a solution between a solid *solute* and a liquid *solvent*. First, energy $E_1$ must be absorbed so that the forces of attraction holding the solute together in the solid state will be overcome. Second, energy $E_2$ must be absorbed so that the forces of attraction holding the solvent molecules together will be overcome at least partially. The relatively few solute particles may then become interspersed between the many solvent molecules. Third, the *solvation energy* $E_3$ is released as solvent molecules bond to solute particles. The solution process is favored when $E_1$ and $E_2$ are low, and when $E_3$ is high. It is especially favored when $E_3$ is greater than $E_1 + E_2$.

## 16.2 Energy and aqueous solutions

In comparing attractive forces in molecular and ionic solids, $E_1$ will be far greater for the latter, in which strong coulombic forces exist between ions of opposite charge. Therefore, we might predict that

# and Electrolytes

molecular solids are more soluble in water than are ionic solids. Experimentally, this is not the case. In general, ionic solids are more water-soluble than molecular solids.

For water, with its highly polar molecules and extensive hydrogen bonding, $E_2$ must also be high. Since there is relatively little attraction between the nonpolar or weakly polar molecules that exist in molecular solids and the highly polar water molecules, the solvation energy, $E_3$, is smaller than the sum, $E_1 + E_2$. This accounts for the low solubility of molecular solids in water.

Since ionic solids do dissolve in water even though $E_1$ and $E_2$ are high, it must be that $E_3$ is also high. For the moment, then, we are left with the problem of accounting theoretically for the high solvation energies that must accompany the solution of ionic solids. Shortly, we shall discover the explanation that we seek.

## 16.3 Energy and solutions formed by nonpolar solvents

For nonpolar solvents, such as benzene and carbon tetrachloride, $E_2$ will usually have low to moderate values. Solvation energies, $E_3$, for molecular solids in such solvents have moderate to high values, while the values of $E_3$ for ionic solute particles in such solvents is low. Thus, experimentally, it is generally found that molecular solids exhibit greater solubility in solutions formed by nonpolar solvents than ionic solids do. Table 16–1 summarizes the general energy effects that help determine relative solubilities of compounds.

347

**TABLE 16–1**     ENERGY EFFECTS AND THE RELATIVE SOLUBILITIES OF COMPOUNDS

| Solute | Solvent | $E_1$ | $E_2$ | $E_3$ | Relative Solubility |
|--------|---------|-------|-------|-------|---------------------|
| Ionic solid | water | high | high | very high | moderate to high |
| Molecular solid | water | moderate | high | low | low |
| Ionic solid | nonpolar liquid | high | moderate | low | low |
| Molecular solid | nonpolar liquid | moderate | moderate | moderate | moderate to high |

### 16.4 Molarity and the concentration of solutions

For soluble substances, it is possible to prepare a wide range of solutions of varying concentrations, from the very dilute to the very concentrated. It is important to be able to express and to use quantitative solution concentrations. There are a number of ways to express concentrations. Perhaps the most commonly used expression, and the one that shall be used predominantly henceforth in this book is *molarity*, *M*. The molarity of a solution is measured and expressed as *the number of moles of solute dissolved in one liter of total solution*. That is:

$$M = \frac{\text{number of moles of solute}}{\text{liter of total solution}}$$

or

$$M = \frac{n}{V}$$

Note carefully that it is the volume of the solution and not the volume of the solvent alone that is involved. The following example will make this clearer.

**EXAMPLE**

Calculate the molarity of the sulfuric acid solution formed when 4.9 g of pure, liquid $H_2SO_4$ are very carefully added to enough water to yield a total of 250 ml of solution.* ($H_2SO_4 =$ 98 g/mole)

**SOLUTION**

1. Find the number of moles of solute, $n_{H_2SO_4}$.

$$n_{H_2SO_4} = \frac{4.9 \text{ g } H_2SO_4}{98 \text{ g/mole } H_2SO_4}$$

$$n_{H_2SO_4} = 0.050 \text{ mole}$$

2. Express the *total* volume of the solution in terms of the liter.

$$250 \text{ ml} = 0.250 \text{ l}$$

---

* In Section 4.2, page 98, reference was made to the distinction between formula weights for ionic compounds and molecular weights for molecular compounds. Many chemists feel the distinction is important enough to limit the term molarity to solutions of molecular compounds whose true formulas are known. For all other solutes, for which only the simplest formulas are known, these chemists define the concentration term *formality* as the number of formula weights of solute per liter of total solution.

3. Calculate the molarity of the solution, $M_{H_2SO_4}$.

$$M_{H_2SO_4} = \frac{n}{V}$$

$$M_{H_2SO_4} = \frac{0.050 \text{ mole } H_2SO_4}{0.250 \text{ l of solution}}$$

$$M_{H_2SO_4} = 0.20 \frac{\text{mole } H_2SO_4}{\text{l of solution}}$$

or, most simply,

$$M_{H_2SO_4} = 0.20 \text{ mole/l}$$

When a solution is diluted, the volume of the solvent, hence of the solution, changes. The number of moles of solute remains the same. Since that same number of moles of solute is now distributed in a greater volume, the *concentration* of the solute, the number of moles per unit volume, is reduced. From the definition of molarity,

$$M = \frac{n}{V},$$

the number of moles of solute can be simply calculated as:

$$n = MV$$

Since $n$ remains the same before and after dilution, then:

$$M_1 V_1 = M_2 V_2$$

This simple relationship allows the quick calculation of concentration after dilution of a solution of known concentration.

**EXAMPLE**

250 ml of $0.20M$ $H_2SO_4$ are added to 1.00 l of water. What is the molarity of the resulting solution?

**SOLUTION**

$M_1 = 0.20 \text{ mole/ l}$ $\qquad$ $M_2 = ?$

$V_1 = 0.25 \text{ l}$ $\qquad$ $V_2 = (0.25 \text{ l} + 1.00 \text{ l}) = 1.25 \text{ l}$

$M_1 V_1 = M_2 V_2$

$M_2 = \frac{M_1 V_1}{V_2}$

$M_2 = \frac{(0.20 \text{ mole/l}) (0.25 \cancel{l})}{(1.25 \cancel{l})}$

$M_2 = 4.0 \times 10^{-2} \text{ mole/l}$

## 16.5 The use of molarity in solving problems

By virtue of the homogeneous nature of solutions, every part of a solution has the same concentration of dissolved solute. That is, if we have a tank car filled with $0.20M$ $H_2SO_4$, then any volume drawn from that tank car—from a drop, to a liter, to the whole carload—will have a sulfuric acid concentration equal to 0.20$M$. Thus, it is possible to measure exact *weights* of dissolved solutes indirectly by measuring exact volumes of solutions of known concentrations.

**EXAMPLE**

What weight of hydrogen chloride gas is dissolved in $2.00 \times 10^2$ ml of 0.400$M$ HCl? (HCl = 36.6 g/mole)

**SOLUTION**

1. Determine the number of moles of solute present.

$$n = MV$$
$$n = (0.400 \text{ mole HCl}/\cancel{l})(0.200 \cancel{l})$$
$$n = 8.00 \times 10^{-2} \text{ mole HCl}$$

2. Determine the weight of the solute.

$$\text{Weight of HCl} = (8.00 \times 10^{-2} \cancel{\text{mole}} \text{ HCl})(36.6 \text{ g}/\cancel{\text{mole}} \text{ HCl})$$
$$\text{Weight of HCl} = 2.93 \text{ g}$$

Since it is possible to calculate weights of dissolved solutes from solutions of known concentration, the study of stoichiometric relationships becomes a broader and more useful one, as the following example may indicate.

**EXAMPLE**

What volume of carbon dioxide gas measured at STP will be produced when an excess amount of solid $CaCO_3$ is treated with 250.0 ml of $4.00 \times 10^{-2} M$ HCl?

**SOLUTION**

Most simply:

1. $CaCO_3(s) + 2HCl(aq) = CaCl_2(aq) + CO_2(g) + H_2O(l)$

2. $$n_{HCl} = MV$$
$$n_{HCl} = (4.00 \times 10^{-2} \text{ mole}/\cancel{l})(0.250\cancel{l})$$
$$n_{HCl} = 1.00 \times 10^{-2} \text{ mole}$$

3. $$n_{CO_2} = \tfrac{1}{2}n_{HCl}$$
$$n_{CO_2} = \tfrac{1}{2}(1.00 \times 10^{-2} \text{ mole})$$
$$n_{CO_2} = 5.00 \times 10^{-3} \text{ mole}$$

4. $$V_{CO_2(STP)} = (5.00 \times 10^{-3} \cancel{\text{mole}})(22.4 \text{ l}/\cancel{\text{mole}})$$
$$V_{CO_2(STP)} = 0.112 \text{ liters}$$

## 16.6 Limits of solubility

When two or more gases are physically combined, they mix homogeneously in all proportions. In some cases, two liquids of very similar

SATURATED SOLUTION

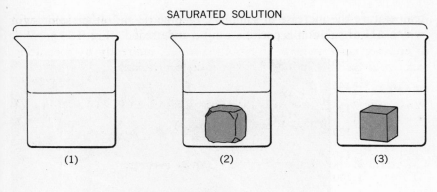

(1)                    (2)                    (3)

**FIGURE 16.1** A saturated solution is a dynamic equilibrium system. Explain the illustration.

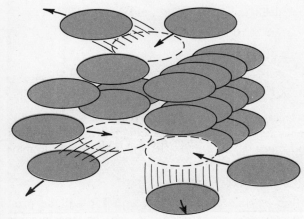

**FIGURE 16.2** When the rate of solution of solid glucose equals its rate of crystallization, the equilibrium state is reached.

structural properties are experimentally found to be infinitely soluble in each other. Such is the case for the ethyl alcohol-water system. However, for any solid solute-liquid solvent system, *at a given temperature*, an experimentally determined solute concentration is reached, at which additional solute added to the solution does not appear to dissolve. When this limit of solubility has been reached, the solution is called a *saturated solution*. Solubilities of solids are recorded as the concentration of the solute in the saturated solution.

When the properties of a saturated solution are carefully studied, it becomes evident that a dynamic equilibrium between dissolved and undissolved solute exists. (Fig. 16.1.) The equilibrium state is reached, at a given temperature, when the rate of solution of the solid equals the rate of crystallization of the solid. (Fig. 16.2.) We may represent the equilibrium state for a saturated solution of glucose, a simple sugar, as:

$$\text{glucose}(s) \rightleftharpoons \text{glucose}(aq)$$

For glucose, as with many soluble solids, the forward reaction is endothermic. Thus, in terms of Le Chatelier's principle, with increasing temperature the increase in solubility of glucose and other solutes for which $\Delta H$ of solution is positive can be understood. (Fig. 16.3.)

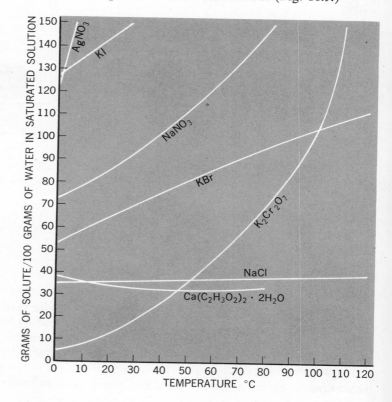

**FIGURE 16.3** Solubility varies with temperature.

## 16.7 Supersaturation: an unstable state

Though it may seem contradictory, with care it is possible at a given temperature to prepare a solution that contains more solute than is usual under saturated conditions. Such a *supersaturated solution* is thermodynamically unstable, and any disturbance of the system will lead to the instantaneous crystallization of the excess solute. A supersaturated solution is prepared by heating a saturated solution until the excess solute present dissolves. When the resulting solution is very carefully cooled, the excess solute will remain dissolved at the lower temperature, and the system will be supersaturated. If a pure *seed crystal* of the solute is added to this supersaturated solution, crystallization of pure crystals of the excess solute will occur on the seed crystal. Dust particles or the surface imperfections of the glass container holding a supersaturated solution can also serve as crystallization sites.

From these considerations of the solubility process we turn to the profound effects dissolved solutes have on the properties of water.

## 16.8 The electrical properties of solutions and electrolytic dissociation

Pure water is a very poor conductor of electricity. Many aqueous solutions, on the other hand, exhibit varying degrees of electrical conductance. A $1M$ NaCl solution is an excellent electrical conductor. So, too, is a $1M$ solution of the polar molecular gas HCl. On the other hand, a $1M$ solution of the polar molecular gas $NH_3$ is a weak electrical conductor whose conductivity increases upon dilution. Finally, a $1M$ solution of the very weakly polar molecular solid glucose shows no enhanced electrical conductance. How are these experimental facts to be interpreted?

In the case of the ionic solid, NaCl, it is reasonable to assume that upon solution the ionic crystal lattice comes apart, or *dissociates*, and $Na^{+1}$ and $Cl^{-1}$ ions are set free. We learned in Chapter 6 that when an ionic solid *melts*, its ions are freed from coulombic attractive influences and can carry an electric current. (See page 162.) Thus, it is reasonable to assume that similar ionic conductance imparts electrical properties to the $1M$ NaCl solution. To explain the electrical properties of solutions, the great Swedish chemist Svante Arrhenius (ahr ANE ee us) in 1887 proposed that ions form in solution. His brilliant assumption was made well before the electrical nature of matter as you understand it was known. All modern theoretical treatments of solutions that conduct electricity, solutions called *electrolytes*, stem from Arrhenius' *theory of electrolytic dissociation*.

**Svante Arrhenius** (1859–1927, Swedish). Although an accomplished chemist, he also speculated in other fields. He developed a theory of the origin of the solar system; suggested that life on earth may have come from some other planet; and dreamed of a universal language.

Arrhenius would have described the electrolytic dissociation of NaCl as:

$$NaCl(s) \xrightarrow{H_2O} Na^{+1}(aq) + Cl^{-1}(aq)$$

We now understand that the ions set free in solution were originally present in the solid NaCl. Thus, we will describe the dissociation as:

$$Na^{+1}Cl^{-1}(s) \xrightarrow{H_2O} Na^{+1}(aq) + Cl^{-1}(aq)$$

Experimentally, ionic solids dissociate to a very high degree upon dissolving. In dilute solutions, dissociation is complete.

## 16.9 Electrolytes and the ionization of covalent molecules

Since solutions of molecular species do not contain ions, electrolytic dissociation does not explain their electrical properties. Why then is a hydrochloric acid solution a strong electrolyte?

When hydrogen chloride gas is dissolved in benzene, albeit to a limited extent, the resulting solution does not conduct a current. We deduce that when molecular HCl dissolves in the nonpolar, molecular solvent benzene, it remains essentially as it was in the gas phase—a polar, covalently bonded molecule. Since an aqueous solution of HCl does conduct a current, we are led to hypothesize a reaction between the HCl and water that leads to the production of ions:

$$HCl(g) \xrightarrow{H_2O} H^{+1}(aq) + Cl^{-1}(aq)$$

Is such a reaction feasible? In terms of the polar nature of molecular HCl and molecular $H_2O$, it is. We assume that the attraction between the oxygen of the water dipole and the proton of the hydrogen chloride dipole is stronger than that between the proton and the chlorine atom in HCl. Therefore, the proton will be pulled away as a positive charge from the chlorine. The latter will be left with an extra electron and, thus, will become the negative chloride ion. Thus we propose a model for the *ionization* of HCl in aqueous solution:

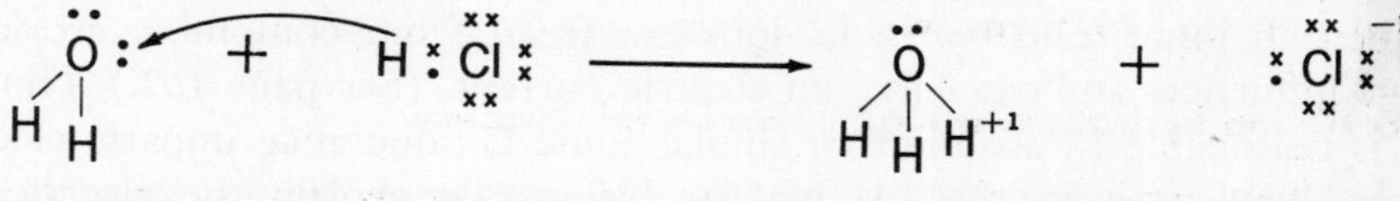

The $(H_3O)^{+1}$ ion is called the *hydronium ion*. In solutions of hydrochloric acid of moderate concentrations, all of which are strong electrolytes, it would appear that the ionization of all HCl molecules is complete. It would further appear that the reaction between HCl gas and water is responsible for the very high solubility of the gas—2.2 moles per 100 milliliters of water.

An incomplete ionization reaction between molecular $NH_3$ and molecular water helps to account for the weak electrolytic properties of aqueous solutions of ammonia, as well as for the extreme solubility of the gas (5.3 moles/100 ml $H_2O$ at 0°C). In this case, however, the hydronium ion is not a product. Experiment indicates the presence of the ammonium ion, $NH_4^{+1}$, in solution. Thus, the ionization reaction may first be written:

$$NH_3(g) + H_2O(l) \rightleftharpoons NH_4^{+1}(aq) + OH^{-1}(aq)$$

In terms of the mechanism of ionization, it would appear that the negative end of the ammonia molecule pulls a proton away from the positive end of a water molecule:

---

* We have assumed that when $NH_3$ gas dissolves in water, $NH_4OH$ molecules are the predominant aqueous species. The existence of this species, however, has *never* been experimentally verified. $NH_3$ (*aq*) is the experimentally indicated species and *will be used henceforth*.

$$H-\overset{\underset{\displaystyle H}{|}}{N}\!:\,\,+\,\,H\!:\!\overset{..}{\underset{\displaystyle H}{O}}\!:\,\,\rightleftharpoons\,\,H-\overset{\underset{\displaystyle H}{|}}{N}-H^{+1}\,\,+\,\,:\!\overset{..}{\underset{\displaystyle H}{O}}\!:^{-1}$$

Since, at a given temperature, the conductivity of aqueous ammonia solutions increases with dilution, the equilibrium pictured must also shift to the right with dilution. We might be tempted to explain this in terms of Le Chatelier's principle. However, Le Chatelier's principle would also lead us to predict an equilibrium shift to the right, leading to enhanced electrical conductivity as the concentration of ammonia is increased. Such a prediction is the precise opposite of the experimental observation. We understand that easy explanations are not always correct. In fact, the modern theory of electrolytic solution behavior has been developed to a very complex, highly mathematical degree. Thus, it will not be possible for us to consider electrolytes in any further theoretical detail. It should be evident, however, that the nonelectrolyte properties of glucose solutions are explained by the fact that ions do not form when glucose molecules dissolve.

### 16.10 Ion hydration: a highly exothermic process

The theory of electrolytic dissociation of ionic solids in solution, and the theory of ionization of covalent molecules to form electrolytes, provide the clue to the problem we were left with in Section 16.2. How can we theoretically account for the high solvation energies necessary for the solution of ionic solids? Since we theorize the formation of ions during any solution process that yields electrolytes, we must consider the solvation of ions to find the necessary energy supply.

Quite simply, when ions are set free in an environment of highly polar water molecules, strong attractive electrostatic forces arise between the ions and neighboring water molecules. Depending upon ion size as well as ion charge, a number of water molecules are strongly attracted and held in a *hydration shell* around the ion.* (Fig. 16.4.) This process of ion hydration is highly exothermic as the values for hydration energies of common ions given in Table 16–2 indicate. It is ion hydration energies, then, that fundamentally constitute the high solvation energies necessary for the solution of ionic solids.

### 16.11 Predominant solution species and the net ionic equation

With an understanding that aqueous solutions may contain ions only (strong electrolytes), solute molecules only (nonelectrolytes), or vary-

---

* Henceforth, water of hydration of ions will not be included in equations involving aqueous ions, unless necessary for the full understanding of the reaction involved.

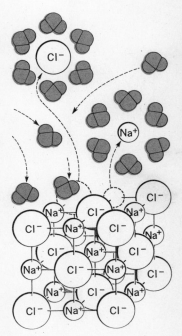

**FIGURE 16.4** A model for the solution of an ionic solid

## TABLE 16–2   COMMON ION HYDRATION ENERGIES

| Ion | Hydration Energy (kcal/mole)* | Ion | Hydration Energy (kcal/mole) |
|---|---|---|---|
| $H^{+1}$ | −256 | $Al^{+3}$ | −1109 |
| $Li^{+1}$ | −121 | $F^{-1}$ | −121 |
| $Na^{+1}$ | −95 | $Cl^{-1}$ | −90 |
| $K^{+1}$ | −75 | $Br^{-1}$ | −82 |
| $Mg^{+2}$ | −456 | $I^{-1}$ | −71 |
| $Fe^{+3}$ | −1041 | $OH^{-1}$ | −120 |

\* These values are *calculated* indirectly and are for the *hypothetical* solvation:
$$Ion(g) \rightarrow Ion(aq).$$

ing combinations of these (weak electrolytes), we can focus our attention on the predominant species in solution. By so doing, we may simplify equations involving solutions by including only the formulas of the predominant species involved in the reaction.

At the outset, then, we must determine what are the predominant species present in a solution. By convention, a *soluble substance* is one that forms *at least a 0.1 M solution* when it dissolves. Conversely, by convention, an *insoluble substance* is one that forms a *less than 0.1M solution* upon dissolving. For soluble substances, two simple rules help us identify the predominant solution species.

**RULE 1.** For soluble substances that yield **strong electrolytes**, the predominant solution species are ions, and **formulas for ions** will appear in the simplified equation.

**RULE 2.** For soluble substances that yield **weak electrolytes** and **nonelectrolytes**, the predominant solution species are molecules, and **molecular formulas** will appear in the simplified equation.

For all insoluble substances, another simple rule is followed.

**RULE 3.** For **insoluble substances, simplest or molecular formulas** will appear in the simplified equation.

The final rules for writing simplified equations are:

**RULE 4.** The *identical species* may not appear both as a reactant and as a product.

**RULE 5.** There must be conservation of mass (atoms) and conservation of charge.

Before we apply the rules to specific cases, we must take stock of our knowledge of soluble and insoluble substances. For soluble substances, we must know which lead to strong electrolytes and which lead to weak electrolytes. Table 16–3 summarizes the solubilities of

**TABLE 16–3** SOLUBILITY OF COMMON IONIC SOLIDS IN WATER

| Anions | Cations | Solubility |
|---|---|---|
| acetate chlorate nitrate | all | soluble |
| chloride bromide iodide | lead(II)*, silver, mercury(I) | insoluble |
| | all others | soluble |
| sulfate | lead(II), mercury(I), barium, calcium | insoluble |
| | all others | soluble |
| carbonate phosphate chromate | Group I metals, ammonium | soluble |
| | all others | insoluble |
| sulfide | Group I metals, ammonium, barium, calcium, magnesium | soluble |
| | all others | insoluble |
| hydroxide | Group I metals, barium | soluble |
| | all others | insoluble |

* Soluble in hot water

common ionic solids and should be used in conjunction with Rules 1 and 3. **Most soluble ionic solids are strong electrolytes.*** Most other strong and weak electrolytes that you will encounter are the strong and weak acids and the strong and weak bases to be discussed in Chapter 17. Water, itself, is a *very* weak electrolyte.

**EXAMPLE**

Write the simplified equation for the neutralization reaction between solutions of hydrochloric acid and sodium hydroxide.

**SOLUTION**

The complete equation for the reaction is:

$$HCl(aq) + NaOH(aq) = NaCl(aq) + H_2O(l)$$

---

* Two relatively important exceptions are $Pb(OOCCH_3)_2$ and $HgCl_2$.

From Table 16–3 and the discussions in this chapter, the equation can be rewritten in terms of Rules 1 and 2:

$$H_3O^{+1}(aq) + Cl^{-1}(aq) + Na^{+1}(aq) + OH^{-1}(aq)$$
$$= Na^{+1}(aq) + Cl^{-1}(aq) + H_2O(l)$$

According to Rule 4, the $Na^{+1}(aq)$ and $Cl^{-1}(aq)$ ions should be deleted:

$$H_3O^{+1}(aq) + OH^{-1}(aq) = H_2O(l)$$

According to Rule 5, two moles of water must be produced to conserve atoms:

$$H_3O^{+1}(aq) + OH^{-1}(aq) = 2H_2O(l)$$

According to Rule 5, charge must be conserved. The sum of the reactant charges is $([+1] + [-1])$, or zero, exactly the charge of the electrically neutral product. This last equation, then, is in its most simplified form. This simplified form is often called the *net ionic equation*.

**EXAMPLE**

Write the net ionic equation for the reaction between aqueous solutions of $NaCl$ and $AgNO_3$.

**SOLUTION**

1.    $NaCl(aq) + AgNO_3(aq) = AgCl(s) + NaNO_3(aq)$

2. $Na^{+1}(aq) + Cl^{-1}(aq) + Ag^{+1}(aq) + NO_3^{-1}(aq)$
$$= AgCl(s) + Na^{+1}(aq) + NO_3^{-1}(aq)$$

3.    $Cl^{-1}(aq) + Ag^{+1}(aq) = AgCl(s)$

A number of simple exercises in writing net ionic equations are provided at the end of the chapter. With practice, you will be able to combine the separate steps involved to arrive quickly at the equations. Until you feel confident in handling net ionic equations, it would be self-instructive to follow the stepwise procedures taken above.

**16.12  Solubility, equilibrium, and solubility products**

We took careful note in Section 16.6 of the equilibrium that exists between a saturated solution in contact with undissolved solute. We may now consider that equilibrium system in more detail, using the principles of chemical equilibrium that we learned in Chapter 15.

We focus our attention especially on solution equilibria involving relatively insoluble ionic solids. For example, let us first consider a saturated solution of $AgCl$. The solid is relatively insoluble— $1.3 \times 10^{-5}$ mole of $AgCl$ dissolving per liter of solution at 25.0°C. In writing the equation for the equilibrium reaction, however, we must not forget that whatever small amount of $AgCl$ does dissolve *will dis-*

*sociate completely into ions.* Thus, the equilibrium reaction is:

$$AgCl(s) \rightleftharpoons Ag^{+1}(aq) + Cl^{-1}(aq)$$

The equilibrium law expression for this system is:

$$K = [Ag^{+1}][Cl^{-1}]$$

Recall that the concentration of a pure solid does not appear in the equilibrium law expression and that the symbol $[Ag^{+1}]$ means the molar concentration of $Ag^{+1}$ ions. The constant, $K$, for a solubility equilibrium is called the *solubility product constant* and is given the special symbol $K_{sp}$. Table 16–4 lists $K_{sp}$ values of some commonly encountered insoluble ionic solids. For solids that are not very insoluble, $K_{sp}$ values are usually calculated from measured solubilities.*

**TABLE 16–4**   SOLUBILITY PRODUCT CONSTANTS (AT 25.0°C)

| Formula | $K_{sp}$ | Formula | $K_{sp}$ |
|---|---|---|---|
| $BaCO_3$ | $4.9 \times 10^{-9}$ | PbS | $7 \times 10^{-28}$ |
| $BaSO_4$ | $1.5 \times 10^{-9}$ | $MgCO_3$ | $1 \times 10^{-5}$ |
| $CdCO_3$ | $2.5 \times 10^{-14}$ | MnS | $1.4 \times 10^{-15}$ |
| CdS | $1 \times 10^{-28}$ | AgBr | $7.7 \times 10^{-13}$ |
| $CaCO_3$ | $4.8 \times 10^{-9}$ | AgCl | $1.7 \times 10^{-10}$ |
| $CaSO_4$ | $6.1 \times 10^{-5}$ | AgCN | $2 \times 10^{-12}$ |
| $PbCO_3$ | $1.6 \times 10^{-13}$ | AgI | $8.3 \times 10^{-17}$ |
| $PbCrO_4$ | $1.8 \times 10^{-14}$ | $SrSO_4$ | $2.8 \times 10^{-7}$ |
| $PbSO_4$ | $1.9 \times 10^{-8}$ | ZnS | $4.5 \times 10^{-24}$ |

Conversely, it is possible to calculate the solubility of an ionic solid if its $K_{sp}$ value is known.

**EXAMPLE**

The solubility of AgCl is $1.3 \times 10^{-5}$ mole/l at 25.0°C. Calculate the $K_{sp}$ of AgCl at that temperature.

**SOLUTION**

From
$$AgCl(s) \rightleftharpoons Ag^{+1}(aq) + Cl^{-1}(aq)$$

when $1.3 \times 10^{-5}$ mole of AgCl dissolve per liter of solution, $1.3 \times 10^{-5}$ mole/l of $Ag^{+1}(aq)$ ions and $1.3 \times 10^{-5}$ mole/l of $Cl^{-1}(aq)$ ions are completely formed. Therefore:

$$K_{sp} = [Ag^{+1}][Cl^{-1}]$$
$$K_{sp} = (1.3 \times 10^{-5} \text{ mole/l})(1.3 \times 10^{-5} \text{ mole/l})$$
$$K_{sp} = 1.7 \times 10^{-10}$$

---

* For solids of very low solubility, more complex and indirect experimental measurements must be made in order to determine $K_{sp}$ values.

**EXAMPLE**

From Table 16–4, $K_{sp}$ of BaSO₄ is seen to be $1.5 \times 10^{-9}$ at 25.0°C. What is the molar solubility of BaSO₄ at that temperature?

**SOLUTION**

The equilibrium reaction is:

$$BaSO_4(s) \rightleftharpoons Ba^{+2}(aq) + SO_4^{-2}(aq)$$

If we let $X$ equal the molar solubility of BaSO₄, then, according to the equation, $X$ will also equal the molar concentration of the $Ba^{+2}(aq)$ and $SO_4^{-2}(aq)$ ions that completely form. Since we know the value for $K_{sp}$, we can solve for $X$:

$$K_{sp} = [Ba^{+2}][SO_4^{-2}]$$
$$1.5 \times 10^{-9} = (X \text{ mole}/1)(X \text{ mole}/1)$$
$$1.5 \times 10^{-9} = X^2$$
$$15 \times 10^{-10} = X^2$$
$$\sqrt{15 \times 10^{-10}} = X$$
$$\sqrt{15} \times 10^{-5} = X$$
$$3.9 \times 10^{-5} \text{ mole}/1 = X$$

The solubility product is most significantly used in determining whether an insoluble precipitate will form upon the mixing of two solutions that contain ions whose chemical combination could lead to the precipitate formation. This predictive use of $K_{sp}$ is amply covered in the bibliographic references noted at the end of this chapter.

## 16.13 Colligative properties of solutions

We have dwelt in this chapter basically on the effect dissolved solutes have on one specific property of water, electrical conductivity. Briefly,

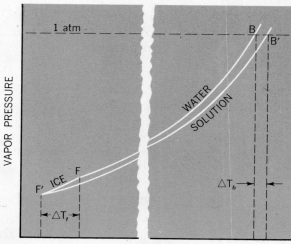

**FIGURE 16.5** The vapor pressures of pure water (F′FB) and a solution containing one mole of a nonvolatile nonionizing solute in 1000 g of pure water. (F′B′). $\Delta T_f$, the *freezing point depression* of water, equals 1.86°C per mole of dissolved particles. $\Delta T_b$, the *boiling point elevation* of water, equals 0.52°C per mole of dissolved particles.

we will conclude our discussion of solutions with an overview of the effect on another property of water, vapor pressure. Figure 16.5 shows clearly the experimental fact that when a *nonvolatile solute* is added to water, the vapor pressure of the resulting solution is lower than that of pure water at the same temperature. The greater the number of solute particles present, the greater is the depression of the vapor pressure. Qualitatively, a model in which nonvolatile solute particles replace surface water molecules, thereby lowering vapor pressure, makes good sense. (Fig. 16.6.)

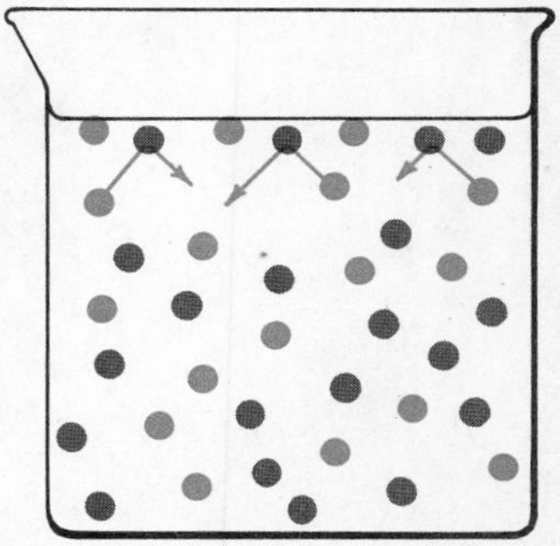

The properties of a solution that depend upon the number of dissolved solute particles are called *colligative properties* of the solution. Aside from vapor pressure itself, Figure 16.5 indicates that boiling points and freezing points are colligative properties. Boiling points are elevated and freezing points are depressed when nonvolatile solutes dissolve in volatile solvents. This is the principle behind the use of antifreeze in automobile radiators and of salt to melt ice.

**FIGURE 16.6**  A model to account for the lowering of the vapor pressure of water containing non-volatile solute particles

## 16.14  Three kinds of solute-solvent systems

Those solute-solvent systems for which there is a homogeneous distribution of solute particles in the solvent and for which the system appears to be, and experimentally has the properties of, a single phase are *true solutions*. The properties of true solutions may be partially explained in terms of the very small size of the solute particles.

There also exist solute-solvent systems for which solute particles are heterogeneously suspended in the solvent. In time, such a system will separate into two distinct phases, solute and solvent. Solute-solvent systems having these properties are called *coarse suspensions*. The properties of coarse suspensions may be partially explained in terms of the very large size of the suspended solute particles.

There exists a range of solute particle sizes for which a third and very vital type of solute-solvent system exists. In these systems, solute particles *appear* to be homogeneously distributed in the solvent, and the system *appears* to be a single phase. Close examination of such systems, however, indicates a heterogeneous suspension of solute in solvent. Further experimentation on such systems can lead to the separation of the system into two phases. These solute-solvent systems are called *colloids*, or colloidal suspensions. The study of colloids has taken on great significance in recent years as it is now realized that all living cells consist mainly of colloidal suspensions of great complexity.

## 16.15  The nature of colloids

Just as the properties of true solutions and coarse suspensions may be partly explained in terms of solute particle size, so, too, may two of the outstanding characteristics of colloidal systems—the optical prop-

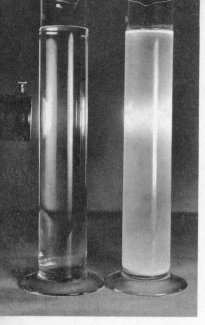

Particles in colloidal suspension are large enough to reflect light. Particles in true solution are not. The optical phenomenon of reflection by colloidal particles is known as the *Tyndall effect.* Where have you encountered this effect?

erties and the surface properties—be explained in terms of the size of the suspended particles. The very fact that some types of colloidal particles remain suspended is partly due to the unending bombardment of these small particles by solvent molecules.

In modern studies, two major size divisions are recognized for colloidal systems. In the first, the suspended part of the system has at least one of its dimensions in the range between 10 to 100 A ($10^{-7}$ – $10^{-5}$ cm). In this division, the properties of films and fibers are the main areas of experimental and theoretical concern. The second major size division includes suspended solid particles, liquid droplets, and gas bubbles with diameters of about $10^4$ A, or $10^{-4}$ cm. Table 16–5 lists some common colloidal systems characterized by suspension of solute particles in a dispersing solvent medium.

**TABLE 16–5**  SOME COMMON COLLOIDAL SYSTEMS

| *Type* | *Examples* |
| --- | --- |
| solid-in-liquid | egg white, gelatin, blood plasma |
| liquid-in-liquid (*emulsion*) | milk, mayonnaise, cold cream |
| gas-in-liquid (*foam*) | froth, meringue, whipped cream |
| solid-in-solid | black diamond, ruby glass |
| liquid-in-solid | opal |
| gas-in-solid | marshmallow, pumice |
| solid-in-gas | smoke, dust |
| liquid-in-gas (*aerosol*) | fog, mist |

In addition to size effects, electrical surface charge effects play a fundamental role in determining the macroscopic properties of colloidal systems. The surfaces of colloidal particles become charged through the adsorption of ions. If the surface charge can be neutralized, *coagulation* or *flocculation* of the colloidal particles will occur. This then results in the separation of the system into phases.

The combination of colloidal size and surface charge effects ultimately determine the attractive forces set up between suspended colloid particles and surrounding solvent particles. These forces, in turn, determine the fluid flow characteristics of a colloidal system. Where there is weak attraction between suspended and suspending media, the colloid is *free-flowing* and is called a *sol.* Where strong attraction exists between colloidal particles and solvent molecules, a *viscous* system results. Such a colloid is classified as a *gel.*

### 16.16 How colloids may be prepared

Since colloidal particles have sizes between those of solutes in true solution and those of particles in coarse suspension, two general methods for preparing colloids are suggested. In one case, it would seem possible to *build up* colloidal-sized particles from smaller particles that are in true solutions. The controlled formation of certain solids from aqueous solutions can be used to form colloidal suspensions of those solids. For example, if hydrogen sulfide gas is bubbled through a solution of sulfur dioxide, a milky colloidal suspension of sulfur forms:

$$2H_2S(g) + SO_2(aq) \rightarrow 3S(s) + 2H_2O(l)$$

The sulfur colloid will pass through filter paper.

The more common method of preparing colloidal suspensions is to break down large particles to colloidal size in a suspending medium. This may be done mechanically. For solids, grinding in a *colloid mill* is an important method for preparing colloidal suspensions, particularly of paint pigments. In the case of liquids, large globules may be forced through fine holes and be broken down to colloidal size in the *homogenization* process.

Division of large particles into colloidal size by chemical means is also common. When certain solids are treated with electrolytes, they form colloidal sols. The process is called *peptization*. The colloidal suspensions of brackish waters are due, in part, to the peptization of clays by the dissolved minerals in those waters.

Colloidal systems of liquids, or *emulsions*, can be established by breaking down large liquid globules by means of a small amount of another liquid, known as an *emulsifying agent*. This agent forms a protective coating on the colloidal-sized liquid particles that are formed and, by preventing their coagulation, permits them to be dispersed in a third liquid, the *dispersing medium*.

Aside from the biochemical significance of colloids, the fact that such everyday words as *homogenization*, *aerosol*, and *emulsion* have come from the study of colloidal systems is a clue to the widespread importance of that study.

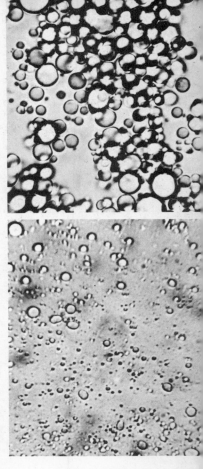

Photomicrographs of nonhomogenized milk (top) and homogenized milk (bottom). By homogenization, large fat globules are irreversibly broken down and dispersed more uniformly in milk.

## SUMMARY

The electrical and colligative properties of a solution differ greatly from those of the pure solvent. The Arrhenius theory of electrolytic dissociation and ionization is helpful in partially explaining how electrical properties of solutions arise. Knowledge of those properties, along with solubility data, allows us to write net ionic equations for reactions that occur in solution.

Solutions of solid solutes can be usefully studied from the point of view of equilibrium. The solubility product, $K_{sp}$, is determined by the solubility limit of an ionic solid at a given temperature. Concentrations of solutions are expressed in terms of molarity, $M$, and, as such, can be used to extend stoichiometric considerations.

True solutions constitute one kind of solute-solvent system. Colloids constitute another, in which solute particle size is larger than in true solutions but smaller than in coarse suspensions. An overview of the properties characteristic of the colloidal state as well as suggestions regarding the widespread importance of colloids is included in this chapter.

## QUESTIONS AND PROBLEMS

16.1   The energy arguments presented in Sections 16.1–16.3 were concerned only with electrostatic attractive forces that exist between particles in solution. What other factors will affect the solution process? Give examples of solute-solvent systems that illustrate the factors chosen.

16.2   At a given temperature, why does a spoonful of granulated sugar dissolve more rapidly than a lump of sugar?

16.3   Describe the entropy effects accompanying the solution of a gas in water and of a crystalline solid in water.

16.4   Calculate the molarity for each of the following solutions.
   a.  $5.00 \times 10^3$ mole of $CH_3COOH$ in $2.00 \times 10^{-2}$ l of solution
   b.  15.0 g of $CH_3COOH$ in $5.00 \times 10^2$ ml of solution
   c.  30.3 g of $KNO_3$ in 500.0 ml of solution
   d.  20.0 g of $NaOH$ in 0.250 l of solution
   Ans.   b. $0.5M$; d. $2.00M$

16.5   Calculate the amount of solute present in each of the following solutions.
   a.  40.0 ml of $2.00M$ $HNO_3$          c.  2 l of $1.0M$ $HgCl_2$
   b.  1.5 l of $18M$ $H_2SO_4$            d.  0.400 l of $0.24M$ $KOH$
   Ans.   b. $2.6 \times 10^2$ g; d. 5.4 g

16.6   How much water must be added to 0.500 l of $6.0M$ $H_2SO_4$ to form a $2.0M$ $H_2SO_4$ solution?

16.7   How many moles of hydrogen gas will be liberated when 0.18 mole of zinc reacts with the following?
   a.  0.400 l of $0.60M$ HCl          b.  0.400 l of $0.60M$ $H_2SO_4$
   Ans.   b. 0.18 mole

16.8   a. What volume of $0.500M$ $AgNO_3$ is required for the complete precipitation of AgCl from 0.160 l of $0.400M$ NaCl?
   b. What weight of AgCl will be precipitated?
   Ans.   b. 9.15 g

**16.9** Write a net ionic equation for the reaction between each of the following pairs of reactants.

a. $BaCl_2(aq) + Na_2SO_4(aq)$    g. $Pb(NO_3)_2(aq) + Na_3PO_4(aq)$
b. $Cl_2(g) + NaBr(aq)$    h. $NH_3(aq) + FeCl_3(aq)$
c. $KOH(aq) + H_2SO_4(aq)$    i. $H_2S(g) + Cu(NO_3)_2(aq)$
d. $Fe(OH)_3(s) + H_2SO_4(aq)$    j. $NaOH(aq) + CH_3COOH(aq)$
e. $NH_3(aq) + H_2SO_4(aq)$    k. $NaHCO_3(s) + HCl(aq)$
f. $Ba(OH)_2(aq) + MgSO_4(aq)$    l. $NH_3(aq) + CH_3COOH(aq)$

**16.10** What would you observe if you added a sugar crystal to each of three beakers containing, respectively, an unsaturated solution of sugar, a saturated solution of sugar, and a supersaturated solution of sugar?

**16.11** Using Table 16–4, calculate the molar solubility at 25.0°C of:
a. calcium carbonate    c. cadmium sulfide
b. lead(II) sulfate    d. silver iodide
ANS. b. $1.4 \times 10^{-4}$ mole/liter; d. $9.1 \times 10^{-9}$ mole/liter

**16.12** Calculate the solubility product constant at 25.0°C for each of the following solids. The solubility of each at 25.0°C is given.
a. barium chromate ($1.4 \times 10^{-2}$ mole/liter)
b. copper(II) oxalate ($1.69 \times 10^{-4}$ mole/liter)
c. thallium(I) bromide (0.57 g/liter)
d. radium sulfate ($2.0 \times 10^{-3}$ g/liter)
ANS. b. $2.86 \times 10^{-8}$; d. $3.9 \times 10^{-11}$

**16.13** a. Which aqueous solution has the lower vapor pressure at a given temperature, a $1M$ solution of the nonelectrolyte ethylene glycol or a $1M$ solution of sodium chloride? b. Why is ethylene glycol rather than sodium chloride used as a permanent antifreeze?

**16.14** Represented at the right are a half-filled beaker of pure solvent and a half-filled beaker of a solution containing that solvent, both having just been placed in a closed container. How will the appearance of the system change, if at all, with the passage of time? Explain your answer.

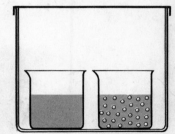

**16.15** One process for neutralizing the surface charge of a colloidal system is by adding an electrolyte to it. Explain how this process has been partially responsible for the formation of the great river deltas on the earth.

## SUGGESTED READINGS

Sisler, H. H. *Chemistry in Non-aqueous Solvents* (paperback). Reinhold, 1961.
Vold, M. J. and R. D. *Colloid Chemistry* (paperback). Reinhold, 1964.

*The paradox is now fully established
that the utmost abstractions
are the true weapons with which
to control our thought of concrete fact.*

*Alfred North Whitehead* (1861–1947)

**CHAPTER 17** | # Acids, Bases, and

Earlier in our studies we touched briefly on the preparation and properties of two classes of solutions of great historical importance—acids and bases. (See Secs. 5.8 and 5.9, pp. 123–124.) In view of the principles considered in the last four chapters, and, in particular, with an understanding of the theory of electrolytic dissociation and ionization, we turn now to seek models that account for their unique behavior.

### 17.1 Acids and bases: a first model

Operationally, you will recall, acids may be defined as solutions that:

1. Liberate $H_2$ gas when they react with certain metals;
2. Neutralize the effects of basic solutions;
3. Cause the blue form of litmus to convert to its red form;
4. Taste sour. (**Caution:** It is dangerous to use taste indiscriminately as a chemical test.)

Operationally, bases may be defined as solutions that:

1. React with solutions of salts of heavy metals to form insoluble hydroxides (in some cases, insoluble oxides form);
2. Neutralize the effects of acid solutions;
3. Cause the red form of litmus to convert to its blue form;
4. Taste bitter; (**Caution.**)
5. Feel slippery to the touch.

The first important conceptual definition of acids and bases that accounted well for most of the experimental facts listed was proposed by Arrhenius at the end of the nineteenth century. From his theory of electrolytic dissociation and ionization, he proposed that

# the Hydronium Ion

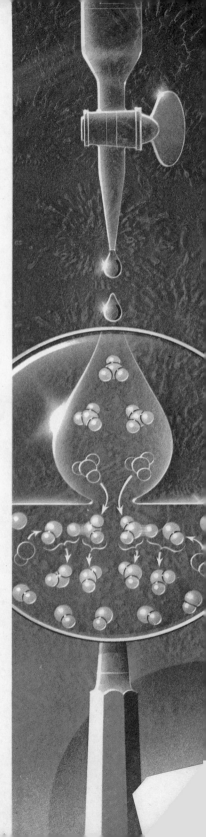

when acid solutions form, the hydrogen ion, $H^{+1}$, is set free in solution:

$$HA(aq) \longrightarrow H^{+1}(aq) + A^{-1}(aq)$$
general acid

The common properties of all acid solutions, then, according to this simple theory were due to the existence of the $H^{+1}$ ion. For example, the reaction of zinc metal with hydrochloric acid,

$$Zn(s) + 2HCl(aq) = ZnCl_2(aq) + H_2(g),$$

could be more simply expressed as:

$$Zn(s) + 2H^{+1}(aq) = Zn^{+2}(aq) + H_2(g)$$

Arrhenius further proposed that when basic solutions form, the hydroxyl ion, $OH^{-1}$, is set free in solution:

$$MOH(aq) \longrightarrow M^{+1}(aq) + OH^{-1}(aq)$$
general base

The common properties of all basic solutions then would be due to the existence of the $OH^{-1}$ ion. For example, the reaction between iron(III) chloride and sodium hydroxide solutions,

$$FeCl_3(aq) + 3NaOH(aq) = Fe(OH)_3(s) + 3NaCl(aq),$$

could be more simply expressed as:

$$Fe^{+3}(aq) + 3OH^{-1}(aq) = Fe(OH)_3(s)$$

## 17.2 Acids, bases, and proton ($H^{+1}$) transfer

As we noted in Section 16.9, the simple existence of the bare proton, $H^{+1}$, in solution is unlikely, if only from a mechanistic point of view.

*367*

We found it necessary, and logical, to assume that at least a monohydrated proton, the hydronium ion, $H_3O^{+1}$, formed when molecular substances formed acid solutions. Thus, Arrhenius' model of an acid must be extended to include the active role of water in the ionization process. For the specific case of the weak electrolyte acetic acid:

$$CH_3COOH(aq) + H_2O(l) \rightleftharpoons H_3O^{+1}(aq) + CH_3COO^{-1}(aq)$$

Arrhenius' model of a base may also be extended to include the active role of water. For metal hydroxides, which are ionic crystalline solids, the role of water is to bring about dissociation of the ionic lattice and hydration of the resulting aqueous ions. A simple equation cannot be written for this very complicated and not well-understood role. For the base aqueous ammonia, however, we can write a simple equation that takes into account the role of water in the ionization of molecular $NH_3$:

$$NH_3(aq) + H_2O(aq) \rightleftharpoons NH_4^{+1}(aq) + OH^{-1}(aq)$$

If we analyze the last two equations given, we can arrive at more general conceptual definitions of acids and bases.

We note that when an acetic acid molecule ionizes, a proton is transferred from the molecule to water. This is the same mechanism that we deduced in Section 16.9, and we are led to define an acid as *any substance that will donate protons* $(H^{+1})$* *to any substance that will accept them.*

We note that when an ammonia molecule ionizes, a proton is transferred *from* the water molecule to the ammonia molecule. We might, therefore, be led to define a base as *any substance that will accept protons from any substance that will donate them.* We can put our new, more general conceptual definitions of acids and bases to an immediate test. Four acid-base neutralization reactions, involving different combinations of strong and weak electrolytes, are represented by the following net ionic equations:

1. Aqueous HCl-aqueous NaOH (two strong electrolytes)

$$\underset{\text{acid}}{H_3O^{+1}(aq)} + \underset{\text{base}}{OH^{-1}(aq)} \rightarrow H_2O(l) + H_2O(l)$$

2. Aqueous HCl-aqueous $NH_3$ (a strong acid electrolyte and a weak basic electrolyte)

$$\underset{\text{acid}}{H_3O^{+1}(aq)} + \underset{\text{base}}{NH_3(aq)} \rightarrow NH_4^{+1}(aq) + H_2O(l)$$

---

* When we use the word *proton* in terms of acids, we are referring specifically to the ionized hydrogen atom, $H^{+1}$, and not to the proton as a nuclear particle.

3. Aqueous $CH_3COOH$-aqueous NaOH (a weak acid electrolyte and a strong basic electrolyte)

$$CH_3COOH(aq) + OH^{-1}(aq) \rightarrow H_2O(l) + CH_3COO^{-1}(aq)$$
$\quad\quad$ acid $\quad\quad\quad\quad$ base

4. Aqueous $CH_3COOH$-aqueous $NH_3$ (two weak electrolytes)

$$CH_3COOH(aq) + NH_3(aq) \rightarrow NH_4^{+1}(aq) + CH_3COO^{-1}(aq)$$
$\quad\quad$ acid $\quad\quad\quad\quad$ base

In each of the four neutralization reactions, the acid species does, indeed, transfer a proton to the basic species.

## 17.3 Acid-base conjugate pairs: the Brønsted-Lowry theory

The extension of Arrhenius' simple acid-base model to involve a proton transfer mechanism was deduced independently in 1923 by the Danish chemist J. N. Brønsted (BRURN sted) and the English chemist T. M. Lowry. The Brønsted-Lowry theory has valuable application in the interpretation of many fascinating experimental facts.

At the outset, since each proton transfer reaction we considered in the last section was an equilibrium reaction, we may consider the reverse of each.

1. $\quad\quad H_2O(l) + H_2O(l) \rightarrow H_3O^{+1}(aq) + OH^{-1}(aq)$
$\quad\quad\quad\quad$ acid $\quad\quad\quad$ base

2. $\quad\quad NH_4^{+1}(aq) + H_2O(l) \rightarrow H_3O^{+1}(aq) + NH_3(aq)$
$\quad\quad\quad\quad$ acid $\quad\quad\quad$ base

3. $\quad\quad H_2O(l) + CH_3COO^{-1}(aq) \rightarrow CH_3COOH(aq) + OH^{-1}(aq)$
$\quad\quad\quad$ acid $\quad\quad\quad$ base

4. $NH_4^{+1}(aq) + CH_3COO^{-1}(aq) \rightarrow CH_3COOH(aq) + NH_3(aq)$
$\quad$ acid $\quad\quad\quad\quad$ base

Combining analyses of the four neutralization reactions of Section 17.2 and the reverse of those reactions, we arrive at a basic principle of the Brønsted-Lowry theory.

*Every acid, upon transfer of a proton, becomes a base:*

$$HA(aq) + H_2O(l) \rightarrow H_3O^{+1}(aq) + A^{-1}(aq)$$
$\quad$ acid$_1$ $\longrightarrow\longrightarrow\longrightarrow\longrightarrow\longrightarrow$ base$_1$

*That base, upon accepting a proton, becomes the original acid:*

$$H_3O^{+1}(aq) + A^{-1}(aq) \rightarrow HA(aq) + H_2O(l)$$
$\quad\quad$ base$_1$ $\longrightarrow\longrightarrow$ acid$_1$

The acid-base pair, $HA(aq)$-$A^{-1}(aq)$, is called a Brønsted-Lowry *conjugate acid-base pair*. In any neutralization reaction, two different conjugate acid-base pairs are involved:

$$HA(aq) + B^{-1}(aq) \rightleftharpoons HB(aq) + A^{-1}(aq)$$
$$\text{acid}_1 \qquad \text{base}_2 \qquad \text{acid}_2 \qquad \text{base}_1$$

Table 17–1 lists some common Brønsted-Lowry conjugate acid-base pairs. When we consider this table in more quantitative detail, we will find it to be of important predictive use.

**TABLE 17–1** Common Conjugate Acid-Base Pairs

| Acid | Base | Acid | Base |
|------|------|------|------|
| $HClO_4$ | $ClO_4^{-1}$ | $H_3PO_4$ | $H_2PO_4^{-1}$ |
| $HCl$ | $Cl^{-1}$ | $CH_3COOH$ | $CH_3COO^{-1}$ |
| $HNO_3$ | $NO_3^{-1}$ | $H_2CO_3$† | $HCO_3^{-1}$ |
| $H_2SO_4$ | $HSO_4^{-1}$ | $H_2S$ | $HS^{-1}$ |
| $HOOCCOOH$ | $HOOCCOO^{-1}$ | $NH_4^{+1}$ | $NH_3$ |
| $H_2SO_3$* | $HSO_3^{-1}$ | $HCO_3^{-1}$ | $CO_3^{-2}$ |
| $HSO_4^{-1}$ | $SO_4^{-2}$ | $H_2O$ | $OH^{-1}$ |

## 17.4 The strengths of acids and bases

Since acids and bases are electrolytes, it is a simple matter to determine relative strengths of acids from electrical conductivity measurements. Since we have defined an acid in aqueous solution in terms of the reaction,

$$HA(aq) + H_2O(l) \rightleftharpoons H_3O^{+1}(aq) + A^{-1}(aq),$$
$$\text{acid}$$

then, at a given concentration:

1. The greater the measured electrical conductivity of an acid solution, the greater is the degree of ionization;
2. The greater the degree of ionization, the greater is the equilibrium concentration of $H_3O^{+1}$ ions;
3. The greater the equilibrium concentration of $H_3O^{+1}$ in an acid solution, the greater is the strength of the solution in terms of its acid properties.

Since the ionization reaction that defines an acid is an equilibrium reaction, experimental determination of the equilibrium constant

---

\* The existence of the species $H_2SO_3$ has never been experimentally verified. The formula $H_2SO_3$ is often more conveniently used than the more correct representations, $SO_2(aq)$ or $[SO_2(aq) + H_2O(l)]$.

† The existence of the species $H_2CO_3$ has never been experimentally verified. The formula $H_2CO_3$ is often more conveniently used than the more correct representations, $CO_2(aq)$ or $[CO_2(aq) + H_2O(l)]$.

for the reaction will give us a quantitative measure of the relative strength of the acid. For the case of a general acid, HA,

$$K_A = \frac{[H_3O^{+1}][A^{-1}]}{[HA]}$$

where $[H_3O^{+1}]$ and $[A^{-1}]$ represent measured equilibrium molar concentrations of aqueous ions, and $[HA]$ represents the measured equilibrium concentration of un-ionized acid. $K_A$ is the symbol chemists use for ionization constants of weak acids.

**EXAMPLE**

A $0.10M$ solution of nitrous acid, $HNO_2$, is found to be 6.50 per cent ionized at a certain temperature. Calculate $K_A$ for $HNO_2$.

**SOLUTION**

1. The ionization reaction is:

$$HNO_2(aq) + H_2O(l) \rightleftharpoons H_3O^{+1}(aq) + NO_2^{-1}(aq)$$

2. Before ionization takes place:

$[HNO_2] = 0.10$ mole/l

$[H_3O^{+1}] = 0.00$ mole/l

$[NO_2^{-1}] = 0.00$ mole/l

3. After ionization, *at equilibrium:*

$[HNO_2] = (0.10 \text{ mole/l} - 6.5\% \, [0.10 \text{ mole/l}])$

$[H_3O^{+1}] = 6.5\% \, (0.10 \text{ mole/l}) = 6.5 \times 10^{-3}$ mole/l

$[NO_2^{-1}] = 6.5\% \, (0.10 \text{ mole/l}) = 6.5 \times 10^{-3}$ mole/l

We have correctly considered the stoichiometry of the reaction by showing equal concentrations of $H_3O^{+1}$ and $NO_2^{-1}$ ions produced.

4. We proceed to calculate $K_A$.

$$K_A = \frac{[H_3O^{+1}][NO_2^{-1}]}{[HNO_2]}$$

$$K_A = \frac{(6.5 \times 10^{-3} \text{ mole/l})(6.5 \times 10^{-3} \text{ mole/l})}{(0.10 \text{ mole/l} - 6.5\% \, [0.10 \text{ mole/l}])}$$

We stop to consider the value of the denominator, the equilibrium concentration of un-ionized $HNO_2$. The data indicates that 93.5 per cent of the initial number of $HNO_2$ molecules present remain unreacted. For all practical purposes, it is not experimentally possible to note the change in the number of unreacted $HNO_2$ molecules. Whenever the degree of ionization of an acid is so small that it is not possible to subtract the concentration of ionized molecules from the concentration of un-ionized molecules, then we arbitrarily assume there is no change in the concentration of the acid before and at equilibrium and

neglect the small number that did react. In this case, we cannot make the subtraction required:    0.10    mole/l    originally
$$-0.0065 \text{ mole/l} \quad \text{ionized}$$
Thus:

$$K_A = \frac{(6.5 \times 10^{-3} \text{ mole/l})(6.5 \times 10^{-3} \text{ mole/l})}{(0.10 \text{ mole/l})}$$

$$K_A = 4.2 \times 10^{-4}$$

**EXAMPLE**

A solution is carefully prepared so that it is initially $1.00 \times 10^{-1} M$ in $HSO_4^{-1}$ ion at 25.0°C. The equilibrium molar concentration of $H_3O^{+1}$ ion is found to be $3.04 \times 10^{-2} M$. Calculate $K_A$ of $HSO_4^{-1}$ at 25.0°C.

**SOLUTION**

1. The ionization reaction is:

$$HSO_4^{-1}(aq) + H_2O(l) \rightleftharpoons H_3O^{+1}(aq) + SO_4^{-2}(aq)$$

2. Before ionization:

$$[HSO_4^{-1}] = 1.00 \times 10^{-1} \text{ mole/l}$$
$$[H_3O^{+1}] = 0.00 \text{ mole/l}$$
$$[SO_4^{-2}] = 0.00 \text{ mole/l}$$

3. After ionization, *at equilibrium:*

$$[H_3O^{+1}] = 3.04 \times 10^{-2} \text{ mole/l}$$

therefore

$$[SO_4^{-2}] = 3.04 \times 10^{-2} \text{ mole/l}$$

and    $[HSO_4^{-1}] = ([1.00 \times 10^{-1} \text{ mole/l}] - [3.04 \times 10^{-2} \text{ mole/l}])$

4.

$$K_A = \frac{[H_3O^{+1}][SO_4^{-2}]}{[HSO_4^{-1}]}$$

$$K_A = \frac{(3.04 \times 10^{-2} \text{ mole/l})(3.04 \times 10^{-2} \text{ mole/l})}{([1.00 \times 10^{-1} \text{ mole/l}] - [3.04 \times 10^{-2} \text{ mole/l}])}$$

What about the value of the denominator in this case? Can we make this subtraction?

$$0.100 \text{ mole/l}$$
$$-0.0304 \text{ mole/l}$$

Indeed, we can and must. Therefore:

$$K_A = \frac{(3.04 \times 10^{-2} \text{ mole/l})(3.04 \times 10^{-2} \text{ mole/l})}{(0.070 \text{ mole/l})}$$

$$K_A = 1.3 \times 10^{-2}$$

From calculations of the type just considered, a table of equilibrium constants for Brønsted-Lowry acids can be derived from experimental measurements. Table 17–2 is such a table.

**TABLE 17–2**   $K_A$ VALUES FOR CONJUGATE ACID-BASE PAIRS

| Acid | | Base | $K_{Acid}$ | Acid Strength |
|------|---|------|------------|---------------|
| $HClO_4$ | — | $ClO_4^{-1}$ | large | strong |
| $HI$ | — | $I^{-1}$ | large | strong |
| $HBr$ | — | $Br^{-1}$ | large | strong |
| $HCl$ | — | $Cl^{-1}$ | large | strong |
| $HNO_3$ | — | $NO_3^{-1}$ | large | strong |
| $H_2SO_4$ | — | $HSO_4^{-1}$ | large | strong |
| $H_3O^{+1}$ | — | $H_2O$ | 1 | strong |
| $HOOCCOOH$ | — | $HOOCCOO^{-1}$ | $5.4 \times 10^{-2}$ | weak |
| $H_2SO_3$ | — | $HSO_3^{-1}$ | $1.7 \times 10^{-2}$ | weak |
| $HSO_4^{-1}$ | — | $SO_4^{-2}$ | $1.3 \times 10^{-2}$ | weak |
| $H_3PO_4$ | — | $H_2PO_4^{-1}$ | $7.1 \times 10^{-3}$ | weak |
| $HF$ | — | $F^{-1}$ | $6.7 \times 10^{-4}$ | weak |
| $HNO_2$ | — | $NO_2^{-1}$ | $5.1 \times 10^{-4}$ | weak |
| $CH_3COOH$ | — | $CH_3COO^{-1}$ | $1.8 \times 10^{-5}$ | weak |
| $H_2CO_3$ | — | $HCO_3^{-1}$ | $4.4 \times 10^{-7}$ | weak |
| $H_2S$ | — | $HS^{-1}$ | $1.0 \times 10^{-7}$ | weak |
| $H_2PO_4^{-1}$ | — | $HPO_4^{-2}$ | $6.3 \times 10^{-8}$ | weak |
| $HSO_3^{-1}$ | — | $SO_3^{-2}$ | $6.2 \times 10^{-8}$ | weak |
| $NH_4^{+1}$ | — | $NH_3$ | $5.7 \times 10^{-10}$ | weak |
| $HCO_3^{-1}$ | — | $CO_3^{-2}$ | $4.7 \times 10^{-11}$ | weak |
| $HPO_4^{-2}$ | — | $PO_4^{-3}$ | $4.4 \times 10^{-13}$ | weak |
| $HS^{-1}$ | — | $S^{-2}$ | $1.3 \times 10^{-13}$ | weak |
| $H_2O$ | — | $OH^{-1}$ | $1.0 \times 10^{-14}$ | weak |

Observe that of the twenty-two acids listed fifteen are molecular species while seven are ions. Of the fifteen molecular acids, six are strong electrolytes—$HClO_4$, $HI$, $HBr$, $HCl$, $HNO_3$, and $H_2SO_4$—and are all represented by the $H_3O^{+1}$ ion in net ionic equations for their reactions as acids. Table 17–2 may now be used in conjunction with the solubility information of Table 16–3 in order to predict predominant species in solution when writing net ionic equations.

We have said little about the relative strengths of bases. It follows, quite simply, from our previous discussion that if an acid is strong, its conjugate base is weak. If an acid is weak, its conjugate base is strong. The $ClO_4^{-1}$, $I^{-1}$, $Br^{-1}$, $Cl^{-1}$, $NO_3^{-1}$, and $HSO_4^{-1}$ aqueous ions that head the list of bases in Table 17–2 are very weak. The strongest base in the water solvent system is, as should be expected, the $OH^{-1}$ ion.

## 17.5 Predicting acid-base reactions

The special value of Table 17–2 to us is in the predictive use to which it may be put. Simply, any acid in the left-hand column should react with any base below it in the right-hand column. In other words, all other things being equal, a stronger acid will react with the conjugate base of a weaker acid. For example, any of the six strong acids listed will react with every conjugate base of the sixteen weak acids listed to form the weak acid. Choosing the acetate ion, $CH_3COO^{-1}$, as an example of the base of a weak acid, the net ionic equation for *each* of the six reactions between $CH_3COO^{-1}$ ion and the six strong acids is:

$$H_3O^{+1}(aq) + CH_3COO^{-1}(aq) \rightleftharpoons CH_3COOH(aq) + H_2O(l)$$

Since this reaction is the reverse of the ionization of $CH_3COOH$, the value of the equilibrium constant for it, at 25.0°C,

$$K = \frac{[CH_3COOH]}{[H_3O^{+1}][CH_3COO^{-1}]},$$

will be equal to the reciprocal of $K_A$ of $CH_3COOH$ at that temperature. That is, $K$ for this predicted reaction will equal:

$$K = \frac{1}{K_{CH3COOH}}$$

$$K = \frac{1}{1.8 \times 10^{-5}}$$

$$K = 5.6 \times 10^4$$

This is an extremely large equilibrium constant, indicating that the products are, indeed, thermodynamically favored over reactants. As always, though we may be able to predict that a reaction should occur, we must resort ultimately to experimental verification to determine whether it does occur. It may be that the rate of the predictable reaction may be so slow as to preclude its occurrence in a reasonable length of time.

Thus, we conclude our consideration of the first practical value of the Brønsted-Lowry theory.

## 17.6 Amphiprotism and the Brønsted-Lowry theory

When a solution of $NaOH$ is slowly added to a solution of $Al(NO_3)_3$, a white, gelatinous precipitate of $Al(OH)_3$ forms. The $Al^{+3}$ ion, being quite small (ionic radius equals 0.51 A) and of high positive charge, exhibits a very high hydration energy in forming what is most likely the $Al(H_2O)_6^{+3}$ aqueous ion ($\Delta H = -1100$ kcal/mole). It is this aqueous species that we choose to use in writing the net ionic equation for the precipitation reaction:

$$Al(H_2O)_6^{+3}(aq) + 3OH^{-1}(aq) \rightleftharpoons Al(H_2O)_3(OH)_3(s) + 3H_2O(l)$$

The species $Al(H_2O)_3(OH)_3(s)$ should be recognized as a hydrated form of $Al(OH)_3(s)$. It is a reasonable species from at least two points of view. When gelatinous $Al(OH)_3$ is heated, hydrated forms of aluminum oxide, $Al_2O_3 \cdot XH_2O$, can be obtained, in which water molecules can experimentally be shown to be bonded to the $Al^{+3}$ ion. Also, the gelatinous nature of the aluminum hydroxide precipitate suggests the inclusion of a large amount of water within the solid structure. Thus, it is reasonable to expect that three of the six water molecules of hydration for the $Al(H_2O)_6^{+3}$ ion will remain bonded during the precipitation of the gelatinous hydroxide.

We carry the experiment further. Treating one part of the precipitate with strong acid leads to its dissolution. Treating a second part of the precipitate with excess strong base also leads to its dissolution. Aluminum hydroxide, then, is amphiprotic. The Brønsted-Lowry explanation of this experimental behavior is:

As a base,

$$Al(H_2O)_3(OH)_3(s) + 3H_3O^{+1}(aq) \rightleftharpoons Al(H_2O)_6^{+3}(aq) + 3H_2O(l)$$

As an acid,

$$Al(H_2O)_3(OH)_3(s) + OH^{-1}(aq) \rightleftharpoons Al(H_2O)_2(OH)_4^{-1}(aq) + H_2O(l)$$

The $Al(H_2O)_2(OH)_4^{-1}$ ion is usually written as $Al(OH)_4^{-1}$, the tetrahydroxoaluminate(III) ion, and is an example of a *complex ion*. (Complex ions and their nomenclature are discussed more fully in Chapter 25.) The experimental amphiprotism of a number of insoluble, gelatinous hydroxides, such as $Cr(OH)_3$, $Zn(OH)_2$, and $Pb(OH)_2$, may be similarly explained.

## 17.7 Hydrolysis

When blue litmus is added to a solution of aluminum nitrate, $Al(NO_3)_3$, the dye turns red. A salt solution is an acid! This seemingly strange conclusion is open to explanation on the basis of the conclusion from the Brønsted-Lowry theory that *aqueous cations, in general, are acids*. Thus, the hydrated $Al^{+3}$ ion reacts with water in an acid-base reaction:

$$Al(H_2O)_6^{+3}(aq) + H_2O(l) \rightleftharpoons H_3O^{+1}(aq) + Al(H_2O)_5(OH)^{+2}(aq)$$

Can this proceed further? Do the following acid-base reactions also occur?

$$Al(H_2O)_5(OH)^{+2}(aq) + H_2O(l) \rightleftharpoons Al(H_2O)_4(OH)_2^{+1}(aq) + H_3O^{+1}(aq)$$

$$Al(H_2O)_4(OH)_2^{+1}(aq) + H_2O(l) \rightleftharpoons Al(H_2O)_3(OH)_3(s) + H_3O^{+1}(aq)$$

If they do, we predict the presence of solid, gelatinous aluminum hydroxide in any solution prepared from an aluminum salt and water. If there is such a solution in your school laboratory that has been made up for some time, you will observe that our prediction was a good one.

The reactions of the hydrated aluminum(III) ionic species are examples of what have been called *hydrolysis reactions*, a term that simply implies a reaction with water. They are more than that, they are true Bronsted-Lowry acid-base reactions.

From the Bronsted-Lowry theory we also conclude that *anions, in general, are bases*. Therefore, should we not expect the aqueous $NO_3^{-1}$ ion to *hydrolyze*,

$$NO_3^{-1}(aq) + H_2O(l) \rightleftharpoons HNO_3(aq) + OH^{-1}(aq)?$$

No, for this would be the case of a weaker acid, $H_2O$, reacting with the conjugate base of a stronger acid, contrary to our conclusions of Section 17.6.

Anion hydrolysis does occur for the sixteen strong anionic bases listed in Table 17–2. For example, when solid sodium acetate is added to water the resulting solution is strongly alkaline. The explanation is that hydrolysis of the acetate ion occurs:

$$CH_3COO^{-1}(aq) + H_2O(l) \rightleftharpoons CH_3COOH(aq) + OH^{-1}(aq)$$

The aqueous sodium ion, $Na^{+1}$, being the very weak conjugate acid of the very strong base NaOH, does not undergo hydrolysis. *Metal cations derived from soluble, strong bases do not hydrolyze. Metal cations derived from insoluble, weak bases do hydrolyze.*

### 17.8  The hydronium ion: a closer look

Since, in essence, all the considerations of this chapter center around the hydronium ion, a closer look at that species is in order. We arrived at the theoretical existence of a monohydrated proton through a mechanism for the ionization of molecular hydrogen chloride in water. Though we did not consider it at the time, experimental evidence strongly suggests an even greater degree of hydration of a proton set free in an aqueous environment than is implied by the formula $H_3O^{+1}$.

The very small size of a bare proton limits the number of water molecules that can be bonded directly to it. At best, a tetrahedral orientation of four molecules is possible. (Fig. 17.1.) This would suggest that $H(H_2O)_4^{+1}$, or $H_9O_4^{+1}$, is the fundamental ionic species formed in acid solutions. Yet it is possible to hypothesize a hydrogen-bonded aggregate based on the $H_3O^{+1}$ ion that also corresponds to a $H_9O_4^{+1}$ species. (Fig. 17.2.) Experiments of all different kinds so far lead to the conclusion that a large number of different species, $H(H_2O)_X^{+1}$, probably exist in acid solution. Moreover, the value of X, as well as the number of different X values in a given acid solution, must be a complex function of acid concentration, nature of the anion and other dissolved particles, and temperature. For simplicity, then, we shall continue to use $H_3O^{+1}$ as the fundamental species that accounts for acidic properties in aqueous solution.

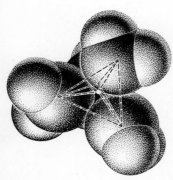

**FIGURE 17.1** A model for the hydronium ion: $H_9O_4^{+1}$

**FIGURE 17.2** Another model for the hydronium ion: $H_9O_4^{+1}$

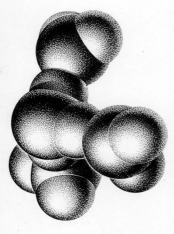

## 17.9 Acid-base neutralization reactions

The most carefully studied reaction involving acid solutions has been the neutralization reaction. In that reaction, in which a salt and water are products, heat is always liberated. Experimentally, it is found that 13.7 kcal *per mole of water formed* is released whenever *any* strong acid neutralizes *any* strong base. This is not surprising when we recognize that the net ionic equation for all such reactions is the same:

$$H_3O^{+1}(aq) + OH^{-1}(aq) \rightleftharpoons 2H_2O(l) \qquad \Delta H = -13.7 \text{ kcal/mole}$$

Thus the heat liberated is for the same reaction of a mole of protons transferring from a mole of hydronium ions to a mole of hydroxyl ions.

When weak acids are neutralized by strong bases, less heat is evolved. For example, results for the neutralization of acetic acid, $CH_3COOH$, and of hydrocyanic acid, HCN, by any strong base are:

$$CH_3COOH(aq) + OH^{-1}(aq) \rightleftharpoons CH_3COO^{-1}(aq) + H_2O(l)$$
$$\Delta H = -13.3 \text{ kcal/mole}$$

$$HCN(aq) + OH^{-1}(aq) \rightleftharpoons CN^{-1}(aq) + H_2O(l)$$
$$\Delta H = -2.9 \text{ kcal/mole}$$

Why are these heats of neutralization smaller? Since the acids are weak, energy is required to ionize them. The amount of energy required will be determined by the strength of the conjugate base of the weak acid. Since HCN ($K_A = 4.0 \times 10^{-10}$) is a far weaker acid than $CH_3COOH$ ($K_A = 1.8 \times 10^{-5}$), the cyanide ion, $CN^{-1}$, is a far stronger base than the acetate ion, $CH_3COO^{-1}$. Thus, more energy should be required to ionize HCN than $CH_3COOH$.

If we consider a two-step mechanism for the neutralization of a weak acid with a strong base, we can calculate the energy of ionization of the acid. For the case of $CH_3COOH$, we postulate:

1. $CH_3COOH(aq) + H_2O(l) \rightleftharpoons H_3O^{+1}(aq) + CH_3COO^{-1}(aq) \quad \Delta H_1$
2. $H_3O^{+1}(aq) + OH^{-1}(aq) \rightleftharpoons 2H_2O(l) \qquad\qquad\qquad\qquad \Delta H_2$

---

$CH_3COOH(aq) + OH^{-1}(aq) \rightleftharpoons CH_3COO^{-1}(aq) + H_2O(l) \; \Delta H_{\text{neut.}}$

Applying Hess's Law, we write:

$$\Delta H_{\text{neutralization}} = \Delta H_1 + \Delta H_2$$

Since it is a value for $\Delta H_1$, the energy of ionization, that we seek, then:

$$\Delta H_1 = \Delta H_{\text{neutralization}} - \Delta H_2$$

Our previous experimental data were:

$$\Delta H_2 = -13.7 \text{ kcal/mole}$$
$$\Delta H_{\text{neutralization}} = -13.3 \text{ kcal/mole}$$

Therefore:

$$\Delta H_1 = (-13.3 \text{ kcal/mole}) - (-13.7 \text{ kcal/mole})$$
$$\Delta H_1 = +0.4 \text{ kcal/mole}$$

To ionize a mole of aqueous $CH_3COOH$ molecules *requires* 400 calories. A similar calculation for the case of HCN shows that 10,800 calories are required for the ionization of one mole of HCN molecules. These results are experimental verification that aqueous HCN is a weaker acid than aqueous $CH_3COOH$.

### 17.10 Water as an acid and as a base

Water, as we have seen, is a very weak electrolyte of itself and is also amphiprotic. The amphiprotism of water accounts for the limited conductivity of pure water:

$$\underset{\text{acid}_1}{H_2O(l)} + \underset{\text{base}_2}{H_2O(l)} \rightleftharpoons \underset{\text{acid}_2}{H_3O^{+1}(aq)} + \underset{\text{base}_1}{OH^{-1}(aq)}$$

The ionization constant for this reaction, denoted by the symbol $K_W$, is simply the product of the molar concentrations of the $H_3O^{+1}$ and $OH^{-1}$ ions at equilibrium:

$$K_W = [H_3O^{+1}][OH^{-1}]$$

At 25.0°C, $K_W$ has the very low value of $1.0 \times 10^{-14}$. It would seem, therefore, that $H_2O$ itself is the weakest acid possible in the water solvent system. Table 17–2 indicates this.*

The equilibrium law expression for the self-ionization of water and the value of $K_W$ are very important. First, we may calculate the $H_3O^{+1}$ and $OH^{-1}$ ion concentrations in pure water at 25.0°C. The ionization reaction is:

$$H_2O(l) + H_2O(l) \rightleftharpoons H_3O^{+1}(aq) + OH^{-1}(aq)$$

---

* Actually, upon careful reasoning, the $OH^{-1}$ ion, being the strongest base in the water solvent system, should therefore be the weakest acid. As an acid, the $OH^{-1}$ aqueous ion has the oxide, $O^{-2}$, ion as its conjugate base:

$$OH^{-1}(aq) + H_2O(l) \rightleftharpoons H_3O^{+1}(aq) + O^{-2}(aq)$$

The equilibrium constant for this reaction is so small—it has been estimated to be of the order of $10^{-36}$—that for all practical purposes $H_2O$, and not $OH^{-1}$ ion, is the weakest aqueous acid.

Before ionization:

$$[H_3O^{+1}] = 0.0 \text{ mole/l}$$
$$[OH^{-1}] = 0.0 \text{ mole/l}$$

After ionization, the stoichiometric requirement is that equal amounts of $H_3O^{+1}$ and $OH^{-1}$ ions have formed. Therefore, if we let $X$ be the unknown equilibrium concentration of $H_3O^{+1}(aq)$:

$$[H_3O^{+1}] = [OH^{-1}] = X$$

and

$$K_W = [H_3O^{+1}][OH^{-1}]$$
$$K_W = (X)(X)$$

or

$$1.0 \times 10^{-14} = X^2$$

and

$$\sqrt{1.0 \times 10^{-14}} = X$$
$$1.0 \times 10^{-7} \text{ mole/l} = X$$

In pure water, at 25.0°C, the concentrations of $H_3O^{+1}$ and $OH^{-1}$ ions have the same value of $1.0 \times 10^{-7}$ mole/l. There being equal amounts of the acid, $H_3O^{+1}$, and the base, $OH^{-1}$, present, pure water is *neutral*.

Next, we must realize that no matter what equilibrium system is caused to exist in aqueous solution by the addition of solute to pure water, the equilibrium law for the $H_3O^{+1}$–$OH^{-1}$ system must always be satisfied. Thus, at the instant an acid is added to water, thereby increasing the $H_3O^{+1}$ ion concentration, the $H_3O^{+1}$–$OH^{-1}$ system must adjust for the change.

**EXAMPLE**

A $0.1M$ solution of HCl is prepared at 25.0°C. What is the concentration of $OH^{-1}$ ions in that solution?

**SOLUTION**

1. The $OH^{-1}$ ion concentration is fixed by the value of $K_W$ at 25.0°C.

$$K_W = [H_3O^{+1}][OH^{-1}]$$
$$[OH^{-1}] = \frac{K_W}{[H_3O^{+1}]}$$
$$[OH^{-1}] = \frac{1.0 \times 10^{-14}}{[H_3O^{+1}]}$$

2. The $H_3O^{+1}$ ion concentration at equilibrium is equal to the sum of the concentration contributed by the two acids in solution:

$$[H_3O^{+1}]_{equilibrium} = [H_3O^{+1}]_{HCl} + [H_3O^{+1}]_{H_2O}$$
$$[H_3O^{+1}]_{equilibrium} = 0.1 \text{ mole/l} + 1.0 \times 10^{-7} \text{ mole/l}$$

Quite obviously, we can neglect the contribution that water makes to the $H_3O^{+1}$ ion concentration, as we shall henceforth.

Therefore:    $[H_3O^{+1}]_{equilibrium} = 0.1$ mole/l

3. We conclude the calculation:

$$[OH^{-1}] = \frac{1.0 \times 10^{-14}}{0.1}$$

$$[OH^{-1}] = 1.0 \times 10^{-13} \text{ mole/l}$$

An *increase* in the $H_3O^{+1}$ ion concentration by a factor of one million ($10^{-7} \times 10^6 = 10^{-1}$) brings about a one-million-fold *decrease* ($10^{-7} \times 10^{-6} = 10^{-13}$) in the $OH^{-1}$ ion concentration, as should be expected.

Any change in the concentration of $H_3O^{+1}$ or $OH^{-1}$ ion concentrations from the value of $10^{-7}$ mole/l upsets the acid-base neutrality of pure water. When $[H_3O^{+1}] > 1.0 \times 10^{-7}$ mole/l, the solution is acidic. When $[OH^{-1}] > 1.0 \times 10^{-7}$ mole/l, the solution is basic.

## 17.11 The concept of pH

Since $K_W$ has such a low value, we are required to deal with cumbersome expressions for $H_3O^{+1}$ and $OH^{-1}$ ion concentration. Such expressions involve negative powers of the base 10. With some simple mathematical manipulations, we can find a simplified way to express $H_3O^{+1}$ and $OH^{-1}$ ion concentrations.

Beginning with the equilibrium law expression,

$$K_W = [H_3O^{+1}][OH^{-1}],$$

find the *logarithm to the base 10* of the expression:

$$\log K_W = \log ([H_3O^{+1}][OH^{-1}])$$

Since the logarithm of a product equals the sum of the logarithms of the quantities being multiplied:

$$\log K_W = \log [H_3O^{+1}] + \log [OH^{-1}]$$

Next, multiply through by $-1$:

$$-\log K_W = (-\log [H_3O^{+1}]) + (-\log [OH^{-1}])$$

Let the combination of the two mathematical operations, finding the logarithm and multiplying by $-1$, be represented by p, that is:

$$p = -\log$$

Therefore:    $pK_W = p[H_3O^{+1}] + p[OH^{-1}]$

Simplifying yet further, we let $H = [H_3O^{+1}]$

$$OH = [OH^{-1}]$$

so that          $pK_W = pH + pOH$

The pH, that is, $-\log [H_3O^{+1}]$, and the pOH, $-\log [OH^{-1}]$, are the simplest ways to express $H_3O^{+1}$ and $OH^{-1}$ ion concentrations, and are universally used as such.*

**EXAMPLE**

What is the pH of a $0.1M$ HCl solution at $25.0°C$?

**SOLUTION**

We have seen that for a $0.1M$ HCl solution, $[H_3O^{+1}] = 0.1$ mole/l. Or, for convenience in finding logarithms, $[H_3O^{+1}] = 1.0 \times 10^{-1}$ mole/l. Therefore:

$$pH = -\log [H_3O^{+1}]$$
$$pH = -\log (1.0 \times 10^{-1})$$
$$pH = (-\log 1.0) + (-\log 10^{-1})$$
$$pH = 0 + 1$$
$$pH = 1$$

**EXAMPLE**

What is the pOH of a $0.1M$ HCl solution at $25.0°C$?

**SOLUTION**

There are two ways to arrive at an answer.

1. Calculate $[OH^{-1}]$ and find pOH. As we saw, for this case, $[OH^{-1}] = 1.0 \times 10^{-13}$ mole/l. Therefore:

$$pOH = -\log [OH^{-1}]$$
$$pOH = -\log (1.0 \times 10^{-13})$$
$$pOH = 13$$

2. Use the relationship

$$pK_W = pH + pOH$$

Since          $K_W = 1.0 \times 10^{-14}$ at $25.0°C$

and            $pK_W = -\log K_W,$

then           $pK_W = 14$

Therefore, $pH + pOH = 14$, and if the pH of a $0.1M$ HCl solution is 1, the pOH is:

$$pOH = 14 - pH$$
$$pOH = 14 - 1$$
$$pOH = 13$$

---

* pH was first defined by the Danish chemist S. P. L. Sorenson in 1909. He chose p as a symbol from the Danish word *potenz*, meaning "power." The base 10 raised to the $-pH$ *power* is the $H_3O^{+1}$ ion molar concentration. That is, if a solution has a pH = 3.0, then $[H_3O^{+1}] = 10^{-3.0}$ mole/l.

Table 17–3 summarizes $[H_3O^{+1}]$, $[OH^{-1}]$, pH, and pOH relationships and how they affect the neutrality of water.

**TABLE 17–3**   THE SCALE OF pH

| $[H^{+1}]$ | $pH$ | $[OH^{-1}]$ | $pOH$ | |
|---|---|---|---|---|
| $10^0$ | 0 | $10^{-14}$ | 14 | |
| $10^{-1}$ | 1 | $10^{-13}$ | 13 | |
| $10^{-2}$ | 2 | $10^{-12}$ | 12 | |
| $10^{-3}$ | 3 | $10^{-11}$ | 11 | ACID SOLUTION |
| $10^{-4}$ | 4 | $10^{-10}$ | 10 | |
| $10^{-5}$ | 5 | $10^{-9}$ | 9 | |
| $10^{-6}$ | 6 | $10^{-8}$ | 8 | |
| $10^{-7}$ | 7 | $10^{-7}$ | 7 | NEUTRAL SOLUTION |
| $10^{-8}$ | 8 | $10^{-6}$ | 6 | |
| $10^{-9}$ | 9 | $10^{-5}$ | 5 | |
| $10^{-10}$ | 10 | $10^{-4}$ | 4 | |
| $10^{-11}$ | 11 | $10^{-3}$ | 3 | BASIC SOLUTION |
| $10^{-12}$ | 12 | $10^{-2}$ | 2 | |
| $10^{-13}$ | 13 | $10^{-1}$ | 1 | |
| $10^{-14}$ | 14 | $10^0$ | 0 | |

### 17.12 Acid-base indicators

Often the chemist finds it convenient to estimate, rather than to determine precisely, the pH of a solution. For this purpose, he uses acid-base indicators. These substances are usually weak organic acids with very complex structures. Conveniently, we will let HIn represent the formula for an acid-base indicator. In solution, this forms an equilibrium system of its own:

$$HIn(aq) + H_2O(l) \rightleftharpoons H_3O^{+1}(aq) + In^{-1}(aq)$$

For the HIn-In$^{-1}$ acid-base system to be an indicating system, the colors of the acid, HIn, and of the base, In$^{-1}$, must be different. Dozens of such systems exist. The mechanism of their indicating action can be understood in terms of Le Chatelier's principle.

When a few drops of HIn are added to water and equilibrium is established, a certain color will be present that is a blend of the different colors of HIn and In$^{-1}$. The precise color is determined by the equilibrium constant value for the HIn-In$^{-1}$ system. If the $K$ value is high, then the color of the In$^{-1}$ ion will be predominant. If $K$ has a low value, the color of HIn predominates. Now if the solution is made acidic—that is, if the $H_3O^{+1}$ ion concentration increases—the HIn-In$^{-1}$ equilibrium will shift to the left according to Le Chatelier's principle, and a color change will occur to indicate qualitatively that the pH has decreased. If the solution is made alkaline—that is, if there is a sudden increase in the concentration of OH$^{-1}$ ion—the HIn-In$^{-1}$

equilibrium will shift to the right. This will occur, since the added $OH^{-1}$ ion will react with $H_3O^{+1}$ ions present and the equilibrium will shift in the direction to replenish $H_3O^{+1}$ ions. Again, a color change will qualitatively indicate that pH has increased.

The pH ranges of acid-base indicators have been carefully determined and tabulated. (Table 17–4.) If he so chooses, the chemist may determine a pH value with high accuracy by selective use of a series of acid-base indicators.

**TABLE 17–4**    SOME ACID-BASE INDICATORS

| *Indicator* | *Color Change with Increasing pH* | *pH Range* |
|---|---|---|
| Thymol blue | red to yellow | 1.2—2.8 |
| Bromphenol blue | yellow to blue | 3.0—4.6 |
| Methyl orange | red to yellow | 3.1—4.4 |
| Bromcresol green | yellow to blue | 3.8—5.4 |
| Methyl red | red to yellow | 4.2—6.2 |
| Litmus | red to blue | 4.5—8.3 |
| Bromthymol blue | yellow to blue | 6.0—7.6 |
| Phenol red | yellow to red | 6.8—8.4 |
| Phenolphthalein | colorless to red | 8.3—10.0 |
| Alizarin yellow R | yellow to violet | 10.1—12.0 |
| 1, 3, 5-Trinitrobenzene | colorless to orange | 12.0—14.0 |

## 17.13 Acid-base titrations

The simplest and quickest method for determining pH is to use a *pH meter*. The electrical properties of a solution are a function of the pH. The pH meter selectively measures one of those electrical properties as a function of the $H_3O^{+1}$ ion concentration. In fact, the meter is usually calibrated on solutions of known pH so that the meter when in use will directly record pH. Since any dissolved ionic species will affect the electrical properties of a solution, you may wonder how the pH meter is selective for $H_3O^{+1}$ ions. This comes about as a result of the development of special glasses that are permeable only by $H_3O^{+1}$ ions. These glasses are used as sheathing for the electrodes in the meter. The electrodes, therefore, are sensitive only to $H_3O^{+1}$ ions—hence, the selectivity of pH meters.

Where pH meters are not available, a classical chemical method known as *acid-base titration* is used to determine pH. Let us consider the case of an acid solution, the pH of which is sought. A base of known concentration is carefully metered out through a *burette* into the acid solution of unknown concentration. When complete neutralization has occurred at the so-called end point of the titration, a sharp color change is observed in an acid-base indicator that is

A glass electrode

present. From the known volume of base of known concentration required for complete neutralization, the pH of the original acid can be calculated.

**EXAMPLE**

40.0 ml of $0.0500M$ NaOH were required for the exact neutralization of 50.0 ml of aqueous HCl. What is the pH of the HCl solution?

**SOLUTION**

1. The number of moles of base required for exact neutralization are:

$$n = MV$$
$$n = (5.00 \times 10^{-2}\,\text{mole/l})(4.00 \times 10^{-2}\,\text{l})$$
$$n = 2.00 \times 10^{-3}\,\text{mole}$$

2. Since the net ionic equation for the neutralization of HCl by NaOH is

$$OH^{-1}(aq) + H_3O^{+1}(aq) \rightleftharpoons 2H_2O(l),$$

the number of moles of base (or $OH^{-1}$ ion) must exactly equal the number of moles of acid (or $H_3O^{+1}$ ion). Thus, there were $2.00 \times 10^{-3}$ mole of HCl in 50.0 ml of solution originally.

3. The molarity of the HCl solution is, therefore:

$$M = \frac{2.00 \times 10^{-3}\,\text{mole}}{5.00 \times 10^{-2}\,\text{l}}$$
$$M = 4.00 \times 10^{-2}\,\text{mole/l}$$

and, therefore, $[H_3O^{+1}] = 4.00 \times 10^{-2}\,\text{mole/l}$.

4. The pH of the HCl solution is, therefore:

$$pH = -\log\,[H_3O^{+1}]$$
$$pH = -\log\,(4.00 \times 10^{-2})$$
$$pH = (-\log 4.00) + (-\log 10^{-2})$$
$$pH = (-0.60) + (2.00)$$
$$pH = 1.40$$

## 17.14 Acids and bases: a practical viewpoint

Just how important is it to understand as much as we have tried to in this chapter? There is first, hopefully, great importance attached to the satisfaction that should come from developing a consistent model to explain diverse experimental results even though such results may not have much practical meaning. But there is more.

Fully four fifths of the cultivated land in the central western United States is too acidic (sour) in natural form to be fully productive.

Therefore, it is necessary to agricultural economy for farmers to understand that the excess soil acidity should be neutralized. Vast amounts of CaO (lime) and Ca(OH)$_2$, a waste product from sugar refining, are used for this. Many industrial processes very heavily depend on pH control. Sugar refiners, brewers, papermakers, electroplaters, sanitary engineers, and bacteriologists, to name a few specialists, require an understanding of the behavior of acids and bases.

Probably the most dramatic processes in which pH control is critical are life processes. As a result of one of the remarkable ways that Nature does its work, the pH of a portion of the human digestive system is less than 7, thereby acidic, while the pH of the human circulatory system is slightly greater than 7, thereby alkaline. Any large change in the pH of either system can have serious physiological effects. Thus, an important part of medical training centers around pH and human physiology.

Indeed, we are walking acid-base equilibrium systems whose physical well-being depends on thousands of other acid-base equilibrium systems. It is assuring to have some understanding of the chemistry of those systems.

## SUMMARY

The experimental behavior of acids and bases in aqueous solution may be explained by use of the Brønsted-Lowry conceptual model of those substances. Such phenomena as acid-base neutralizations, amphiprotism, hydrolysis, and acid-base indicators may be understood in terms of this proton donor (acid)—proton acceptor (base) model. In conjunction with experimental and theoretical understanding of ionization reactions in solution, the model leads to a quantitative tabulation of conjugate acid-base equilibrium pairs. It is then possible to predict acid-base neutralizations.

The hydronium ion, $H_3O^{+1}(aq)$, must be the *simplest* form of the aqueous proton in terms of the Brønsted-Lowry model. It is the strongest acid in aqueous solution, and all strong acid electrolytes are represented by it in water. As a consequence of the weak, but significant, self-ionization of water, we must often deal with very small concentrations of the $H_3O^{+1}(aq)$ ion. The pH has been defined in a way that makes the handling of such concentrations convenient.

## QUESTIONS AND PROBLEMS

**17.1**  Define acids and bases operationally. Define acids and bases conceptually in two different ways.

**17.2** It requires three moles of NaOH to neutralize completely one mole of arsenic acid, $H_3AsO_4$. Show by equations the three acid-base systems that are present in an aqueous solution of $H_3AsO_4$. Pair up the conjugate acids and bases present, and write equilibrium-law expressions for each.

**17.3** Calculate $K_A$ for each of the following acids at 25.0°C and the experimental conditions cited.

a. A $0.010M$ solution of HCN that is 0.020 per cent ionized

b. A $1.0 \times 10^{-2}M$ solution of $CH_3COOH$ that is 4.2 per cent ionized

c. A solution is initially made $1.0M$ in $H_3AsO_4$. At equilibrium, the concentration of $H_2AsO_4^{-1}$ ion is found to be $1.6 \times 10^{-2}M$.

d. A solution is initially made $1.4 \times 10^{-2}M$ in cyanic acid, HOCN. At equilibrium, the concentration of $H_3O^{+1}$ ion is found to be $1.2 \times 10^{-2}M$.

Ans.    b. $1.8 \times 10^{-5}$; d. $7.2 \times 10^{-2}$

**17.4** Using Table 17–2, predict whether a reaction will occur between each member of the following aqueous systems. Write net ionic equations for the reactions that you predict should occur.

a. $HBr + NaF$                   e. $H_3PO_4 + NaHSO_3$

b. $NaHSO_4 + NaNO_2$          f. $NaHS + H_2O$

c. $NaHS + Na_3PO_4$           g. $Na_2HPO_4 + Na_2CO_3$

d. $CO_2(aq) + NaHS$          h. $Na_2CO_3 + H_2O$

**17.5** On long standing, an aqueous solution of iron(III) chloride becomes clouded with a brownish-red gelatinous solid. Using net ionic equations, explain this observation. Assume that $Fe(H_2O)_6^{+3}$ represents the aqueous iron(III) ion.

**17.6** When anhydrous samples of liquid HF and liquid HCN are mixed, they form an anhydrous weak electrolyte system. If $K_{HF} = 6.7 \times 10^{-4}$ and $K_{HCN} = 4.0 \times 10^{-10}$, write the net ionic equation to account for the observation.

**17.7** Write equations for the self-ionization that occurs in anhydrous liquid HF and in anhydrous liquid HCN.

**17.8** Using the data of Section 17.9, calculate the ionization energy per mole of HCN molecules in aqueous solution.

**17.9** Derive the value of the equilibrium constant of ammonia as a base, $NH_3(aq) + H_2O(l) \rightleftharpoons NH_4^{+1}(aq) + OH^{-1}(aq)$, using $K_{NH_4^{+1}}$ from Table 17–2 and $K_W$.

**17.10** Calculate the pH and pOH for each of the following solutions.

a. $1.00 \times 10^{-4}\ M$ HCl          e. $3.00\ M$ NaOH

b. $2.0 \times 10^{-3}\ M$ NaOH          f. $1.00 \times 10^{-6}\ M$ HCl

c. $1.00 \times 10^{-3}\ M$ $HClO_4$      g. $4.2 \times 10^{-3}\ M$ $HNO_3$

d. $0.10\ M$ $H_2S$                       h. $1.0\ M$ $NH_3$

Ans.    b. pOH = 2.7; d. pH = 4.0; f. pH = 5.96; h. pOH = 2.4

**17.11** Calculate $[H_3O^{+1}]$ and $[OH^{-1}]$ for solutions having the following pH or pOH values.

a. pH = 2.00      c. pH = 2.80      e. pOH = 6.00
b. pOH = 9.00     d. pH = 8.20     f. pOH = 4.80

Ans. b. $[OH^{-1}]$ = 1.00 × $10^{-9}$ m/l; d. $[H_3O^{+1}]$ = 6.3 × $10^{-9}$ m/l; f. $[OH^{-1}]$ = 1.6 × $10^{-5}$ m/l

**17.12** It requires 26.5 ml of a 0.100 *M* HCl solution to neutralize exactly 10.0 ml of a solution of NaOH of unknown concentration. Calculate a. the molar concentration of the base; b. the weight of salt produced.

Ans. b. 0.155 g

**17.13** Calculate the weight of $Al_2O_3$ that will be dissolved by reaction with 200.0 ml of 0.50 *M* HCl.

**17.14** Describe, with appropriate equations, a model for the behavior of a chemical acid-base indicator.

**17.15** Explain why bromthymol blue (Table 17–4) can be used in the titration of HCl with NaOH but not in the titration of $CH_3COOH$ with NaOH.

**17.16** a. Using data from Table 17–2, calculate the molar concentrations of all species present in a solution that is 0.010 *M* in $CO_2$.
b. What is the pH of the solution? c. Show that $K_{CO_2} \times K_{HCO_3^{-1}}$ yields the value for the equilibrium constant for the following system.

$$CO_2(aq) + 3H_2O(l) \rightleftharpoons 2H_3O^{+1}(aq) + CO_3^{-2}(aq)$$

Ans. b. 4.2

## SUGGESTED READINGS

Butler, J. N. *Solubility and pH Calculations* (paperback). Addison-Wesley Publishing Co., 1965.

Christensen, H. N. *pH and Dissociation* (paperback). W. B. Saunders Co., 1963.

VanderWerf, C. A. *Acids, Bases, and the Chemistry of the Covalent Bond* (paperback). Reinhold, 1961.

*And so it must always be;*
*the great experimentalist must*
*ever be the habitual theorist ....*

*John Tyndall* (1820–1893)

**CHAPTER 18** | # Oxidation, Reduction,

Perhaps the largest number of chemical reactions occurs between re-actants whose electron configurations are changed by the reaction. The first series of reactions of this nature that we came across was that between oxygen and elements in which oxides of the elements were products. We learned that such reactions historically were called *oxidation reactions.* (See Sec. 5.3, p. 118.) In Chapter 7, we singled out halogen displacement reactions as special cases of *oxidation-reduction reactions.* (See Sec. 7.7, pp. 173–174.) Finally, in Chapter 9, a narrow, historical definition of *reduction reactions* as deoxidation re-actions was given. (See Sec. 9.7, pp. 212–213.) If we return to examples of each reaction type cited—classical oxidation, halogen displacement, and reduction as deoxidation—we shall see that in each case the elec-tron configurations of the elements involved change when reactants form products. Further, we will seek general principles that we may apply to all reactions of which electron configuration changes are the primary characteristics—reactions that are now all called *oxidation-reduction,* or *redox,* reactions.

### 18.1 Classical oxidation: a closer look

We consider first a classical oxidation reaction—that between elemen-tal sodium and oxygen gas. When sodium slowly reacts with oxygen gas, sodium oxide is the chief product:

$$2\mathrm{Na}(s) + \tfrac{1}{2}\mathrm{O}_2(g) = \mathrm{Na}_2^{+1}\mathrm{O}^{-2}(s)$$

This reaction is a case not only of a classical oxidation but, more gen-erally, of an ionic reaction. Electrically neutral sodium atoms *donate*

# and $E°$

electrons to electrically neutral oxygen atoms, yielding $Na^{+1}$ ions and $O^{-2}$ ions:

$$_{11}Na^0 \ (1s^2 2s^2 2p^6 3s^1) \rightarrow {_{11}Na^{+1}} \ (1s^2 2s^2 2p^6) + e^{-1}$$
$$_8O^0 \ (1s^2 2s^2 2p^4) + 2e^{-1} \rightarrow {_8O^{-2}} \ (1s^2 2s^2 2p^6)$$

Since electrical neutrality, as well as conservation of atoms, must be maintained, we see why *two* neutral sodium atoms must ionize for each oxide ion that forms:

$$2[Na^0(s) \rightarrow Na^{+1} + e^{-1}]$$
$$\tfrac{1}{2}O_2{}^0(g) + 2e^{-1} \rightarrow O^{-2}$$

Net reaction: $2Na(s) + \tfrac{1}{2}O_2(g) = Na_2^{+1}O^{-2}(s)$

## 18.2 Halogen replacement: a closer look

A simple halogen replacement reaction may be similarly analyzed:

$$\tfrac{1}{2}Cl_2(g) + Br^{-1}(aq) = \tfrac{1}{2}Br_2(l) + Cl^{-1}(aq)$$

1.
$$_{35}Br^{-1} \ (1s^2 2s^2 2p^6 3s^2 3p^6 4s^2 3d^{10} 4p^6) \rightarrow {_{35}Br^0} \ (1s^2 2s^2 2p^6 3s^2 3p^6 4s^2 3d^{10} 4p^5) + e^{-1}$$
$$_{17}Cl^0 \ (1s^2 2s^2 2p^6 3s^2 3p^5 + e^{-1} \rightarrow {_{17}Cl^{-1}} \ (1s^2 2s^2 2p^6 3s^2 3p^6)$$

2.
$$Br^{-1}(aq) \rightarrow \tfrac{1}{2}Br_2^0(l) + e^{-1}$$
$$\tfrac{1}{2}Cl_2(g) + e^{-1} \rightarrow Cl^{-1}(aq)$$

Net reaction: $\tfrac{1}{2}Cl_2(g) + Br^{-1}(aq) = \tfrac{1}{2}Br_2(l) + Cl^{-1}(aq)$

389

## 18.3 Reduction as deoxidation: a closer look

Finally, the same kind of analysis of a hydrogen reduction, or deoxidation reaction,

$$H_2(g) + Cu^{+2}O^{-2}(s) \overset{\Delta}{=} Cu^0(s) + H_2O(g),$$

leads to some complexity. First, it is easy to see that the $Cu^{+2}$ ion in solid copper(II) oxide must gain two electrons to be *reduced* to elemental copper:

$$_{29}Cu^{+2} \; (1s^2 2s^2 2p^6 3s^2 3p^6 3d^9) + 2e^{-1} \rightarrow {}_{29}Cu^0 \; (1s^2 2s^2 2p^6 3s^2 3p^6 4s^2 3d^9)$$

However, it is not so simple to hypothesize a mechanism for the source of the electrons. It is true that there is a marked change in the electron environment of a hydrogen atom when it is transformed from the element into a covalently bonded hydrogen atom in steam. However, there is also a marked change in the electron environment of an oxygen atom when it is changed from the $O^{-2}$ *ion* into a covalently bonded oxygen *atom* in steam.

To parallel our first two analyses, therefore, we will postulate a two-step mechanism for the changes involving hydrogen and oxygen atoms. The first of these involves the formation of the *hypothetical* $(H^{+1})$ ion:

$$_1H^0 \; (1s^1) \rightarrow ({}_1H^{+1}) + e^{-1}$$

Since the $(H^{+1})$ ion is not an experimentally verifiable species, the next step of our mechanism assumes that a reaction between *ionic* $(H^{+1})$ and $O^{-2}$ ions results, *on electron rearrangements, in the formation of covalently bonded atoms:*

$$2(H^{+1}) + O^{-2} \rightarrow H_2O(l)$$

The intermediate formation of an $(H^{+1})$ ion allows us to complete our analysis of the deoxidation of reduction of copper(II) oxide:

$$H_2(g) \rightarrow 2(H^{+1}) + 2e^{-1}$$

$$\underline{Cu^{+2}O^{-2}(s) + 2e^{-1} + 2(H^{+1}) \rightarrow Cu^0(s) + H_2O(l)}$$

$$H_2(g) + Cu^{+2}O^{-2}(s) = Cu^0(s) + H_2O(l)$$

## 18.4 Oxidation and reduction broadly defined

Each of the three reactions that we have just considered has been analyzed via a two-step mechanism. The first step in each case involved *the formation of free electrons*, as a species of one electrical charge formed a species of *more positive* electrical charge:

$$Na^0 \rightarrow Na^{+1} + e^{-1}$$
$$Br^{-1} \rightarrow \tfrac{1}{2}Br_2{}^0 + e^{-1}$$
$$\tfrac{1}{2}H_2^0 \rightarrow (H^{+1}) + e^{-1}$$

Each of these reactions, and all reactions that lead to the formation of free electrons, are called *oxidation reactions*.

The second step involved a species of one electrical charge *accepting with electrons* to produce a species of *more negative* electrical charge: 

$$\tfrac{1}{2}O_2^0 + 2e^{-1} \rightarrow O^{-2}$$

$$\tfrac{1}{2}Cl_2^0 + e^{-1} \rightarrow Cl^{-1}$$

$$Cu^{+2}O^{-2} + 2e^{-1} + 2(H^{+1}) \rightarrow Cu^0 + H_2O$$

Each of these reactions, and all reactions that lead to the acceptance of electrons, are called *reduction reactions*.

Whenever an oxidation reaction occurs, it *must* be accompanied by a reduction reaction. During oxidation-reduction, or redox, reactions there is a *transfer of electrons from the substance being oxidized to the substance being reduced*. Substances that *donate* electrons are oxidized. Substances that *accept* electrons are reduced.

What situation might arise, we may wonder, if the electrons that are produced in an oxidation step can first be routed through a metal wire before they become consumed in a reduction step? Since electrons moving along a metallic wire constitute an electric current, a very practical situation suggests itself. If the two reactions that constitute a redox reaction can be physically separated into oxidation and reduction systems that are connected through an external conducting circuit, a useful electrical current in that circuit may be produced.

## 18.5 Chemical energy to electrical energy: electrochemical cells

The physical separation of the oxidation and reduction *half-reactions* that constitute a total redox reaction has been accomplished. This has not only provided chemical sources of electrical energy, but has also allowed the quantitative study of redox reactions.

When a zinc strip is immersed in a solution of copper(II) sulfate, the immediate deposition of copper metal on the zinc is observed. As the finely divided metallic grains of copper grow larger, the color of the deposit changes from black to the familiar reddish-gold color of copper.

The net ionic equation for the redox reaction is:

$$Zn^0(s) + Cu^{+2}(aq) = Zn^{+2}(aq) + Cu^0(s)$$

Two half-reactions may be postulated:

Oxidation: $\qquad\qquad Zn^0(s) \rightarrow Zn^{+2}(aq) + 2e^{-1}$

Reduction: $\qquad Cu^{+2}(aq) + 2e^{-1} \rightarrow Cu^0(s)$

When a zinc strip is immersed in a copper(II) sulfate solution, the two half-reactions occur *simultaneously* on the surface of the zinc,

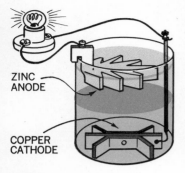

**FIGURE 18.1** In the *Daniell* cell, a copper cathode is immersed in a copper sulfate solution. A zinc anode is immersed in a zinc sulfate solution, which *floats* on the denser copper sulfate solution. What serves as a barrier to the bulk diffusion of ions?

and there is no opportunity to obtain electrical energy from the system. If the two half-reactions are physically separated, however, they serve as the basis of the electrochemical cell called the Daniell cell. (Fig. 18.1.)

Considering a more complex redox reaction, the oxidation of lead by lead(IV) oxide in sulfuric acid solution,

$$Pb(s) + PbO_2(s) + 4H_3O^{+1}(aq) + 2SO_4^{-2}(aq) = 2PbSO_4(s) + 6H_2O(l),$$

we may postulate two half-reactions:

Oxidation: $\qquad\qquad\qquad Pb(s) + SO_4^{-2}(aq) \rightarrow PbSO_4(s) + 2e^{-1}$

Reduction:

$$PbO_2(s) + SO_4^{-2}(aq) + 4H_3O^{+1}(aq) + 2e^{-1} \rightarrow PbSO_4(s) + 6H_2O(l)$$

(Note that insoluble $PbSO_4$ is a product of both the oxidation and reduction steps.) When these half-reactions are physically separated, they serve as the basis of the electrochemical cells that comprise the economically invaluable *lead storage battery*.

In recent years, many new and economically important electrochemical cells have been invented. These are based on the simple principle of physically separating the half-reactions that constitute an over-all redox reaction. These cells have found use in such diverse areas as space exploration and household appliances.

### 18.6 Electrochemical cells and oxidation potential

Redox reactions are, in general, reversible. You need only think of the discharging and charging of the lead storage battery to realize this. Because of the reversibility of redox half-reactions, and our ability to separate them physically, we can study quantitatively the relative tendencies of substances to be oxidized or reduced.

We may reconsider the two half-reactions that constitute the Daniell cell, both written as oxidations under reversible conditions:

$Zn(s) \rightleftharpoons Zn^{+2}(aq) + 2e^{-1}$ (abbreviated $Zn/Zn^{+2}$, and called the zinc–zinc plus two *couple*, or *half-cell*)

$Cu(s) \rightleftharpoons Cu^{+2}(aq) + 2e^{-1}$ (the $Cu/Cu^{+2}$, or copper–copper plus two, *couple*)

Associated with each of these oxidation half-reactions are a thermodynamic free energy change and associated equilibrium constant. These are measures of the spontaneity and extent to which each occurs. Related to these properties is another property, the tendency for a substance to be oxidized. This property is called the *oxidation potential* and is symbolized by $E$. Since an oxidation reaction cannot occur unless, simultaneously, a reduction reaction occurs, it is not possible to measure the individual tendencies for substances to oxidize.

However, by setting up two oxidation half-reactions in an electrochemical cell, the *difference* between their oxidation potentials can be quantitatively measured.

### 18.7 Measuring oxidation potential differences

In Figure 18.2 are depicted the carefully controlled conditions under which the difference between the oxidation potential of the $Zn/Zn^{+2}$ couple and of the $Cu/Cu^{+2}$ couple can be measured. The measuring device, symbolized by $V$, is a *voltmeter* and measures the *electrical potential*, or *voltage*, generated by the cell. The voltage of an electrochemical cell is a measure of the "pressure" of the electron flow produced by the cell. That voltage, or electrical potential, is equal to the *difference* in oxidation potentials between the two half-cells constituting the over-all cell.

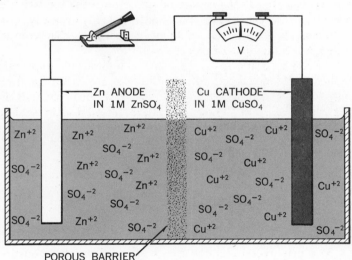

FIGURE 18.2    When the switch is closed in this system at 25.0°C, an electrochemical cell is operating under *standard conditions.*

When the switch is closed to complete the circuit in the setup of Figure 18.2, several observations and conclusions may be made:

1. Current flows in the external circuit, and the voltmeter registers +1.10 volts.

2. Oxidation occurs on the surface of the zinc strip, and electrons leave the cell by moving along the zinc and into the metal wires of the external circuit:

$$Zn(s) \rightleftharpoons Zn^{+2}(aq) + 2e^{-1}$$

A conducting surface at which an electron-involving reaction occurs is called an *electrode*. If the reaction is an oxidation, the electrode is more specifically called an *anode*. *Oxidation always occurs at an anode.*

3. Reduction occurs on the surface of the copper strip as electrons enter the cell from the metallic wires of the external circuit:

$$Cu^{+2}(aq) \rightleftharpoons Cu(s) + 2e^{-1}$$

The electrode at which reduction occurs is called a *cathode. Reduction always occurs at a cathode.**

4. The rate of ion migration through the porous plate increases. The concentration of sulfate ions in the $Zn/Zn^{+2}$ half-cell increases. The concentration of zinc(II) ions in the $Cu/Cu^{+2}$ half-cell increases.

You are left with two questions:

a. What *experimental observations* would lead us to conclude that oxidation occurs at the zinc electrode and reduction at the copper electrode?

b. Why do the observed *enhanced* ion migrations through the porous plate occur?

What conclusions can we make regarding the cell voltage, $E_{cell}$, and the oxidation potentials, $E$, of the individual half-cells present? Quite clearly, the oxidation potential of the $Zn/Zn^{+2}$ couple is greater than that of the $Cu/Cu^{+2}$ couple. It is great enough to cause $Cu^{+2}$ ions to be reduced. Experimentally, the oxidation potential of the $Zn/Zn^{+2}$ couple is greater than that of the $Cu/Cu^{+2}$ couple by 1.10 volts:

$$E_{cell} = E_{Zn/Zn^{+2}} - E_{Cu/Cu^{+2}}$$
$$E_{cell} = 1.10 \text{ volts}$$
$$E_{Zn/Zn^{+2}} = E_{Cu/Cu^{+2}} + 1.10 \text{ volts}$$

## 18.8 Predicting redox reactions

Let us consider another redox system in our attempt to understand, and then make use of, oxidation potential differences between redox couples. The reaction of zinc metal with strong acids to liberate hydrogen gas,

$$Zn(s) + 2H_3O^{+1}(aq) \rightleftharpoons Zn^{+2}(aq) + H_2(g) + 2H_2O(l),$$

---

* In an electrochemical cell, the anode, *in the external circuit,* is negatively charged. This makes sense, since negative electrons are donated at the anode. The electrons move through the circuit to the *positive* cathode, where they are accepted. An unfortunate situation concerning electrode signs arises when a long-standing convention is recalled. An electric current, by this convention, flows from a positive to a negative "pole." Thus, while electrons may be moving from − to +, current is, by convention, moving from + to −. Because such a situation is confusing, and because electrode signs in electrolytic cells (Chapter 19) are the reverse of those in electrochemical cells, we shall not be concerned with electrode signs. Just remember: oxidation—anode; reduction—cathode.

may be broken down into the two half-reactions:

Oxidation: $\qquad\qquad\qquad Zn(s) \rightleftharpoons Zn^{+2}(aq) + 2e^{-1}$

Reduction: $\quad 2H_3O^{+1}(aq) + 2e^{-1} \rightleftharpoons H_2(g) + 2H_2O(l)$

Under conditions similar to those holding in the previous consideration of the $Zn/Zn^{+2}$–$Cu/Cu^{+2}$ system, we may experimentally measure the difference between the oxidation potential of the $Zn/Zn^{+2}$ couple and the $H_2/H_3O^{+1}$ couple. (Fig. 18.3.) Remember that now we are concerned with the reverse of the reduction reaction given above.

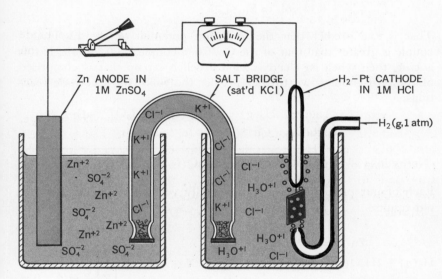

**FIGURE 18.3** When the switch is closed in this system at 25.0°C, an electrochemical cell is operating under *standard conditions*.

When the circuit in the setup of Figure 18.3 is closed, several observations may be made:

1. The voltmeter registers +0.76 volt.
2. At the zinc electrode, oxidation of zinc occurs, as expected.
3. At the platinum electrode, reduction of $H_3O^{+1}$ ions occurs, as expected. Experimentally, the pH *rises* in the vicinity of this electrode as soon as the circuit is closed.
4. Enhanced ion migration through the salt bridge occurs, and the $Zn/Zn^{+2}$ half-cell becomes more concentrated in $Cl^{-1}$ ions. The $H_2/H_3O^{+1}$ half-cell becomes more concentrated in $K^{+1}$ ions.

The important conclusion we sought is:

$$E_{cell} = E_{Zn/Zn^{+2}} - E_{H_2/H_3O^{+1}}$$
$$E_{cell} = +0.76 \text{ volt}$$
$$E_{Zn/Zn^{+2}} = E_{H_2/H_3O^{+1}} + 0.76 \text{ volt}$$

Experimentally, the oxidation potential of the $Zn/Zn^{+2}$ couple is greater than that of the $H_2/H_3O^{+1}$ couple.

As a result of our two experimental studies, we found:

$$E_{Zn/Zn^{+2}} = E_{Cu/Cu^{+2}} + 1.10 \text{ volts}$$
$$E_{Zn/Zn^{+2}} = E_{H_2/H_3O^{+1}} + 0.76 \text{ volt}$$

Therefore, we predict:

$$E_{Cu/Cu^{+2}} + 1.10 \text{ volts} = E_{H_2/H_3O^{+1}} + 0.76 \text{ volt}$$

or

$$E_{Cu/Cu^{+2}} + 0.34 \text{ volt} = E_{H_2/H_3O^{+1}}$$

That is, we predict that the oxidation potential of the $H_2/H_3O^{+1}$ couple is greater than that of the $Cu/Cu^{+2}$ couple by 0.34 volt. If this is true, then when an electrochemical cell is set up that is comprised of the two couples, we further predict the following electrode reactions:

$$\text{Anode:} \quad H_2(g) + 2H_2O(l) \rightleftharpoons 2H_3O^{+1}(aq) + 2e^{-1}$$
$$\text{Cathode:} \quad Cu^{+2}(aq) + 2e^{-1} \rightleftharpoons Cu(s)$$

$$\text{Net redox:} \quad H_2(g) + Cu^{+2}(aq) + 2H_2O(l) \rightleftharpoons 2H_3O^{+1}(aq) + Cu(s)$$

Each of our predictions is experimentally verified. We now tabulate our results:

$$E \text{ (volts)}$$

$$Zn(s) \rightleftharpoons Zn^{+2}(aq) + 2e^{-1}$$
$$H_2(g) + 2H_2O(l) \rightleftharpoons 2H_3O^{+1}(aq) + 2e^{-1} \quad X - Z = 1.10 \begin{cases} X \\ Y \\ Z \end{cases} \begin{matrix} X - Y = 0.76 \\ \\ Y - Z = 0.34 \end{matrix}$$
$$Cu(s) \rightleftharpoons Cu^{+2}(aq) + 2e^{-1}$$

## 18.9 Standard oxidation potentials

In dealing with redox reactions, chemists face the problem of being able to measure only differences in oxidation potentials. But these differences, as we have indicated, are related to thermodynamic properties of the redox system dependent only on initial and final states. Thus, while it is not possible to measure single half-cell $E$ values, it is possible *to assign* an arbitrary $E$ value to one such half-cell, and relate all other half-cell oxidation potentials to the arbitrary standard.

By convention, for the $H_2/H_3O^{+1}$ couple, under the carefully specified conditions,

$$H_2(g, 1 \text{ atm}) + 2H_2O(l) \overset{25.0\,°C}{\rightleftharpoons} 2H_3O^{+1}(1M) + 2e^{-1},$$

chemists have agreed that the oxidation potential for this half-cell shall have the value of *exactly* zero volts. Moreover, under these arbitrarily set conditions, the chemist refers to the oxidation potential of the $H_2/H_3O^{+1}$ couple as the *standard oxidation potential* of the couple, symbolized $E^0$.

Thus, under the carefully specified electrochemical *standard* cell conditions,

$$Zn(s) + 2H_3O^{+1}(1M) \overset{25.0°C}{\rightleftharpoons} Zn^{+2}(1M) + H_2(g, 1 \text{ atm}) + 2H_2O(l),$$

since

$$E^0_{Zn/Zn^{+2}} = E^0_{H_2/H_3O^{+1}} + 0.76 \text{ volt},$$

then

$$E^0_{Zn/Zn^{+2}} = 0.00 \text{ volt} + 0.76 \text{ volt},$$

and

$$E^0_{Zn/Zn^{+2}} = +0.76 \text{ volt}.$$

Likewise, under the carefully specified electrochemical standard cell conditions,

$$H_2(g, 1 \text{ atm}) + Cu^{+2}(1M) + 2H_2O(l) \rightleftharpoons Cu(s) + 2H_3O^{+1}(1M),$$

since

$$E^0_{Cu/Cu^{+2}} + 0.34 \text{ volt} = E^0_{H_2/H_3O^{+1}},$$

then

$$E^0_{Cu/Cu^{+2}} + 0.34 \text{ volt} = 0.00 \text{ volt},$$

and

$$E^0_{Cu/Cu^{+2}} = -0.34 \text{ volt}.$$

Our tabulated results of $E$ values become, in terms of $E^0$:

| Half-reaction | $E^0$ (volts) |
|---|---|
| $Zn(s) \rightleftharpoons Zn^{+2}(1M) + 2e^{-1}$ | $+0.76$ |
| $H_2(g, 1 \text{ atm}) + 2H_2O(l) \rightleftharpoons 2H_3O^{+1}(1M) + 2e^{-1}$ | $0.00$ |
| $Cu(s) \rightleftharpoons Cu^{+2}(1M) + 2e^{-1}$ | $-0.34$ |

Observe carefully that because $E^0_{H_2/H_3O^{+1}}$ is defined to have the value of exactly zero volts, the $E^0$ value for the $Cu/Cu^{+2}$ couple and for *all other redox couples that have lower oxidation potentials than the $H_2/H_3O^{+1}$ couple* will be negative.

## 18.10 Oxidation numbers: redox redefined

In practice, scores of $E^0$ values for different half-cell reactions have been measured relative to the $H_2/H_3O^{+1}$ couple under *standard conditions*. Before considering how valuable the tabulation of this $E^0$ data can be, we might first consider half-reactions more generally.

We have previously defined oxidation and reduction in terms of electron-donating and electron-accepting half-reactions. We also saw, however, that it is not always possible to determine which atom in a species is the actual donor or acceptor of electrons during redox reactions. It has proved convenient, therefore, for chemists to define a fictional property of atoms to help keep track of electron changes during redox reactions. The fictional property is called the *oxidation number*, or *oxidation state*, of the element. It is defined as the valence of the element, to which a + or − sign is affixed.

In the elemental state, the oxidation number of an element is zero. For simple cations, such as $Na^{+1}$, $Fe^{+2}$, and $Al^{+3}$, and for simple anions, such as $H^{-1}$, $Cl^{-1}$, $O^{-2}$, and $P^{-3}$, the oxidation number of the element is its *true ionic charge*. In complex ions or neutral covalent molecules, the oxidation number of an element is a fictional or apparent ionic charge.

The oxidation number for elements in complex ions or neutral molecular compounds may be found according to three simple rules:

1. The oxidation number of hydrogen *is defined to be* +1.

2. The oxidation number of oxygen *is defined to be* −2 except in peroxides when it is −1.

3. The oxidation number of any other element is such that the sum of the oxidation numbers of all the elements in a complex ion equals the charge of that ion or in a molecular compound equals zero.

Table 18–1 indicates how these rules are applied in some familiar complex ions and covalent molecules.

**TABLE 18–1** OXIDATION NUMBERS

| Complex Ion or Covalent Molecule | Oxidation Numbers | Conservation of Charge |
|---|---|---|
| $H_2O$ | $\overset{+1\ -2}{H_2O}$ | $2(+1) + (-2) = 0$ |
| $H_3O^{+1}$ | $\overset{+1\ -2}{(H_3O)}{}^{+1}$ | $3(+1) + (-2) = +1$ |
| $NH_3$ | $\overset{-3\ +1}{NH_3}$ | $(-3) + 3(+1) = 0$ |
| $NH_4{}^{+1}$ | $\overset{-3\ +1}{(NH_4)}{}^{+1}$ | $(-3) + 4(+1) = +1$ |
| $CH_3COOH$ | $\overset{0+1\ \ 0-2-2+1}{CH_3COOH}$ | $4(+1) + 2(-2) + 2(0) = 0$ |
| $CH_3COO^{-1}$ | $\overset{0+1\ \ 0-2-2}{(CH_3COO)}{}^{-1}$ | $3(+1) + 2(-2) + 2(0) = -1$ |

If we reconsider each of the oxidation and reduction half-reactions studied thus far in light of the concept of the oxidation number, a useful redefinition of oxidation and reduction becomes apparent. *Oxidation is the process in which the oxidation number of an element is increased. Reduction is the process in which the oxidation number of an element is decreased* (or *reduced* in value). Examples in support of these redefinitions are given in Table 18–2.

## 18.11 Oxidation numbers and net ionic equations for half-reactions

If an element, either by itself or in combination with other elements, can be assigned more than one oxidation number, we may write a half-

**TABLE 18–2**   REDOX REACTION AND CHANGE IN OXIDATION NUMBER

| *Half-reaction* | *Change in Oxidation Number* | *Process* |
|---|---|---|
| $\overset{0}{\mathrm{Na}}(s) \rightarrow \mathrm{Na}^{+1}(aq) + \mathrm{e}^{-1}$ | For Na: $0 \rightarrow +1$ | oxidation |
| $\frac{1}{2}\overset{0}{\mathrm{Cl}_2}(g) + \mathrm{e}^{-1} \rightarrow \mathrm{Cl}^{-1}(aq)$ | For Cl: $0 \rightarrow -1$ | reduction |
| $\overset{0}{\mathrm{H}_2}(g) + 2\mathrm{H}_2\mathrm{O}(l) \rightarrow 2(\overset{+1\ -2}{\mathrm{H}_3\mathrm{O}})^{+1}(aq) + 2\mathrm{e}^{-1}$ | For H: $0 \rightarrow +1$ | oxidation |

$$\overset{4+\ -2}{\mathrm{PbO}_2}(s) + (\overset{+6-2}{\mathrm{SO}_4})^{-2}(aq) + 4(\overset{+1\ -0}{\mathrm{H}_3\mathrm{O}})^{+1}(aq) + 2\mathrm{e}^{-1} \rightarrow \overset{+2+6-2}{\mathrm{PbSO}_4}(s) + 6\overset{+1\ -2}{\mathrm{H}_2\mathrm{O}}(l)$$

For Pb: $+4 \rightarrow +2$     reduction

reaction in which the element is *oxidized* from the state of lower oxidation number to the state of higher oxidation number.

**EXAMPLE**

Iron may be found as the iron(II) and iron(III) ions in neutral or acid solution. Write a net ionic equation for a half-cell reaction involving these two species.

**SOLUTION**

Since iron(II) is a state of lower oxidation number than iron(III), iron(II) can be oxidized to iron(III) in neutral or acid solution:

$$\mathrm{Fe}^{+2}(aq) \rightleftharpoons \mathrm{Fe}^{+3}(aq) + \mathrm{e}^{-1}$$

Experimentally, $E^0_{\mathrm{Fe}^{+2}/\mathrm{Fe}^{+3}}$ equals $-0.77$ volt.

**EXAMPLE**

Chromium may be found as the chromium(III) and dichromate ions in acid solution. Write a net ionic equation for a half-cell reaction involving these two species.

**SOLUTION**

1. The two ionic species are $\mathrm{Cr}^{+3}(aq)$ and $\mathrm{Cr}_2\mathrm{O}_7{}^{-2}(aq)$. The *ionic charge*, hence the oxidation number, in the $\mathrm{Cr}^{+3}(aq)$ ion is, of course, $+3$. We may simply determine the oxidation number of chromium in the $(\mathrm{Cr}_2\mathrm{O}_7)^{-2}(aq)$ ion:

$$(\overset{X\ \ -2}{\mathrm{Cr}_2\mathrm{O}_7})^{-2}: \qquad 2X + 7(-2) = -2$$
$$2X - 14 = -2$$
$$2X = +12$$
$$X = +6$$

The value of $+6$ for the oxidation number of chromium in $(\mathrm{Cr}_2\mathrm{O}_7)^{-2}(aq)$ must be recognized as a *fictional* charge.

2. Since chromium in $\mathrm{Cr}^{+3}(aq)$ ion has a lower oxidation number than in $(\mathrm{Cr}_2\mathrm{O}_7)^{-2}(aq)$ ion, $\mathrm{Cr}^{+3}(aq)$ can be oxidized to $(\mathrm{Cr}_2\mathrm{O}_7)^{-2}(aq)$ ion in acid solution:

$$\mathrm{Cr}^{+3}(aq) \rightleftharpoons (\mathrm{Cr}_2\mathrm{O}_7)^{-2}(aq)$$

Since *one* $Cr^{+3}(aq)$ ion could not possibly lead to a $(Cr_2O_7)^{-2}(aq)$ ion containing *two* chromium atoms, we consider:    $2Cr^{+3}(aq) \rightleftharpoons (Cr_2O_7)^{-2}(aq)$

In any oxidation half-reaction, *electrons appear as products.* The *number* of electrons is found by subtracting the *total* lower oxidation number of an element in its reduced form from the *total* higher oxidation number in its oxidized form. In this case:

$$2Cr^{+3} \rightleftharpoons (\overset{+6}{Cr}_2O_7)^{-2}(aq)$$

$$2(+3) \longrightarrow 2(+6)$$

$$+6 \longrightarrow +12$$

$$12 - 6 = 6$$

Therefore:    $2Cr^{+3}(aq) \rightleftharpoons Cr_2O_7^{-2}(aq) + 6e^{-1}$

3. At the moment, *true* electrical charge is unbalanced:

$$2Cr^{+3}(aq) \rightleftharpoons Cr_2O_7^{-2}(aq) + 6e^{-1}$$

$$(+6) \quad \rightleftharpoons (-2) \quad\quad + (-6)$$

Since the solution is acidic, we can balance the charge and maintain the electroneutrality by assuming the formation of $14\,H_3O^{+1}(aq)$ ions for each $Cr_2O_7^{-2}(aq)$ ion formed:

$$2Cr^{+3}(aq) \rightleftharpoons Cr_2O_7^{-2}(aq) + 6e^{-1} + 14H_3O^{+1}(aq)$$

$$(+6) \quad \rightleftharpoons (-2) \quad\quad + (-6) + (+14)$$

$$(+6) \quad \rightleftharpoons (+6)$$

4. We balance for atoms, realizing that water is the only electrically neutral species that we may use that will provide the 21 oxygen atoms and 42 hydrogen atoms in the products:

$$2Cr^{+3}(aq) + 21H_2O(l) \rightleftharpoons Cr_2O_7^{-2}(aq) + 14H_3O^{+1}(aq) + 6e^{-1}$$

Experimentally, $E^0_{Cr^{+3}/Cr_2O_7^{-2}}$ equals $-1.33$ volts.

**EXAMPLE**

Manganese may be found in solid manganese(IV) oxide and the permanganate ion, $MnO_4^{-1}$, in alkaline solution. Write a net ionic equation for a half-cell reaction involving these two species.

**SOLUTION**

1.    $(\overset{X}{Mn}\overset{-2}{O}_2)^0$:    $X + 2(-2) = 0$

$$X - 4 = 0$$

$$X = +4$$

$(\overset{Y}{Mn}\overset{-2}{O}_4)^{-1}(aq)$:    $Y - 8 = -1$

$$Y = +7$$

Both the $+4$ and $+7$ oxidation numbers of manganese in $MnO_2$ and $(MnO_4)^{-1}(aq)$ are fictional charges.

2.
$$\overset{+4}{Mn}O_2(s) \rightleftharpoons (\overset{+7}{Mn}O_4)^{-1}(aq)$$

$$+4 \longrightarrow +7$$

$$7 - 4 = 3$$

thus:    $MnO_2(s) \rightleftharpoons (MnO_4)^{-1}(aq) + 3e^{-1}$

3. Electrical imbalance currently holds:

$$MnO_2(s) \rightleftharpoons (MnO_4)^{-1}(aq) + 3e^{-1}$$

$$(0) \rightleftharpoons (-1) \qquad + (-3)$$

In this case, since we are dealing with an alkaline solution, we use the $OH^{-1}(aq)$ ion to balance for charge:

$$MnO_2(s) + 4OH^{-1}(aq) \rightleftharpoons MnO_4^{-1}(aq) + 3e^{-1}$$

$$(0) \qquad + (-4) \qquad \rightleftharpoons (-1) \qquad + (-3)$$

$$(-4) \rightleftharpoons (-4)$$

4. To balance for atoms, water must be a product:

$$MnO_2(s) + 4OH^{-1}(aq) \rightleftharpoons MnO_4^{-1}(aq) + 2H_2O(l) + 3e^{-1}$$

Experimentally, $E^0_{MnO_2/MnO_4^{-1}}$ equals $-0.60$ volt.

Exercises in writing net ionic equations for oxidation half-cell reactions in acid, alkaline, and neutral solutions are provided at the end of the chapter.

### 18.12 Predicting redox reactions: the table of $E^0$ values

Some of the more commonly encountered of the very many half-re-actions whose $E^0$ values have been measured are listed in Table 18–3. In analogous fashion to the use of the table of conjugate acid-base pairs in Chapter 17, we can make vital predictive use of Table 18–3. Let us first quickly note the characteristics of the table.

Each couple in the table is written as an oxidation half-reaction, the reduced form of the couple yielding the oxidized form of the couple. The reduced form of a couple is most simply called a *reducing agent*. The oxidized form of a couple is, simply, an *oxidizing agent*. The more positive the $E^0$ for a couple, the greater is the tendency of the reducing agent to be oxidized. *Strong reducing agents are in couples having high $E^0$ values.* The less positive the $E^0$ for a couple, the greater is the tendency for the reverse reaction, reduction of the oxidizing agent, to occur. *Strong oxidizing agents are in couples having low $E^0$ values.* The strongest reducing agent in Table 18–3 is lithium metal. The strongest oxidizing agent is fluorine gas.

## TABLE 18-3 STANDARD OXIDATION POTENTIALS*

| No. | Half-reaction | $E^0$ volts |
|:---:|:---:|:---:|
| 1. | $Li(s) \rightleftharpoons Li^{+1}(aq) + e^{-1}$ | +3.05 |
| 2. | $K(s) \rightleftharpoons K^{+1}(aq) + e^{-1}$ | +2.93 |
| 3. | $Rb(s) \rightleftharpoons Rb^{+1}(aq) + e^{-1}$ | +2.93 |
| 4. | $Cs(s) \rightleftharpoons Cs^{+1}(aq) + e^{-1}$ | +2.92 |
| 5. | $Ba(s) \rightleftharpoons Ba^{+2}(aq) + 2e^{-1}$ | +2.90 |
| 6. | $Sr(s) \rightleftharpoons Sr^{+2}(aq) + 2e^{-1}$ | +2.89 |
| 7. | $Ca(s) \rightleftharpoons Ca^{+2}(aq) + 2e^{-1}$ | +2.87 |
| 8. | $Na(s) \rightleftharpoons Na^{+1}(aq) + e^{-1}$ | +2.71 |
| 9. | $Mg(s) \rightleftharpoons Mg^{+2}(aq) + 2e^{-1}$ | +2.37 |
| 10. | $Al(s) \rightleftharpoons Al^{+3}(aq) + 3e^{-1}$ | +1.66 |
| 11. | $Mn(s) \rightleftharpoons Mn^{+2}(aq) + 2e^{-1}$ | +1.18 |
| 12. | $H_2(g) + 2OH^{-1}(aq) \rightleftharpoons 2H_2O(l) + 2e^{-1}$ | +0.83 |
| 13. | $Zn(s) \rightleftharpoons Zn^{+2}(aq) + 2e^{-1}$ | +0.76 |
| 14. | $Cr(s) \rightleftharpoons Cr^{+3}(aq) + 3e^{-1}$ | +0.74 |
| 15. | $S^{-2}(aq) \rightleftharpoons S(s) + 2e^{-1}$ | +0.48 |
| 16. | $Fe(s) \rightleftharpoons Fe^{+2}(aq) + 2e^{-1}$ | +0.44 |
| 17. | $H_2(g) + 2H_2O(l) \rightleftharpoons 2H_3O^{+1}(1.0 \times 10^{-7} M) + 2e^{-1}$ | +0.41 |
| 18. | $Pb(s) + SO_4^{-2}(aq) \rightleftharpoons PbSO_4(s) + 2e^{-1}$ | +0.36 |
| 19. | $Ni(s) \rightleftharpoons Ni^{+2}(aq) + 2e^{-1}$ | +0.25 |
| 20. | $Sn(s) \rightleftharpoons Sn^{+2}(aq) + 2e^{-1}$ | +0.14 |
| 21. | $Pb(s) \rightleftharpoons Pb^{+2}(aq) + 2e^{-1}$ | +0.13 |
| 22. | $H_2(g) + 2H_2O(l) \rightleftharpoons 2H_3O^{+1}(1.0M) + 2e^{-1}$ | 0.00 |
| 23. | $H_2S(g) + 2H_2O(l) \rightleftharpoons S(s) + 2H_3O^{+1}(aq) + 2e^{-1}$ | −0.14 |
| 24. | $Sn^{+2}(aq) \rightleftharpoons Sn^{+4}(aq) + 2e^{-1}$ | −0.15 |
| 25. | $Cu^{+1}(aq) \rightleftharpoons Cu^{+2}(aq) + e^{-1}$ | −0.15 |
| 26. | $SO_2(g) + 6H_2O(l) \rightleftharpoons SO_4^{-2}(aq) + 4H_3O^{+1}(aq) + 2e^{-1}$ | −0.17 |
| 27. | $Ag(s) + Cl^{-1}(aq) \rightleftharpoons AgCl(s) + e^{-1}$ | −0.22 |
| 28. | $Cu(s) \rightleftharpoons Cu^{+2}(aq) + 2e^{-1}$ | −0.34 |
| 29. | $Cu(s) \rightleftharpoons Cu^{+1}(aq) + e^{-1}$ | −0.52 |
| 30. | $2I^{-1}(aq) \rightleftharpoons I_2(s) + 2e^{-1}$ | −0.54 |
| 31. | $MnO_2(s) + 4OH^{-1}(aq) \rightleftharpoons MnO_4^{-1}(aq) + 2H_2O(l) + 3e^{-1}$ | −0.60 |

---

* Unless specified otherwise, all aqueous ions are at $1.0M$ concentration. All gases are at partial pressures of 1.0 atmosphere. The temperature is 25.0°C for each couple.

| No. | Half-reaction | $E^0$ volts |
|---|---|---|
| 32. | $H_2O_2(aq) + 2H_2O(l) \rightleftharpoons O_2(g) + 2H_3O^{+1}(aq) + 2e^{-1}$ | $-0.68$ |
| 33. | $Fe^{+2}(aq) \rightleftharpoons Fe^{+3}(aq) + e^{-1}$ | $-0.77$ |
| 34. | $NO_2(g) + 3H_2O(l) \rightleftharpoons NO_3^{-1}(aq) + 2H_3O^{+1}(aq) + e^{-1}$ | $-0.78$ |
| 35. | $2Hg(l) \rightleftharpoons Hg_2^{+2}(aq) + 2e^{-1}$ | $-0.79$ |
| 36. | $Ag(s) \rightleftharpoons Ag^{+1}(aq) + e^{-1}$ | $-0.80$ |
| 37. | $6H_2O(l) \rightleftharpoons O_2(g) + 4H_3O^{+1}(1.0 \times 10^{-7}\,M) + 4e^{-1}$ | $-0.82$ |
| 38. | $Hg(l) \rightleftharpoons Hg^{+2}(aq) + 2e^{-1}$ | $-0.85$ |
| 39. | $Cl^{-1}(aq) + 2OH^{-1}(aq) \rightleftharpoons OCl^{-1}(aq) + H_2O(l) + 2e^{-1}$ | $-0.89$ |
| 40. | $Hg_2^{+2}(aq) \rightleftharpoons 2Hg^{+2}(aq) + 2e^{-1}$ | $-0.92$ |
| 41. | $NO(g) + 6H_2O(l) \rightleftharpoons NO_3^{-1}(aq) + 4H_3O^{+1}(aq) + 3e^{-1}$ | $-0.96$ |
| 42. | $2Br^{-1}(aq) \rightleftharpoons Br_2(l) + 2e^{-1}$ | $-1.07$ |
| 43. | $6H_2O(l) \rightleftharpoons O_2(g) + 4H_3O^{+1}(1.0\,M) + 4e^{-1}$ | $-1.23$ |
| 44. | $2Cr^{+3}(aq) + 21H_2O(l) \rightleftharpoons Cr_2O_7^{-2}(aq) + 14H_3O^{+1}(aq) + 6e^{-1}$ | $-1.33$ |
| 45. | $2Cl^{-1}(aq) \rightleftharpoons Cl_2(aq) + 2e^{-1}$ | $-1.36$ |
| 46. | $Cl_2(g) + 18H_2O(l) \rightleftharpoons 2ClO_3^{-1}(aq) + 12H_3O^{+1}(aq) + 10e^{-1}$ | $-1.47$ |
| 47. | $Cl^{-1}(aq) + 2H_2O(l) \rightleftharpoons HOCl(aq) + H_3O^{+1}(aq) + 2e^{-1}$ | $-1.49$ |
| 48. | $Au(s) \rightleftharpoons Au^{+3}(aq) + 3e^{-1}$ | $-1.50$ |
| 49. | $Mn^{+2}(aq) + 12H_2O(l) \rightleftharpoons MnO_4^{-1}(aq) + 8H_3O^{+1}(aq) + 5e^{-1}$ | $-1.51$ |
| 50. | $PbSO_4(s) + 6H_2O(l) \rightleftharpoons PbO_2(s) + 4H_3O^{+1}(aq) + SO_4^{-2}(aq) + 2e^{-1}$ | $-1.69$ |
| 51. | $4H_2O(l) \rightleftharpoons H_2O_2(aq) + 2H_3O^{+1}(aq) + 2e^{-1}$ | $-1.77$ |
| 52. | $O_2(g) + 3H_2O(l) \rightleftharpoons O_3(g) + 2H_3O^{+1}(aq) + 2e^{-1}$ | $-2.07$ |
| 53. | $2F^{-1}(aq) \rightleftharpoons F_2(g) + 2e^{-1}$ | $-2.87$ |
| 54. | $2HF(aq) + 2H_2O(l) \rightleftharpoons F_2(g) + 2H_3O^{+1}(aq) + 2e^{-1}$ | $-3.06$ |

The table is used in the following predictive manner. *In theory, any reducing agent of a couple will react with any oxidizing agent of a couple of lower $E^0$ value.* Stated in another way, if the *algebraic difference* between the $E^0$ values for two half-reactions constituting a hypothetical cell is positive, the cell will operate in theory. That is, if the cell potential, $E^0{}_{cell}$, for a hypothetical cell, is positive under standard conditions,

$$E^0{}_{cell} = E^0{}_{anode} - E^0{}_{cathode}$$
$$E^0{}_{cell} > 0,$$

then a redox reaction between the reducing agent of the anode reaction and the oxidizing agent of the cathode reaction will occur in theory.

**EXAMPLE**

Will metallic manganese react with strong acids to liberate $H_2$ gas?

**SOLUTION**

From Table 18–3, the two half-reactions are:

11.  $\qquad$ $Mn(s) \rightleftharpoons Mn^{+2}(aq) + 2e^{-1}$ $\qquad\qquad$ $E^0 = 1.18$ volts

17.  $H_2(g) + 2H_2O(l) \rightleftharpoons 2H_3O^{+1}(aq) + 2e^{-1}$ $\qquad$ $E^0 = 0.00$ volt

Since we are hypothesizing *the oxidation of manganese metal* by aqueous $H_3O^{+1}$ ion, we consider a hypothetical cell for which:

$$E^0_{cell} = E^0_{Mn/Mn^{+2}} - E^0_{H_2/H_3O^{+1}}$$
$$E^0_{cell} = (+1.18 \text{ volts}) - (0.00 \text{ volt})$$
$$E^0_{cell} = +1.18 \text{ volts}$$

Since $E^0_{cell}$ is positive, we predict that manganese should react with strong acids to liberate $H_2$ gas.

**EXAMPLE**

Will metallic manganese *displace* magnesium metal from solutions containing $Mg^{+2}$ ions?

**SOLUTION**

From Table 18–3, the two half-reactions are:

9.  $\qquad$ $Mg(s) \rightleftharpoons Mg^{+2}(aq) + 2e^{-1}$ $\qquad$ $E^0 = +2.37$ volts

11.  $\qquad$ $Mn(s) \rightleftharpoons Mn^{+2}(aq) + 2e^{-1}$ $\qquad$ $E^0 = +1.18$ volts

Since we are hypothesizing the oxidation of manganese metal by aqueous $Mg^{+2}$ ions, we consider a hypothetical cell for which: $E^0_{cell} = E^0_{Mn/Mn^{+2}} - E^0_{Mg/Mg^{+2}}$

$$E^0_{cell} = (+1.18 \text{ volts}) - (+2.37 \text{ volts})$$
$$E^0_{cell} = -1.19 \text{ volts}$$

Since $E^0_{cell}$ is negative, we predict that manganese metal *will not displace* magnesium metal from solutions containing $Mg^{+2}$ ions. What displacement reaction involving the $Mn/Mn^{+2}$ and $Mg/Mg^{+2}$ couples can you predict? What is the basis for your prediction?

**EXAMPLE**

Will an acid solution of hydrogen peroxide reduce a potassium permanganate solution?

**SOLUTION**

At the outset, we observe from Table 18–3 that $H_2O_2$ may act both as a mild reducing agent and as a strong oxidizing agent:

32.  $H_2O_2(aq) + 2H_2O(l) \rightleftharpoons O_2(g) + 2H_3O^{+1}(aq) + 2e^{-1}$
$$E^0 = -0.68 \text{ volt}$$

51.  $$4H_2O(l) \rightleftharpoons H_2O_2(aq) + 2H_3O^{+1}(aq) + 2e^{-1}$$
$$E^0 = -1.77 \text{ volts}$$

It is the first of these half-reactions in combination with the $Mn^{+2}/MnO_4^{-1}$ half-reaction (No. 49) that we must consider. For the hypothetical cell in which $H_2O_2$ would react as a reducing agent with respect to $MnO_4^{-1}$ ion, both in acid solution:

$$E^0_{cell} = E^0_{H_2O_2/O_2} - E^0_{Mn^{+2}/MnO_4^{-1}}$$
$$E^0_{cell} = (-0.68 \text{ volt}) - (-1.51 \text{ volts})$$
$$E^0_{cell} = +0.83 \text{ volt}$$

Thus, we predict that the reaction will occur. We realize that five moles of $H_2O_2$ must be oxidized for every two moles of $MnO_4^{-1}$ ion reduced, in order that the same number of electrons are donated that are accepted. However, under the same conditions, the oxidation potential for five moles of $H_2O_2$ is the same as for one mole of $H_2O_2$ —the tendency for a substance to oxidize is *dependent on the nature of the substance and not on the amount** of substance—hence, $E^0_{H_2O_2/O_2}$ and $E^0_{Mn^{+2}/MnO_4^{-1}}$ are not multiplied when calculating $E^0_{cell}$. Finally, since $E^0_{cell}$ is positive, $+0.83$ volt, we would predict the reduction of $MnO_4^{-1}$ ion by $H_2O_2$ in acid solution.

## 18.13 Thermodynamics, kinetics, and E⁰

The rules for predicting redox reactions from $E^0$ values may lose some of their apparent arbitrariness if we briefly consider redox reactions as thermodynamic systems. We have already noted in passing that oxidation potentials are related to the free energy change accompanying redox reactions. In the thermodynamic treatment of redox systems occurring in electrochemical cells, it is found that the free energy change under standard conditions, $\Delta G^0$, and the $E^0$ value for the cell under those conditions are simply related:

$$\Delta G^0_{reaction} = -n\mathscr{F}E^0_{cell}$$

where n is the number of electrons transferred per redox process, and $\mathscr{F}$ is a positive number constant called the *faraday*.

---

* In Section 18.15, however, we shall see that oxidation potentials do change with *concentration*. The important distinction arises because when concentration changes, the *conditions* under which the oxidation takes place change. Since we are dealing with equilibria, a change in conditions affects the equilibrium states. On the other hand, *under the same conditions*, no matter how much of a substance is present, each of its atoms will have the same tendency to be oxidized.

For any process to occur spontaneously at constant pressure, it is necessary from thermodynamic theory that the Gibbs free energy change for that process be negative, that is:

$$\Delta G_{\text{reaction}} < 0 \text{ (spontaneity)}$$

Thus, for any redox reaction under standard conditions to be theoretically spontaneous—that is, to occur—it is necessary that:

$$E^0{}_{\text{cell}} > 0$$

so that                                   $\Delta G^0{}_{\text{reaction}} < 0.$

Thus, our rules for predicting redox reactions from Table 18–3, like our rules for predicting acid-base reactions from Table 17–2, stem from chemical thermodynamics.

Since chemical thermodynamics is independent of time, as usual we must verify predicted redox reactions by laboratory test. In many cases, the rates of predicted redox reactions are too slow to be measurable or of practical significance.

### 18.14  Balancing redox equations

We have seen how simple it is to use Table 18–3 to predict the theoretical occurrence of redox reactions. Going a step further, we may use the table to write net ionic equations for the predicted reactions. Four simple rules are followed:

1. For the couple containing the reducing agent, write the half-reaction exactly as it appears in Table 18–3.
2. For the couple containing the oxidizing agent, write the half-reaction exactly the *reverse* of the way it appears in Table 18–3.
3. Since the reducing agent must donate as many electrons as the oxidizing agent accepts, multiply by the least common multiple where necessary.
4. Add the two equations and simplify the results to arrive at the net ionic equation.

**EXAMPLE**

Write net ionic equations for the two redox reactions in Section 18.12 that were predicted to occur.

**SOLUTION**

1. Manganese reacts with strong acids to liberate hydrogen gas.

$$\text{Mn}(s) \rightleftharpoons \text{Mn}^{+2}(aq) + 2\text{e}^{-1}$$

$$2\text{H}_3\text{O}^{+1}(aq) + 2\text{e}^{-1} \rightleftharpoons \text{H}_2(g) + 2\text{H}_2\text{O}(l)$$

$$\text{Mn}(s) + 2\text{H}_3\text{O}^{+1}(aq) + 2\text{e}^{-1} \rightleftharpoons \text{Mn}^{+2}(aq) + \text{H}_2(g) + 2\text{H}_2\text{O}(l) + 2\text{e}^{-1}$$

or        $\text{Mn}(s) + 2\text{H}_3\text{O}^{+1}(aq) \rightleftharpoons \text{Mn}^{+2}(aq) + \text{H}_2(g) + 2\text{H}_2\text{O}(l)$

2. An acid solution of hydrogen peroxide reduces a potassium permangate solution.

$$5[H_2O_2(aq) + 2H_2O(l) \rightleftharpoons O_2(g) + 2H_3O^{+1}(aq) + 2e^{-1}]$$
$$2[MnO_4^{-1}(aq) + 8H_3O^{+1}(aq) + 5e^{-1} \rightleftharpoons Mn^{+2}(aq) + 12H_2O(l)]$$

$$5H_2O_2(aq) + 10H_2O(l) + 2MnO_4^{-1}(aq) + 16H_3O^{+1}(aq) + 10e^{-1}$$
$$\rightleftharpoons 5O_2(g) + 10H_3O^{+1}(aq) + 10e^{-1} + 2Mn^{+2}(aq) + 24H_2O(l)$$

Finally, upon considering the *net* consumption or production of $H_3O^{+1}$ ions and $H_2O$ molecules:

$$5H_2O_2(aq) + 2MnO_4^{-1}(aq) + 6H_3O^{+1}(aq)$$
$$\rightleftharpoons 5O_2(g) + 2Mn^{+2}(aq) + 14H_2O(l)$$

### 18.15 Le Chatelier's principle and redox equilibria

Since $E^0$ is the standard oxidation potential for an oxidation half-reaction, we may expect that under any nonstandard condition the measured oxidation potential will be different from $E^0$. Since oxidation half-reactions are chemical equilibria, we may fruitfully use Le Chatelier's principle to predict the effect of concentration changes on oxidation potentials.

How does the oxidation potential for the standard $H_2/H_3O^{+1}$ couple itself change with changes of pH, for example? By definition, $E^0$ is exactly zero for this couple at 25°C and at a pH of zero—that is, when $H_2$ gas at one atmosphere is in equilibrium with a solution that is $1M$ in $H_3O^{+1}$ ions. What if we are dealing simply with pure water, however, for which the pH is 7? From the equilibrium involved,

$$H_2(g) + 2H_2O(l) \rightleftharpoons 2H_3O^{+1}(aq) + 2e^{-1},$$

we predict that if the $H_3O^{+1}$ ion concentration is decreased, the equilibrium should shift to the right. A shift to the right is evidence of an increased tendency to be oxidized on the part of $H_2$ molecules. Thus, we would predict that the oxidation potential for the $H_2/H_3O^{+1}$ couple should *increase* as the pH increases. Indeed, such is the experimental fact. The $E$ value for the $H_2/H_3O^{+1}$ couple in pure water is +0.41 volt. *Any half-reaction in which $H_3O^{+1}$ or $OH^{-1}$ ions take part will have an oxidation potential that is pH dependent.* In many cases, then, we find that the strengths of oxidizing or reducing agents are markedly changed with a change in pH.

Full understanding of oxidation-reduction reactions through redox half-reaction equilibria and standard oxidation potentials is essential to understanding some of the most practical problems and achievements of modern chemical science. The appalling and exorbitantly expensive annual waste of natural metal resources through metallic *corrosion* can be understood and retarded, as we shall later see, through a knowledge and application of the principles behind redox reactions. Conversion of the grossly inefficient production of energy from the burning of carbon fuels into an efficient, clean, and potentially invaluable energy source can be understood on those same principles, as we shall also see later. Major products of modern chemical industry depend on redox reactions, as we shall *now* see.

## SUMMARY

The model for all redox reactions involves the transfer of electrons from a donor (reducing agent) to an acceptor (oxidizing agent). The quantitative study of a redox process is possible only by breaking it down into the two half-reactions of which it is comprised. The physical separation of oxidation and reduction half-cells, connected only by an ion migration linkage, is also the basis for the production of useful electrical energy from redox reactions.

Relative oxidation potentials can be experimentally obtained by opposing oxidation half-cells. By *defining* the oxidation potential of the $H_2(1 \text{ atm})/H_3O^{+1}(1 \text{ } M)$ half-cell to be exactly zero volts at 25.0°C, a table of standard oxidation potentials, $E^0$, can be established. Important predictive use is made of such a table.

It is useful to define *fictitious* oxidation numbers as an electron bookkeeping device. These are very useful in writing net ionic equations for oxidation half-cell reactions. In those reactions, the role of $H_3O^{+1}$ or $OH^{-1}$ ions can often have an important effect on the oxidation potential.

## QUESTIONS AND PROBLEMS

**18.1**  Give an operational definition for redox reactions. Give two conceptual definitions for such reactions.

**18.2**  On the basis of your conceptual definitions for redox reactions, show that each of the following is a redox reaction.
  **a.** $Mg(s) + Cl_2(g) = MgCl_2(s)$
  **b.** $CH_4(g) + 2O_2(g) = CO_2(g) + 2H_2O(g)$
  **c.** $(IO_3)^{-1}(aq) + 5I^{-1}(aq) + 6H_3O^{+1}(aq) = 3I_2(s) + 9H_2O(l)$
  **d.** $C_2H_4(g) + Cl_2(g) = C_2H_4Cl_2(g)$

**18.3**  Draw and label in detail experimental setups whereby the following reactions could be quantitatively studied.
  **a.** $3Ag(s) + NO_3^{-1}(aq) + 4H_3O^{+1}(aq)$
$$\rightleftharpoons 3 \text{ } Ag^{+1}(aq) + NO(g) + 6H_2O(l)$$
  **b.** $Fe^{+3}(aq) + Sn^{+2}(aq) \rightleftharpoons Fe^{+2}(aq) + Sn^{+4}(aq)$

**18.4**  Explain why it is not possible to measure absolute single half-cell oxidation potentials.

18.5 How would you redefine the value for $E^0_{H_2/H_3O^{+1}}$ in order that *all $E^0$* values be positive?

18.6 Determine the oxidation number for the atom that appears in boldface in each of the following.
   a. **H**OCl        c. Na$_2$**O**$_2$        e. K$_2$(**Mn**O$_4$)    g. **Fe**$_3$O$_4$
   b. **N**$_2$H$_4$        d. H$_2$**S**$_2$O$_7$        f. Na$_2$(**S**$_4$O$_6$)        h. HO**Cl**O$_2$
   Ans.  b. $-2$; d. $+6$; f. $+2\frac{1}{2}$; h. $+5$

18.7 Write net ionic half-reactions for each of the couples given. For those cases where from your prior knowledge you cannot know whether the system is acid or basic, the information is given.

   a. $Ca(s)/Ca(OH)_2(s)$
   b. $S^{-2}(aq)/SO_2(aq)$
   c. $Ta(s)/Ta_2O_5(s)$ $(H_3O^{+1})$
   d. $Cr(OH)_3(s)/CrO_4^{-2}(aq)$
   e. $N_2H_4(g)/NO_3^{-1}(aq)$ $(H_3O^{+1})$
   f. $NH_3(g)/NO_3^{-1}(aq)$
   g. $VO^{+1}(aq)/VO_2^{+1}(aq)$ $(H_3O^{+1})$
   h. $O_2(g)/O_3(g)$ $(OH^{-1})$

18.8 Using Table 18–3, predict whether a reaction will occur when the following reactants are brought together under standard conditions. To facilitate use of Table 18–3, the number of the position of the half-reaction in which a reactant appears is given.

   a. $Mg(s)(9)$ and $Ag^{+1}(aq)(36)$
   b. $Fe^{+3}(aq)(33)$ and $NO_3^{-1}(41)$
   c. $Cr(s)(14)$ and $Zn^{+2}(aq)(13)$
   d. $H_2S(g)(23)$ and $NO_3^{-1}(aq)(41)$
   e. $Cr_2O_7^{-2}(aq)(44)$ and $H_2O_2(aq)(32$ and $51)$
   f. $MnO_4^{-1}(aq)(49)$ and $H_2O_2(aq)(32$ and $51)$
   g. $SO_2(g)(26)$ and $Hg_2^{+2}(aq)(35)$

18.9 Write a net ionic equation for each of the reactions in Problem 18.8 that occurs and calculate the voltage of the electrochemical cell utilizing that reaction.

18.10 a. Explain why concentrated sulfuric acid is a more powerful oxidizing agent than dilute sulfuric acid is. (26) b. Compare the pH dependence of the oxidizing strength of sulfuric acid and of nitric acid. (41)

18.11 On long standing, or on heating, a colorless solution containing $Cu^{+1}(aq)$ ions turns blue, and a reddish solid also forms. Explain this observation. (25 and 29)

## SUGGESTED READINGS

Chemistry
Meloan, C. E., "Balancing Oxidation-Reduction Equations." July 1964
Taube, Henry, "How Do Redox Reactions Occur?" Mar. 1965

*It is no paradox to say that
in our most theoretical moods
we may be nearest to our most
practical applications.*

*Alfred North Whitehead* (1861–1947)

**CHAPTER 19** | # Electrolytic Reactions

All of the redox reactions that we have just studied are characterized by the conversion of chemical potential energy into electrical energy by means of electron transfer. Such redox reactions are called *galvanic* or *voltaic* reactions after Luigi Galvani, Italian physiologist, and Alessandro Volta, Italian chemist and physicist, who discovered some basic electrical phenomena near the close of the eighteenth century. We now focus our interest on a second class of redox reactions. These are characterized by the conversion of electrical energy into chemical energy, again by means of electron transfer. Such redox reactions are called *electrolytic reactions*, and the vital process wherein chemical changes occur as a result of the input of electrical energy into a chemical system is called *electrolysis*.

### 19.1 Electrolysis: a first approach

Most of the significant principles underlying electrolytic reactions can be discovered by careful study of the electrolysis of sodium chloride under three different sets of conditions:

1. Electrolysis of a $1M$ solution of NaCl
2. Electrolysis of a saturated solution of NaCl, or brine
3. Electrolysis of anhydrous, molten NaCl

We consider the first case to learn of the relationship of $E^0$ values to electrolytic reactions.

When a $1M$ NaCl solution is electrolyzed (Fig. 19.1), hydrogen gas is produced at one electrode and oxygen gas is produced at the other. Moreover, the volume of hydrogen produced is twice that of

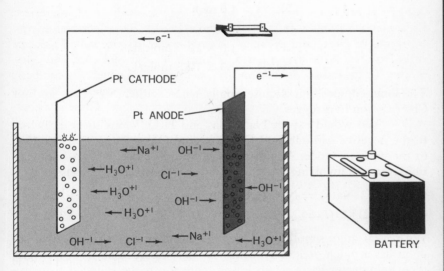

**FIGURE 19.1** A diagrammatic representation of the mechanism for the electrolysis of a 1M NaCl solution

oxygen. With little analysis, it is quite clear that the electrolysis of $1M$ NaCl corresponds simply to the electrolysis of water:

$$2H_2O(l) \overset{\text{D.C.}}{=\!=} 2H_2(g) + O_2(g)$$

Why is this the result?

During any electrolytic reaction, electrons tend to move from a source of *direct electric current* onto a conducting electrode immersed in the electrolytic cell. This electrode tends, therefore, to be much more negatively charged than the second electrode in the cell, which, therefore, tends to be relatively positive in charge. Electrolysis occurs if the externally produced electrons are accepted at the negative electrode, or cathode, in a *reduction* half-reaction while, simultaneously, electrons are donated at the positive electrode, or anode, in an oxidation half-reaction. The primary factor that determines whether electrolysis occurs is the "pressure," that is, the voltage under which electrons are "pumped" into the cell. Within the electrolytic cell, ion movement between cathode and anode completes the total electrical circuit.

### 19.2 The electrolysis of 1M NaCl solution: the role of oxidation potential

What is the ionic composition of a $1M$ NaCl solution, and how will the ions present behave with respect to the negatively charged cathode and positively charged anode? Since aqueous NaCl is a strong electrolyte, the molar ionic composition of a $1M$ solution is:

$$[Na^{+1}] = 1.0 \text{ mole/l}$$
$$[Cl^{-1}] = 1.0 \text{ mole/l}$$
$$[H_3O^{+1}] = 1.0 \times 10^{-7} \text{ mole/l}$$
$$[OH^{-1}] = 1.0 \times 10^{-7} \text{ mole/l}$$

The ionic composition is quite simple, since neither $Na^{+1}(aq)$ ion nor $Cl^{-1}(aq)$ ion hydrolyzes.

We would expect $Na^{+1}$ ions and $H_3O^{+1}$ ions to be attracted to the negative cathode, and $Cl^{-1}$ ions and $OH^{-1}$ ions to be attracted to the positive anode. At the cathode we first consider two half-reactions, the first involving $Na^{+1}$ ions, and the second, $H_3O^{+1}$ ions:

$$Na(s) \rightleftharpoons Na^{+1}(1M) + e^{-1} \qquad E^0 = +2.71 \text{ volts}$$
$$H_2(g) + 2H_2O(l) \rightleftharpoons 2H_3O^{+1}(1.0 \times 10^{-7} M) + 2e^{-1} \quad E = +0.41 \text{ volt}$$

We reason quite simply. If, under the conditions of this reaction, sodium has a much greater tendency to be oxidized than hydrogen gas, then sodium ion has a much lower tendency to be reduced than hydronium ion. For our immediate purposes, this means that the hydronium ion has the greater tendency to be reduced, and will be reduced, while the sodium ion remains in solution:

$$2H_3O^{+1}(1.0 \times 10^{-7} M) + 2e^{-1} \rightleftharpoons H_2(g, 1 \text{ atm}) + 2H_2O(l)$$

This not only is supported by the presence of $H_2$ gas at the cathode during the electrolysis of $1M$ NaCl, but can be verified by another experimental test. If $H_3O^{+1}$ ion is reduced at the cathode, then the immediate aqueous environment of the cathode should be alkaline. When phenolphthalein is added to the cell, it turns pink at the cathode when electrolysis begins, indicating removal of $H_3O^{+1}$ ions from the solution.

Turning our attention to a predicted anode reaction, we must determine whether the $Cl^{-1}$ ion or the $OH^{-1}$ ion will be oxidized under the conditions of the original electrolysis reaction. The two half-reactions we must consider are:

$$4OH^{-1}(1.0 \times 10^{-7} M) \rightleftharpoons O_2(g) + 2H_2O(l) + 4e^{-1} \quad E = -0.82 \text{ volt}$$
$$2Cl^{-1}(1M) \rightleftharpoons Cl_2(g) + 2e^{-1} \quad E^0 = -1.36 \text{ volts}$$

Both of these are, directly, oxidation reactions. Hence, we must clearly predict that when $1M$ NaCl is electrolyzed, $OH^{-1}$ ion will be oxidized at the anode and $O_2$ gas produced. Our prediction is supported by experimental observation and may also be verified by an independent chemical test. What is that test? (Fig. 19.2.)

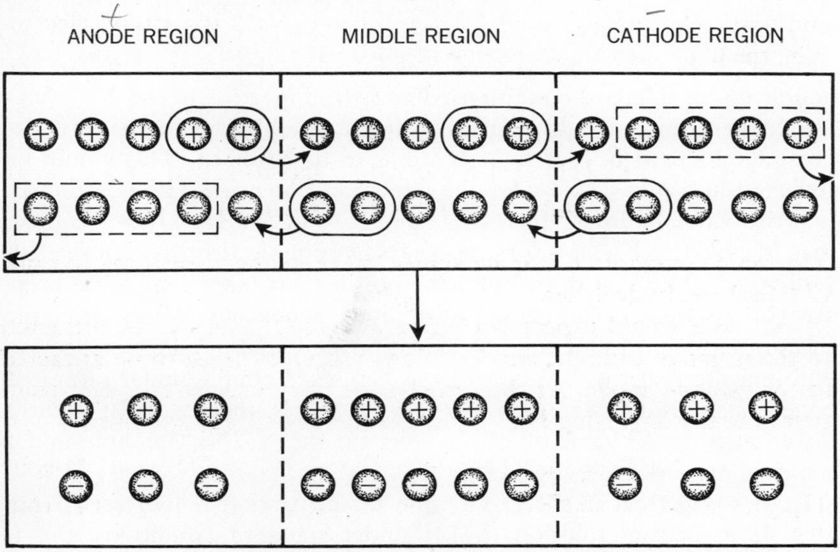

ANODE REGION          MIDDLE REGION          CATHODE REGION

FIGURE 19.2 Though cations are reduced at the cathode and anions are oxidized at the anode and there is enhanced ion migration during electrolysis, the electrolyte remains electrically neutral.

The principles that we have discovered in analyzing the electrolysis of a $1M$ NaCl solution may be conveniently summarized:

1. In the electrolysis of a solution containing more than one reducible cation, that cation involved in the redox couple of least positive oxidation potential will be reduced first.
2. In the electrolysis of a solution containing more than one oxidizable anion, that anion involved in the redox reaction of most positive oxidation potential will be oxidized first.

### 19.3 The electrolysis of saturated brine

Now we consider any changes in the electrolysis products as we electrolyze very concentrated solutions of NaCl, known as *brines*. Under saturated conditions, at 25.0°C, a brine solution is approximately $6M$ in NaCl. Thus, the molar ionic composition of such a solution is:

$$[Na^{+1}] = 6 \text{ moles/l}$$
$$[Cl^{-1}] = 6 \text{ moles/l}$$
$$[H_3O^{+1}] = 1.0 \times 10^{-7} \text{ mole/l}$$
$$[OH^{-1}] = 1.0 \times 10^{-7} \text{ mole/l}$$

As for the case of $1M$ NaCl, we consider the half-reactions involving $Na^{+1}$ and $H_3O^{+1}$ ions for predicting the cathode reaction during the electrolysis of saturated brine:

$$Na(s) \rightleftharpoons Na^{+1}(6M) + 1e^{-1} \qquad\qquad E = ?$$
$$H_2(g) + 2H_2O(l) \rightleftharpoons 2H_3O^{+1}(1.0 \times 10^{-7}\ M) + 2e^{-1} \quad E = +0.41 \text{ volt}$$

To make our prediction, we must know the value of $E$ for the $Na/Na^{+1}$ couple under these conditions. From Le Chatelier's principle, we can predict that the value of $E$ will be less than that of $E^0$ for the couple under standard conditions. The sixfold increase in the $Na^{+1}(aq)$ ion concentration would tend to shift the equilibrium to the left, decreasing the tendency of sodium atoms to be oxidized. This would be reflected in a *lower value* for the oxidation potential. The question is, will this value be lower than the $+0.41$ volt of the $H_2/H_3O^{+1}$ couple; that is, will the $E$ value for the $Na/Na^{+1}$ couple drop by more than 2.30 volts? Only if it does, will it be possible for $Na^{+1}$ ions to be preferentially reduced instead of $H_3O^{+1}$ ions, according to our principle relating cathodic reductions to oxidation potentials. A little reflection will indicate that the $E$ value for the $Na/Na^{+1}$ couple under saturated conditions is *not* lower than $+0.41$ volt and is, in fact, only slightly lower than the $E^0$ value of $+2.71$ volts for the $Na/Na^{+1}$ couple under standard conditions.

Recall that if the $H_3O^{+1}$ ion concentration is increased from $10^{-7}\ M$ in neutral solution to $1M$ under standard conditions, the $E$ value of the $H_2/H_3O^{+1}$ couple drops only 0.41 volt—from $+0.41$ volt to 0.00 volt. Thus, if a ten-million-fold increase in this case leads to a voltage change of 0.41 volt, we could hardly expect a sixfold increase in the $Na^{+1}$ ion concentration to cause a decrease in the oxidation potential of more than 2.30 volts. In fact, a voltage decrease of approximately 0.05 volt is found. Thus, even in saturated brine solution, we must conclude that $H_3O^{+1}$ ion should be electrolytically discharged at the cathode while $Na^{+1}$ ion remains in solution.

For predicting an anode reaction, as before, we consider the half-reactions involving $Cl^{-1}$ and $OH^{-1}$ ions:

$$4OH^{-1}(1.0 \times 10^{-7}\,M) \rightleftharpoons O_2(g) + 2H_2O(l) + 4e^{-1} \quad E = -0.82 \text{ volt}$$
$$2Cl^{-1}(6M \rightleftharpoons Cl_2(g) + 2e^{-1} \qquad\qquad E = ?$$

Again, it is necessary to know the $E$ value for the $Cl^{-1}/Cl_2$ couple under the new concentration conditions before a prediction can be made. Le Chatelier's principle leads us to recognize that the value of $E$ for the $Cl^{-1}/Cl_2$ couple under saturated conditions should be more positive than the $E^0$ value of $-1.36$ volts for the $Cl^{-1}/Cl_2$ couple under standard conditions. Increasing the $Cl^{-1}$ ion concentration causes an equilibrium shift to the right, indicating an enhanced tendency for $Cl^{-1}$ ion to be oxidized. This should be reflected by an increase in the oxidation potential. An increase of only 0.60 volt would lead to the formation of $Cl_2$ gas rather than $O_2$ gas at the anode. However, again we can only account for a very small change, about 0.05 volt, from the $E^0$ value. Thus, we predict that $O_2$ gas should form. Therefore, as in the case of $1M$ NaCl, the electrolysis of saturated brine should correspond to the electrolysis of water.

Testing our predictions experimentally, we do, indeed, find that $H_2$ gas is evolved at the cathode when saturated brine is electrolyzed. At the anode, however, $Cl_2$ gas, and not the predicted $O_2$ gas, is evolved. Has chemical thermodynamics, a pillar of modern chemical thought, failed us?

## 19.4 Overvoltage and practical electrolysis

We must recall that thermodynamics is concerned with the initial and final states of a system. For reactions occurring on electrode surfaces, those surfaces are an integral part of the system. While the physics and chemistry of surface phenomena are still not well understood, it is quite clear that electrode surface characteristics can severely affect oxidation potentials. This is particularly true for electrode reactions involving gases. As gases form on electrode surfaces, they tend to remain *adsorbed* on those surfaces. Different gases have markedly different adsorption properties, as, of course, do electrode surfaces of different materials.

To explain the fact that chlorine gas and not oxygen gas is discharged during the electrolysis of saturated brine, it must be assumed that oxygen gas would be much more highly adsorbed on electrode surfaces than is chlorine gas. Thus, in the final analysis, it would be energetically more favorable for $Cl_2$ gas to form during electrolysis of saturated brine than for $O_2$ gas to form.

Experimentally, it is found that both the anodic evolution of oxygen gas and the cathodic evolution of hydrogen gas only occur at voltages higher than those predicted from theory. The difference between the theoretical electrolysis voltage required for the evolution of these gases and the actual voltage used is called *overvoltage*. The overvoltage effect plays an important role in practical electrolytic reactions. As we have seen, for example, it is the overvoltage effect that

The overvoltage effect in the service of man—the commercial production of chlorine

leads to the anodic formation of chlorine rather than oxygen when saturated brine is electrolyzed. During the same electrolysis reaction, as we have also seen, cathodic reduction of $H_3O^{+1}$ ion occurs. Thus, the electrolytic solution becomes highly alkaline as the electrolysis proceeds. The total change effected may be described as:

$$2NaCl \text{ (saturated)} + 2H_2O(l) \xrightarrow{\text{D.C.}} 2NaOH(aq) + H_2(g) + Cl_2(g)$$

Because of the overvoltage effect, then, the electrolysis of saturated brine leads to the production of two vitally important chemicals, sodium hydroxide and chlorine gas. Industry has long taken advantage of this. Annually, some six million tons of chlorine and seven million tons of sodium hydroxide are produced in the United States alone by the electrolysis of concentrated brine solutions. It goes without saying that the hydrogen gas produced is, additionally, a vital by-product.

## 19.5 The electrolysis of molten NaCl and Faraday's first law

Another industrially important electrolytic reaction involves molten, anhydrous sodium chloride. As we know, when an ionic solid melts, ions are set free from the strong coulombic forces binding them in the ionic lattice. When an ionic melt is electrolyzed, then simple cationic reduction and anionic oxidation take place. For *molten* sodium chloride:

$$2Na^{+1}(l) + 2Cl^{-1}(l) \xrightarrow[\text{D.C.}]{\Delta} 2Na(l) + Cl_2(g)$$

Well over 100,000 tons of sodium are produced in this country as a result of this reaction.

We may consider the electrolysis of molten sodium chloride more closely to learn the quantitative relationships existing between the electrical current passing through the electrolytic cell and the *amount* of chemical change that takes place at the electrodes.

Though it is true that whether an electrolytic reaction takes place depends upon the *voltage* at which electric current passes through a cell, the amount of chemical change during an electrolysis depends on the *amount* of current passed. Early in the nineteenth century, the brilliant English scientist Michael Faraday discovered the quantitative relationship of the amount of current to the amount of chemical change that exists during an electrolysis. This relationship, in modern language, is:

**FARADAY'S FIRST LAW.**   The amount of chemical change occurring during an electrolysis is directly proportional to the quantity of electricity passing through the electrolytic cell.

The unit of quantity of electricity, $Q$, is the coulomb. Amount of electricity, however, is not measured directly. It is *derived* from the measured *rate of flow* of electricity, or the current, $I$, and the time of flow, $t$. That is:

$$Q = I \times t$$

where $I$ is electrical current measured in *amperes*, and $t$ is time in seconds. Thus,

$$1 \text{ coulomb} = 1 \text{ ampere} \times 1 \text{ second}.$$

If enough current flows through molten sodium chloride for a long enough period of time so that one mole of sodium forms at the cathode,

$$Na^{+1}(l) + e^{-1} \rightarrow Na^0(l),$$

and one half mole of chlorine gas simultaneously forms at the anode,

$$Cl^{-1}(l) \rightarrow \tfrac{1}{2}Cl_2(g) + e^{-1},$$

it can be determined that the amount of electricity that has passed through the cell is 96,500 coulombs. *Thus, 96,500 coulombs is equivalent to a mole of electrons.* This quantity of electricity is called a *faraday* and is symbolized, as we have seen, by $\mathscr{F}$.

**Michael Faraday** (1791–1867, English). Faraday began his career as a bookbinder's apprentice, became an assistant to Humphry Davy, and finally became the foremost scientist of his day. Although his discoveries in chemistry were minor, his contributions in the fields of electricity and magnetism were epochal. The *faraday*, a unit of amount of electricity, and the *farad*, a unit of electrical capacity, are named in honor of his achievements.

## 19.6 The electrochemical equivalent weight

One faraday of electricity leads to the electrolytic formation of a mole of sodium atoms. Simultaneously, a faraday is produced when a mole of chlorine atoms (a half mole of diatomic chlorine molecules) forms electrolytically. Thus we might say that a mole of sodium atoms and a mole of chlorine atoms are *electrochemically equivalent*.

In the electrolytic deposition of metallic copper from solutions containing aqueous $Cu^{+2}$ ions,

$$Cu^{+2}(aq) + 2e^{-1} \rightarrow Cu^0(s),$$

it is apparent that *two faradays are required per mole of copper atoms formed*. In the electrolytic discharge of oxygen from water,

$$6H_2O(l) \rightarrow O_2(g) + 4H_3O^{+1}(aq) + 4e^{-1},$$

it is apparent that two faradays are produced per mole of oxygen atoms (one half mole of $O_2$ molecules) formed. Thus, a mole of copper atoms and a mole of oxygen atoms, *under the conditions cited*, will be electrochemically equivalent to each other. However, a mole of copper atoms and a mole of oxygen atoms are electrochemically equivalent to *two moles* of sodium atoms and *two moles* of chlorine atoms.

It would be convenient to be able to compare amounts of different elements that are *exactly* electrochemically equivalent. From the above relationships it is not hard to see that one half mole each of copper atoms and oxygen atoms will be exactly the electrochemical equivalents of one mole each of sodium and chlorine atoms, as well as of each other. The weights of one half mole each of copper atoms and oxygen atoms are called *electrochemical equivalent weights*. The electrochemical equivalent weight of an element, which we shall symbolize E.E.W., equals the atomic weight of the element divided by the number of moles of electrons involved per mole of atoms of the element formed. Thus, the electrochemical equivalent weight of copper under the conditions described above is:

$$E.E.W._{Cu} = \frac{63.5 \text{ g/mole of Cu}}{2 \text{ moles of electrons/mole of Cu}}$$

$$E.E.W._{Cu} = 31.8 \text{ g/mole of electrons}$$

$$E.E.W._{Cu} = 31.8 \text{ g/faraday}$$

What are the electrochemical equivalent weights of sodium, chlorine, and oxygen in the electrolytic reactions that we have been considering?

## 19.7 Faraday's second law

The concept of the electrochemical equivalent weight was proposed by Faraday as a result of his quantitative studies of electrochemical systems. Those results are conveniently summarized in terms of the electrochemical equivalent weight.

**FARADAY'S SECOND LAW.** The weights of electrolytically discharged elements are proportional to their electrochemical equivalent weights.

We make use of both of Faraday's laws in calculating amounts of chemical change occurring during electrolysis.

**EXAMPLE**

A current of 3.00 amp flows for 20.0 hours through a concentrated solution of copper(II) chloride. What weights of copper and chlorine gas will form at the electrodes? (Cu = 63.5 g/mole; Cl = 35.5 g/mole.)

**SOLUTION**

1. Calculate the number of faradays passing through the cell.

$$Q = It$$

$$Q = (3.00 \text{ amps}) (20.0 \text{ hr}) \times \left( 3600 \frac{\text{sec}}{\text{hour}} \right) \left( \frac{1 \text{ coulomb}}{\text{amp-sec}} \right) \left( \frac{1 \text{ faraday}}{96,500 \text{ coulombs}} \right)$$

$$Q = 2.24 \text{ faradays}$$

2. Calculate the weight of copper formed at the cathode.

$$Cu^{+2}(aq) + 2e^{-1} \rightarrow Cu^0(s)$$

$$\text{Weight of Cu} = 2.24 \text{ faradays} \left( \frac{63.5 \text{ g}}{2 \text{ faradays}} \right)$$

Weight of Cu = 71.1 g

3. Calculate the weight of chlorine gas formed at the anode.

$$2Cl^{-1}(aq) \rightarrow Cl_2(g) + 2e^{-1}$$

$$\frac{\text{Weight of chlorine}}{\text{E.E.W.}_{Cl}} = \frac{\text{Weight of copper}}{\text{E.E.W.}_{Cu}}$$

$$\text{Weight of chlorine} = \text{weight of copper} \left( \frac{\text{E.E.W.}_{Cl}}{\text{E.E.W.}_{Cu}} \right)$$

$$\text{Weight of chlorine} = 71.1 \text{ g} \left( \frac{\dfrac{35.5 \text{ g}}{1 \text{ faraday}}}{\dfrac{63.5 \text{ g}}{2 \text{ faradays}}} \right)$$

$$\text{Weight of chlorine} = 71.1 \text{ g} \left( \frac{2 \times 35.5}{63.5} \right)$$

Weight of chlorine = 79.6 g

Verify this result by an independent calculation.

## 19.8 Electrolytic reactions: putting electrons to work

As we have already seen in the cases of the industrial production of sodium, chlorine, and sodium hydroxide, electrolysis is a most important manufacturing process. Fluorine, the most powerful oxidizing agent known, is also prepared industrially by an electrolytic reaction.

Comparing the half-reactions,

$$4OH^{-1}(aq) \rightleftharpoons O_2(g) + 2H_2O(l) + 4e^{-1} \qquad E^0 = -0.41 \text{ volt}$$
$$2F^{-1}(aq) \rightleftharpoons F_2(g) + 2e^{-1} \qquad E^0 = -2.87 \text{ volts}$$

it is quite obvious that when aqueous solutions of soluble fluorides, which tend to be slightly alkaline (why?), are electrolyzed, oxygen, and not fluorine, will be discharged at the anode, oxygen overvoltage notwithstanding. Accordingly, fluorine is electrolytically generated under anhydrous conditions. A solution of potassium hydrogen fluoride, $KHF_2$, in *anhydrous*, liquid hydrogen fluoride is electrolyzed, leading to the production of hydrogen gas and fluorine gas:

$$HF_2^{-1} \rightleftharpoons H^{+1} + 2F^{-1}$$
$$H^{+1} + HF_2^{-1} \xrightarrow{\text{D.C.}} H_2(g) + F_2(g)$$

Electrolytic reaction, as we shall learn in later chapters, is the basis for the industrial production of magnesium and aluminum metals, elemental phosphorus, and silicon; the refining of copper; and the electroplating of many metals. Thus, it is not difficult to realize how important electrolytic reactions are to the economic climate of this nation, and, as before, it is assuring to have some understanding of those reactions.

## SUMMARY

Electrolysis is the process in which an input of electrical energy into a chemical system causes a chemical change to occur. Knowledge of oxidation potentials for the components of the system permits the prediction of electrode reactions. In the case of electrolytic evolution of gases, the overvoltage effect may lead to an unpredicted result.

The amount of chemical change occurring during an electrolysis may be determined from Faraday's laws. The basis of such a determination is that the electrochemical equivalent weight of any element under given conditions is electrolytically discharged by the same amount of electricity—the faraday.

## QUESTIONS AND PROBLEMS

**19.1**  Describe galvanic and electrolytic reactions from the energy transformations involved.

**19.2**  Cite rules for predicting electrode reactions during electrolysis.

**19.3**  If a solution that is 1.0 $M$ in $NiCl_2$ and 1.0 $M$ in $CrBr_3$ was electrolyzed, what would you expect to observe happening first at each electrode? Explain your answer. (See Table 18–3, half-reactions 14, 17, 19, 37, 42, and 45.)

**19.4**  When a solution containing $0.1M$ $CuSO_4$ and $0.1M$ $SnCl_2$ in $0.1$ $M$ HCl is electrolyzed, the deposition of copper, followed by the deposition of tin, followed by the evolution of hydrogen, is observed at the cathode. Explain these observations on the basis of data in Table 18–3, Le Chatelier's principle, and the overvoltage effect.

**19.5**  Write net equations for the half-reactions that occur at the electrodes of a lead storage battery during *charging*.

**19.6**  What is meant by the overvoltage effect? Discuss how it applies in the commercial production of chlorine gas.

**19.7**  Calculate the electrochemical equivalent weight of manganese in **a.** $MnCl_2$; **b.** $MnO_2$; **c.** $KMnO_4$?
Ans.  **b.** 13.7 g/equiv

**19.8**  A current of 80.0 amp flows for 12.0 hours through an electrolytic cell. **a.** Determine the number of coulombs, faradays, and electrons that pass through the cell. **b.** How many grams of copper would deposit at the cathode of the cell from a copper(II) sulfate cell solution?
Ans.  **b.** 1.13 kg

**19.9**  Given that the charge on the electron is $1.60210 \times 10^{-19}$ coulomb and that one faraday equals 96,487.0 coulombs, calculate Avogadro's number. (Give correct units with your answer.)

**19.10**  In the electrolysis of a solution of copper(II) sulfate, 0.318 g of copper was deposited. **a.** How many electrons were involved? **b.** How many faradays were involved? **c.** If the electrolysis required 20.0 minutes, how many amperes were involved? **d.** For the same amount of electricity, how much silver could be plated from a silver nitrate solution?
Ans.  **b.** $1.00 \times 10^{-2}$ faraday; **d.** 1.08 g

**19.11**  How could electrolysis be applied to the analysis of the composition of a stainless steel containing iron, nickel, chromium, and carbon?

## SUGGESTED READINGS

Dibner, Bern. *Galvani-Volta*. Burndy Library, Norwalk, Conn., 1952.
MacDonald, D. K. C. *Faraday, Maxwell, and Kelvin* (paperback). Doubleday, 1964.

*Gott würfelt nicht.*
("God does not play dice.")
*Albert Einstein* (1879–1955)

**CHAPTER 20** | # Orbital Shapes and

In Chapter 10 we described the theoretical model of atomic structure in which electrons exist in atoms in energy levels. Those energy levels were called orbitals and were defined by two quantum numbers, $n$ and $l$. According to whether the quantum number $l$ had a value of 0, 1, 2, or 3, the orbitals were designated $s$, $p$, $d$, or $f$. In Chapter 11 we learned more about these atomic orbitals and their importance in chemical bonding between atoms. Chemical bonds, both ionic and covalent, formed as a result of the stability associated with filled orbitals, particularly for a filled orbital pattern identical to that possessed by noble gas atoms. Thus, we could explain why sodium forms +1 ions while fluorine forms −1 ions in chemical reactions. In similar fashion, it was possible to understand why chlorine combined with only one hydrogen atom to form HCl, whereas carbon combined with four hydrogen atoms to form $CH_4$. Actually, chemists believe that it is possible to relate a great many more aspects of chemical bonds to the properties of atomic orbitals than just the number of bonds that atoms form. Let us consider some of these aspects as we study more deeply the nature of atomic orbitals and their relationship to chemical bonding.

## 20.1 One model for explaining the structure of $H_2S$

To begin our advanced consideration of orbitals and bonding, let us first review some of the concepts developed in Chapters 10 and 11. How did we describe the bonding in, and the shape of, a molecule based on those concepts? Let us consider the compound between sulfur and hydrogen for such a description.

The sulfur atom has the electron configuration:

$$_{16}S \quad 1s^2 2s^2 2p^6 3s^2 3p^4 \quad \text{or} \quad \frac{\uparrow\downarrow}{1s}\left|\frac{\uparrow\downarrow}{2s}\right|\frac{\uparrow\downarrow}{2p}\ \frac{\uparrow\downarrow}{2p}\ \frac{\uparrow\downarrow}{2p}\left|\frac{\uparrow\downarrow}{3s}\right|\frac{\uparrow\downarrow}{3p}\ \frac{\uparrow}{3p}\ \frac{\uparrow}{3p}$$

*422*

# the Sizes of Atoms

Two more electrons in the $3p$ orbitals would complete the valence shell for sulfur and give it an electron configuration identical to that of the noble gas argon. Two atoms of hydrogen, each with a simple $1s$ electron configuration, can provide the two electrons. What then could we expect about the molecule that sulfur forms with hydrogen?

Since both elements are nonmetals, we would predict covalent bonding between them in the formation of a compound whose simplest formula would be $H_2S$.

From Table 11–2 it is learned that the difference in electronegativity between hydrogen (2.1) and sulfur (2.5) is rather small, so that the covalent bond between them would have only a slight per cent of ionic character. Finally, since the electron pairs in the completed valence shell of sulfur will be localized in four separate positions in space, the Lewis electron dot structure for $H_2S$ should reflect a tetrahedral orientation of those electron pairs. Thus, we would represent $H_2S$ as:

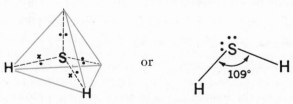

or

What are the experimental facts? The formula for the binary compound between hydrogen and sulfur is, indeed, $H_2S$. The compound is a gas at ordinary temperatures, indicating covalent bonding within the molecules and little intermolecular attraction. The molecule is bent,

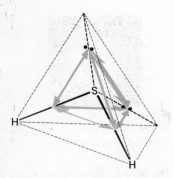

**FIGURE 20.1** Lone-pair—bond-pair electron interaction: a model for hydrogen sulfide

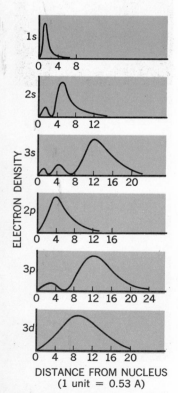

**FIGURE 20.2** Radial probability distribution curves for the electron in hydrogen

but instead of the expected tetrahedral bond angle of 109° for the H—S—H angle, an experimental angle of 92° is observed. The 17° difference between the theoretical and the observed bond angle has been interpreted in terms of the repulsive forces present among the nonbonding and bonding electron pairs around the sulfur atom. (Fig. 20.1.)

We have been able to arrive at a fairly successful model for $H_2S$ based on our first considerations of atomic orbitals. We now turn to more advanced considerations of atomic orbitals and to the bonding and structural characteristics that can be derived from them.

### 20.2 The spatial extension of orbitals

We should recall from Chapter 10 (Sec. 10.2) that one of the pillars that support the great intellectual structure that is the quantum mechanical theory of atomic and molecular structure is the Heisenberg Uncertainty Principle. We also saw (Sec. 10.5) that on the basis of the Uncertainty Principle the quantum mechanical model deals strictly with *probable* electron positions in atoms. For an electron in the 1s orbital of hydrogen, for example, a probability calculation for different electron distances from the nucleus results in the curve shown in Figure 20.2. Similarly, the probability curves for an electron in the 2s, 2p, 3s, 3p, and 3d orbitals of hydrogen are shown. The maximum in the probability curve for the 1s orbital occurs at approximately 0.50 A, while for the 2s orbital it occurs at 2.6 A, and for the 3s orbital at 6.9 A. It is important to recognize that *these are not the values for definite orbital positions*. Careful study of Figure 20.2 shows that even for the 1s orbital there is a definite, albeit small, probability for the electron to be 2.6 A from the nucleus, while there is, also, a definite but small probability for an electron in the 2s orbital to be at 0.50 A from the nucleus at any particular moment. The maxima in the probability curves represent the most probable distance from the nucleus at which an electron of specific energy characteristics will be found.

### 20.3 The angular distribution of orbitals

At this point it would be logical to ask the question: Does the electron in the 1s orbital have the same probability to be at a certain distance from the nucleus in all directions from the nucleus? For example, if the calculation of probability versus distance gives a value of 0.50 A for the maximum probability in one direction, is the maximum probability still at 0.50 A along a direction that is at an angle of 90° to the first? When the appropriate calculation is made, it is found that probability as a function of distance is *independent* of angle for the 1s electron. Thus, the 1s electron has an equal probability in all directions of being at a certain distance from the nucleus. That is, the 1s electron has a spherically symmetrical probability distribution. (Fig. 20.3.)

It is clear from Figure 20.2 that the probability curves for the 1s and 2s orbitals are different. Thus, it is more likely that a 1s electron will be found 1 A from the nucleus at a given moment than will a 2s electron. However, the probability for each at 1 A is the same in all directions. (Fig. 20.4.)

**FIGURE 20.3** The 1s electron: a model in space

### 20.4 Orbital probabilities are directed in space.

We recall that $p$ electron orbitals which have a quantum number value $l = 1$ can have values of $+1$, 0, and $-1$ for the quantum number $m$. We interpreted three $m$ values physically to indicate that three $p$ orbitals of identical energy characteristics exist, but are oriented differently in space. Probability distribution for $p$ electrons support that interpretation.

**FIGURE 20.4** The 1s and 2s electrons in space

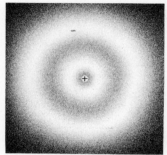

The probability of finding a $p$ electron at a given distance from the nucleus, unlike that of finding an $s$ electron, *is dependent upon angle.* Appropriate calculations indicate that $p$ electron orbitals should be found most probably in three mutually perpendicular directions. Common practice is to orient those directions in a familiar *cartesian coordinate system* ($x$, $y$, $z$ axes). Then the $p$ orbital probability distribution oriented along the $x$ axial direction is referred to as the $p_x$ orbital probability distribution. Similarly, there are $p_y$ and $p_z$ orbital probability distributions. (Fig. 20.5.)

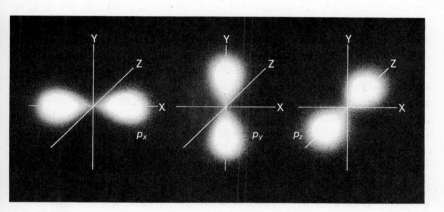

**FIGURE 20.5** Probability distributions for 2p orbitals. The mutual perpendicularity arises in a magnetic field.

### 20.5 Orbital shapes to be used

Strictly speaking, the spherical probability distribution of $s$ electron orbitals and the dumbbell-shaped probability distribution of $p$ electron orbitals *are not the shapes of the orbitals themselves.* It becomes convenient, however, to think of those shapes and to use them in just such

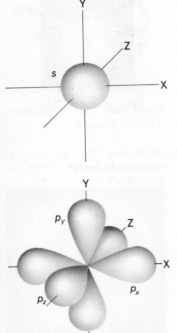

**FIGURE 20.6**    *s* and *p* orbitals

**FIGURE 20.7** The overlap of 1*s* orbitals: a model for the hydrogen molecule

a way. Following common practice among chemists, we shall use a simpler form of the probability distributions. That form is a bounded shape that encloses 90 per cent of the probability of finding the electron at any distance from the nucleus. It is these bounded shapes that we shall henceforth for convenience refer to as orbital shapes. (Fig. 20.6.) It might be valuable, however, to remember that there is still one chance in ten, or a 10 per cent probability, that the electron will be located outside these arbitrarily chosen orbital shapes at any given instant. This is the essence of the modern theory of atomic structure. It is a theory which predicts that there is a finite probability that an electron in a given energy state will be at any distance from the nucleus at any instant in time.

### 20.6  Orbital overlap and chemical bonding

The fact that orbital "shapes" really represent electron probability distributions gives meaning to the use of such shapes in depicting chemical bonds. If we consider the simple case of $H_2$, we recall that the Lewis structure for this molecule is **H ⋮ H**. We are now able to extend our understandings of the probability nature of modern theory of atomic structure and chemical bonding to this simple case. In words, we might say that when a diatomic hydrogen molecule forms, the probability of finding the two bonding electrons is greatest between the two nuclei. Chemists can calculate that probability from quantum mechanical theory. They also can picture that probability in terms of the *overlap* of the orbital shapes for each of the two bonding electrons. (Fig. 20.7.)

The region of high electron probability brought about by the merging, or overlap, of the 1*s* orbitals represents the covalent bond between the two nuclei. Since for this simple case of $H_2$ we have been dealing with spherically symmetrical *s* orbitals, the same degree of overlap would occur no matter how the two atoms were oriented, provided that the internuclear distance remained constant. When, however, *p* orbitals are involved in covalent bonding, their inherent orientations in space impose similar orientations upon the bonds that are formed. We turn next to such cases.

### 20.7  Orbital direction and bond direction

When an atom uses *p* orbitals to form bonds, the electron probability for bond formation is not equal in all directions from the nucleus. The degree of overlap between the orbitals of the two bonding atoms will depend on the directional character of the *p* bonding orbital.

In Figure 20.8 is represented the hypothetical case of a covalent bond formed by an *s* and a *p* electron. At the left, the *s* orbital of atom A overlaps with the $p_y$ orbital of atom B along the *Y* axis. At the right in Figure 20.8, the *s* orbital of atom A is also overlapping with the $p_y$ orbital of atom B at the same internuclear distance, but not along the preferred *y axis* orientation of the $p_y$ orbital of atom B. It is easy to see that under these conditions very much less overlap occurs. It follows that the larger the degree of overlapping of electron orbitals, the larger the probability of the bonding pair of electrons being between the two nuclei. When the bonding electrons are between the two nuclei, there is less repulsion between those nuclei. Consequently, the bond between the nuclei is more stable. *Thus, the greater the overlapping of bonding orbitals, the more stable the bond formed between them.* As a result, the situation at the left in Figure 20.8 represents a stable bond, whereas that at the right does not.

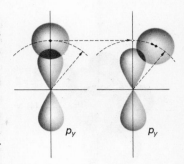

**FIGURE 20.8** Which model is more stable?

## 20.8 The structure of H₂S: another view

We may now return to a consideration of the molecular structure of hydrogen sulfide in view of the more advanced knowledge of orbitals that we now have.

Again, we begin with the electron configuration for sulfur. This time we will consider only the valence electrons and make note of the mutual perpendicularity of the 3*p* orbitals. We now have two ways to pictorialize those valence electron orbital distributions, most simply as

$$\underset{3s}{\uparrow\downarrow}\;\bigg|\;\underset{3p_x}{\uparrow\downarrow}\;\underset{3p_y}{\uparrow}\;\underset{3p_z}{\uparrow}$$

and in terms of orbital shapes as:

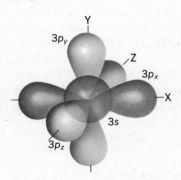

Several points should be made. First, it is simply arbitrary to label the 3*p* orbital that has two electrons of opposite spin as the $3p_x$ orbital.* We normally think in terms of *x, y, z,* rather than some other combination of those letters. The important point is that the three 3*p*

---

* Full occupancy of an orbital will henceforth be shown by shading.

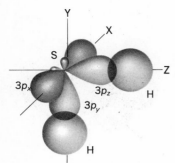

**FIGURE 20.9** *s-p orbital overlap: a model for hydrogen sulfide*

orbitals are mutually perpendicular regardless of how they are labeled. Next, the fact that one of the $3p$ orbitals does have its maximum electron occupancy makes it a *nonbonding orbital*. That is, were such an orbital to become involved in overlap it would possess three electrons. Recalling the Pauli Exclusion Principle (Section 10.7), we determine that, according to the quantum mechanical theory, three electrons in a given orbital are forbidden. Thus, to simplify our new view of the bonding and structure in $H_2S$, we need only consider the bonding $3p_y$ and $3p_z$ orbitals of sulfur overlapping with two $1s$ electrons of hydrogen atoms. (Fig. 20.9.)

If you have examined Figure 20.9 carefully, you have noted a change in the shape of the $3p_y$ and $3p_z$ orbitals *after bonding*. This is simply a reflection of the fact that each bonding electron pair in $H_2S$ is localized between the sulfur nucleus and one of the hydrogen nuclei. Thus, there is little probability of finding bonding electrons other than directly between nuclei. The shape of a bonded $p$ orbital is based on quantum mechanical probability calculations for a bonding situation.

Since three $3p$ orbitals are all at right angles to each other, if any two are used to form bonds then the angle between the bonds would be expected to be 90° or very close to that. The experimental bond angle of 92° for the H—S—H bond angle in $H_2S$ is quite close to the expected 90° shown in Figure 20.9. In fact, for $H_2S$ we see that the prediction of bond angles from our new model involving $p$ orbitals overlapping with $s$ orbitals is in much closer agreement than the 109° expected from the tetrahedral electron pair model of Chapter 11. The success of our new model is encouraging. Let us consider some more of its applications.

### 20.9 The structure of PH₃

Phosphorus has the electron configuration:

$$_{15}P \quad 1s^2 2s^2 2p^6 3s^2 3p^3 \quad \text{or} \quad \frac{\uparrow\downarrow}{1s}\frac{\uparrow\downarrow}{2s}\frac{\uparrow\downarrow}{2p_x}\frac{\uparrow\downarrow}{2p_y}\frac{\uparrow\downarrow}{2p_z}\frac{\uparrow\downarrow}{3s}\frac{\uparrow}{3p_x}\frac{\uparrow}{3p_y}\frac{\uparrow}{3p_z}$$

By concentrating on the valence electrons we see that phosphorus may form three covalent bonds using its three $3p$ orbitals. Since, in our new model, these three orbitals are mutually perpendicular, we expect a pyramidal structure for a molecule formed using those orbitals. (Fig. 20.10.) The experimental bond angles in $PH_3$ are all 93°, again an encouraging support for the orbital overlap model for molecular structure.

### 20.10 The structure of methane: orbital hybridization

When we consider methane, $CH_4$, we meet with a difficult problem that did not arise in the cases of hydrogen sulfide and phosphine.

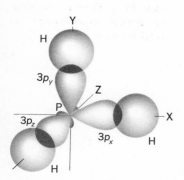

**FIGURE 20.10** *Orbital overlap and the shape of phosphine*

From the electron configuration of carbon,

$$_6C \quad 1s^2 2s^2 2p^2 \quad \text{or} \quad \frac{\uparrow\downarrow}{1s}\frac{\uparrow\downarrow}{2s}\frac{\uparrow}{2p_x}\frac{\uparrow}{2p_y}\frac{}{2p_z},$$

and the spatial representation thereof (Fig. 20.11), it becomes evident that we can account for the formation of a compound of formula $CH_2$ but not $CH_4$. When we first met with this problem in Section 11.9, using simple electrostatic considerations, we were able to solve this problem by extending our model to include *orbital hybridization*. From the mathematical mixing of a $2s$ and three $2p$ orbitals, we arrived at four identical hybrid $2(sp^3)$ orbitals that assumed a tetrahedral orientation in space. How does our new approach to molecular structure fare when it comes to orbital hybridization?

When quantum mechanical probability calculations are made on the orbitals that would be formed from the mathematical mixing of one $s$ and three $p$ orbitals, the satisfying results of Figure 20.12 are obtained. Not only do the probability calculations lead to the possibility of hybrid $(sp^3)$ bonding orbitals, but their spatial orientation is tetrahedral! Thus, we can now readily account for the bonding properties of methane in terms of our new model and hybrid orbitals. (Fig. 20.13.)

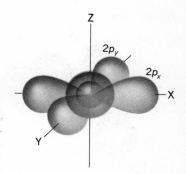

**FIGURE 20.11** The shape of orbitals in unbonded gaseous carbon atoms

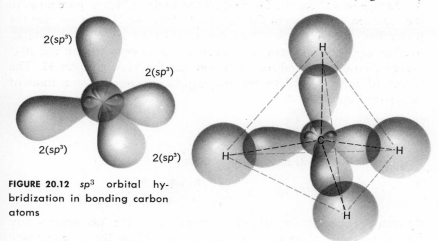

**FIGURE 20.12** $sp^3$ orbital hybridization in bonding carbon atoms

**FIGURE 20.13** Orbital overlap and orbital hybridization: a model for methane

## 20.11 Orbital shapes: successes and uncertainties

The successful application of the quantum mechanical model of orbital shapes to molecular structures in a number of cases has been spectacular. Figure 20.14 shows how it is applied in the case of water. Figure 20.15 shows how it helps explain the properties of ammonia. Indications of the powerful support it gives to other types of orbital hybridizations are summarized in Figures 20.16 and 20.17.

**FIGURE 20.14**

Quantum mechanical model for water, $H_2O$,

$_8O$    $1s^2 2s^2 2p_x{}^2 2p_y{}^1 2p_z{}^1$   or   $\underset{1s}{\uparrow\downarrow}\,\underset{2s}{\uparrow\downarrow}\,\underset{2p_x}{\uparrow\downarrow}\,\underset{2p_y}{\uparrow}\,\underset{2p_z}{\uparrow}$

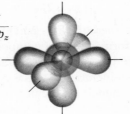

On forming water, $H_2O$,

$_8O$  $\underset{1s}{\uparrow\downarrow}\,\underset{2s}{\uparrow\downarrow}\,\underset{2p_x}{\uparrow\downarrow}\,\underset{2p_y}{\uparrow}\,\underset{2p_z}{\uparrow}$  hybridizes to  $\underset{1s}{\uparrow\downarrow}\,\underset{2(sp^3)}{\uparrow\downarrow}\,\underset{2(sp^3)}{\uparrow\downarrow}\,\underset{2(sp^3)}{\uparrow}\,\underset{2(sp^3)}{\uparrow}$ .

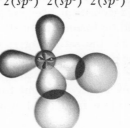

Thus, the quantum mechanical model for water is:

**FIGURE 20.16**

Quantum mechanical model for beryllium bifluoride, $BeF_2$,

$_4Be$  $1s^2 2s^2$   or   $\underset{1s}{\uparrow\downarrow}\,\underset{2s}{\uparrow\downarrow}\,\underset{2p_x}{\quad}\,\underset{2p_y}{\quad}\,\underset{2p_z}{\quad}$

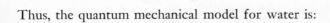

On forming beryllium bifluoride, $BeF_2$,

$_4Be$  $\underset{1s}{\uparrow\downarrow}\,\underset{2s}{\uparrow\downarrow}\,\underset{2p_x}{\quad}\,\underset{2p_y}{\quad}\,\underset{2p_z}{\quad}$  hybridizes to  $\underset{1s}{\uparrow\downarrow}\,\underset{2(sp)}{\uparrow}\,\underset{2(sp)}{\uparrow}$ .

Thus, the quantum mechanical model of beryllium bifluoride is:

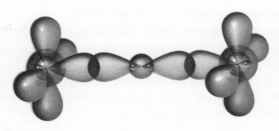

**FIGURE 20.15**

Quantum mechanical model for ammonia, $NH_3$,

$_7N$    $1s^2 2s^2 2p_x{}^1 2p_y{}^1 2p_z{}^1$   or   $\underset{1s}{\uparrow\downarrow}\,\underset{2s}{\uparrow\downarrow}\,\underset{2p_x}{\uparrow}\,\underset{2p_y}{\uparrow}\,\underset{2p_z}{\uparrow}$

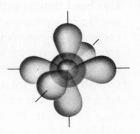

On forming ammonia, $NH_3$,

$_7N$   $\underset{1s}{\uparrow\downarrow}\,\underset{2s}{\uparrow\downarrow}\,\underset{2p_x}{\uparrow}\,\underset{2p_y}{\uparrow}\,\underset{2p_z}{\uparrow}$   hybridizes to   $\underset{1s}{\uparrow\downarrow}\,\underset{2(sp^3)}{\uparrow\downarrow}\,\underset{2(sp^3)}{\uparrow}\,\underset{2(sp^3)}{\uparrow}\,\underset{2(sp^3)}{\uparrow}$.

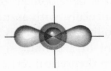

Thus, the quantum mechanical model for ammonia is:

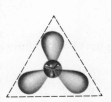

**FIGURE 20.17**

Quantum mechanical model for boron trifluoride, $BF_3$,

$_5B$   $1s^2 2s^2 2p^1$   or   $\underset{1s}{\uparrow\downarrow}\,\underset{2s}{\uparrow\downarrow}\,\underset{2p_x}{\uparrow}\,\underset{2p_y}{\,}\,\underset{2p_z}{\,}$

On forming boron trifluoride, $BF_3$,

$_5B$   $\underset{1s}{\uparrow\downarrow}\,\underset{2s}{\uparrow\downarrow}\,\underset{2p_x}{\uparrow}\,\underset{2p_y}{\,}\,\underset{2p_z}{\,}$   hybridizes to   $\underset{1s}{\uparrow\downarrow}\,\underset{2(sp^2)}{\uparrow}\,\underset{2(sp^2)}{\uparrow}\,\underset{2(sp^2)}{\uparrow}$.

Thus, the quantum mechanical model for boron trifluoride is:

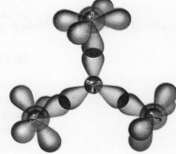

All of our considerations thus far have centered on simple covalent bonds. The quantum mechanical model of orbital shapes has also been dramatically successful in explaining multiple covalent bonding. In its extension to double and triple bonds, though, the model becomes quite complex. Its basic characteristic, for example, involves the *side-to-side* overlap of *p* orbitals. Single bonds only involve the *end-to-end* overlap of orbitals. Since multiple bonding is considerably more complex in its interpretation, you are directed to the bibliographic references at the end of this chapter for further information.

Despite its power and intellectual beauty, the quantum mechanical model for atomic and molecular structures is far from complete. You are aware, for example, that $H_2O$ and $H_2S$ are related chemically just as $PH_3$ and $NH_3$ are. Yet it is easier to explain the bond angles in $H_2S$ and $PH_3$ from a model with only the *p* orbitals of sulfur and phosphorus considered. On the other hand, $H_2O$ and $NH_3$ have angles that are quite a bit larger than the 90° expected for simple *p* orbital involvement. To explain $H_2O$ and $NH_3$, a model based on the formation of hybrid ($sp^3$) orbitals is found to be better. The necessity of using two different kinds of models for such related compounds as $H_2O$ and $H_2S$, or $NH_3$ and $PH_3$, indicates that we still have a great deal to learn about chemical bonds, molecular structure, and the role of orbitals.

### 20.12 Atomic size

One aspect of atomic and molecular systems to which little attention has been paid thus far is the size of the atoms and molecules of such systems. From the development of the preceding eleven sections of this chapter, and especially with an understanding that we can learn only about the probabilities of electron position in atoms, it is easy to foresee that the concept of a definite size for atoms is not likely to be acceptable in modern theoretical terms. Strictly speaking, there are no sharp boundaries or limits to atoms. There is always a finite probability for electrons to be at large distances from the nucleus. Arbitrarily, the shapes used in this book for orbitals included 90 per cent of the total over-all electron probability distribution. In the same sense, we should be able to arrive at a set of practical atomic sizes. There are several approaches that can be taken. In all of these approaches, the quantity actually measured is the distance between neighboring nuclei.

### 20.13 Atomic volumes

The simplest measurement of atomic size is derived from a measurement of the volume occupied in the solid state by one mole of atoms of an element. This volume is known as the *atomic volume*. With a knowledge of the number of atoms contained in that volume, $6.02 \times 10^{23}$, and assuming the atoms are spherical, it is possible to calculate the relative

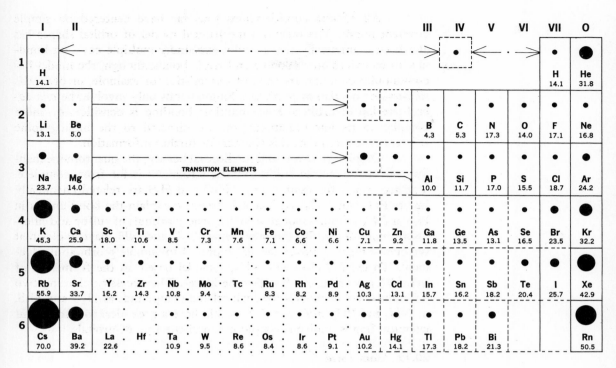

**FIGURE 20.18** Atomic volumes of the elements. (Adapted from *Chemical Periodicity* by R. T. Sanderson. New York: Reinhold Publishing Corporation; by permission of the publisher.)

diameters of different atoms. While such measurements and calculations lead to relative sizes of atoms, as shown in Figure 20.18, there is much experimental uncertainty involved. The solid elements exist in a wide variety of structures. Some have atoms that are closely packed with little empty space between them. Other solid elements, however, have more loosely packed atoms with a fair amount of unfilled space between them. Based on the calculation used to arrive at Figure 20.18, the atoms in loosely packed structures would have larger sizes than they should, since the empty space between them would be unavoidably added to their size. It is known from independent measurements, for example, that individual phosphorus atoms are smaller than individual silicon atoms. The atomic volume of phosphorus, however, is larger than that of silicon, since it has a more open solid state structure. (Fig. 20.19.)

## 20.14 Ionic crystal radii

A more accurate measurement of atomic size involves the diffraction of X rays as they pass through crystals. Although this is a more com-

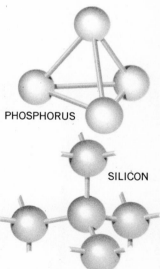

PHOSPHORUS

SILICON

**FIGURE 20.19** Structure of molecular phosphorus, $P_4$, (above), and atomic silicon (below).

plex measurement than that of atomic volume, it avoids the problem of empty spaces in the solid structure. Using X-ray diffraction techniques, the distance between sodium and chlorine nuclei in a crystal of sodium chloride is found to be 2.81 A. The problem now arises over how much of this 2.81 A distance is due to the sodium and how much to the chlorine. By measuring a very large number of compounds, it has been possible to arrive at a set of consistent sizes for crystal radii. Table 20–1 lists some of these radii.

Several trends are observable in these data. The ionic size *increases* regularly from $Li^{+1}$ to $Cs^{+1}$, which is to be expected from the curves in Figure 20.2. The outermost electrons in $Li^{+1}$ ions are in the $1s$ orbital ($_3Li$ $1s^22s^1$; $_3Li^{+1}$ $1s^2$), whereas those in $Cs^{+1}$ ions are in the $5p$ orbitals. (Verify this by checking the electron configuration of Cs atom.) From Figure 20.2 we see that the electrons in orbitals of higher values of $n$, the principal quantum number, are more probably found further from the nucleus. Similarly, we can understand the increase in radii between $Mg^{+2}$ and $Ba^{+2}$, between $B^{+3}$ and $Tl^{+3}$, between $Cu^{+1}$ and $Au^{+1}$, between $Zn^{+2}$ and $Hg^{+2}$, between $Sc^{+3}$ and $Y^{+3}$, between $Ti^{+4}$ and $Zr^{+4}$, and between $F^{-1}$ and $I^{-1}$.

Another trend observed is the *decrease* in size for ions of the same number of electrons as the atomic number *increases*. Thus, $Na^{+1}$ (11 protons, 10 electrons) is larger than $Mg^{+2}$ (12 protons, 10 electrons), and $Mg^{+2}$ is larger than $Al^{+3}$ (13 protons, 10 electrons). Fluoride ion, $F^{-1}$, which has 10 electrons also but only 9 protons in its nucleus, is even larger than $Na^{+1}$. This trend is also simple to understand. The ions $F^{-1}$, $Na^{+1}$, $Mg^{+2}$, and $Al^{+3}$ all have the electron configuration

$$1s^22s^22p^6.$$

As we would expect, these electrons are more tightly attracted to the nucleus the larger the number of positive charges present. In $F^{-1}$, there is a deficiency of one positive charge ($9^+$, $10^-$), so the electrons experience weaker attraction and the ionic size is largest. Progressively, from $Na^{+1}$ to $Al^{+3}$, there is an increasing surplus of positive charge and, consequently, the electrons are attracted more closely to the nucleus.

## 20.15 Radius ratios and ionic crystal structure

Using the ionic radii values in Table 20–1, and assuming spherical shapes for ions, it is possible to calculate how many anions of a certain radius can be packed around a cation of a definite size. Thus, for the $Na^{+1}$ ion of 0.95 A radius, it is possible to calculate that six $Cl^{-1}$ spheres of 1.81 A radius will pack around it symmetrically. Experimentally, this is verified. (See Figure 6.8, page 162.) Thus, from simple calculations

## TABLE 20–1 Ionic Crystal Radii

| Ion | Radius(A) | Ion | Radius(A) | Ion | Radius(A) | Ion | Radius(A) | Ion | Radius(A) |
|-----|-----------|-----|-----------|-----|-----------|-----|-----------|-----|-----------|
| $Li^{+1}$ | 0.60 | $Be^{+2}$ | 0.31 | $B^{+3}$ | 0.20 | $Ti^{+4}$ | 0.68 | $F^{-1}$ | 1.36 |
| $Na^{+1}$ | 0.95 | $Mg^{+2}$ | 0.65 | $Al^{+3}$ | 0.50 | $Zr^{+4}$ | 0.80 | $Cl^{-1}$ | 1.81 |
| $K^{+1}$ | 1.33 | $Ca^{+2}$ | 0.99 | $Ga^{+3}$ | 0.62 | | | $Br^{-1}$ | 1.95 |
| $Rb^{+1}$ | 1.48 | $Sr^{+2}$ | 1.13 | $In^{+3}$ | 0.81 | | | $I^{-1}$ | 2.16 |
| $Cs^{+1}$ | 1.69 | $Ba^{+2}$ | 1.35 | $Tl^{+3}$ | 0.95 | | | | |
| $Cu^{+1}$ | 0.96 | $Zn^{+2}$ | 0.74 | $Sc^{+3}$ | 0.81 | | | | |
| $Ag^{+1}$ | 1.26 | $Cd^{+2}$ | 0.97 | $Y^{+3}$ | 0.93 | | | | |
| $Au^{+1}$ | 1.37 | $Hg^{+2}$ | 1.10 | | | | | | |

of geometry it is possible to predict the number of anions that will surround a cation if the value of the ratio of the radii of the two ions is
known. The results of these radius ratio calculations are given in
Table 20–2 and shown in Figure 20.20.

## TABLE 20–2 Predictions of Packing in Ionic Crystals from the Radius Ratio

| Radius Ratio $\left(\dfrac{Cation\ Radius}{Anion\ Radius}\right)$ | Number of Nearest Neighbors | Structure |
|---|---|---|
| 0.16–0.23 | 3 | Triangular |
| 0.23–0.41 | 4 | Tetrahedral |
| 0.41–0.73 | 6 | Octahedral |
| 0.73–1.00 | 8 | Cubic |

In most cases, the actual packing as determined by experiment
agrees with the predictions. For some crystals, however, there is disagreement. In $Cs^{+1} F^{-1}$, the radius ratio (1.24) predicts eight small $F^{-1}$
ions surrounding each large $Cs^{+1}$ ion. The experimental value, however,
is six. In $Li^{+1}I^{-1}$, the radius ratio (0.28) predicts four large $I^{-1}$ ions
surrounding each small $Li^{+1}$ ion, whereas six are found experimentally.
Obviously, then, the model of packing is too simple. If we recall our
introductory remarks about sizes and the difficulty of knowing just
what they mean, an explanation for the $Cs^{+1}F^{-1}$ and $Li^{+1}I^{-1}$ cases is
suggested. Maybe it is an oversimplification to expect the radius of a
particular ion to have the same value in all compounds. Perhaps ions
change radii somewhat, depending on the other ions they are near.
Perhaps $Cs^{+1}$ being rather large is more sensitive to this change than
the smaller $Na^{+1}$ and, similarly, maybe the large $I^{-1}$ is more sensitive
than the smaller $F^{-1}$.

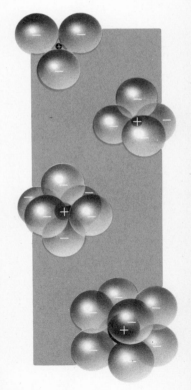

**FIGURE 20.20** Radius ratio determines ionic crystal structure.

Data exist that allow this idea to be checked. While it is not possible to single out molecules in ionic solids, ionic molecules do exist in the gaseous state. It is possible to measure the distances between nuclei in gaseous ionic molecules as well as in ionic crystals. If ionic radii change depending upon their electrical environment, it is reasonable to expect to see such a change reflected in a difference in the internuclear distance. This difference would be most pronounced between ionic gaseous molecules, where a cation has only one anion near it, and ionic crystals, where a cation may have 4, 6, or 8 anions around it. For $Cs^{+1}F^{-1}$, the internuclear distance in the gas molecules is 2.35 A compared to 3.00 A in the crystal; for $Li^{+1}I^{-1}$, the values are 2.39 A in the gas and 3.00 A in the crystal. Thus, ionic internuclear distances are more than 25 per cent shorter in the gas phase than in crystals. This confirms our suspicion that it is naïve to believe the values in Table 20–1 are valid in all compounds or even in all ionic compounds.

### 20.16 Covalent radii

Since you now have evidence for believing that the radius of an ion should be somewhat dependent on its surrounding ions, it will come as no surprise to learn that an atom in a predominantly covalent compound has a different radial length than it has in a predominantly ionic compound.

The distance between nuclei in gaseous diatomic molecules of identical atoms (e.g., $H_2$, $Cl_2$, $Na_2$) are measured. These internuclear distances are referred to as covalent *bond lengths*. One half the internuclear distance is called the covalent radius of the atom. Figure 20.21 depicts values of covalent radii.

Notice that the covalent radius for sodium is 1.54 A compared to the ionic crystal radius of 0.95 A. The covalent radius is based on a sodium atom that has an electron in the $3s$ orbital. The ionic radius is derived from a sodium atom that has lost the $3s$ electron and that has the $2p$ orbitals as the last filled. As before, the spatial extension of orbitals of different principal quantum numbers predicts the smaller size for the ion.

In the case of chlorine, the ionic radius of 1.81 A is larger than the covalent radius of 0.99 A. Unlike the case of sodium, we are now dealing with the same electron orbitals for both ion and atom in a covalent bond. However, simple explanations are available to account for the size difference. When the $Cl^{-1}$ ion forms, the incoming extra electron brings about repulsion among the five already present $3p$ electrons. This repulsion leads to an expansion of the $3p$ orbital extension in space, and a large ion size. In a covalent bond, on the other hand, while the chlorine atom gains a share in an extra electron, it also loses a share of one of its own $3p$ electrons. In addition, the localization of

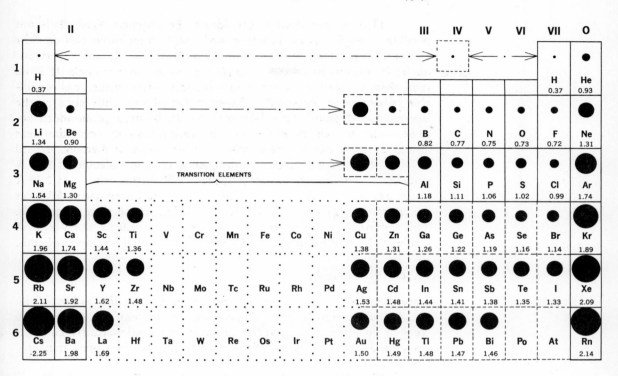

**FIGURE 20.21** Covalent radii of the elements. (Adapted from *Chemical Periodicity* by R. T. Sanderson. New York: Reinhold Publishing Corporation; by permission of the publisher.)

the bonding electron pair between the two nuclei of the bonding atoms tends to draw the nuclei closer together. In all, then, the covalent radius of chlorine is small compared to $Cl^{-1}$ ion size.

It would be useful to be able to compare covalent and ionic radii to the radius of a non-bonded atom. Fortunately, another kind of atomic size allows such a comparison.

## 20.17 Van der Waals radii

If we consider a molecular model of two neighboring $Cl_2$ molecules, in the solid state two internuclear distances become evident. (Fig. 20.22.)

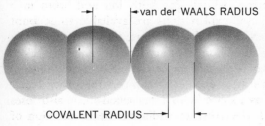

van der WAALS RADIUS

COVALENT RADIUS

**FIGURE 20.22** The covalent and van der Waals radii of a diatomic molecule

As you can see, one of those internuclear distances is the covalent bond length, the distance between the centers of two covalently bonded atoms. It is an *intra*molecular distance. The other, a longer internuclear distance, is the closest that the centers of two atoms in neighboring molecules can approach each other. In the case of liquid or solid chlorine, such closeness is brought about by the presence of van der Waals forces of attraction between neighboring molecules. (See Section 12.3.) The longer internuclear distance, which is also *inter*molecular in nature, is called the van der Waals diameter. One half of this measured quantity is, then, the van der Waals radius of an atom. Table 20–3 lists some of these radii.

**TABLE 20–3**  VAN DER WAALS RADII (A)

| Na | 1.86 | Cl | 1.40 | Ne | 1.60 |
|----|------|-----|------|-----|------|
| K  | 2.31 | Br | 1.65 | Ar | 1.92 |
| Rb | 2.44 | I  | 1.77 | Kr | 1.97 |
| Cs | 2.62 | Xe | 2.17 |    |      |

Thus, in comparing the sizes of Cl, Ar, and K, the van der Waals radii are in the order:

$$K > Ar > Cl$$
$$2.31 \text{ A} \quad 1.92 \text{ A} \quad 1.40 \text{ A}$$

We may assume that the van der Waals radii reflect the size of unbonded neutral atoms of these elements.

On the other hand, the sizes for the *isoelectronic* (same number of electrons) species, $Cl^{-1}$, Ar, $K^{+1}$, are in the order

$$K^{+1} < Cl^{-1} < Ar$$
$$1.33 \text{ A} \quad 1.81 \text{ A} \quad 1.92 \text{ A}$$

and we are hard put to explain why $Cl^{-1}$ with only 17 protons and 18 electrons is smaller than Ar atom with 18 of each.

Finally, in comparing the sizes of neutral chlorine atom, $Cl^0$, covalently bonded chlorine atom, Cl, and chloride ion, $Cl^{-1}$, the order is, as we should expect:

$$Cl < Cl^0 < Cl^{-1}$$
$$0.99 \text{ A} \quad 1.40 \text{ A} \quad 1.81 \text{ A}$$

We thus conclude twenty chapters in which the underlying concepts that constitute the skeletal structure of the great edifice of chemical science have been developed. We proceed now to studies of large chemical systems—systems whose orderliness is made clear through an understanding of the structure we have built.

# SUMMARY

Basic to the quantum mechanical model of the atom is the fact that we deal only with the probability distributions of electron positions in the atom. For $s$ electrons, those distributions are independent of angle. On the other hand, $p$ electrons have angularly dependent distributions that are, therefore, directed in space. Molecules in which $p$ electrons are involved in covalent bonds will have structures determined, in part, by the spatial orientation of bonding $p$ electron probability distributions. Nonbonding electrons will also influence molecular structures through electrostatic interactions with bonding electrons.

The covalent bond can be represented in terms of the overlap of the probability distributions for the electrons in the bond. For the carbon compounds, especially, as well as for a number of other compounds, hybrid orbitals are required to explain bonding characteristics. In general, the calculated probability distributions for electrons in such orbitals lead to quite satisfying explanations.

Measurements of atomic size and ionic size are important experimental quantities, which support modern chemical bonding theory. Atomic size and ionic size are subject to varying influences, especially the number of neighbors nearest to the atom or ion whose size is being measured. On the other hand, atomic size and ionic size determine the number of nearest neighbors and, therefore, greatly influence solid state structures.

In considering molecular compounds, intramolecular and intermolecular distances, measured as covalent and van der Waals radii respectively, are important in determining the structural characteristics of these compounds.

# QUESTIONS AND PROBLEMS

**20.1** Describe the spatial orientations of $s$ and $p$ electron orbitals and their effect on molecular structure.

**20.2** Pictorially represent and describe the molecular structure of a water molecule in terms of: **a.** simple electron pair interactions; **b.** overlap involving unhybridized orbitals and interactions of lone pairs and bond pairs of electrons; **c.** overlap involving $sp^3$ hybrid orbitals and interactions of lone pairs and bond pairs of electrons. **d.** Which model of those described in parts **a**, **b**, and **c** most closely approximates the experimentally determined structure?

**20.3** Repeat the exercises of Question 20.2 for the ammonia molecule and for the phosphine molecule. In each case, which model most satisfactorily approximates the experimental evidence?

**20.4** Pictorially represent the electron probability distributions for: a. F in $F_2$; b. Be in $BeF_2$; c. B in $BCl_3$; d. C in $CCl_4$.

**20.5** Describe and explain the variation in ionic size among the alkali metal ions given in Table 20–1.

**20.6** Describe and explain the variation in ionic size given in Table 20–1 among the isoelectronic ions $F^{-1}$, $Na^{+1}$, $Mg^{+2}$ and $Al^{+3}$.

**20.7** The experimentally determined atomic radius of the sodium atom in metallic sodium is 1.90 A. a. Calculate the volume of a mole of sodium atoms in metallic sodium. b. What per cent of the atomic volume of sodium ($23.7$ $cm^3$) is occupied by atoms? Ans.  b. $72.8\%$

**20.8** From Tables 20–1 and 20–2, pictorially represent the orientation of the anions surrounding one cation in each of the following: LiF, LiBr, KF, KBr.

**20.9** How would you explain the fact that ionic internuclear distances are 25 per cent shorter in the gas phase than they are in the solid state?

**20.10** The covalent radius of a sodium atom is 1.54 A. [$Na_2(g)$ is a covalent molecule.] The atomic radius of a sodium atom in metallic sodium is 1.90 A. The ionic radius of a sodium ion is 0.95 A. Account qualitatively for these values.

**20.11** The covalent radius of chlorine is 0.99 A. The van der Waals radius of chlorine is 1.40 A. The ionic radius of the chloride ion is 1.81 A. Account qualitatively for these values.

## SUGGESTED READINGS

Barrow, G. M. *The Structure of Molecules* (paperback). W. A. Benjamin, 1963.

De Jong, W. F. *General Crystallography: A Brief Compendium*. W. H. Freeman and Co., Publishers, 1959.

Sebera, Donald K. *Electronic Structure and Chemical Bonding*. Blaisdell Publishing Co., 1964.

Wells, Alexander F. *The Third Dimension in Chemistry*. Oxford University Press, 1956.

CHEMISTRY
King, L. Carroll, "Molecular Architecture." Feb. 1964

SCIENTIFIC AMERICAN
Derjaguin, Boris V., "The Force Between Molecules." July 1960
Dirac, P. A. M., "The Evolution of the Physicist's Picture of Nature." May 1963

# Spectroscopy

## THE SCIENCE OF MEASURING MOLECULES

These spectral images of the visible radiation emitted by stars are
clues to many of the properties of the stars. In the same way, the
spectral images of the radiant energy emitted and absorbed by
matter lead to a fuller understanding of the properties of matter.

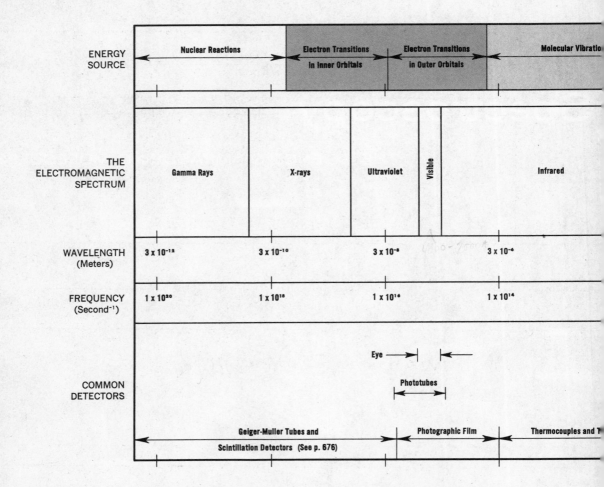

**RADIANT ENERGY**  Generated by the violent fusions of hydrogen nuclei in the sun, radiant energy streams through space to sustain and make visible all life on the earth. Generated on earth by electronic devices created by man, radiant energy provides radar for his defense and safety, television and radio for his amusement, and electric power for his economy.

As shown above, there exists an enormous range of radiant energies—from the ultra high, death-dealing energies resulting from cataclysmic cosmic reactions, to the very low energies characteristic of direct electrical current. The most satisfactory model of the source and properties of those energies stems from the work of the English physicist James Clerk Maxwell. In one of the greatest triumphs of abstract reasoning in the history of intellectual thought, Maxwell arrived at a mathematical formulation that exactly described electrical and related magnetic phenomena. His theory, fully enunciated in 1873, focused attention on the conditions in space around interacting particles rather than on the particles themselves. Thus, a significant transi-

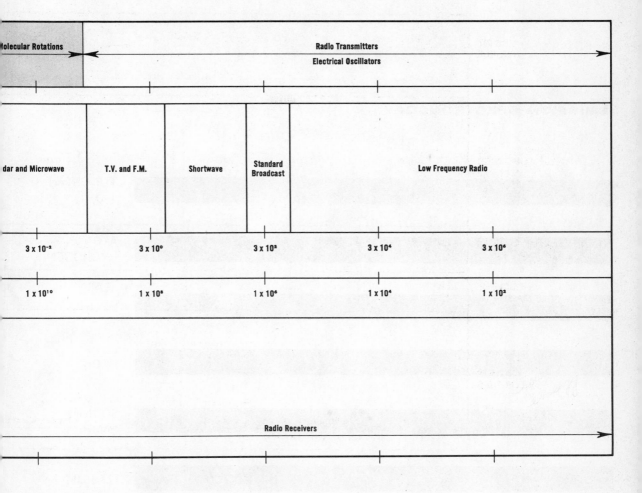

tion, *from particles to fields*, was brought about in physical thinking. The epochal conclusion of Maxwell's theory was that electricity, magnetism, and light were identical in nature. Thus, the classical model of radiant energy, still applicable to a host of observations, holds that radiant energy is produced whenever an electric charge *oscillates* or is *accelerated*. Moving outward from the charge is a disturbance characterized by the presence of electric and magnetic fields. This disturbance we call an *electromagnetic wave*. (Sec. 9.11.)

The chemist has learned that atoms and molecules interact differently with radiations from different parts of the spectrum. The measurement of the emission or absorption of radiant energy by atoms and molecules, and the deduction of atomic and molecular properties from such measurements, constitute *spectroscopy*, the science of measuring molecules. Above, you can see that there are spectral regions of particular importance for the spectroscopist. We turn to a brief consideration of each of those regions.

## EMISSION SPECTROSCOPY

TUNGSTEN LAMP

ATOMIC HYDROGEN

HELIUM

NEON

SODIUM LAMP

LITHIUM

Emission spectroscopy began in 1664 when Newton allowed sunlight to pass through a prism. It was not until the nineteenth century, however, that it blossomed into a full-blown science. By 1859 enough spectral data had been gathered to permit Gustav Kirchoff to deduce that each element had a uniquely characteristic emission spectrum. Some of the emission lines in the visible region for eight pure elements may be seen above. In order to obtain spectra for the high-boiling elements lithium, iron, and barium, each was vaporized in a carbon arc. The white light emitted by the arc leads to the continuous visible spectrum backgrounds in the spectra of these elements.

444

BARIUM

MOLECULAR
HYDROGEN

MERCURY
LAMP

FLUORESCENT
LAMP

IRON ARC

FRAUNHOFER
LINES

Interesting comparisons that might be made among the above spectra are between those of elemental and molecular hydrogen, and between those of a tungsten filament lamp and a fluorescent lamp. Also of great interest is the spectrum of the sun showing many "missing lines," an observation first made by Joseph von Fraunhofer, a German physicist, in 1814. These missing lines are believed to indicate the *absorption* of energy by electrons in the relatively cool elemental vapors of the sun's atmosphere. The principle involved is simply that if an element, on de-excitation, emits radiation of a given frequency, it will, upon excitation, absorb radiant energy of the same frequency.

# INFRARED SPECTROSCOPY

Note from the information given on pages 442–443 that electron excitations in *atoms* are manifested by emission lines in the ultraviolet, the visible, and the near infrared regions of the electromagnetic spectrum. It is when the more moderate energies of the infrared spectral region, especially of the far end of that region, are considered that we come upon a source of inestimable importance to the elucidation and understanding of *molecular* structure and properties.

At a given instant in time, a molecule in the gas phase may exhibit three distinct motions simultaneously. There is, of course, the *translational motion* through space of the entire molecule. Then, the molecule as a whole may be moving with respect to some imaginary axis passing through it. That is, there may be *molecular rotations*. Finally, the atoms comprising the molecule may be moving relative to each other while bonded to each other. That is, there may be internal *molecular vibrations*.

One of the most powerful extensions of the quantum theory of atomic structure indicates that any molecular vibration that *maintains or creates a dipole* will have quantum vibrational energy levels for which molecular excitations will occur. These are manifested in the infrared spectral region. As a result, a major science—infrared spectroscopy—has developed, through which the molecular structures of tens of thousands of compounds have been elucidated.

The highly developed techniques and instrumentation of infrared spectroscopy have been so widely applied that probably no modern chemical research laboratory is without some type of *infrared spectrophotometer.* Shown is a commonly used laboratory bench-top instrument that automatically exposes a sample to infrared radiation from 2.5 to 40 *microns.* (One micron = 1 X $10^{-6}$m.) Any molecular vibrational excitation that occurs in the sample in this region appears as an *absorption peak* on the spectrum, which is automatically recorded by this instrument.

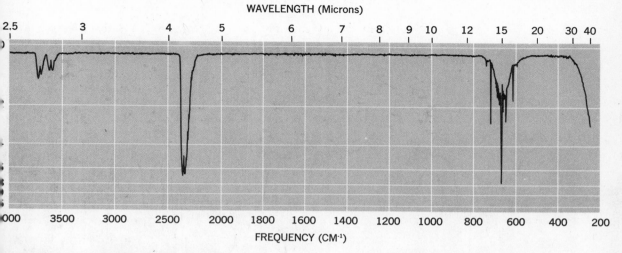

WAVELENGTH (Microns)

FREQUENCY (CM⁻¹)

Above is the infrared spectrum of carbon dioxide gas. How might we interpret it in terms of the model for the structure of carbon dioxide molecules that we previously established? (Sec. 11.13.)

We should recognize that the normally linear $CO_2$ molecule must be nonpolar. Present are two polar C=O bonds oriented in opposite directions. At the right are pictured the three *fundamental modes of vibration* for carbon dioxide. Two of them—the *bending mode* (top) and the *asymmetric stretching mode* (center)—lead to dipole formation. The *symmetric stretching mode* (bottom) does not. Thus we might predict that the two dipole-forming modes will be infrared active, while the symmetric stretching mode will not. Two major absorption peaks should, therefore, be apparent in the infrared spectrum of carbon dioxide gas, and they are.

On the basis of the spectra of other molecules containing the C=O bond, the assignments of energy absorption to vibrational modes for carbon dioxide are: asymmetric stretching vibration absorbs radiation at 4.1 microns; bond-bending vibration absorbs energy at 15 microns. (The minor peaks below three microns are due to absorption of *overtones* of the fundamental frequencies that are due to bond bending.)

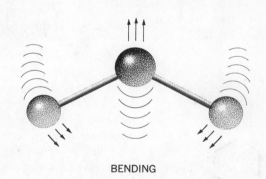

BENDING

ASYMMETRICAL STRETCHING

SYMMETRICAL STRETCHING

447

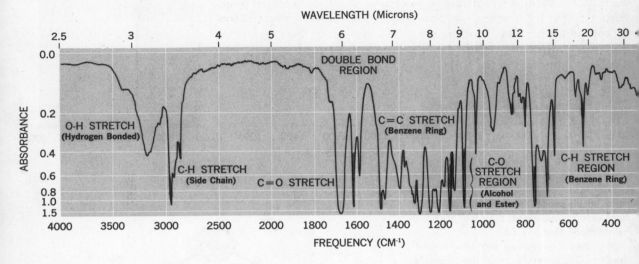

WAVELENGTH (Microns)

ABSORBANCE

FREQUENCY (CM⁻¹)

Infrared spectroscopy has found its widest use, and has led to its most significant results, in the investigation of chemical structure. After long years of infrared absorption studies, made on literally tens of thousands of compounds, chemists have found it possible to assign narrow spectral regions in the infrared to specific vibrational modes for specific groups of bonded atoms. Thus, for example, the stretching vibration for the C=O bond found in twelve distinctly different types of compounds absorbs energy in the wavelength region between 5.4 and 7.1 microns.

This region of the spectrum is not limited in assignment, however, to C=O stretching modes. In the same region, for example, are found energy absorptions that are due to stretching vibrations of the C=C, C=N, and O=N=O bonds as well as to bending vibrations of the $-NH_2$ and $-CH_3$ groups. Thus, infrared spectroscopic information must be used in conjunction with other chemical data in arriving at correct assignments of molecular structure when a choice of structures is available.

On this page is shown the infrared spectrum of the pure organic compound *isoamyl salicylate*. On the basis of the bond assignments also shown, along with other chemical information, the chemist arrives at the structural formula given for this compound.

isoamyl salicylate

# INFRARED SPECTROSCOPY: Industrial Tool

As a logical corollary to its use in helping to elucidate chemical structure, infrared spectroscopy finds widespread use as an analytical tool in both academic and industrial research laboratories. The qualitative and quantitative analyses of complex mixtures lend themselves, in particular, to this technique.

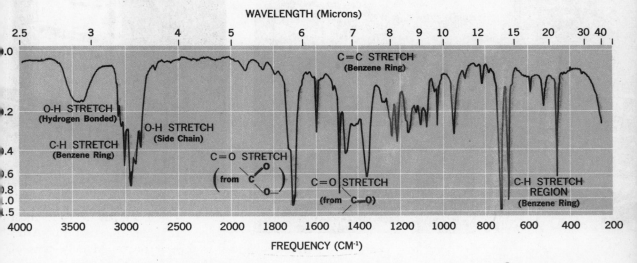

Shown on this page is the infrared spectrum of an industrial lacquer thinner of originally unknown composition. By comparing the spectrum of this complex mixture of solvents with spectra of mixtures of known composition, it was possible to determine the composition of the unknown to be 60% toluene, 15% methyl isobutyl ketone, 10% isopropyl alcohol, 9% acetone, and 3% each of isopropyl acetate and methyl ethyl ketone. Structural formulas for these solvents are given. Note that all the different bonding groups of isoamyl salicylate appear among the six compounds. This accounts for similar absorption peaks on the spectra on these facing pages.

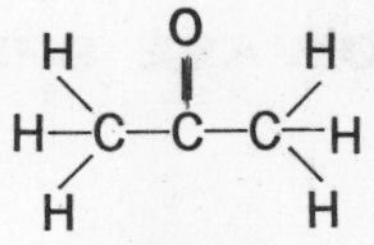

acetone

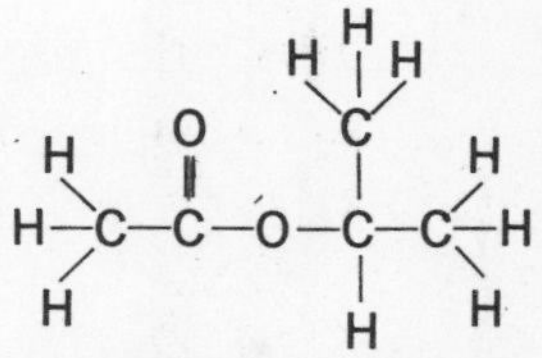

isopropyl acetate

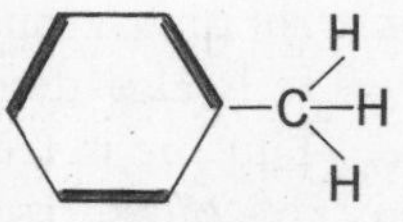

toluene

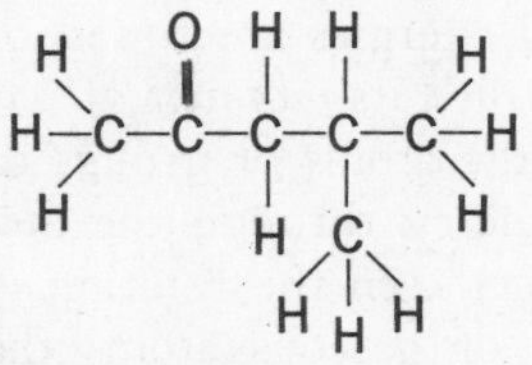

methyl isobutyl ketone

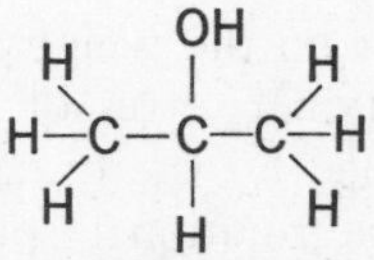

isopropyl alcohol

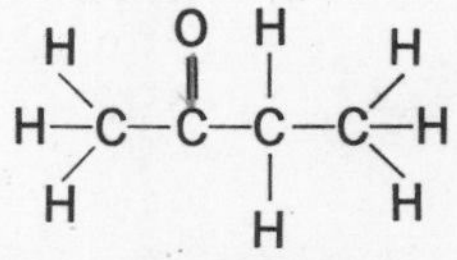

methyl ethyl ketone

**MICROWAVE SPECTROSCOPY** We have noted that in addition to other motions, a molecule in the gas phase may experience free rotations. Molecular rotational energies, as we might have predicted, are quantized. Rotations of *molecular dipoles* can be activitated free from vibrational modes only if low-incident energies, corresponding to the microwave region of the electromagnetic spectrum, impinge upon them. Higher energies will activate vibrational and rotational modes *simultaneously* and will lead to *vibration-rotation* spectra, found mainly in the near infrared. The latter are important in molecular structure determinations.

Pure rotational microwave absorption spectra assume importance because rotational energies are found to depend on a property of a rotating molecule called its *moment of inertia*. The latter depends first on the weights of the atoms or groups of atoms rotating around imaginary axes of symmetry through the molecule. It is also determined by the distance between the rotating groups. Thus, it is from pure rotational spectra of gaseous atoms that most of our present knowledge of internuclear distances comes.

Much microwave work has been accomplished with "home-made" equipment, such as that seen in the photograph at the left above. The long rectangular tube on the bench top is a *wave guide,* through which the long-wavelength microwaves travel. Using such apparatus, the microwave absorption spectrum is manually scanned and can be observed on an oscilloscope screen. At the right are oscilloscope photographs from the microwave spectrum of carbonyl sulfide, $O{=}C{=}S$. Recently, commercial microwave equipment, such as that shown above, has become available. Its great advantage lies in its use to scan and record a microwave spectrum continuously. Below is seen such a spectrum for methyl alcohol, $CH_3OH$.

FREQUENCY (MC)

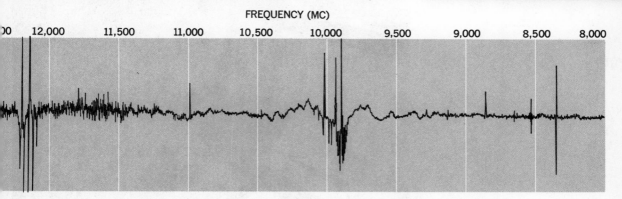

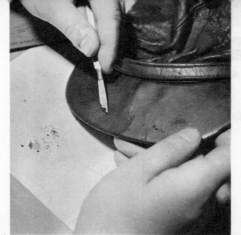

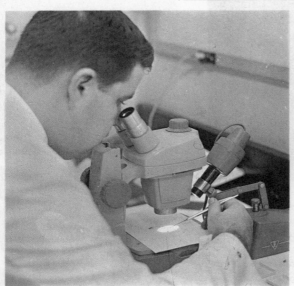

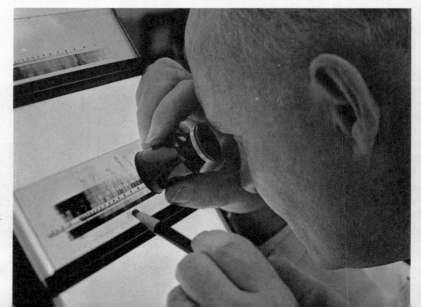

## IN CRIME DETECTION

As has been implied in the last eight pages, spectroscopic analyses are vital tools in the chemist's attempt to unravel atomic and molecular mysteries. In recent years, such analyses have become equally vital in the attempts of law enforcement agencies, at all levels, to solve mysteries of crime. Indeed, spectroscopic analysis is but one of a whole arsenal of modern chemical techniques being used in the apprehension of criminals and, thereby, in the interests of public safety. From the routine analysis of a blood sample taken from a suspect to the complex analysis of a speck of paint that may be several layers thick, the police chemist applies the principles and techniques of modern chemical science. It is often his expert testimony, based on virtually irrefutable evidence, that stands strongest in the defense of innocence or in the exposition of guilt. A visit to a modern crime detection laboratory—the lair of this Sherlock Holmes in laboratory dress that is found in every major city of this nation, in many of its counties, and, especially, at the Federal Bureau of Investigation in Washington, D.C.—is both an educational and an edifying experience.

A speck of matter is scraped from evidence gathered at the scene of an actual crime. It is examined microscopically (center left), then a small part of it is analyzed in an emission spectrometer (center right). Elements present in the speck are determined, in part, from the emission spectrum obtained. Some more of the speck is analyzed by infrared spectroscopy, and interpretation of the infrared spectrum (right) gives further clues as to its composition. From these and other analyses, the occupation of the cap's owner may be determined, or his presence at the scene of the crime may be verified.

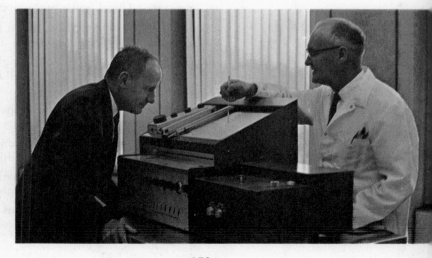

## QUESTIONS AND PROBLEMS

1. Explain the assertion that radiant energy sustains and makes visible all life on earth.

2. Describe in simple terms a model for electromagnetic radiation.

3. Cite practical applications of each of the ten spectral regions, classified in the diagram of the electromagnetic spectrum on pages 442–443.

4. Relate the energy of an electromagnetic radiation to its wavelength and frequency.

5. Give a reason for the difference in appearance of the atomic hydrogen emission spectrum and the molecular hydrogen emission spectrum.

6. Examine the emission spectra of a tungsten lamp, a fluorescent lamp, and mercury vapor, shown on pages 444–445. a. Contrast the spectra of the lamps. b. To what would you attribute the bright lines in the fluorescent lamp spectrum? c. Determine the content of a fluorescent lamp to test your prediction.

7. a. A qualitative test for the presence of sodium in a substance is to examine the color imparted to a flame by the substance. From the emission spectrum of sodium shown on page 444, what is the predicted color of a "sodium flame"? b. From the emission spectra of barium and lithium, shown on pages 444-445, predict colors for the flame tests for each of these elements. c. Test your predictions in the laboratory.

8. From the neon emission spectrum shown on page 444, predict which of all the colored lamps called "neon lamps" are filled solely with neon gas. Check your prediction.

9. Examine the emission spectra on pages 444–445 and indicate which elements are *clearly* indicated as being in the sun's atmosphere.

10. Pure white light is passed through sodium vapor and then through a diffraction grating. What will be the appearance of the resulting visible spectrum?

11. Describe the effect emission spectra had on the development of modern atomic theory.

12. Using a model of a water molecule, illustrate three different modes of motion that the molecule exhibits in the gas phase.

13. a. Illustrate the three fundamental vibrational modes of a water molecule. b. Which of these modes are active in the infrared?

14. Describe the behavior of gaseous carbon dioxide molecules as they are exposed to infrared radiation of continuously increasing wavelength from 3 to 20 microns.

15. Why is it reasonable to expect that the stretching vibration of the carbonyl bond, C=O, may be active in a short *region* of the infrared, rather than at one specific wavelength?

16. The C=C stretching vibration of $H_2C=CH_2$ absorbs energy at 6.16 microns. In $D_2C=CD_2$, the stretching vibration is active at 6.60 microns. Give a reasonable explanation for these data.

17. Describe how you might use infrared spectroscopy in an experiment on determining the rate of a certain chemical reaction.

18. Using models of a carbon dioxide molecule, draw *axes of symmetry* through the model and illustrate different rotational motions for the molecule.

19. Why does carbonyl sulfide, OCS, but not "carbonyl oxide," OCO, show a pure rotational microwave spectrum?

20. Using a model of the water molecule, show that it is reasonable to expect interaction between vibrational and rotational modes of energies.

## SUGGESTED READINGS

Barrow, G. M. *The Structure of Molecules* (paperback). W. A. Benjamin, 1963.

CHEMISTRY

Jones, Paul R., "Infrared Spectroscopy and Molecular Architecture." Feb. 1965

SCIENTIFIC AMERICAN

Alder, B. J., and T. E. Wainwright, "Molecular Motions." Oct. 1959
Crawford, B., Jr., "Chemical Analysis by Infrared." Oct. 1953

*But al thyng which that shineth as the gold
Nis nat gold, as that I have herd it told.*

*Geoffrey Chaucer* (1340?–1400)
*from "The Canterbury Tales"*

**CHAPTER 21** | # Metals and the

We now begin a general study of the elements based on the conceptual foundations of modern chemical science—atomic theory and molecular structure, thermodynamics, and chemical kinetics. We recognize that other conceptual schemes that will aid our understandings—chemical periodicity, principles of chemical equilibria, the theory of electrolytic dissociation and ionization in solution, acid-base theory, and principles of electrochemistry—stem from these primary creations of the intellect. And so we start by remembering that there exists a structuring principle that brings order to the chaotic multiplicity of chemical facts—the principle of chemical periodicity.

### 21.1 The periodic table: a backward glance before moving on

As we have often implied in past discussions, there exists a large group of elements having similar properties that permit us to classify these elements as *metals*. For example, elements whose oxides yield alkaline solutions are, in general, metals. A smaller group of elements, those whose oxides are acid anhydrides, we called nonmetals. Let us reconsider the periodic classification of the elements in terms of metallicity and nonmetallicity.

Close analysis of the periodic table on pages 178–179 will reveal that approximately eighty of the chemical elements are classified as metals. These elements are found on the left side of the table. Further study reveals that the elements become less metal-like as we move from left to right and from bottom to top of the periodic table. Thus, element 87, francium, should be the most metallic element. Since francium is very radioactive and exists only for a few minutes after its synthetic production (see Sec. 32.6, p. 678), it is difficult to

# Elements of Group I

synthesize enough of it for careful study of its chemistry. Therefore, to cesium, the element above francium in the periodic table, falls the distinction of being the most metallic. Fluorine, the element in the upper right-hand corner of the chart, is the most nonmetallic.

Recall that in progressing from left to right in a period, more electrons are added to the electron shell being filled. Further, that in progressing from top to bottom in a group, the valence electrons are in shells of higher energy. Then, elements have lower ionization energies the farther to the left and the lower they are in the periodic table. Thus, for elements with significant chemical activity, cesium has the lowest first ionization energy, 90 kcal per mole of gaseous atoms, and fluorine the highest, 402 kcal per mole of gaseous atoms. It seems logical, therefore, to associate metallic character with the property of ease of electron loss. *Metals are those elements that tend to donate electrons, that is, to become cations. Nonmetals are those elements which have a strong tendency to accept electrons, that is, to become anions.*

There are a small number of elements, such as antimony and arsenic, that behave both as metals and nonmetals. These are known as *metalloids.* As you might have anticipated, these metalloids lie on the border region between the metals and the nonmetals. (Fig. 21.1.) We focus our attention, for a while, on the metals.

### 21.2 Characteristic physical properties of metals

Metals have a number of characteristic physical properties:

1. Metals are *lustrous;* the shining surfaces of gold, silver, nickel, and copper are familiar examples of this property.

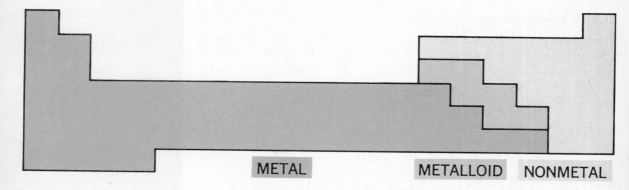

**METAL**      **METALLOID**  NONMETAL

FIGURE 21.1  A broad classification of the elements

2. They are *malleable*—able to be hammered into very thin sheets or foil. The most malleable metal is gold, which has been beaten into sheets so thin that 300,000 of them placed one above the other make a pile only one inch thick.
3. Metals are *ductile*—able to be drawn into wire. Platinum, for example, can be drawn into a wire so fine that it cannot be seen by the unaided eye. A gram of gold can be drawn into a fine wire one and a quarter miles in length.
4. Metals are *good conductors of heat*. Experimentally, however, the heat conductivity of a metal decreases as its temperature increases.
5. They are *good conductors of electricity*. Silver has the highest electrical conductivity among the metals, but copper is used most generally because of its much lower cost. Just as the capacity to conduct heat decreases, so, too, does the electrical conductivity of metals decrease as their temperatures are raised.

Individual metals may not possess all of these properties. These are, however, the general properties of the metallic state, and a *perfect metal* would exhibit them all. To the degree that a real metal lacks these properties, it is less perfect as a metal.

Metals, of course, do have widely differing physical properties. All, with the exception of mercury, are solids at room temperatures. Their melting points range widely—from −39°C for mercury to 3380°C for tungsten (wolfram). Metals differ greatly in their *tensile strength*, that is, the ease with which they can be pulled in two. For example, lead has a tensile strength of about 3000 pounds per square inch of cross section, while that for tungsten is nearly 600,000 pounds per square inch. Metals range in density from very light lithium, whose density is only 0.534 g/ml, to the very heavy osmium, whose density is 22.5 g/ml.

Pure iron "whiskers" have tensile strengths approaching 2,000,000 pounds per square inch.

## 21.3 Characteristic chemical properties of a metal

In addition to their common physical properties, metals also have characteristic chemical properties. As we have noted, their most characteristic chemical property is the tendency to lose electrons and form cations, while their second most characteristic property is the formation of nonvolatile oxides, which are basic anhydrides. Also:

1. Many, but not all metals, have $E^0$ values greater than zero volts. Such metals, therefore, will theoretically displace hydrogen gas from acid solutions. For example, for element 27, cobalt, $E^0_{Co/Co^{+2}} = 0.28$ volt. Therefore, in theory:

$$Co(s) + 2H_3O^{+1}(1M) = Co^{+2}(aq) + H_2(g) + 2H_2O(l)$$

2. Metals that have $E^0$ values greater than 0.41 volt theoretically should liberate hydrogen gas from pure water. Strontium ($E^0_{Sr/Sr^{+2}} = +2.89$ volts), for example, will do so:

$$Sr(s) + 2H_2O(l) = H_2(g) + Sr^{+2}(aq) + 2OH^{-1}(aq)$$

In some cases, an initial reaction may occur that results in the formation of an insoluble metal hydroxide coating on the remaining free metal that precludes further reaction. In other cases, the hydrogen overvoltage effect prevents a reaction. (See Sec. 19.4, p. 415.)

A very few metals will liberate hydrogen gas in strongly alkaline solution by forming complex ions with hydroxyl ions. Zinc, for example, will do so:

$$Zn(s) + 2OH^{-1}(aq) + 2H_2O(l) = H_2(g) + \underset{\text{tetrahydroxozincate(II) ion}}{Zn(OH)_4^{-2}(aq)}$$

Chromium, aluminum, tin, and lead, in forming the $Cr(OH)_4^{-1}$, $Al(OH)_4^{-1}$, $Sn(OH)_4^{-2}$, and $Pb(OH)_4^{-2}$ aqueous ions, respectively, exhibit the same behavior.

3. Some metals reduce steam. We have seen that in the case of iron, such a reaction was once used as an industrial preparation of hydrogen gas. (See Sec. 9.4, p. 210.)

## 21.4 A model for the metallic state

The chemical properties of metals may be explained by the principles of atomic theory and chemical bonding considered in Chapters 10, 11, and 20. The physical properties of metals, however, require explanations for which we have no prior model. Those same general physical properties of metals, along with additional experimental findings, will lead us to a model for the metallic state that will help us to understand the physical behavior of metals.

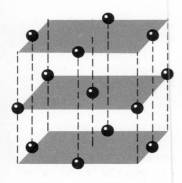

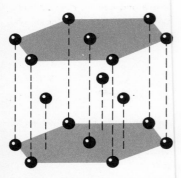

**FIGURE 21.2** The packing of atoms in metal crystals: cubic (top) and hexagonal (bottom) close packing

Scientists have learned by X-ray analysis that metals form crystals that are like spheres packed closely together in either cubical or hexagonal patterns. (Fig. 21.2.) Aluminum, copper, and gold are examples of metallic crystals having the cubic structure, while magnesium and beryllium form hexagonal solid state structures. In the metal, each sphere is surrounded by the maximum number of spheres that is geometrically possible.

To explain the physical properties of metals, the model of closely packed spheres in solid state metal structures is extended. It is assumed that each sphere represents a positively charged ion. That is, a useful model of the metallic state is one in which *metal atoms exist as spherical cations in a regular crystalline lattice network*. In order to account for the stability of such lattices, it is assumed that the electrons still present in the metal crystal are distributed among the cations. In this manner, coulombic attractive forces are set up that prevent the mutually repulsive cations from flying apart. The binding electrons are not held in the energy levels of any *particular* atom. Rather, the assembly of closely packed atoms produces a set of energy levels associated with the *whole* metal crystal in which the electrons exist. The electrons, in fact, belong to the crystal *as a whole,* so that, in a sense, the groups of positive metal ions exist in a lattice "floating in a sea of metallic electrons." The negative sea of *delocalized* electrons constitutes the bonding electrostatic force that holds the positive ions together. The *metallic bond* differs, then, from the typical covalent bond in that the atoms in metals are not held together in pairs. Instead, there exists the mutual attraction of a large number of electrons for a large number of positively charged atomic nuclei.

### 21.5 How metallic bonding explains metallic properties

Since there are neither ionic nor covalent bonds between the metallic ions in a metal, there is greater freedom of cation and electron movement within a metal. High malleability and ductility of metals are pictured as a result of metallic bonds not being strictly oriented in space as are ionic and covalent bonds. It is easy for metal atoms to be moved about without destroying the bonding. (Fig. 21.3.)

Since the electrons in metals are not attached to a single definite ion (as in an ionic solid) nor confined between two atoms (as in a covalent bond) but, instead, exist in energy levels for the metal as a whole, they are, thus, less restricted in their movement. We may infer from our model for the metallic bond that electrons can easily move from one place in the metal crystal to another. Assuming that electrical conductivity in solids is directly related to the ease of electron movement, we are thus able to explain the high electrical conductivity of metals.

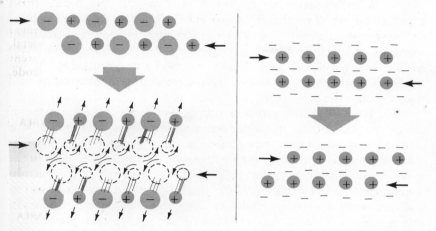

**FIGURE 21.3** Ionic crystals (left) are generally brittle; metallic crystals (right) are generally malleable and ductile. How do these models account for these observed properties?

Heat conduction involves the transport of thermal energy. In ionic and covalent solids, this is accomplished by slight vibrations of the ions or atoms in the positions they occupy. In metals, however, the thermal energy can be transported through the solid metal by the very mobile electrons, but the mobility of electrons in metals is hindered as the vibrational motion of the metal cations in the lattice increases. Hence, we can explain the facts that electrical and heat conductivities for metals both decrease with increasing temperatures.

The surface luster of metals can be explained by the mobility of the electrons, also. The light striking a metal surface is absorbed by loosely bonded electrons in the surface. These electrons are caused to oscillate rapidly back and forth. These oscillating electrons, like any moving electrical charge, emit radiant energy. The net effect of the absorption and emission of radiant energy is that the metallic surface "reflects" light and takes on a luster.

An iron rod, half of which is sealed in dry air. What is a necessary factor for rusting to occur?

### 21.6 Metallic corrosion: the silent destroyer

The very chemical property that is the identifying feature of metals —ease of oxidation—in a practical context may be defined as *corrosion*. The corroding chemical action of atmospheric water, oxygen, and carbon dioxide on metal surfaces leads to an annual economic loss that totals in the billions of dollars. Though the full understanding of the mechanism of corrosion still eludes us, its basic nature as an electrochemical process is known.

If any one part of a metal is in contact with another element, has an impurity, or is under greater stress than another part of the metal, it is found to have a greater oxidation potential than the rest of the metal. If an electrolytic solution, such as that formed when atmospheric oxygen and carbon dioxide dissolve in water, covers the metal, a galvanic cell is formed. Generally, the metal area that is different from the rest of the metal will function as an anode and will corrode. (Fig. 21.4.)

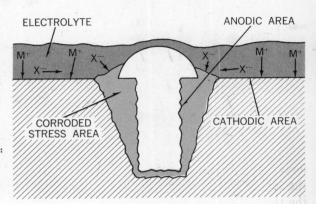

**FIGURE 21.4** A metal under stress plus air plus moisture: corrosion

Corrosion can be prevented in a number of ways. If a metal surface can be kept free from the action of atmospheric oxygen, carbon dioxide, and water vapor, the surface will not corrode. Classical methods of painting metal surfaces or plating them with noncorroding metallic films can accomplish this. Some metals, notably aluminum, naturally form very thin and impermeable surface oxide films, which impart some protection from further atmospheric chemical action without greatly impairing the lustrous qualities of the surface. Industrially, a very strong protective oxide film is formed on aluminum by making it the *anode* in an electrolytic reaction. The product, known as *anodized aluminum,* is an important structural material in the building industries. In addition, the surface of anodized aluminum adsorbs dyes exceedingly well. This has led to its widespread ornamental use in the automotive and housewares industries.

More recently developed anti-corrosion methods involve changing the electrochemical properties of a corrosion-prone metal. If a more active metal is connected to it, for example, the more active metal will preferentially corrode. This is called *cathodic protection,* wherein the metal being protected becomes cathodic relative to the more easily oxidized, hence anodic, active metal. Magnesium is used extensively in the cathodic protection of buried iron pipelines, canal gates, water tanks, and ship hulls. The electrochemical properties of a corrosion-prone metal may also be altered by the addition of small amounts of other elements to it, resulting in the formation of metal *alloys.*

$E^0_{Mg/Mg^{+2}} = 2.37$ volts; $E^0_{Fe/Fe^{+2}}$ $= 0.44$ volt: cathodic protection against corrosion

## 21.7 Alloys: metals in partnership

Other than the copper metal used in electrical wiring, the mercury used in thermometers and barometers, and the gold, silver, and platinum of some ornamental jewelry, most metallic substances are composed of more than one metal. Such substances are known as alloys and are complex *solid solutions* of metals with metals or nonmetals, and, in some cases, with metal-metal or metal-nonmetal compounds. Alloys of copper and tin, the *bronzes*, have been known since ancient times. Alloys of copper and zinc—the *brasses;* of mercury and almost all other metals—the *amalgams;* of iron, carbon, and other elements— the *steels*, are all familiar and vitally important. No matter where you turn, the metallic objects that you use daily are mainly alloys—from the coins you carry, to the fillings in your teeth; from the cutlery that you use, to the car that you may drive.

With this brief introduction to metals in general, we turn our attention specifically to a group of metals that we first encountered in Chapter 7—the *alkali metals*.

## 21.8 The elements of Group I: the alkali metals

We have already learned that the alkali metal family—Li, Na, K, Rb, Cs, and Fr—exemplifies the periodic nature of physical and, especially, chemical properties of elements. Review the properties of these chemically active elements as presented in Section 7.9 on pages 174 and 175. In Table 21–1 are brought together additional properties of the alkali metals that were in most cases previously presented.

**TABLE 21–1**   ADDITIONAL PROPERTIES OF THE ALKALI METALS

| | Li | Na | K | Rb | Cs |
|---|---|---|---|---|---|
| Metallic atomic radius (A) | 1.55 | 1.90 | 2.35 | 2.48 | 2.67 |
| Covalent radius (A) | 1.34 | 1.54 | 1.96 | 2.11 | 2.25 |
| Ionic radius, $M^{+1}$ (A) | 0.60 | 0.95 | 1.33 | 1.48 | 1.69 |
| First ionization energy (kcal/mole) | 124 | 118 | 100 | 96 | 90 |
| $\Delta H$ of ion hydration (kcal/mole) | −121 | −95 | −75 | −69 | −61 |
| $E^0{}_{M/M^{+1}}$ (volts) | +3.05 | +2.93 | +2.71 | +2.93 | +2.92 |

### 21.9 The reaction of alkali metals with oxygen

Generally speaking, the alkali metals exhibit chemical behavior subject to simple interpretation. There are, however, a number of unusual chemical properties of these elements that require more careful analysis and thought before they can be understood. For example, when the alkali metals are burned in pure oxygen, three different types of oxide products are formed. Lithium, alone, forms the simple oxide:

$$2Li(s) + \tfrac{1}{2}O_2(g) = Li_2O(s)$$

Sodium, on the other hand, mainly forms the *peroxide:*

$$2Na(s) + O_2(g) = Na_2O_2(s)$$

Finally, potassium, rubidium, and cesium mainly form *colored super-oxides:*

$$M(s) + O_2(g) = MO_2(s)$$
$$\text{where } M = \text{K, Rb, or Cs}$$

The superoxides are ionic compounds in which the orange-colored $O_2{}^{-1}$ ion is present. Potassium superoxide has found application as a source of oxygen for breathing purposes in submarines and at high altitudes. The solid releases oxygen when it absorbs exhaled carbon dioxide in the presence of copper(II) chloride as a catalyst:

$$2KO_2(s) + CO_2(g) \xrightarrow{\text{CuCl}_2} K_2CO_3(s) + \tfrac{3}{2}O_2(g)$$

A possible explanation for the differing behaviors of the alkali metals toward oxygen may lie in a comparison of the sizes of the alkali metal ions. Only the very large ions—$K^{+1}$, $Rb^{+1}$, and $Cs^{+1}$ for example—are naturally associated with the superoxide ion. In fact, calcium, strontium, and barium, which are in Group II and also form quite large cations, have stable ionic superoxides. It would appear then that the large superoxide ion forms to promote ionic crystal stability, while neither the smaller peroxide ion nor the even smaller oxide ion could lead to as great stability.

Though in its behavior toward oxygen lithium may seem to be the most chemically "normal" of the alkali metals, it is, in fact, the most abnormal.

## 21.10 The anomalous behavior of lithium

In many of its reactions, lithium behaves more like magnesium, a Group II element, than like the rest of the alkali metals. For example, unlike the other alkali metal carbonates, lithium carbonate, like magnesium carbonate, is thermally unstable:

$$Li_2CO_3(s) \overset{\Delta}{=} Li_2O(s) + CO_2(g)$$

$$MgCO_3(s) \overset{\Delta}{=} MgO(s) + CO_2(g)$$

$$M_2CO_3(s) \overset{\Delta}{=} \text{no reaction}$$

where $M =$ Na, K, Rb, Cs

All the alkali metal nitrates, except that of lithium, thermally decompose to yield oxygen gas:

$$MNO_3(s) \overset{\Delta}{=} MNO_2(s) + \tfrac{1}{2}O_2(g)$$

where $M =$ Na, K, Rb, Cs

Lithium nitrate, on the contrary, yields oxygen and nitrogen(IV) oxide gases, paralleling the behavior of magnesium nitrate:

$$2LiNO_3(s) \overset{\Delta}{=} Li_2O(s) + \tfrac{1}{2}O_2(g) + 2NO_2(g)$$

$$Mg(NO_3)_2(s) \overset{\Delta}{=} MgO(s) + \tfrac{1}{2}O_2(g) + 2NO_2(g)$$

Finally, the solubilities of lithium fluoride and lithium hydroxide are low—comparable to the limited solubilities of the corresponding magnesium compounds—in contrast with the high solubilities of the other alkali metal fluorides and hydroxides.

All of these unique properties of lithium, relative to the other alkali metal atoms, can be explained in terms of the very small size of the $Li^{+1}$ ion. Because of that size, the positive charge on the $Li^{+1}$ ion is much more highly concentrated than is the charge on the other alkali metal ions. Lithium ion is said to have a very high *charge density*. This high concentration of positive charge on the $Li^{+1}$ ion tends to make it attract electrons away from anions to which it is bonded. The net effect is that lithium compounds, though predominantly ionic, have a relatively higher degree of covalency than do the compounds of the other alkali metal ions, which are quite ionic. This fundamental difference in bonding characteristics can, of course, help explain differences in chemical behavior.

The high charge density of the $Li^{+1}$ ion also accounts for its relatively high hydration energy when compared with those of the other alkali metal ions. It is that high hydration energy, a measure of the great stability of the aqueous $Li^{+1}$ ion, that can be shown to account for the high $E^0$ value of the $Li/Li^{+1}$ couple.

### 21.11 Preparation of the alkali metals

The alkali metals, being far too chemically active to exist in elemental form naturally, are found in some abundance in compounds of the earth's crust. Though lithium, rubidium, and cesium compounds are rare, sodium and potassium compounds are so widespread, particularly in the oceans, that sodium and potassium are the fifth and ninth most abundant elements.

Because of their extreme chemical activity, it is only through electrolytic decomposition of molten salts that the alkali metals can be economically obtained. The versatile, brilliant Sir Humphry Davy was the first man to isolate potassium and sodium through electrolysis, in England in 1807. As we saw in Chapter 19, vast amounts of sodium metal are still produced through the same process today.

### 21.12 Uses of the alkali metals

The usefulness of the alkali metals is reduced to some extent by the expense of their production and by the handling problems associated with their high chemical activity. Nonetheless, sodium metal is used in the manufacture of several compounds such as sodium hydride, sodium peroxide, sodium cyanide, and sodamide ($NaNH_2$). By far the largest use for sodium is in the formation of a sodium-lead alloy needed in the manufacture of tetraethyl and tetramethyl lead, the antiknock additives of gasoline. (See Sec. 7.19, pp. 184–185.)

Liquid sodium, because it is an excellent heat conductor, is employed as a coolant and heat transfer medium in some nuclear reactors. The ease with which cesium loses electrons is made use of in photoelectric cells. This property is also the basis for the exploratory development of a cesium *ion-engine* for use in space exploration.

### 21.13 Sodium chloride: a chemical cornucopia

Certainly one of the outstanding mineral products of the earth is common salt. Whether it is mined from the underground remains of some long dried out and buried sea, or scooped from the shores of a great, evaporating salt lake, sodium chloride is the precursor of major industrial chemicals and a vital constituent of living matter.

Well over twenty million tons of salt are consumed annually in the United States. A small percentage of this finds its way into our bodies—directly, through the table salt that we use to spice our foods, and indirectly, through the use of salt in animal feeds and in the preserving and canning of foods.

**Humphry Davy** (1778–1829, English). Besides discovering sodium, potassium, and boron, Davy isolated calcium, magnesium, barium, and strontium and did other extensive work in electrochemistry. For his many contributions, including the invention of a coal miner's safety lamp, he was knighted in 1812. The poet Coleridge declared that if Davy "had not been the first chemist, he would have been the first poet of his age."

Dispersions of sodium in nonaqueous solvents are widely used in industry. Of what economic advantage are such dispersions?

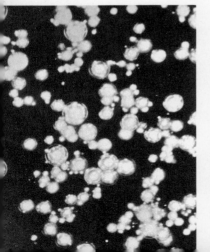

The mining of salt: from the depths of the earth or from its surface—a great mineral wealth

Of all uses for sodium chloride, none is equal to its use in the industrial preparation of a host of products whose own myriad uses underscore the importance of salt in modern society. Salt is a precursor, as we have seen, of hydrochloric acid, chlorine, hydrogen, sodium hydroxide, and sodium. It is also used in the synthesis of the most important industrial base *sodium carbonate*.

## 21.14 Sodium carbonate, hydrolysis, and the Solvay process

In many processes, the requirements of industry for alkalies cannot be most economically met by the use of sodium hydroxide. However, a compound that has been known since antiquity is inexpensively and widely used as a substitute. The compound is sodium carbonate, or soda ash,* $Na_2CO_3$, which is an alkali by virtue of the fairly strong Bronsted-Lowry base properties of the carbonate ion, $CO_3^{-2}(aq)$:

$$CO_3^{-2}(aq) + H_2O(l) \rightleftharpoons HCO_3^{-1}(aq) + OH^{-1}(aq)$$

Soda ash is still mined extensively in the United States. Annually, upwards of 1.5 million tons are extracted, mainly from brine wells in California and deposits of *trona*, a mineral containing $Na_2CO_3 \cdot 2H_2O$, in Wyoming. Industry, however, requires so much

---

* Potash, $K_2CO_3$, and soda ash, $Na_2CO_3$, were originally found in the ashes of burned plants. The Arabic words for "the ashes" are *al-qili*, hence, the word *alkali*.

sodium carbonate that some five million more tons are synthesized annually.

The synthesis of sodium carbonate is achieved mainly through a process invented more than a century ago by two Belgian chemists, Ernest and Alfred Solvay. The Solvay process is an example of the efficient use of raw materials. Those materials are limestone, salt, and ammonia gas.

Limestone is first thermally decomposed:

$$1. \quad CaCO_3(s) \stackrel{\Delta}{=} CaO(s) + CO_2(g)$$

The $CO_2$ gas is mixed with $NH_3$ gas in large absorption towers. A cold, very concentrated, and purified brine solution is sprayed in at the top of the tower. The gas mixture dissolves in the brine solution, forming ammonium and bicarbonate ions:

$$2. \quad Na^{+1}(aq) + Cl^{-1}(aq) + NH_3(g) + CO_2(g) + H_2O(l)$$
$$= NH_4^{+1}(aq) + HCO_3^{-1}(aq) + Na^{+1}(aq) + Cl^{-1}(aq)$$

Of the four most likely salts that could form from the concentrated solution—$NH_4HCO_3$, $NH_4Cl$, $NaHCO_3$, or $NaCl$—the sodium bicarbonate is least soluble under the reaction conditions, and crystallizes from solution. Most of the sodium bicarbonate, or sodium hydrogen carbonate, is then heated to form the desired sodium carbonate end product:

$$3. \quad 2NaHCO_3(s) \stackrel{\Delta}{=} Na_2CO_3(s) + CO_2(g) + H_2O(l)$$

The efficiency of the Solvay process stems from its treatment of by-products. The $CO_2$ gas of the last step is recycled for consumption in step 2. The calcium oxide, or lime, produced in step 1 is treated with water to form calcium hydroxide, or *slaked lime:*

$$CaO(s) + H_2O(l) = Ca(OH)_2(s)$$

The slaked lime reacts with the $NH_4Cl$ product of step 2 to form ammonia gas, which is then recycled for consumption in step 2:

$$Ca(OH)_2(s) + 2NH_4Cl(aq) \stackrel{\Delta}{=} 2NH_3(g) + CaCl_2(aq) + 2H_2O(l)$$

In essence, then, the Solvay process in total leads to $Na_2CO_3$ as its main product, and $CaCl_2$ as its only by-product. The $CaCl_2$, being deliquescent, finds wide industrial application. (See Sec. 6.14, p. 152.)

Aside from its major uses in industry, particularly in the manufacture of glass, soap, and paper pulp and in the tanning of hides, crystalline sodium carbonate is packaged and sold as *washing soda.* The alkaline properties of carbonate solutions give them cleansing properties. Washing soda is a highly efflorescent decahydrate, which readily converts to a stable monohydrate on exposure to air.

As was noted, not all the $NaHCO_3$ produced in the Solvay process is converted to soda ash. A large amount of the bicarbonate is sold as *baking soda*. When used as such in baking, thermal decomposition leads to the release of $CO_2$ gas and the consequent "rising" of bread and cakes. Baking soda is also a constituent of all baking powders. The latter contains another solid, which hydrolyzes to release hydronium ion. The hydronium ion then reacts with the baking soda to release $CO_2$ gas for the *leavening* effect:

$$H_3O^{+1}(aq) + NaHCO_3(s) = CO_2(g) + Na^{+1}(aq) + 2H_2O(l)$$

On this effervescent note, we conclude our brief look at the elements of Group I and some of their compounds.

## SUMMARY

On the basis of both its physical and its chemical properties, an element may be broadly classified as a metal or a nonmetal. A few elements show properties of both metals and nonmetals. These elements are called metalloids.

The characteristic physical properties of metals lead to a useful model of the metallic state as one in which metal atoms exist as cations in close-packed crystalline arrangements. The highest energy electrons of the metal atoms are delocalized in the crystal. In serving to bind the crystal together, they constitute the metallic bond.

The chemical properties of metals may be understood in light of past principles of atomic structure and chemical bonding. In particular, metallic corrosion can be understood and dealt with in terms of the principles of oxidation and reduction.

The elements of Group I, the alkali metals, are the most nearly perfect metals. The anomalous behavior of lithium is probably due to its high charge density.

Compounds of the alkali metals are important to the economy. Common salt, NaCl, and sodium carbonate, $Na_2CO_3$, are especially valuable. The Solvay process is an efficient industrial method for synthesizing the latter from the former.

## QUESTIONS AND PROBLEMS

21.1  Describe the model for the metallic state developed in this chapter. Indicate how this model helps to explain metallic conduction of electricity and heat, and metallic luster.

21.2  Many metals become *superconductors* of electricity when cooled to temperatures near absolute zero. Use the model for the metallic state as it was developed in this chapter to explain this experimentally derived fact.

**21.3** Cite four *different* ways in which structural iron can be protected against corrosion. Indicate the mechanism of protection in each case.

**21.4** Using data from Table 7–4 on page 175, describe the differences in metallic bonding among the alkali metals. How does this variation explain the use of cesium in photoelectric cells?

**21.5** Using data from Table 21–1, plot the metallic atomic radii and first ionization energies of the alkali metals as functions of atomic number. Predict values of these properties for francium, the synthetic, radioactive alkali metal of period 7.

**21.6** Citing chemical evidence, describe what is meant by the anomalous behavior of lithium. What data for lithium in Table 21–1 may also be classified as anomalous? Explain.

**21.7** Write chemical equations for each of the following. Where appropriate, net ionic equations should be given.
**a.** Rubidium is added to water.
**b.** Aluminum is heated in concentrated sodium hydroxide.
**c.** Steam is passed over hot zinc.
**d.** Molten potassium chloride is electrolyzed.
**e.** Concentrated brine is electrolyzed.
**f.** The hydrolysis of sodium carbonate
**g.** The amphiprotic nature of the bicarbonate ion
**h.** Commercial production of hydrochloric acid from salt

**21.8** Comment on the appropriateness of the title for Section 21.13.

**21.9** Describe the Solvay process in detail. Chemical equations must be part of your description.

**21.10** A common baking soda mixture contains sodium bicarbonate and *sodium alum*, $NaAl(SO_4)_2$. Describe by chemical equation the sequence of reactions leading to the production of carbon dioxide gas when the mixture is exposed to moisture.

**21.11 a.** Write the electron configuration for potassium and cesium.
**b.** Draw Lewis structures for the oxide, peroxide, and superoxide ions.

**21.12** Assuming 100 per cent efficiency, how many tons of each of the following are required to produce 5.0 tons of anhydrous sodium carbonate: **a.** limestone; **b.** salt; **c.** ammonia?
ANS. **b.** 5.5 tons

**21.13** What volume of $0.500\ M$ HCl is required to react completely with **a.** 1.06 g of $Na_2CO_3$? **b.** 1.06 g of $NaHCO_3$?
ANS. **b.** 25.2 ml

**21.14** Derive a value of the equilibrium constant of the bicarbonate ion as a base,

$$HCO_3^{-1}(aq) + H_2O(l) \rightleftharpoons [CO_2(aq) + H_2O(l)] + OH^{-1}(aq),$$

using data from Table 17–2, page 373.

**21.15 a.** Assuming 100 per cent efficiency, how many amperes are required to produce $5.00 \times 10^2$ pounds of sodium from molten salt in 12.0 hours? (454 g = 1.00 pound) **b.** What volume of chlorine (STP) will be produced simultaneously?

ANS. **b.** $1.10 \times 10^5$ l

**21.16** What is meant by each of the following?

| | | |
|---|---|---|
| **a.** anodized aluminum | **d.** charge density | **g.** brass |
| **b.** tensile strength | **e.** steel | **h.** superoxide |
| **c.** bronze | **f.** chemical periodicity | **i.** amalgam |

## SUGGESTED READINGS

**CHEMISTRY**

Fullmer, June Z., "Discovery of Potassium." Aug. 1964
Verhoek, Frank H., "What Is a Metal?" Nov. 1964

**SCIENTIFIC AMERICAN**

Bloch, M. R., "The Social Influence of Salt." July 1963
Gilman, Henry, and John J. Eisch, "Lithium." Jan. 1963
Williams, L. Pearce, "Humphry Davy." June 1960

**CHAPTER 22** | # The Alkaline Earth

We shift our attention from the elements of Group I to those of Group II. As we do so, we move from a group of elements closely approximating perfect metallic behavior—the alkali metals—to a group of metals much less perfect—the alkaline earth metals.

### 22.1 Some properties of the alkaline earth metals

The alkaline earth metals—beryllium, Be; magnesium, Mg; calcium, Ca; strontium, Sr; barium, Ba; and radium, Ra—appear physically more like metals than do the alkali metals. These Group II metals are good conductors of heat and electricity, have a silvery luster, and tarnish upon exposure to air, but not as rapidly as do the alkali metals. They are malleable but are not nearly as soft as the alkali metals. A number of the important properties of the Group II metals are summarized in Table 22–1. The properties of radium, a radioactive, naturally occurring element, are not included in the table.

An alkaline earth atom and ion are *smaller* than the neighboring alkali metal atom and ion. (Compare data of Table 21–1, p. 464.) The Group II atoms each contribute two *s* electrons to metallic bonds, whereas the alkali metal atoms each contribute only one *s* electron. As a consequence, metallic bonding is stronger in the alkaline earth metals. This results in closer packing of the lattice ions, which explains the greater density of the alkaline earth metals compared to the density of the alkali metals.

472

# Elements: Group II

**TABLE 22–1**  PROPERTIES OF THE GROUP II ELEMENTS

|  | Be | Mg | Ca | Sr | Ba |
|---|---|---|---|---|---|
| Atomic weight (amu) | 9.013 | 24.32 | 40.08 | 87.63 | 137.36 |
| Boiling point (°C) | 2477 | 1120 | 1492 | 1370 | 1638 |
| Melting point (°C) | 1285 | 650 | 845 | 757 | 710 |
| Heat of fusion (kcal/mole) | 2.8 | 2.14 | 2.1 | 2.2 | 1.8 |
| Heat of vaporization (kcal/mole) | 70.4 | 30.75 | 35.84 | 33.2 | 36.1 |
| Density of metal (g/ml) | 1.86 | 1.74 | 1.54 | 2.60 | 3.74 |
| Metallic atomic radius (A) | 1.12 | 1.60 | 1.97 | 2.15 | 2.22 |
| Covalent radius (A) | 0.90 | 1.30 | 1.74 | 1.92 | 1.98 |
| Ionic radius, $M^{+2}$ (A) | 0.31 | 0.65 | 0.99 | 1.13 | 1.35 |
| First ionization energy (kcal/mole) | 215 | 176 | 141 | 131 | 120 |
| Second ionization energy (kcal/mole) | 420 | 347 | 274 | 254 | 231 |
| $\Delta H$ of ion hydration (kcal/mole) | −570 | −456 | −377 | −342 | −308 |
| $E^0{}_{M/M^{+2}}$ (volts) | +1.85 | +2.37 | +2.87 | +2.89 | +2.90 |

## 22.2 The anomalous behavior of beryllium

One aspect that the Group I and II families have in common is the abnormal behavior of the *first* member of each group. We have seen how lithium behaves more like magnesium than like a typical alkali metal. (See Sec. 21.10, p. 465.) It is interesting that beryllium behaves more like aluminum of Group III than like a typical Group II element.

The oxide of each of the alkaline earth metals, *except that of beryllium*, is a basic anhydride:

$$MO(s) + H_2O(l) = M(OH)_2$$

Furthermore, when $M$ is Mg or Ca, $M(OH)_2$ is insoluble; when $M$ is Sr or Ba, $M(OH)_2$ is soluble.

Beryllium hydroxide, like aluminum hydroxide, is amphiprotic:

$$Be(OH)_2(s) + 2H_3O^{+1}(aq) \rightleftharpoons Be^{+2}(aq) + 4H_2O(l)$$

and

$$Be(OH)_2(s) + 2OH^{-1}(aq) \rightleftharpoons \underset{\text{tetrahydroxoberyllate(II) ion}}{Be(OH)_4{}^{-2}(aq)}$$

By virtue of its small ionic size and double positive charge, the $Be^{+2}$ ion has a very high charge density. Thus, compounds containing beryllium in the +2 oxidation state are highly covalent, comparable to many aluminum(III) compounds. For example, just as aluminum(III) chloride exists as a *molecular dimer*, $Al_2Cl_6$, beryllium(II) chloride has the true formula $Be_2Cl_4$. Just as the $Al(H_2O)_6{}^{+3}(aq)$ ion is extensively hydrolyzed, so, too, is the $Be(H_2O)_4{}^{+2}(aq)$ ion:

$$Be(H_2O)_4{}^{+2}(aq) + H_2O(l) \rightleftharpoons Be(H_2O)_3(OH)^{+1}(aq) + H_3O^{+1}(aq)$$

Finally, unlike any of the other metals of Group II, beryllium displaces hydrogen gas from strongly alkaline, as well as from acid, solution:

$$Be(s) + 2OH^{-1}(aq) + 2H_2O(l) = H_2(g) + Be(OH)_4{}^{-2}(aq)$$

This chemical property we learned was also peculiar to aluminum (see Sec. 21.3, p. 459).

## 22.3 Ionization energies, crystal energies, and Hess's law

In Section 11.6, pages 263–264, we considered why magnesium formed +2 ions rather than +1 or +3 ions. We were satisfied then to accept the +2 ionic species in light of ionization energy data and the natural tendency for elements to assume rare gas electron configurations. We now re-examine the ionization energy data for the Group II elements as they appear in Table 22–1, and seek energy-releasing processes that will help account for the stability of +2 ionic state.

Reactions between the alkaline earth metals and nonmetals to produce ionic solids are, in general, *highly exothermic*. Those reactions may be interpreted, according to Hess's law, in terms of a stepwise sequence of reactions. For example, the formation of solid magnesium chloride from its elements,

$$Mg(s) + Cl_2(g) = Mg^{+2}Cl_2^{-1}(s),$$

may be analyzed by a cyclic reaction sequence involving six steps:

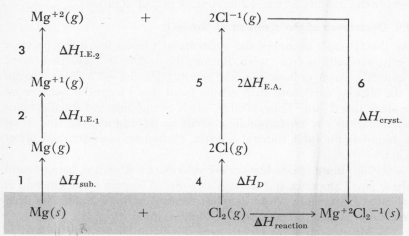

where

$\Delta H_{sub.} = $ *sublimation energy* of magnesium $= +32.9$ kcal/mole

$\Delta H_{I.E._1} = $ *first ionization energy* of magnesium $= +176$ kcal/mole

$\Delta H_{I.E._2} = $ *second ionization energy* of magnesium $= +347$ kcal/mole

$\Delta H_D = $ *energy of dissociation* of $Cl_2(g) = +57.2$ kcal/mole

$2\Delta H_{E.A.} = $ twice the *electron affinity** of $Cl(g) = 2(-92.5$ kcal/mole$)$

$\Delta H_{cryst.} = $ *energy of crystallization*

$\Delta H_{reaction} = $ calorimetric *heat of reaction* $= -153.4$ kcal/mole

Since the over-all reaction between solid magnesium and gaseous diatomic chlorine may be considered as this six-step reaction sequence, from Hess's Law of Constant Heat Summation we may write:

$$\Delta H_{reaction} = \Delta H_{sub.} + \Delta H_{I.E._1} + \Delta H_{I.E._2} + \Delta H_D + 2\Delta H_{E.A.} + \Delta H_{cryst.}$$

The experimental values for each of the energy terms, except the heat of crystallization, are given. By substituting, we can determine $\Delta H_{cryst.}$:

$$(-153.4 \text{ kcal/mole}) = ([+32.9] + [+176] + [+347] + [+57.2]$$
$$+ 2[-92.5]) \text{ kcal/mole} + \Delta H_{cryst.}$$

$$\Delta H_{cryst.} = -581 \text{ kcal/mole}$$

---

* See Section 11.16, page 280.

Thus, the formation of an ionic crystalline lattice from gaseous $Mg^{+2}$ and $Cl^{-1}$ ions is the highly exothermic process that accounts for the stability of the +2 ionic state for magnesium as well as for the other Group II elements.*

In aqueous solutions, it is the high ion hydration energies for the alkaline earth metal ions that can be shown to be partially responsible for the stability of the +2 ionic state in such solutions.

### 22.4 Occurrence of the elements of Group II

Like the Group I elements, the elements of Group II are too reactive to exist naturally as free metals. Rather, they occur in combined forms as minerals. Stronger ionic bonding results from the +2 cationic charge of the alkaline earth ions than results from the +1 cationic charge of the alkali metal ions. Thus, alkaline earth compounds are usually more insoluble than the corresponding alkali metal compounds, and they are found as insoluble mineral silicates, carbonates, sulfates, and phosphates.

Beryllium is rare but widely distributed in nature, being found only in small amounts, not in large deposits. The gem stone emerald is a silicate of beryllium whose simplest formula is $Be_3Al_2Si_6O_{18}$. Its deep green color is due to traces of a chromium impurity.

Magnesium is the eighth most abundant element in the earth's crust. It is found in brine wells and in salt deposits as $MgCl_2$ and as the *double salt* $MgCl_2 \cdot KCl$, *carnallite*. *Dolomite*, consisting mainly of the double salt $MgCO_3 \cdot CaCO_3$, is very widely distributed throughout the world, forming entire mountain ranges. There is also an almost unlimited supply of magnesium in the sea. Every ton of sea water contains the equivalent of twenty-four pounds of $MgCl_2$. This is the main commercial source of magnesium today—the first metal obtained from the sea.

Calcium is the most abundant of the elements of this group, being widely found as silicates, carbonates, phosphates, sulfates, and fluorides. It is the sixth most abundant of the earth's elements. Strontium is less plentiful than barium, which ranks eighteenth in order of abundance.

---

* The cyclic sequence of reactions that we have considered in this section is called a *Born-Haber cycle*, after Max Born and Fritz Haber, who independently first applied Hess's law in this manner. Professor Born (1882–   ) is one of the great theoretical physicists of this century and was honored with a Nobel prize in 1954. In 1932, with the young Dr. Maria Goeppert Mayer, Born formulated a complex equation from which lattice energies may be *theoretically calculated*. Experimental (Born-Haber) and theoretical (Born-Mayer) values for lattice energies agree well for compounds of high ionic character. It is of interest to note that Maria Mayer, now at the University of California, was awarded the Nobel Prize for Physics in 1963 in recognition of her outstanding contributions to the theory of the structure of atomic nuclei.

## 22.5 Preparation and uses of the alkaline earth metals

These metals are prepared from their compounds by reduction with a chemical reducing agent or by electrolysis of their molten salts. At Freeport, Texas, the Dow Chemical Company, pioneer producer of magnesium, dredges oyster shells ($CaCO_3$) from the sea. These are converted to lime ($CaO$), which is then added to sea water. The magnesium ions in the sea water form the insoluble hydroxide. This is separated by filtration and treated with hydrochloric acid. The magnesium chloride that forms is then fused and electrolyzed in an airtight iron container. Pure magnesium metal forms at iron cathodes. Chlorine gas is the by-product formed at graphite anodes. Nearly 80,000 tons of magnesium metal are produced annually in the United States.

Beryllium fluoride ($BeF_2$) and beryllium chloride ($BeCl_2$) are so covalent that, when molten, they have too few ions to conduct electrical current. Thus, these fused compounds cannot be electrolyzed. When sodium chloride is dissolved in the melts, the resulting solutions are electrolytes and, upon electrolysis, beryllium forms in each case at the cathode. Beryllium is also extracted from fused $BeF_2$, by reduction with magnesium.

Calcium is prepared commercially by the electrolysis of fused $CaCl_2$, just as Davy first obtained it in 1808. Barium and strontium may also be prepared by the electrolysis of fused salt mixtures. They are, however, more economically produced by aluminum reduction of their oxides.

Among the elements of Group II only magnesium finds important industrial use. Though they have high oxidation potentials, pure magnesium and its alloys corrode very slowly even in moist air. A thin, durable, and impermeable self-protecting film of $Mg(OH)_2$ • $MgCO_3$, a *basic carbonate*, forms on the exposed metal, which then resists further oxidative corrosion. Structural alloys of magnesium are widely used, particularly in the aircraft industry. The alloys may be made corrosion-resistant by anodizing their surfaces.

By virtue of its high oxidation potential, magnesium finds use as a reducing agent in the metallurgy of beryllium, titanium, and zirconium, and, as we learned, as cathodic protection against corrosion of iron and steel.

Beryllium metal has been used to a limited extent as a *neutron moderator* in some nuclear reactors. (See Sec. 32.16, p. 688.) It is more widely used as an alloying element. Copper-beryllium alloys are formed into very high-strength springs of long-lasting elasticity.

## 22.6 Calcium carbonate, the ubiquitous mineral

We have noted that calcium is the sixth most abundant element in the earth's crust. This fact is due to the terrestrial existence of the

Limestone—source of lasting beauty. At the left, one of the majestic caves of the Carlsbad Caverns in New Mexico. At the right, a quarry in Carrara, Italy. From this quarry came the marble that was shaped by Michelangelo.

remarkable compound, calcium carbonate. Not only is this compound the second most widely distributed mineral on earth, but it exists in four distinctly different forms.

As *limestone*, $CaCO_3$ is a major part of the great *sedimentary rock* formations of the earth. These formations have resulted from the *alluvial* deposits of shells of minute aquatic animals, over eons of time. Much of the fossil history of the earth is contained in these formations.

While most limestone quarried in the United States is converted to lime, a large amount is used directly as a building material. The exteriors of the buildings in Rockefeller Center in New York City, for example, contain 150,000 tons of Indiana limestone.

Limestone that has been greatly compressed by natural forces so that it is dense, hard, and has a close-textured surface that takes a high polish is *marble*. Limestone that is fine-grained, porous, and easily crumbled is *chalk*. Pure, crystalline $CaCO_3$ is colorless and transparent and is found as the mineral *calcite*, or *Iceland spar*.

The magnificent limestone caverns found throughout the world have resulted from the internal erosion of massive limestone deposits. The erosion is chemical in nature and involves the slow conversion of insoluble $CaCO_3$ to soluble $Ca(HCO_3)_2$. This conversion is brought about by the action of dissolved $CO_2$ gas:

$$CaCO_3(s) + H_2O(l) + CO_2(aq) \rightleftharpoons Ca^{+2}(aq) + 2HCO_3^{-1}(aq)$$

When water rich in dissolved calcium bicarbonate slowly seeps into the caves, solid residues build up from the cave floors and down from the cave ceilings as evaporation takes place. Over eons of time the soluble solid calcium bicarbonate residues convert to the more lasting, insoluble calcium carbonate,

$$Ca(HCO_3)_2(s) \rightleftharpoons CaCO_3(s) + CO_2(g) + H_2O(g),$$

and often, a veritable fairyland of *stalagmites* and *stalactites* is left to bedazzle the eye.

### 22.7 Lime, the versatile chemical

Each year many tons of shells are dredged from the sea, and many tons of limestone are stripped from the earth and *calcined* in huge *rotary kilns*. Calcination of these $CaCO_3$-bearing substances leads to one of the major products of the chemical industry—lime:

$$CaCO_3(s) \overset{\Delta}{=} CaO(s) + CO_2(g)$$

An ancient alchemical process in modern dress: calcination

Of the more than 17 million tons of lime produced in this country, second in tonnage only to sulfuric acid, a great amount is used by the building industry. Pure lime, by virtue of its very high melting point (2580°C), is used as a *refractory* brick to line furnaces. When used in *mortar*, *stucco*, and *plaster*, the lime is usually present as slaked lime. The dry, slaked lime will set to a very hard mass in the presence of water, carbon dioxide from the air, and *silica*, $SiO_2$, by forming very complex mixtures of calcium carbonate and calcium silicate over lengths of time:

$$Ca(OH)_2(s) + CO_2(g) \overset{H_2O}{\rightleftharpoons} CaCO_3(s) + H_2O(l)$$

$$Ca(OH)_2(s) + SiO_2(s) \overset{H_2O}{\rightleftharpoons} CaSiO_3(s) + H_2O(l)$$

When lime is produced in combination with *alumina*, $Al_2O_3$, silica, and iron(III) oxide in carefully controlled proportions, the resulting dry, pulverized mixture is a *Portland cement*. This vital product is a *hydraulic cement* that *sets* in water to a very hard mass as a very complex mixture of calcium aluminate, $Ca(AlO_2)_2$, calcium silicate, and calcium carbonate. *Concrete*, the major nonmetal structural material of modern times, is a suspension of sand, gravel, or crushed stone, in Portland cement.

Large amounts of lime are used in metallurgy to combine, as a base, with the acidic silica impurities of ores:

$$CaO(s) + SiO_2(s) \overset{\Delta}{=} CaSiO_3(l)$$

When used in this way, lime is termed a *flux*. The alkaline properties of lime permit a myriad of uses, which range in diversity from the "sweetening" of soils whose pH is too low to the production of magnesium.

*Bleaching powder* is produced when chlorine gas is passed through freshly slaked lime. The resulting solid is heterogeneous and is a variable mixture of calcium hypochlorite, $Ca(OCl)_2$, hydrated calcium chloride, and unreacted calcium hydroxide. The hypochlorite part of the mixture is a mild oxidizing agent, $E^0_{Cl^{-1}/OCl^{-1}} = -0.89$ volt, that increases in oxidizing strength on acidification, $E^0_{Cl^{-1}/HOCl} = -1.49$ volts. Bleaching powder finds important use in the textile industry. And on this bright note, we conclude our brief study of the elements of Group II and some of their compounds.

"The Blessings of Peace" by Charles Clement. Beauty and symbolism in concrete.

## SUMMARY

The Group II elements are less nearly ideal metals than are the elements of Group I. They are chemically active elements isolated in pure form by electrolyzing a melt of their compounds. These compounds, especially those of calcium, are of vital economic importance. Beryllium and its compounds exhibit properties more similar to those of aluminum and its compounds than to those of the other Group II elements and compounds.

The Born-Haber extension of Hess's law is a useful tool for analyzing the formation of energetically stable ionic crystals and attempting to understand the anomalous behavior of ions of high charge density.

## QUESTIONS AND PROBLEMS

**22.1** Cite chemical evidence for the anomalous behavior of beryllium relative to the other elements of Group II.

**22.2** Write equations for *all* the reactions involved in extracting magnesium from the sea.

**22.3** a. How many tons of oyster shells would be required in the production of 1.20 tons of magnesium from the sea? (Assume that the shells are entirely calcium carbonate.) b. How much current would be necessary to produce this much magnesium? Ans. b. $8.62 \times 10^9$ coulombs

**22.4** Set up a Born-Haber cycle for the *sublimation* of magnesium and, using data from Table 22–1, calculate $\Delta H_{\text{sub}}$.

**22.5** From the following data, using the Born-Haber approach, calculate the energy of crystallization per mole of KBr.
$\Delta H_{\text{sub}}$ = 19.1 kcal/mole of potassium metal
$\Delta H_{\text{I.E.1}}$ = 100.0 kcal/mole of gaseous potassium atoms
$\Delta H_{\text{vap}}$ = 7.6 kcal/mole of liquid bromine molecules
$\Delta H_D$ = 46.1 kcal/mole of gaseous bromine molecules
$\Delta H_{\text{E.A.}}$ = −84.6 kcal/mole of gaseous bromine atoms
$\Delta H_{\text{reaction}}$ = −94.2 kcal/mole of KBr formed from the elements
Ans. $\Delta H_{\text{cryst.}}$ = −155.6 kcal/mole of KBr formed

**22.6** Using a Born-Haber analysis, qualitatively explain which step is probably primarily responsible for the anomalously high $E^0$ value for the $Li(s)/Li^{+1}(aq)$ couple.

**22.7** Give a chemical explanation for the following.
a. Crushed limestone is used to "sweeten sour soil."
b. Anhydrous calcium chloride is spread on dry dirt roads.
c. Calcium chloride is spread on icy roads.
d. Commercial hydrochloric acid, or *muriatic* acid, is often used to clean excess mortar from bricks and tiles.

**22.8** What is meant by each of the following?
a. Portland cement      d. refractory
b. concrete             e. alluvial deposit
c. slaked lime          f. Hess's law

## SUGGESTED READING

Scientific American
Brunauer, S., and L. E. Copeland, "The Chemistry of Concrete." Apr. 1964

*No age is shut against great genius.*

Seneca (8? B.C.–A.D. 65)

**CHAPTER 23**

# Boron, Aluminum,

In moving from the alkali metals of Group I to the alkaline earth metals of Group II, a slight, but notable, decrease in metallic character was observed. In particular, the covalent character of beryllium compounds is a feature of the chemistry of nonmetals rather than of metals. It should not be surprising to find then—as we continue our survey of the elements by considering now the elements of Group III—that the behavior of these elements becomes more nonmetallic in nature. Of the five elements of this group—boron, B; aluminum, Al; gallium, Ga; indium, In; and thallium, Tl—only the first, boron, is a true nonmetal. Though aluminum appears to be a metal in a physical sense, it is a metalloid in a chemical sense. The bulk of the chemist's attention to the Group III elements is directed to the study of boron and aluminum. While due in part to the greater accessibility of compounds of these elements, relative to those of gallium, indium, and thallium, the emphasis on boron and aluminum is due mainly, as we shall now see, to the rich variety in the chemical behavior of these elements.

### 23.1 Some properties of the Group III elements

The properties that were previously tabulated for the elements of Groups I and II are presented for the Group III elements in Table 23–1. A study of this table indicates that boron is not similar in properties to the other elements of the group. Observe the high melting and boiling points of boron, as well as the high heats of fusion and vaporization determined for it experimentally. These data point to stronger bonding between boron atoms in the solid state than that which exists between atoms of other elements. If the boron-to-boron bonds in the solid were

*482*

# and Group III

**TABLE 23—1**  PROPERTIES OF THE GROUP III ELEMENTS

| | B | Al | Ga | In | Tl |
|---|---|---|---|---|---|
| Atomic weight (amu) | 10.82 | 26.98 | 69.72 | 114.82 | 204.39 |
| Boiling point (°C) | 3927 | 2447 | 2237 | 2047 | 1470 |
| Melting point (°C) | 2027 | 660 | 29.8 | 156 | 304 |
| Heat of fusion (kcal/mole) | 5.3 | 2.55 | 1.34 | 0.78 | 1.02 |
| Heat of vaporization (kcal/mole) | 129 | 70.2 | 61.2 | 54.1 | 38.7 |
| Density (g/ml) | 2.34 | 2.70 | 5.91 | 7.31 | 11.83 |
| Metallic atomic radius (A) | 0.98 | 1.43 | 1.41 | 1.66 | 1.71 |
| Covalent radius (A) | 0.82 | 1.18 | 1.26 | 1.44 | 1.48 |
| Ionic radius, $M^{+3}$ (A) | 0.20 | 0.50 | 0.62 | 0.81 | 0.95 |
| I.E.$_1$ (kcal/mole) | 191 | 138 | 138 | 133 | 141 |
| I.E.$_2$ (kcal/mole) | 580 | 434 | 473 | 435 | 471 |
| I.E.$_3$ (kcal/mole) | 874 | 656 | 708 | 646 | 687 |
| $\Delta H$ of ion hydration (kcal/mole) | | −1109 | −1115 | | −77* |
| $E^0_{\mathrm{M/M}^{+3}}$ (volts) | 0.87† | 1.66 | 0.53 | 0.34 | −0.72 |

* For $Tl^{+1}(g) \rightarrow Tl^{+1}(aq)$
† For $B(s) + 6H_2O(l) \rightleftharpoons H_3BO_3(aq) + 3H_3O^{+1}(aq) + 3e^{-1}$

more covalent than metallic in nature, then greater bonding strength between the atoms would result. Covalent bonding in solid boron suggests low thermal and electrical conductivity, both of which are borne out by experiment. The covalent nature of the bonding in boron, then, gives it nonmetallic rather than metallic properties.

In attempting to analyze transitions in properties of the Group III elements, we are met with seemingly irregular changes in values of the ionization energies—in particular, in going from aluminum to gallium, and in going from indium to thallium. The presence of a filled *d* electron subshell in gallium, where none exists in aluminum, and a filled *f* electron subshell in thallium, where none such exists in indium, is undoubtedly the basic factor that leads to the observed irregularities.

Unquestionably, the most startling departure from true periodicity among the Group III elements occurs with boron. Recall the observation that lithium, at the head of Group I, behaves more like an element of Group II. Also, recall that beryllium, at the head of Group II, behaves more like an element of Group III. It is no surprise to learn that boron, at the head of Group III, behaves more like an element of Group IV.

### 23.2  Boron, borides, and the boranes

At high temperatures, boron reacts with a number of different metals to form very hard, refractory solids. X-ray analysis of these compounds indicates that the metal atoms are incorporated in the spaces between the boron atoms. Such *interstitial* compounds are called *borides*. Corresponding compounds of carbon, the *carbides*, and of silicon, the *silicides*, exist. Though the borides are, of themselves, fascinating subjects of chemical study, they are the precursors of an even more unusual series of compounds—the *boranes*.

If magnesium boride, $MgB_6$, is treated with an acid, a complex mixture of gases that are all *boron hydrides* evolves. The simplest of these gases is *diborane*, $B_2H_6$, and not $BH_3$ as might have been expected. Indeed, there is nothing at all usual about the boranes, the most complex of which is *decaborane*, $B_{10}H_{14}$. The fact that they all have positive heats of formation suggests potential thermodynamic instability. In fact, they oxidize readily in highly exothermic reactions—and thus, they are being intensively studied for their potential value as high energy rocket fuels.

Of most interest to chemists are the remarkable bonding characteristics of the boranes. In diborane, for example, there are twelve valence electrons—three each from two boron atoms, and one each from six hydrogen atoms. On the basis of our model for covalent bonding, these twelve electrons cannot account for the minimum number of *seven* chemical bonds that must be present among the eight atoms of $B_2H_6$. Obviously, the covalent bonding in diborane does not conform to our simple electron-pair-per-bond model. Figure 23.1 shows some of the proposed bonding structures for diborane.

### 23.3 The resemblance of boron to carbon

If boron is heated in the presence of nitrogen gas or ammonia gas, it reacts to form a white, refractory solid. The solid has the simplest formula, BN, and is known as *boron nitride*. It is very similar in its physical properties to graphite, and X-ray analysis suggests the two have similar solid state structures. (Fig. 23.2.) Just as graphite can be converted to diamond at high temperatures and pressures, so, too, under similar conditions can the graphite structure of boron nitride be converted to a diamond-like structure. (Fig. 23.3.) As might be expected, this form of boron nitride, called *borazon*, is as hard as diamond.

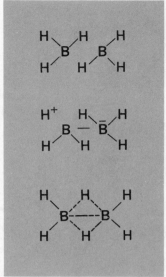

FIGURE 23.1 Diborane. Proposed structures: a covalent model with a "no-electron" bond (top); an ionic model (center); and a more successful "hydrogen bridge" model (bottom)

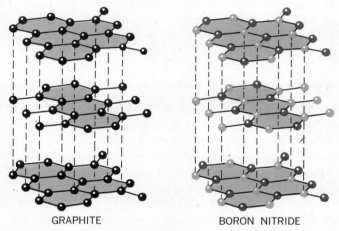

GRAPHITE

BORON NITRIDE

FIGURE 23.2 The resemblance of boron to carbon: models for graphite and boron nitride

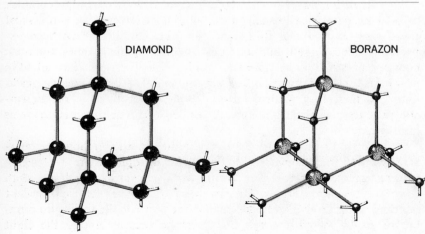

DIAMOND

BORAZON

FIGURE 23.3 The resemblance of boron to carbon: models for diamond and borazon

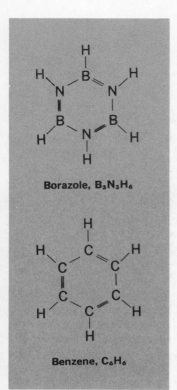

**Borazole, B₃N₃H₆**

**Benzene, C₆H₆**

**FIGURE 23.4** The resemblance of boron to carbon: models for borazole and benzene

Another interesting boron-nitrogen compound forms when a mixture of diborane and ammonia is heated. This compound, which is a liquid at room temperature, is called *borazole* and has the true molecular formula $B_3N_3H_6$. Borazole greatly resembles benzene, $C_6H_6$, in a number of ways, though it is chemically more reactive. It would appear that the bonding characteristics of the two compounds are quite similar. (Fig. 23.4.)

The similarity of the boron nitrides to graphite and diamond, and of borazole to benzene, suggests a similarity between the boron-nitrogen bond and the carbon-carbon bond. It is not difficult to hypothesize how this similarity may arise. The eight valence electrons of the B-N bond make it isoelectronic with the C-C bond. Moreover, the covalent radius of boron (0.82 A) and that of nitrogen (0.75 A) do not differ greatly from that of carbon (0.77 A). In all, it might be expected that the B-N and C-C bonds should have similar characteristics.

Thus, while boron does not occur naturally in the free state as does carbon, the similarities that exist between interstitial borides and carbides, between the boron nitrides and the allotropes of carbon, and between borazole and benzene, highlight the fact that boron behaves more like an element of Group IV than as one of Group III.

### 23.4 Boron as a nonmetal: the boric acids

In considering the covalent nature of the bonding in elemental boron (Sec. 23.1) and the similarity in behavior of boron to carbon (Sec. 23.3), we have touched upon the nonmetallic nature of the element. Most characteristically, boron behaves as a nonmetal by forming an *acidic* oxide, $B_2O_3$.

Boron(III) oxide is the acid anhydride of a number of *boric* acids, only two of which exist as such—*metaboric* acid, $HBO_2$, and *orthoboric* acid, $H_3BO_3$. Orthoboric acid occurs naturally as a solid in volcanic ash. Large amounts of the white powder are also found in borax deposits, and in the steam issuing from *fumaroles* in Nevada and in Tuscany, Italy.

Prolonged and intensified heating of orthoboric acid leads to its stepwise dehydration:

$$H_3BO_3(s) \overset{\Delta}{=} HBO_2(s) + H_2O(g)$$

$$2HBO_2(s) \overset{\Delta}{=} B_2O_3(s) + H_2O(g)$$

Neutralization of orthoboric acid results in the formation of the tetraborate ion rather than the orthoborate ion:

$$4H_3BO_3(s) + 2OH^{-1}(aq) \rightleftharpoons B_4O_7^{-2}(aq) + 7H_2O(l)$$

Though reported in older chemical literature, the independent existence of tetraboric acid, $H_2B_4O_7$, has not been verified. Tetraborates,

however, are more common in nature than are metaborates and ortho-
borates.

The most common compound of boron is *borax*, sodium tetraborate 10-hydrate, $Na_2B_4O_7 \cdot 10H_2O$. It is obtained mainly from saline
lakes, such as Searles Lake in the Mojave Desert of California. Approximately a half million tons of borax, most of which is used in the
making of glass, are mined annually in the United States. Borax is also
used in the production of glazes and enamels, and it is found in millions of homes, where it is used for cleaning purposes.

A number of complex *polyborates*, such as $KH_4B_5O_{10}$, $Ca_2B_6O_{11}$,
and $Mg_3B_8O_{15}$, have been identified. Their structures are very complex
and not as yet well understood.

Since orthoboric acid is very weak,

$$H_3BO_3(aq) + H_2O(l) \rightleftharpoons H_3O^{+1}(aq) + H_2BO_3^{-1}(aq) \qquad K_A = 7.3 \times 10^{-10},$$

borates undergo extensive hydrolysis to form alkaline solutions:

$$BO_2^{-1}(aq) + 2H_2O(l) \rightleftharpoons H_3BO_3(aq) + OH^{-1}$$
$$BO_3^{-3}(aq) + 3H_2O(l) \rightleftharpoons H_3BO_3(aq) + 3OH^{-1}$$
$$B_4O_7^{-2}(aq) + 7H_2O(l) \rightleftharpoons 4H_3BO_3(aq) + 2OH^{-1}$$

Observe that it is orthoboric acid that forms, regardless of what type
of borate hydrolyzes.

Since boron(III) oxide is an acid, it reacts with basic metal
oxides. The reaction is the basis for a classical analysis for metals—
*the borax bead test*. If an unknown metal salt is *fused* with borax, a
bead of boron(III) oxide forms in which the unknown metal oxide dissolves and reacts to form a borate. The color of the bead is often specific for a given element. For example, cobalt salts yield blue beads,
and manganese salts yield violet beads.

## 23.5 The story of aluminum

Aluminum is the third most abundant element in the earth's crust,
found both in *clays* and *feldspars*. Of the other elements of Group III,
gallium is only 1/10,000 as abundant, while boron, indium, and thallium are still rarer. *Impure* aluminum was first isolated in 1825 by Hans
Christian Oersted (ERR sted), the Danish scientist who performed the
first recorded experiment in electromagnetism. It was another sixty
years, however, before a young American discovered an inexpensive
method of producing metallic aluminum. This event made available
to the world an abundant metal whose versatility has in no small way
shaped our present way of life.

One day, as Professor Jewett of Oberlin College spoke of the
fortune that awaited the man who would develop a simple method for
extracting aluminum, one of his students nudged a young classmate,

Charles Martin Hall. The response of Hall, a chemistry enthusiast, was, "I am going after that metal," and soon thereafter Hall went to work in his father's woodshed, seeking his goal and fortune. He attacked the problem scientifically. He knew that only the most active metals, such as sodium and potassium, were strong enough reducing agents to liberate aluminum from molten aluminum chloride:

$$Al^{+3}(l) + 3K(l) \overset{\Delta}{\rightleftharpoons} 3K^{+1}(l) + Al(l)$$

But both potassium and sodium were too expensive to use in commercial mass production of the metal. Hall finally discarded all methods that depended upon action of a reducing agent and turned to electrolysis, in spite of his knowledge that Davy, who had isolated the alkali metals by electrolysis, had failed to get *pure* aluminum in this way.

*Alumina*, $Al_2O_3$, was the natural starting point. In hydrated form, alumina is the chief component of *bauxite*, the ore richest in aluminum. But alumina has such an extremely high melting point (2045°C) that Hall realized it would be commercially impracticable to melt the oxide. However, if an electric current was to liberate free aluminum from it, alumina had to be either melted or dissolved. Perhaps—the thought came to Hall in one of those flashes of genius—some mineral that would act as a solvent for aluminum oxide might be found. After trying a number of these, he came across a milky-white, glassy solid called *cryolite*, $Na_3AlF_6$. He melted this with some difficulty (mp = 1000°C) and then threw in some alumina. The alumina dissolved readily. He passed a direct current through the solution of alumina in cryolite and, to his intense joy, found that metallic aluminum was deposited at the cathode. On February 26, 1886, some eight months after he had graduated from Oberlin, the twenty-two-year-old Hall burst excitedly into the laboratory of Professor Jewett and, holding a few aluminum "buttons," exclaimed, "I've got it."

Hall soon obtained a patent on his process and two years later the Pittsburgh Reduction Company, which later became the Aluminum Company of America, was founded. Two months after Hall first produced metallic aluminum, Paul Héroult (AY rue), a twenty-three-year-old Frenchman, independently prepared aluminum by a method identical to that used by Hall.

In the history of science, this is not a rare example of simultaneous discoveries. Advances in science often are made in different parts of the world at almost the same time. They are frequently the final step in a long series of experiments conducted by many research workers in widely separated laboratories. The scientist who is fortunate enough to achieve the final result is always aware that he owes an immeasurable debt to all the others whose ideas and measurements showed him the correct path.

A fitting tribute to a brilliant alumnus: an aluminum statue of Charles Martin Hall at Oberlin College

### 23.6 The Hall-Héroult process

With the introduction and development of the Hall-Héroult process, the price of aluminum fell from \$8.00 a pound to \$0.33 a pound in little more than a decade. Today, aluminum sells for around \$0.25 a pound in the United States, and more than two million tons are produced each year by essentially this same process. (Fig. 23.5.)

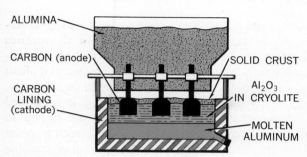

ALUMINA

CARBON (anode)

CARBON LINING (cathode)

SOLID CRUST

Al$_2$O$_3$ IN CRYOLITE

MOLTEN ALUMINUM

**FIGURE 23.5** A diagram of a most important electrolytic cell: the Hall-Héroult cell

The large structures in which aluminum is extracted serve a dual purpose. First, they are electric furnaces in which cryolite is melted. Second, they are electrolytic cells. After Al$_2$O$_3$ is dissolved in the molten cryolite, in which it dissociates,

$$Al_2O_3(l) \xrightarrow[\text{Na}_3\text{AlF}_6]{\Delta} 2Al^{+3}(l) + 3O^{-2}(l),$$

electrolysis leads to the formation of aluminum at the carbon cathode that serves as the cell lining. Simultaneously, oxygen gas is discharged at graphite anodes where, since the temperature is so high, extensive reaction occurs that wears away the anodes:

$$C(s) + O_2(g) = CO_2(g)$$

The process is a continuous one. Aluminum oxide is added, aluminum is removed, and the carbon anodes are replaced from time to time. The original cryolite, Na$_3$AlF$_6$, acts only as a solvent and does not become electrolyzed. Commercial cells, consuming huge amounts of current, each day produce about 500 pounds of aluminum that is more than 99 per cent pure.

Bauxite, found in large amounts in Surinam (Dutch Guiana), Jamaica (British West Indies), and British Guiana, contains a fair percentage of the oxides of iron, silicon, and titanium. If these impurities are not removed before the bauxite is put in the electric furnace, the aluminum produced is impure. Arkansas leads the United States in the production of this ore.

After the aluminum is drawn from the electrolytic cells, the *pig metal* is remelted so that the nonmetal impurities may be skimmed off. If aluminum alloys, rather than pure aluminum, are desired, the alloying materials may be added during the remelting. The chief alloying elements include copper, magnesium, manganese, silicon, zinc, iron, nickel, and chromium.

The Hall-Héroult process gives *primary* aluminum, that is, metal produced directly from its ore. An additional significant supply of aluminum lies in *secondary* sources—those in which the metal is recovered after one use, to be reused in another way. By far the largest users of aluminum are the transportation industries. The lightness of aluminum—its density is one-third of iron—in combination with its great structural strength, means larger payloads at smaller operating costs.

Because of its metallic nature, aluminum is a very good conductor of electricity. Each year, thousands of tons of it are used in the manufacture of cables, reinforced with a steel core, that are used extensively for long distance transmission lines. Requiring fewer supporting towers than heavier copper cables do, these lines economically carry electricity to areas that were formerly virtually inaccessible.

2785 miles of aluminum pipe to be used as a heat exchange unit in the fractional distillation of liquid air

Since aluminum is an excellent conductor of heat as well as a light metal, cooking utensils made of aluminum have long been popular. In recent years, aluminum has come to play an increasingly important role in the packaging industry. With great ingenuity, a myriad of uses have been found for aluminum, from foil wrappings to "flip open" cans.

The construction industry finds wide application for this wondrous metal. Many buildings and homes are now constructed with aluminum window frames, panels, screens, and insulation.

### 23.7 Some chemical properties of aluminum

Aluminum is silvery white in color and, as we saw, is rendered naturally passive to further chemical action by an impermeable oxide film that forms on its surface. The metal is attacked by both nonoxidizing acids and bases, releasing hydrogen in each case:

$$Al(s) + 3H_3O^{+1}(aq) = Al^{+3}(aq) + \tfrac{3}{2}H_2(g) + 3H_2O(l)$$
$$Al(s) + OH^{-1}(aq) + 3H_2O(l) = \tfrac{3}{2}H_2(g) + Al(OH)_4^{-1}(aq)$$
$$\text{tetrahydroxoaluminate(III) ion}$$

In both cases, reaction of the amphiprotic oxide surface film must first occur:

$$Al_2O_3(s) + 6H_3O^{+1}(aq) = 2Al^{+3}(aq) + 9H_2O(l)$$
$$Al_2O_3(s) + 2OH^{-1}(aq) + 3H_2O(l) = 2Al(OH)_4^{-1}(aq)$$

In the presence of strong oxidizing acids, such as nitric and sulfuric acids, the oxide film remains intact, and the underlying metal is protected from reaction.

By virtue of its small ionic radius (0.50 A) and high positive charge, the $Al^{+3}$ ion has a very high charge density. As a consequence, most aluminum compounds are highly covalent in nature. In addition, the $Al^{+3}$ aqueous ion is very strongly hydrated and is a relatively strong Brønsted-Lowry acid; both of these features have been discussed in detail previously. (See Secs. 16.10 and 17.7.)

### 23.8 Aluminothermy

The outstanding chemical property of aluminum is its great reducing strength. Because of this property, one of the classic uses to which aluminum has been put is on-the-spot welding. When a mixture of powdered aluminum and iron(III) oxide, known as *Thermit* (THUR mit), is ignited by means of a fuse, such as a strip of burning magnesium ribbon, a highly exothermic reaction takes place:

$$2Al(s) + Fe_2O_3(s) = Al_2O_3(s) + 2Fe(l) \qquad \Delta H = -204 \text{ kcal}$$

The temperature produced by the reaction is so high that the iron formed is molten, and can be used directly to weld broken propeller shafts, rudder frames, and similar pieces of heavy iron or steel equipment.

Chromium, manganese, molybdenum, and vanadium, as well as the alloys ferrovanadium (Fe-V), and ferrotitanium (Fe-Ti), are produced in reduction reactions similar to the *Thermit reaction*. These reductions are all highly exothermic and result in exceptionally pure metal products, making *aluminothermy* one of the more important metallurgical processes of recent years.

### 23.9 Alumina: ore, gem, abrasive, refractory

When white, gelatinous aluminum hydroxide is heated, it forms the white, insoluble oxide alumina:

$$2Al(OH)_3(s) \stackrel{\Delta}{=} Al_2O_3(s) + 3H_2O(g)$$

The hydrated forms of aluminum(III) oxide, $Al_2O_3 \cdot 3H_2O$ and $Al_2O_3 \cdot H_2O$, are found widely distributed in bauxite. The precious gem stones *ruby* and *sapphire* are composed of alumina, colored by the presence of small amounts of metal oxides. Successful methods of preparing synthetic rubies and sapphires by growing them from a molten mixture of pure aluminum oxide and chromium oxide have been developed. These artificial stones, not easily distinguishable from natural gems, are widely used in a variety of ways in modern precision instruments and in jewelry.

    *Emery*, a natural alumina, is extremely hard and is used as an abrasive for grinding, polishing, drilling, and cutting. Fused alumina (*Alundum*), used as an abrasive, is prepared in large quantities by the fusion of natural alumina (*corundum*) in an electric furnace. Because of its high melting point, fused alumina is also an excellent *refractory*. It is used for furnace linings, and in bricks, spark plugs, crucibles, and high temperature cements. Because alumina is also quite inert chemically, it is employed as a catalyst support and is used in some laboratory ware, such as porous plates used in filtering chemical solutions. *Activated alumina* is a highly porous $Al_2O_3$ that is used to adsorb moisture in some air-conditioning systems and to dry such gases as propane and butane, both important fuels.

### 23.10 The hydroxides of Group III: a study of change

The clearest indication of the changing chemical nature of the Group III elements, going from boron to thallium, is shown by the properties of the hydroxides of the elements. We have already seen that the nonmetallic nature of boron is evidenced by the complete acid properties of $B(OH)_3$, or $H_3BO_3$, orthoboric acid. The metalloid nature of aluminum is indicated by the amphiprotic nature of $Al(OH)_3$. Proceeding down the group, we find that gallium(III) hydroxide, $Ga(OH)_3$, is also amphiprotic, forming the *tetrahydroxogallate*(III) ion, $Ga(OH)_4^{-1}$, in the presence of a strong base. Indium(III) hydroxide, $In(OH)_3$, is very much less amphiprotic, and thallium(III) hydroxide, finally, is quite basic and does not react with strong bases.

For gallium, indium, and thallium, the +1 oxidation state has been identified. Thallium(I) compounds, in fact, are very stable and well characterized. Thallium(I), or *thallous*, hydroxide is a soluble, strong base comparable to an alkali metal hydroxide. The fact that the +1 oxidation states exist for the elements of Group III in periods 4, 5, and 6 is related, unquestionably, to the prior appearance in those periods of the *transition elements*. Since the existence of the transition elements markedly influences the properties of the elements succeeding them in a period, and since the transition elements are nominally all metals, we turn our attention next to a brief overview of those elements.

## SUMMARY

The elements of Group III exhibit a greater degree of nonmetallic character than do the metals of Groups I and II. Boron, especially, is a nonmetal, forming an acidic oxide and behaving more like carbon in Group IV. The boranes and compounds containing B-N bonds are the subjects of intensive modern research and development.

The story of the first practical synthesis of aluminum is one of drama and inspiration. The Hall-Héroult process has led to an inexpensive, continuous supply of this metal of many uses. Though physically a metal, aluminum behaves chemically as a metalloid, a tendency that becomes less pronounced among the heavier elements of Group III.

## QUESTIONS AND PROBLEMS

23.1   a. What physical properties of boron clearly distinguish it as being unique among the Group III elements? b. Account for this uniqueness in terms of a bonding model for elemental boron.

23.2   Cite chemical evidence for the resemblance of boron to carbon.

23.3   What is meant by each of the following?
   a. interstitial compound
   b. isoelectric
   c. fumarole
   d. primary aluminum
   e. allotropes
   f. anodized aluminum
   g. aluminothermy
   h. activated alumina

23.4   Write chemical equations for each of the following. Where appropriate, net ionic equations should be given.
   a. complete combustion of diborane
   b. hydrolysis of borax
   c. both anode reactions of the Hall-Héroult process
   d. amphiprotic nature of alumina
   e. aluminothermy of *chromite* ore, $FeO \cdot Cr_2O_3$
   f. neutralization of metaboric acid with thallium(I) hydroxide

**23.5**  On the basis of boron chemistry, suggest names for the two phosphoric acids, $H_3PO_4$ and $HPO_3$.

**23.6**  What is the pH of a 0.01 $M$ $H_3BO_3$ solution?

**23.7**  a. Using data from Table 23–1 and a Born-Haber analysis, calculate a value for the energy change for the reaction $Al(s) \rightleftharpoons Al^{+3}(aq) + 3e^{-1}$. b. What factor associated with the reaction accounts for its spontaneity?
Ans.  a. $\Delta H = +192$ kcal/mole

**23.8**  a. What amperage is required for the electrolytic aspect alone in the production of $5.00 \times 10^2$ pounds of aluminum from a Hall-Héroult cell operating for 12.0 hours? b. Why is additional amperage required? c. Determine where major aluminum-producing facilities are located, and comment on a common characteristic of the sites.

**23.9**  How much aluminum can be extracted from 4.00 tons of a bauxite ore containing 37.0 per cent $Al_2O_3 \cdot H_2O$?
Ans.  0.666 ton

**23.10**  No visible reaction occurs when a piece of aluminum foil is placed in nitric acid. When a piece of the foil is placed in hydrochloric acid, no reaction is observed for a short time. Then a very vigorous, highly exothermic dissolution of the foil occurs. Explain these observations and their relevance to the rise of aluminum and its alloys as structural metals.

**23.11**  Analyze the Thermit reaction, using Hess's law to calculate $\Delta H_f$ of iron(III) oxide. ($\Delta H_f$ of $Al_2O_3 = -404$ kcal/mole)

**23.12**  Using data from Table 23–1 and that given below, calculate the energy of crystallization for aluminum(II) oxide.
Data:   $\Delta H_f = -404$ kcal/mole of $Al_2O_3$
$\Delta H_D = 118.9$ kcal/mole of $O_2$
$\Delta H_{E.A.} = 178$ kcal/mole of $O(g)$ atoms

**23.13**  Using data from Table 11–1 on page 262, plot the first ionization energies of the elements of periods 2 and 3 as a function of atomic number. Account for any dips or peaks in your graph on the basis of modern atomic theory.

**23.14**  From the data below, quantitatively compare ethane, $C_2H_6$, and diborane, $B_2H_6$, as fuels.
$\Delta H_f = -20.2$ kcal/mole $C_2H_6(g)$
$\Delta H_f = +7.5$ kcal/mole $B_2H_6(g)$
$\Delta H_f = -57.8$ kcal/mole $H_2O(g)$
$\Delta H_f = -94.0$ kcal/mole $CO_2(g)$
$\Delta H_f = -298.7$ kcal/mole $B_2O_3(s)$

## SUGGESTED READINGS

McCabe, Charles L., and C. L. Bauer. *Metals, Atoms, and Alloys* (paperback). Scholastic Book Services, 1964.

SCIENTIFIC AMERICAN
Massey, A. G., "Boron." Jan. 1964

*Where order in variety we see,*
*And where, though all things*
*differ, all agree.*

*Alexander Pope* (1688–1744)

**CHAPTER 24** | # The Transition and

For all the elements of Groups I, II, and III that we have just studied, the valence electrons were in "outer" electron orbitals, that is, in $s$ and $p$ orbitals. For example, sodium loses its $3s$ electron in forming $Na^{+1}$; magnesium loses both $3s$ electrons in forming $Mg^{+2}$; and aluminum loses the two $3s$ electrons and a $3p$ electron to form $Al^{+3}$. In the middle of the periodic table, in period 4 between calcium ($Z = 20$) and gallium ($Z = 31$), and in period 5 between strontium ($Z = 38$) and indium ($Z = 49$), there are, in each case, ten elements in which $d$ orbitals are being occupied for the first time in electron configurations. You will recall that such elements are called *transition elements*. (Review Sec. 10.12, pp. 249–254.) The $d$ orbitals of transition elements have a major quantum number $n$ value one less than that of the $s$ and $p$ orbitals in the same energy shell. Thus, those transition elements in period 4 are $3d$ elements; those in period 5 are $4d$ elements, and so forth.

In period 6, between barium ($Z = 56$) and thallium ($Z = 81$), there are not ten, but twenty-four, elements. In addition to ten transition elements, there are fourteen so-called "rare earth," or *lanthanide*, elements. In these fourteen elements, the $f$ orbitals are being occupied for the first time in electron configurations. These $f$ orbitals have a major quantum number $n$ value that is *two less* than that of the $s$ and $p$ orbitals in the same energy shell in which the $f$ orbitals are first being occupied. As a consequence, these elements are also called the *inner transition elements*. Period 6 contains, therefore, $5d$ transition elements and $4f$ inner transition elements. There is a second group of inner

*496*

# Rare Earth Elements

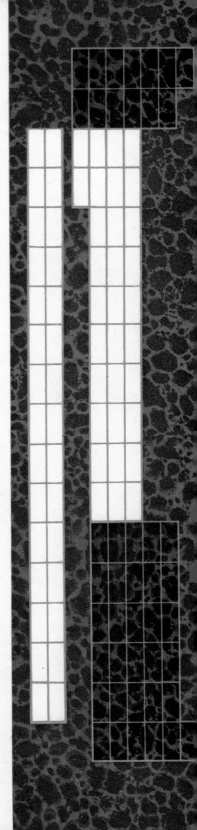

transition elements known as the *actinide* elements. These include the fourteen elements beyond actinium ($Z = 89$) in period 7, which have the $5f$ orbitals being occupied for the first time.

It is obviously impossible to discuss in any detail thirty-two transition elements and twenty-eight inner transition elements within the space of a single chapter. However, it is important to be able to relate these sixty elements to the other elements of the periodic classification. Moreover, a number of these elements have played a role in the development of civilizations since ancient times, and are still a vital factor in modern times. Hence, we shall touch upon general characteristics of all these elements and specific details for some of them, in order to broaden our understanding of the rich chemical variety in nature.

## 24.1 Electron configurations: a review

The electron configurations, *experimentally* suggested, of the elements between potassium ($Z = 19$) and krypton ($Z = 36$) are given in Table 24–1. These are orbital configurations for individual gaseous atoms and may not be the same in metals or compounds. Notice that *chromium* ($3d^5 4s^1$) and *copper* ($3d^{10} 4s^1$) are the only transition elements of period 4 to deviate from the $4s^2$ configuration. The deviation leads to a $3d$ subshell that is half filled in chromium ($3d^5$), and completely filled in copper ($3d^{10}$). *We may conclude, therefore, that there is more stability connected with a half-filled or a completely filled d subshell than with a filled s subshell.*

**TABLE 24–1** ELECTRON CONFIGURATIONS FOR ELEMENTS OF PERIOD 4

| Element | Electron Configuration* |
|---------|------------------------|
| $_{19}$K | $1s^2$ $2s^22p^6$ $3s^23p^6$ $4s^1$ |
| $_{20}$Ca | $1s^2$ $2s^22p^6$ $3s^23p^6$ $4s^2$ |
| $_{21}$Sc | $1s^2$ $2s^22p^6$ $3s^23p^63d^1$ $4s^2$ |
| $_{22}$Ti | $1s^2$ $2s^22p^6$ $3s^23p^63d^2$ $4s^2$ |
| $_{23}$V | $1s^2$ $2s^22p^6$ $3s^23p^63d^3$ $4s^2$ |
| $_{24}$Cr | $1s^2$ $2s^22p^6$ $3s^23p^63d^5$ $4s^1$ |
| $_{25}$Mn | $1s^2$ $2s^22p^6$ $3s^23p^63d^5$ $4s^2$ |
| $_{26}$Fe | $1s^2$ $2s^22p^6$ $3s^23p^63d^6$ $4s^2$ |
| $_{27}$Co | $1s^2$ $2s^22p^6$ $3s^23p^63d^7$ $4s^2$ |
| $_{28}$Ni | $1s^2$ $2s^22p^6$ $3s^23p^63d^8$ $4s^2$ |
| $_{29}$Cu | $1s^2$ $2s^22p^6$ $3s^23p^63d^{10}$ $4s^1$ |
| $_{30}$Zn | $1s^2$ $2s^22p^6$ $3s^23p^63d^{10}$ $4s^2$ |
| $_{31}$Ga | $1s^2$ $2s^22p^6$ $3s^23p^63d^{10}$ $4s^24p^1$ |
| $_{32}$Ge | $1s^2$ $2s^22p^6$ $3s^23p^63d^{10}$ $4s^24p^2$ |
| $_{33}$As | $1s^2$ $2s^22p^6$ $3s^23p^63d^{10}$ $4s^24p^3$ |
| $_{34}$Se | $1s^2$ $2s^22p^6$ $3s^23p^63d^{10}$ $4s^24p^4$ |
| $_{35}$Br | $1s^2$ $2s^22p^6$ $3s^23p^63d^{10}$ $4s^24p^5$ |
| $_{36}$Kr | $1s^2$ $2s^22p^6$ $3s^23p^63d^{10}$ $4s^24p^6$ |

\* These configurations, based on experimental evidence, are for individual gaseous atoms.

### 24.2 Physical properties of the transition elements

All the transition elements are metals showing true metallic luster and high conductivity of heat and electricity. In Table 24–2, some of the properties of the transition elements of period 4 are listed. It is among these $3d$ elements that some of the most abundant, as well as the most important, of all the transition elements appear.

**TABLE 24–2** SOME PROPERTIES OF THE TRANSITION ELEMENTS OF PERIOD 4

|  | Sc | Ti | V | Cr | Mn | Fe | Co | Ni | Cu | Zn |
|---|----|----|---|----|----|----|----|----|----|----|
| Atomic weight (amu) | 44.96 | 47.90 | 50.95 | 52.01 | 54.94 | 55.85 | 58.94 | 58.71 | 63.54 | 65.38 |
| Boiling point (°C) | 2730 | 3260 | 3450 | 2665 | 2150 | 3000 | 2900 | 2730 | 2595 | 906 |
| Melting point (°C) | 1539 | 1668 | 1900 | 1875 | 1245 | 1536 | 1495 | 1453 | 1083 | 419.5 |
| Heat of fusion (kcal/mole) | 3.8 | 3.7 | 4.2 | 3.3 | 3.50 | 3.67 | 3.64 | 4.21 | 3.11 | 1.76 |
| Heat of vaporization (kcal/mole) | 81 | 106.5 | 106 | 72.97 | 53.7 | 84.6 | 93 | 91.0 | 72.8 | 27.4 |
| Density (g/ml) | 3.0 | 4.51 | 6.1 | 7.19 | 7.43 | 7.86 | 8.9 | 8.9 | 8.96 | 7.14 |
| Metallic atomic radius (A) | 1.62 | 1.47 | 1.34 | 1.27 | 1.26 | 1.26 | 1.25 | 1.24 | 1.28 | 1.38 |

We should notice several aspects of these data. These metals are more dense and have higher melting and boiling points and heats of fusion and vaporization than do the elements of Groups I, II, and III (with the exceptions of beryllium and boron). Also, we note that the values for the properties listed are low for scandium, manganese, and zinc compared with those for neighboring elements. As an additional fact, it should be noted that these metals, in general, have high tensile strengths. All of these properties suggest a high degree of covalency between transition element atoms in the solid state.

## 24.3 Covalency in the transition elements

When covalent bonding is added to metallic bonding, the over-all attraction between the atoms in a metal should be higher than the attraction between atoms that are bonded by metallic bonding only. However, this comparison may *only* be made provided the atoms all have the same ionic charge in the cationic metal lattice so that the metallic bond strength is relatively the same. Except for manganese, copper, and zinc, in which +2 ions are probably present in the metal lattice, the ionic charge in the metallic state for the other transition metals is probably +3. This conclusion is based on the observed oxidation states shown by these elements in their compounds. The melting and boiling points and heats of fusion and vaporization for scandium, titanium, vanadium, chromium, iron, cobalt, and nickel are higher than those of aluminum, gallium, indium, and thallium in Group III, which also form metal lattices of +3 ions. This leads us to conclude that there is some degree of covalent bonding in the transition metals. Only beryllium and boron of the first three groups showed comparably high values for these properties, and it was seen that these elements exhibit a high degree of covalency.

Can this model of metals with both covalent and metallic bonding also explain the *trends* in the properties? Let us examine that question briefly. If the transition elements exhibit covalency but Group III elements do not, it seems reasonable to suggest that the mutual sharing of $3d$ electrons may cause this covalency. In zinc, the $3d$ orbitals are filled. Ten *paired* $3d$ electrons are present that cannot mutually participate in covalent bonding. Thus, there should be little, if any, covalent bonding between zinc atoms. We see in Table 24–2 that the properties of zinc do indeed have much lower values than those of the other $3d$ elements and basically reflect metallic bonding only. For manganese it might be expected that the $3d^5$ half-filled shell configuration, of noted stability, would reduce the tendency of manganese atoms to share electrons mutually in covalent bonds. Thus, we can explain the lower values for the properties of manganese. For the early members of the transition elements of period 4, few unpaired electrons are present in the $3d$ orbitals, so the amount of covalency in scandium and titanium, for example, is low. With succeeding elements, more unpaired $d$ electrons become available for bonding, and covalency increases. However, after manganese, although the number of $d$ electrons continues to increase, *pairing* within orbitals occurs according to the principle of maximum multiplicity. This intra-atomic pairing takes precedence over the interatomic pairing necessary for covalent bonds. Thus, the degree of covalency decreases from iron to zinc. We see, therefore, that by extending our model of the metallic state to include covalent bonding involving $d$ electrons we can account well for the properties in Table 24–2.

### 24.4 Chemical activity of the transition elements

The transition metals vary widely in their chemical activity. Scandium, yttrium, and lanthanum are chemically very active, and have oxidation potentials comparable to those of the alkali metals. The others are not as active. Polished iron slowly rusts in moist air; copper and silver both tarnish slowly. A few of the transition elements, such as platinum and gold, are extremely inert to oxidation. Even when heated to a red glow in the air, neither platinum nor gold oxidizes. Some metals, such as chromium and zinc, have relatively high oxidation potentials but are rendered passive by tough oxide or basic carbonate films that form naturally on their surfaces.

### 24.5 Oxidation numbers of the transition elements

One of the outstanding characteristics of the transition elements is the multiplicity of oxidation states they possess. Many of the transition elements have two, three, and even four different oxidation states. This diversity results in a chemistry whose subtle variations and rich variety offer a special challenge to the student of chemistry.

Table 24–3 summarizes the common oxidation states of the transition elements of period 4. It is possible to obtain other oxidation

**TABLE 24–3**   COMMON OXIDATION STATES OF THE TRANSITION ELEMENTS OF PERIOD 4

| Sc | Ti | V | Cr | Mn | Fe | Co | Ni | Cu | Zn |
|----|----|----|----|----|----|----|----|----|----|
|    |    |    |    |    |    |    |    | +1 |    |
|    | +2 | +2 | +2 | +2 | +2 | +2 | +2 | +2 | +2 |
| +3 | +3 | +3 | +3 | +3 | +3 | +3 | +3 |    |    |
|    | +4 | +4 |    | +4 |    |    |    |    |    |
|    |    | +5 |    |    |    |    |    |    |    |
|    |    |    | +6 | +6 |    |    |    |    |    |
|    |    |    |    | +7 |    |    |    |    |    |

states (e.g., +3 for Cu; +4 for Fe, Ni) but the conditions are usually rather severe. Except for scandium, all these elements can exist with an ionic oxidation state of +2, which must result from the process:

$$M^0(3d^n4s^2) \rightarrow M(3d^n)^{+2} + 2e^{-1*}$$

The abundance of high oxidation numbers does not mean that chromium, for example, can exist as a $Cr^{+6}$ ion by losing the two $4s$ and four $3d$ electrons. Rather, the small difference in energy between the $3d$, $4s$, and $4p$ orbitals allows them to be involved in hybrid covalent bonds. (Hybrid covalent bonds involving $s$ and $p$ electrons were discussed in Chapters 11 and 20.) As we shall see in the next chapter, such hybrid covalent bonds are responsible for an important aspect of transition metal chemistry.

To summarize then, the variety of oxidation states in the transition elements is due to the small difference in energy between the $3d$, $4s$, and $4p$ orbitals, which allows involvement of both $3d$ and $4s$ electrons and $3d$, $4s$, and $4p$ orbitals in bond formation.

## 24.6 Transition element compounds and color

The ions of the elements of Groups I, II, and III are colorless. When one of their compounds shows color, it is due to the anion. Chloride, sulfate, and nitrate anions, to name just three, are colorless, so the chloride, sulfate, and nitrate compounds of the elements of Groups I, II, and III are all white. For the transition elements, however, the existence of colored cations is as characteristic as is the variety of oxidation numbers. Moreover, anions of the transition elements, such as permanganate, $MnO_4^{-1}$, (a deep purple) and dichromate, $Cr_2O_7^{-2}$ (a bright orange), also show color. Table 24–4 summarizes some of the colors observed for aqueous solution species of the $3d$ transition metal oxidation states.

---

* An element of confusion has been injected into the above discussion without comment. In Chapter 10 and here, we assumed the order of energy among the $4s$, $4p$, and $3d$ orbitals to be $4s < 3d < 4p$. Only in this way could we explain the appearance of elements of Groups I and II followed by the transition elements followed by elements of Groups III–0, in periods 4–7. If the $3d$ electrons are higher in energy than the $4s$ electrons when the transition elements are being formed, how is it that we have been ionizing the $4s$ rather than the $3d$ electrons in forming transition metal ions? The answer is not simple. We recall that Figure 10.6 is a calculated orbital pattern for a many-electron atom based on quantum mechanical considerations and approximations. In reality, the electron orbital pattern for such an atom is far more complicated. It must suffice for us to note that there is much *experimental* evidence to indicate that in reality, *after formation*, the observed order of energies among the $4s$, $4p$, and $3d$ orbitals is $3d < 4s < 4p$. Thus, $4s$ electrons have lower rather than higher ionization energies than $3d$ electrons.

**TABLE 24–4**  OXIDATION STATES AND COLORS OF TRANSITION
ELEMENTS OF PERIOD 4

|    | +2 | +3 | +4 | +5 | +6 | +7 |
|----|----|----|----|----|----|----|
| Sc |    | colorless |    |    |    |    |
| Ti |    | violet | colorless |    |    |    |
| V  | violet | green | blue | red |    |    |
| Cr | blue | green |    |    | orange-yellow |    |
| Mn | pink |    |    |    | green | purple |
| Fe | pale green | amber |    |    |    |    |
| Co | pink | blue |    |    |    |    |
| Ni | green |    |    |    |    |    |
| Cu | blue |    |    |    |    |    |
| Zn | colorless |    |    |    |    |    |

The colors listed in Table 24–4 may vary considerably with the chemical state. For example, the hydrated $Fe^{+3}$ ion in a solution of iron(III) chloride is amber. Upon addition of colorless sodium thiocyanate, $NaSCN$, to the solution, an intense blood-red color develops. This color is that of the complex $Fe(SCN)_6^{-3}$ anion that forms. Inorganic chemists have used the slight changes in color in different compounds to learn a great deal about the types of bonding, the geometrical structure, and many other facets of transition element compounds.

In the ions of Groups I, II, and III the energy difference between the last occupied set of orbitals and the next highest to which an electron can be excited is greater than the energies of visible light. For example, for the excitation process,

$$Na^{+1}(1s^2,\ 2s^2,\ 2p^6) \xrightarrow{h\nu} Na^{+1}(1s^2,\ 2s^2 2p^5,\ 3s^1),$$

the energy needed to promote an electron from a $2p$ orbital to a $3s$ orbital cannot be obtained by the absorption of radiant energy having any of the frequencies present in visible light. Consequently, light in this range is not absorbed, and the ion is colorless. For transition metal ions, the energy difference between the $3d$ and $4s$ levels is much smaller than between the $2p$ and $3s$ in $Na^{+1}$ ion. Consequently, absorption of radiant energy in the visible region of the electromagnetic spectrum does occur with transition metal ions. For example, excitation in the aqueous $Cu^{+2}$ ion,

$$Cu^{+2}(1s^2,\ 2s^2 2p^6,\ 3s^2 3p^6 3d^9) \xrightarrow{h\nu} Cu^{+2}(1s^2,\ 2s^2 2p^6,\ 3s^2 3p^6 3d^8,\ 4s^1),$$

is achieved by absorption of radiant energy whose frequency corresponds to that of red light. Since it is a red component of light that is absorbed by the aqueous $Cu^{+2}$ ion, the light transmitted by the ion appears blue in color. Note from Table 24–4 that the aqueous $Zn^{+2}$ ion is colorless. This is not difficult to understand. For the excitation process,

$$Zn^{+2}(1s^2, 2s^22p^6, 3s^23p^63d^{10}) \xrightarrow{h\nu} Zn^{+2}(1s^2, 2s^22p^6, 3s^23p^63d^9, 4s^1),$$

enough energy must be absorbed first to unpair two electrons of opposite spin, and then to raise one of them to a higher energy level. So much energy is required for the unpairing step alone that radiant energy in the ultraviolet, rather than the visible region of the spectrum is required. Thus, as with oxidation numbers, the color of transition metal compounds is due to the relatively small energy difference between the $(n-1)d$ and the $(n)s$ and $(n)p$ energy levels of transition metal atoms and ions.

## 24.7 The transition elements are paramagnetic.

A substance that is not attracted by a magnetic field is termed *diamagnetic*. The simple compounds of the ions of Groups I, II, and III are diamagnetic. A substance that is attracted into a magnetic field is said to be *paramagnetic*. Many transition element compounds are paramagnetic. Paramagnetism is believed to be due *to the presence of unpaired electrons in the ions.* A spinning electron, being a moving charge, engenders weak electrical and magnetic fields. It is the magnetic field of a spinning electron that leads to paramagnetism, a relatively easily measured property of matter.

A diamagnetic ion has only paired electrons. In $Na^{+1}$ ion or $Cl^{-1}$ ion, all the electrons exist in pairs in orbitals, and sodium chloride exhibits diamagnetism. The presence of unpaired electrons in the $d$ orbitals of transition element ions is the source of their paramagnetism. Paramagnetism should not be confused with the type of magnetism exhibited by certain metals and alloys, particularly iron. The latter type of magnetism is known as *ferromagnetism* and is much stronger than paramagnetism. Another important difference between the two types of magnetism is that paramagnetism is only exhibited in the presence of an applied magnetic field, whereas ferromagnetism exists spontaneously in the absence of such a field. Thus, ferromagnetic solids will strongly attract one another, while paramagnetic solids will not. The observed paramagnetism of certain gaseous atoms and ions is an important experimental foundation for the proposed electron configurations of those species. In particular, verification of the principle of maximum multiplicity by measurement of paramagnetic properties has been accomplished. (See Sec. 10.12, p. 249.)

## 24.8 The transition elements are catalysts.

Another characteristic property of the transition elements that differentiates them from the elements of all other groups of elements is the catalytic activity of the free metals and their compounds. This catalytic activity is believed to be due to the presence of unfilled, or partially filled, $d$ orbitals. By forming transient, intermediate complexes utilizing those $d$ orbitals, transition metal atoms and ions can provide reaction paths of lower activation energy for normally slow reactions to bring about increased reaction rates.

With an overview of the general properties of the transition elements behind us, we turn now to brief considerations of the specific elements themselves, in the order of their appearance in the periodic classification of the elements.

### 24.9 Scandium, yttrium, and lanthanum

The three elements scandium, yttrium, and lanthanum form $+3$ ions in compounds. Those compounds are colorless and diamagnetic. The metals have high oxidation potentials and react vigorously with water. Their compounds show some resemblance to those of aluminum, but $Sc^{+3}$ (0.81 A), $Y^{+3}$ (0.93 A), and $La^{+3}$ (1.15 A) are much larger than $Al^{+3}$ (0.50 A). The compounds are increasingly less covalent as the radius increases. The radioactive element actinium, Ac, is also a member of this group.

### 24.10 Titanium, zirconium, and hafnium

The elements titanium, zirconium, and hafnium are more abundant than those of the scandium group. In fact, they are more abundant than some more commonly known metals, such as lead and copper. They are difficult to prepare as free metals, requiring such strong reducing agents as metallic sodium and magnesium to displace them from compounds:

$$TiCl_4(g) + 2Mg(s) \xrightarrow{\Delta} Ti(s) + 2MgCl_2(s)$$

Titanium occurs abundantly in the United States in the ore *ilmenite*, $FeTiO_3$, nearly one million tons of which are mined annually. Titanium has oxidation states of $+2$, $+3$, and $+4$. However, the $+2$ titanium compounds are unstable and are oxidized by air and by water ($E^0_{Ti^{+2}/Ti^{+3}} = +0.34$ volt). Solutions containing $Ti^{+3}$ ion are also good reducing agents because of the tendency for the ion to be oxidized to the $+4$ state ($E^0_{Ti^{+3}/TiO^{+2}} = -0.1$ volt).

Zirconium has a $+3$ and a more stable $+4$ state, while hafnium has only a $+4$ state. Ions in the $+4$ oxidation state of all three elements hydrolyze strongly in aqueous solution to form *oxycations*:

$$M^{+4}(aq) + 3H_2O(l) \rightarrow MO^{+2}(aq) + 2H_3O^{+1}(aq)$$
$$M = Ti, Zr, Hf$$

The strong attraction between the $+4$ ions, of very high charge density, and oxygen atoms results in the formation of oxycations called the *titanyl* ($TiO^{+2}$), *zirconyl* ($ZrO^{+2}$), and *hafnyl* ($HfO^{+2}$) ions.

Titanium metal is very strong, has a high melting point, and is very resistant to corrosion, forming surface layers of protective oxide and nitride. Because of its properties, titanium is used widely as a structural material in jet engines. Zirconium metal is used in nuclear reactors, since it has a very small tendency to absorb neutrons necessary to maintain the nuclear reaction. $TiO_2$ is used as a white pigment in both the paint and cosmetic industries, while $ZrO_2$ and $HfO_2$ are refractories used for high temperature insulation.

### 24.11 Vanadium, niobium, and tantalum

Although vanadium has oxidation states of +2, +3, +4, and +5, niobium shows only the +3 and +5 states, while tantalum exhibits only the +5 state. This pattern of predominance of the higher oxidation states for the heavier elements of a group—seen already in titanium, zirconium, and hafnium—is a typical pattern for the transition elements. The high oxidation states make the chemistry of these elements rather complicated, since these states are exhibited in complex oxycations.

Vanadium is added to steel to increase its strength. Tantalum is so resistant to corrosion that it finds use in chemical plants in apparatus for handling corrosive liquids, such as acids. Tantalum has found recent use in the electronics industry in electron and neon tubes. It is also used in surgical and dental instruments. Niobium finds some use in certain stainless steels. (See Sec. 24.12.)

### 24.12 Chromium, molybdenum, and tungsten

Chromium, molybdenum, and tungsten, all metals of great hardness, have very high melting points and show high resistance to corrosion. Chromium metal is used as a thin surface plating on other metals, where it can serve as a protective coating as well as provide a bright mirror-like finish. The chromium itself is protected from corrosion by a thin surface oxide film. Addition of chromium to steel makes the steel harder and more resistant to corrosion. Steels with high chromium content (more than 10 per cent chromium) are called the *stainless steels*.

Chromium is obtained by aluminothermy of its chief ore, *chromite*, $Cr_2O_3 \cdot FeO$. Though chromium is a relatively active metal ($E^0_{Cr/Cr^{+3}} = +0.74$ volt), it is rendered passive in oxidizing acids, but will liberate hydrogen gas from warm, dilute sulfuric acid or hydrochloric acid.

Molybdenum is produced by the hydrogen reduction of molybdenum(VI) oxide:

$$MoO_3(s) + 3H_2(g) \overset{\Delta}{\rightleftharpoons} Mo(s) + 3H_2O(g)$$

Tungsten is produced by aluminothermy of tungsten(VI) oxide, or by carbon reduction of the oxide in an electric furnace:

$$WO_3(s) + 3C(s) \stackrel{\Delta}{=} W(s) + 3CO(g)$$

Both molybdenum (2610°C) and tungsten (3410°C) have melting points that are too high to permit economic melting of the elemental powder after its formation by chemical reduction. Hence, the powder is pressed together and heated to cause *sintering* in which the heat and pressure cause enough localized fusion within the mass to hold it together. To make tungsten wire to be used in light bulbs, the sintered tungsten is drawn into wire which then has an electric current passed through it at high temperatures. This current causes additional fusion of particles in the wire.

The largest use of tungsten is as an alloying material in steel that is used in high-speed tools, for steels that contain tungsten remain hard even at red heat. Molybdenum finds similar alloying uses in the steel industry. About 90 per cent of the world's known store of molybdenum is found in the *molybdenite*, $MoS_2$, of Bartlett Mountain in Colorado. More than 35,000 tons of the metal are extracted annually from that source. Pure $MoS_2$ finds important use as a high temperature dry lubricant. The soft, black solid behaves much like graphite in this respect, and it is not surprising to learn that both have similar hexagonal layered structures.

Of the three elements of this group, chromium has been studied in most detail. In the +2 oxidation state, chromium is found to be readily and rapidly oxidized to the +3 state ($E^0_{Cr^{+2}/Cr^{+3}} = +0.41$ volt), the oxidation state in which chromium forms many *complex ions* and *coordination compounds*. This aspect of the chemistry of chromium will be covered in the next chapter. Chromium(III) hydroxide is amphiprotic, the $Cr^{+3}(aq)$ and $Cr(OH)_4^{-1}(aq)$ ions existing in acid and strongly alkaline solutions, respectively.

As we have seen, one of the common and interesting solution equilibria encountered is that involving the oxyanions of chromium in the +6 oxidation state:

$$2CrO_4^{-2}(aq) + 2H_3O^{+1}(aq) \rightleftharpoons Cr_2O_7^{-2}(aq) + 3H_2O(l)$$

The equilibrium shifts brought about by changing conditions, can be followed by the change in color from the yellow chromate ion, $CrO_4^{-2}$, to the orange dichromate ion, $Cr_2O_7^{-2}$.

An interesting, but very complex, feature of the chemistry of molybdenum and tungsten is the tendency for the +6 oxidation state of these elements to form polymolybdates and polytungstates. These are compounds in which the molybdenum and tungsten appear in oxyanions involving –O–Mo–O– and –O–W–O– bonds, often with rather large numbers of metal atoms involved.

### 24.13 Manganese, technetium, and rhenium

It is in this family of transition elements—manganese, technetium, and rhenium—that the height of chemical versatility among the metals is attained. Manganese, for example, exists in five well-characterized oxidation states. In the +7 oxidation state, manganese exists in the familiar, purple permanganate ion, $MnO_4^{-1}$, a useful, strong oxidizing agent ($E^0_{Mn^{+2}/MnO_4^{-1}} = -1.51$ volts). Rhenium is even more unusual in that it also exists in a $-1$ oxidation state, a rather nonmetallic property for a metal. Technetium exists only in radioactive forms, none of which currently are found in nature. In its chemistry, technetium resembles rhenium more than manganese.

Manganese is the thirteenth most abundant element in nature and occurs mainly as *pyrolusite*, $MnO_2$. More than two million pounds of the metal are consumed annually in this country, almost all for alloying steels. Thus, while pure manganese metal can be obtained by aluminothermy of pyrolusite, most of the oxide is reduced along with iron(III) oxide by coke in blast furnaces to form alloys of iron and manganese:

$$Fe_2O_3(s) + MnO_2(s) + 5C(s) \stackrel{\Delta}{=} 2Fe\text{-}Mn(l) + 5CO(g)$$

Two main types of alloys are formed. The one that is low in manganese content (15–20 per cent) is called *spiegeleisen*. The other, quite high in manganese content (75–81 per cent), is called *ferromanganese*. These alloys serve two main purposes in steelmaking. The manganese in them acts as a *scavenger* by removing traces of oxygen and sulfur in steel by forming MnO and MnS which are removed in the *slag* of the steelmaking process. The alloys also serve as the source of manganese in manganese-steel alloys, which are of carefully controlled composition and very hard and resistant to wear and abrasion.

### 24.14 The iron family: iron, cobalt, nickel

The elements iron, cobalt, and nickel show more similar chemical properties relative to each other than to the elements below them in the periodic table. Accordingly, the three are treated as members of a *horizontal family*. Iron and its alloy, steel, are so important to the economy of the nation and the world that their metallurgy and use are treated separately in the special photographic essay beginning on page 519.

The three metals are stronger reducing agents than hydronium ion; hence, theoretically they will liberate hydrogen gas from acid solutions. The hydrogen overvoltage on nickel ($E^0_{Ni/Ni^{+2}} = +0.25$ volt) is high enough, however, to make evolution of the gas very slow. Iron and cobalt, however, can be rendered passive by treatment with

Potential wealth from the sea. Large manganese-containing nodules nearly four miles below the surface of the Pacific Ocean.

concentrated nitric acid. The most notable difference in chemical behavior among the three elements is that iron exists most stably in the +3 oxidation state, while nickel and cobalt are found in the +2 state. The enhanced stability of $Fe^{+3}$ must be due to the formation of a half-filled $3d$ subshell. Cobalt may also exist in the +3 oxidation state. However, $Co^{+3}$ ion is such a powerful oxidizing agent ($E^0_{Co^{+2}/Co^{+3}} = -1.84$ volts) that cobalt(III) salts will react vigorously with water:

$$4Co^{+3}(aq) + 6H_2O(l) = 4Co^{+2}(aq) + O_2(g) + 4H_3O^{+1}(aq)$$

The electrochemical properties of nickel compounds have been put to important practical use. In 1908, Thomas Alva Edison invented a reversible galvanic cell that is the basis for a widely used storage battery. The *Edison cell* is comprised of a $Ni(OH)_2(s)/NiO_2(s)$ half-cell ($E^0 = -0.49$ volt) and a $Fe(s)/Fe(OH)_2(s)$ half-cell ($E^0 = +0.88$ volt) in a potassium hydroxide electrolyte. The entire assembly is sealed in airtight containers to prevent the oxidation of iron(II) hydroxide, a reaction that occurs with ease and one that curtails the life of the Edison cell. In more recent years, the $Ni(OH)_2(s)/NiO_2(s)$ half-cell has been used more effectively with the $Cd(s)/Cd(OH)_2(s)$ half-cell ($E^0 = +0.81$ volt) in the *nickel-cadmium storage battery*, which is lighter and more durable than the lead storage battery.

Nickel is used extensively for electroplating metal surfaces. In the process, the surface to be plated is made the cathode, a pure nickel bar is the anode, and a solution of nickel(II) sulfate and nickel(II) chloride at low pH serves as the electrolyte.

More than 125,000 tons of nickel are used in the United States each year. Most of this must be imported, mainly from Canada. Several hundred tons of nickel are produced in this country, but as a by-product in the metallurgy of copper. Most of the nickel is used in alloys, some of whose names—Monel, Invar, Alnico—are almost household words. Much smaller amounts of cobalt (around 5000 tons annually) are used for alloying purposes, also.

## 24.15 The platinum group elements

The six elements that fall below the "iron family" in the periodic table are generally considered together as the *platinum group elements*—ruthenium, rhodium, palladium, osmium, iridium, and platinum. These metals have very high melting and boiling points and are so unreactive that they are found uncombined in nature. They are, however, rather rare. The hardness and chemical inertness of these metals have led to their use in jewelry, in special laboratory equipment such as crucibles, and in special alloys used for phonograph needles and fountain pen points. They are also used as catalysts—platinum, especially, is so used in the manufacture of both sulfuric acid and nitric acid.

## 24.16 The coinage metals: copper, silver, gold

Copper, silver, and gold have been known since antiquity in the free state. Gold and silver found use in coins in early civilizations. Then the discovery was made that copper, added to such coins, made the coins less costly to produce and increased their circulation life because of increased hardness. Today, American coinage silver is an alloy containing 90 per cent silver and 10 per cent copper. Sterling silver contains 92.5 per cent silver and 7.5 per cent copper.

Native silver and gold are still economically very important, though silver is also found in important ore deposits of *argentite*, $Ag_2S$. In addition, the two elements are significant by-products of the metallurgy of copper. The uses of gold are based on its scarcity, color, and luster, and most of the gold produced is used in jewelry. However, most importantly, gold has long been used by nations of the world to stabilize their currencies. Pure gold is known as 24-karat gold. A gold alloy containing 25 per cent copper is 18-karat gold ($\frac{18}{24}$, or 75 per cent pure).

Egyptian gold ring money, ca. 1000 B.C.

Aztec gold bell money, pre-Columbian

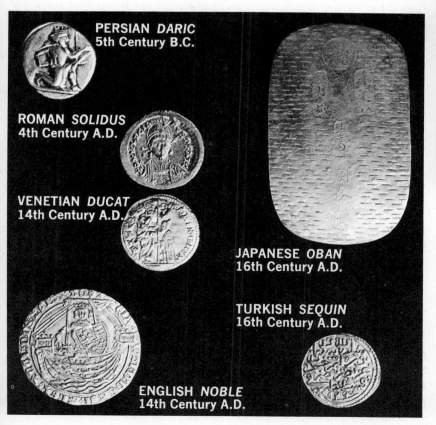

PERSIAN *DARIC*
5th Century B.C.

ROMAN *SOLIDUS*
4th Century A.D.

VENETIAN *DUCAT*
14th Century A.D.

JAPANESE *OBAN*
16th Century A.D.

TURKISH *SEQUIN*
16th Century A.D.

ENGLISH *NOBLE*
14th Century A.D.

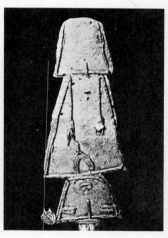

Gold, the coinage metal, through history

Silver, being the best conductor of electricity among the metals, finds some use in special electronic equipment. Its greatest uses, however, are in the preparation of alloys, in silver plating, and in the production of silver nitrate. In silver plating, pure silver sheets serve as anodes, and the electrolyte contains the complex dicyanoargentate(I) ion, $Ag(CN)_2^{-1}$.

Silver nitrate is prepared by the reaction of cold nitric acid on silver:

$$3\,Ag(s) + NO_3^{-1}(aq) + 4H_3O^{+1}(aq) \rightleftharpoons 3\,Ag^{+1}(aq) + NO(g) + 6H_2O(l)$$

The colorless salt $AgNO_3$ is crystallized from the resulting solution. Silver nitrate is a mild oxidizing agent ($E^0_{Ag/Ag^{+1}} = -0.80$ volt) and is photosensitive. It is used mainly to prepare insoluble silver halides, especially the bromides that are the light-sensitive components of photographic emulsions. When silver nitrate solution is treated with an excess of aqueous ammonia, the complex $Ag(NH_3)_2^{+1}$ ion is formed:

$$Ag^{+1}(aq) + 2NH_3(aq) \rightleftharpoons \underset{\text{diamminesilver(I) ion}}{Ag(NH_3)_2^{+1}(aq)}$$

Reduction of the diamminesilver(I) complex ion by a mild reducing agent, such as *formaldehyde*, HCHO, on glass surfaces is the basis of the commercial preparation of mirrors:

$$4Ag(NH_3)_2^{+1}(aq) + HCHO(aq) + 4OH^{-1}(aq)$$
$$= 4Ag(s) + CO_2(g) + 8NH_3(aq) + 3H_2O(l)$$

Both silver and gold ($E^0_{Au/Au^{+3}} = -1.50$ volts) are relatively inactive chemically. Silver does *tarnish* in air in which minute amounts of sulfur-containing compounds are present, or in contact with sulfur-containing foods. A black film of silver sulfide, $Ag_2S$, forms under such conditions. Silver, unlike gold, will also react with warm nitric acid and with warm, concentrated sulfuric acid. Gold, in fact, will not react with any one of the common acids, but does with the solution of concentrated hydrochloric acid and concentrated nitric acid that is known as *aqua regia*. The formation of the complex $AuCl_4^{-1}$ ion is a factor contributing to the spontaneity of the reaction:

$$Au(s) + NO_3^{-1}(aq) + 4Cl^{-1}(aq) + 4H_3O^{+1}(aq)$$
$$\overset{\Delta}{=} \underset{\text{tetrachloroaurate(III) ion}}{AuCl_4^{-1}(aq)} + NO(g) + 6H_2O(l)$$

### 24.17  The metallurgy of copper

Nearly a million and a half tons of primary copper are produced in the United States each year. Thus, copper not only is the most economically important "coinage metal," but also ranks third in tonnage production among all metals, only behind iron and aluminum. Consideration of the metallurgy of copper leads to a practical summary of methods that find use in the production of many other metals.

Copper ores are first concentrated, or *beneficiated*. This is most usually accomplished by the process of *froth flotation*. The copper-bearing minerals of the ore—*chalcopyrite*, $CuFeS_2$, and *chalcocite*, $Cu_2S$—are preferentially *wetted* by oil. The metal silicate impurities of the ore, known as *gangue*, are preferentially wetted by water. If air is blown through a suspension of copper ores in an oil-water mixture, an oily froth, consisting largely of the copper-bearing mineral portion of the ore, forms, which may be separated from the gangue.

The beneficiation of copper ore by froth flotation (left). The mechanism of this process as it occurs in the beneficiation of potash, $K_2CO_3$, ores is seen in close-up at the right.

The enriched sulfide ore is then *roasted* in air to form some copper oxide, but primarily to rid the ore of arsenic and antimony impurities:

$$Cu_2S(s) + \tfrac{3}{2}O_2(g) \overset{\Delta}{\rightleftharpoons} Cu_2O(s) + SO_2(g)$$

$$As_2S_3(s) + \tfrac{5}{2}O_2(g) \overset{\Delta}{\rightleftharpoons} As_2O_3(g) + SO_2(g)$$

$$Sb_2S_3(s) + \tfrac{5}{2}O_2(g) \overset{\Delta}{\rightleftharpoons} Sb_2O_3(g) + SO_2(g)$$

The roasted ore, mainly $Cu_2S$ with some $Cu_2O$, is mixed with limestone and sand, and heated in a furnace. A calcium silicate *slag* forms:

$$CaCO_3(s) \overset{\Delta}{\rightleftharpoons} CaO(s) + CO_2(g)$$

$$CaO(s) + SiO_2(s) \overset{\Delta}{\rightleftharpoons} CaSiO_3(l)$$

The iron(II) silicate impurities remaining in the ore dissolve in the slag, which is immiscible with the liquid $Cu_2S$ in the furnace. The slag and refined ore are separated from each other, and the molten $Cu_2S$ *matte* is then converted to copper by blasting air through it:

$$Cu_2S(l) + O_2(g) \stackrel{\Delta}{=} 2Cu(l) + SO_2(g)$$

The $Cu_2O$ portion of the matte is also reduced:

$$2Cu_2O(l) + Cu_2S(l) \stackrel{\Delta}{=} 6Cu(l) + SO_2(g)$$

As the molten copper solidifies, entrained sulfur dioxide gas bubbles break through the surface, giving it a blistered effect. The final solid, known as *blister copper*, is 97–99 per cent pure. This product is too impure for most purposes, particularly for use in electrical equipment, since as little as 0.03 per cent of arsenic in copper decreases its conductivity by about 14 per cent. The blister copper is *electrorefined* to produce a final product that is better than 99.95 per cent pure. (Fig. 24.1.)

By far the greatest use for copper is in electrical transmission wires and cables. Large amounts are used in alloys, such as the bronzes

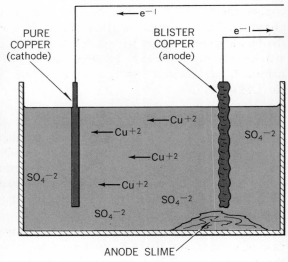

**FIGURE 24.1** A diagram showing the electrolytic refining of copper. Describe the anode and cathode reactions. (See Ques. 24.4, p. 517.) The magnitude of the electrorefining process is indicated in the photograph. Shown are blister copper anodes about to be immersed in an electrolyte bath.

Art in bronze, separated by some 3000 years. A Chinese vase of the 11th century B.C. and an abstract sculpture of the 20th century A.D.

(with tin) and the brasses (with zinc). Copperplating, in which pure copper anodes and copper(II) sulfate electrolytes are used, is an important industry. Copper and its alloys are still used decoratively in the building industry, as well as for water and gas lines. In time, such articles take on a familiar blue-green *patina*, which is due to the formation of a protective surface film of basic copper(II) carbonate, $Cu(OH)_2 \cdot CuCO_3$.

## 24.18 Oxidation states of the coinage metals

It might be expected from their electron configurations—$(n-1)d^{10}ns^1$—that the coinage metals would all exhibit a stable +1 oxidation state. Silver alone, however, exists commonly and stably in such a state. In the +1 state, the coinage metal ions show properties similar to those of the alkali metal ions. As should be expected, $Ag^{+1}$, $Cu^{+1}$, and $Au^{+1}$ ions are all colorless and diamagnetic.

The +2 oxidation state is more commonly observed in the case of copper, and the +3 oxidation state is most common for gold, though, of course, it is an easily reducible state.

## 24.19 Zinc, cadmium, and mercury

The chemistry of zinc, cadmium, and mercury tends to be the simplest among the transition elements. Except for mercury ($E^0_{Hg/Hg^{+2}} = -0.85$ volt), these elements are more chemically active than the coinage metals. Each of the metals forms a +2 oxidation state, while mercury also exhibits a *dimeric* +1 oxidation state, $Hg_2^{+2}$. Cadmium and zinc compounds resemble each other closely, though zinc hydroxide, unlike cadmium hydroxide, is amphiprotic.

More than a half million tons of primary zinc are produced annually in this country, mainly from ores containing the mineral *sphalerite*, or *zinc blende*, ZnS. The ore is concentrated by flotation, roasted to the oxide, and then reduced, or *smelted*, by coke:

$$\mathrm{ZnS}(s) + \tfrac{3}{2}\mathrm{O}_2(g) \overset{\Delta}{\rightleftharpoons} \mathrm{ZnO}(s) + \mathrm{SO}_2(g)$$

$$\mathrm{ZnO}(s) + \mathrm{C}(s) \overset{\Delta}{\rightleftharpoons} \mathrm{Zn}(g) + \mathrm{CO}(g)$$

The smelting temperatures are well above the boiling point of zinc (906°C), so that zinc vapor is distilled from the furnace and condensed. Cadmium is usually found in the same ores with zinc, and most of the 5000 tons of primary cadmium produced annually is produced as a by-product of zinc metallurgy. The two metals may be separated by distilling the cadmium (bp = 765°C) from molten zinc.

Mercury is obtained most simply from the roasting of its main ore, *cinnabar*, HgS, a dark-red mineral:

$$\mathrm{HgS}(s) + \mathrm{O}_2(g) \overset{\Delta}{\rightleftharpoons} \mathrm{Hg}(g) + \mathrm{SO}_2(g)$$

A modern use of mercury to extend man's senses. The metallic wafer is a galvanic cell consisting of a Zn/ZnO anode and a Hg/HgO cathode in a KOH electrolyte. The cell potential is about 1.3 volts, and the cell operates for at least one year.

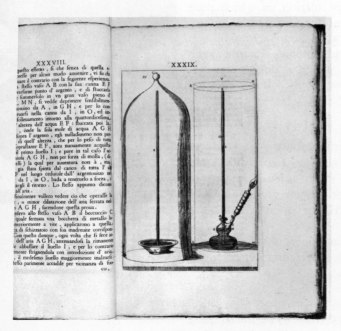

An early use of mercury to extend man's senses. Torricelli's original paper, appearing in the *Saggi di naturali Esperienze, Academia del Cimento*, Florence, 1657–1667, that described the mercury barometer. (See footnote on p. 51.)

Mercury, by virtue of its electrical and heat-conducting properties, finds important use in electrical switches and measuring instruments. It also finds use in the preparation of *amalgams*, mercury alloys of all the common metals except iron and platinum.

The major use of zinc is in the protective coating of iron. Ordinary *galvanized iron* is prepared by immersing a pickled iron object in molten zinc. Zinc ($E^0_{Zn/Zn^{+2}} = +0.76$ volt), being more chemically active than iron ($E^0_{Fe/Fe^{+2}} = +0.44$ volt), preferentially corrodes when a galvanized iron surface is broken and exposed to an oxidizing environment. The second major use for zinc is in alloy formation, particularly of the brasses.

Cadmium finds direct use as a neutron absorber in nuclear reactors, in electroplating, and, as we saw, in the nickel-cadmium storage battery. It finds wide use in alloys used in bearings, and is the starting material in the production of cadmium sulfide, $CdS$, an intense yellow powder used as a pigment in paints and printing inks.

Zinc oxide, $ZnO$, called *zinc white*, is the major industrially produced compound of zinc. It is used in paints as a pigment, and in tires as a heat conductor to keep tires running cooler—thereby prolonging their life. Mercury forms a number of interesting and useful compounds. Mercury(I) chloride, or *calomel*, $Hg_2Cl_2$, is a very insoluble salt ($K_{sp} = 2 \times 10^{-18}$) and has long been used medicinally as a mild *purgative*. Two familiar household antiseptics, *Mercurochrome* and *Merthiolate*, are complex mercury-containing organic compounds. Mercury(II) chloride, a soluble salt, is the violent poison the alchemists named *corrosive sublimate*. It is important to recognize that soluble mercury salts and mercury vapor are extremely toxic.

## 24.20 The rare earth elements

The first series of inner transition elements have been inappropriately called rare earth elements. They neither are rare, relatively speaking, nor are they "earths." They are so chemically alike, however, that it has only been in recent years that they have been separated from each other. They were first discovered in the early nineteenth century in compounds associated with two rare and complex oxide (earth) mixtures, *yttria*, $YO_2$, and *ceria*, $CeO_2$.

By general agreement, the fifteen elements from lanthanum ($Z = 57$) to lutetium ($Z = 71$) are included in this lanthanide series of elements, which is characterized by a $P$ electron shell configuration, $4f^n 5d^1 6s^2$ ($n = 0[La]$ to $14[Lu]$). Each lanthanide element forms a stable $+3$ ionic state with relative ease. Since the $4f$ electrons that distinguish one lanthanide element from the next are buried so deeply within the atoms and ions, they have very little influence on the chemistry of those elements. Thus, the lanthanide atoms and ions are very similar in their physical properties and, especially, in their chemical properties.

It is beyond the scope and intent of this book to pursue the lanthanides further. It is important to note, though, that a second complete series of inner transition elements now exists. This is comprised of the radioactive elements from actinium ($Z = 89$) to lawrencium ($Z = 103$), the actinide elements, and is characterized by a $Q$ electron shell configuration $5f^n6d^17s^2$ ($n = 0[Ac]$ to $14[Lw]$).

With this general overview of the properties of the transition elements behind us, we move on to consider in more detail a unique chemical characteristic of those elements—the formation of complex ions and coordination compounds.

## SUMMARY

More than half of the elements known to man are classified as transition or inner transition elements. These are elements in which $d$ or $f$ orbitals are partially filled. (Zinc, cadmium, mercury, lutetium, and nobelium are exceptions to this definition.) The elements all are essentially metals and exhibit a wide variety of physical and chemical properties. Among the latter is the multiplicity of oxidation states.

Compounds of the transition metals are usually colored and paramagnetic. These properties may be attributed to unpaired $d$ electrons within the compounds. The availability of unoccupied $d$ orbitals within them may account for the important catalytic properties of these compounds.

Modern technology depends on a variety of uses to which the transition and inner transition elements and their compounds are put.

## QUESTIONS AND PROBLEMS

**24.1** **a.** Write the electron configurations *that you would expect* the elements with atomic numbers 25, 42, 79, and 104 to have. **b.** For each element indicate which electron shells are completely filled, and pictorially represent the unfilled shells.

**24.2** What is meant by each of the following?

| | | |
|---|---|---|
| **a.** paramagnetism | **e.** froth flotation | **i.** 14-karat gold |
| **b.** ferromagnetism | **f.** gangue | **j.** transition element |
| **c.** sintering | **g.** smelting | **k.** scavenger |
| **d.** beneficiation | **h.** actinides | **l.** storage battery |

**24.3** Write chemical equations for each of the following. Where appropriate, use net ionic equations.

**a.** Lanthanum [$E^0_{La/La^{+3} (aq)}$ = 2.52 volts] is added to water

b. The aluminothermy of tungsten(VI) oxide
c. The electrode reactions during the discharge cycle of the Edison cell
d. The electrode reactions during nickel plating
e. The reaction of gold(III) chloride with water
f. Copper is added to nitric acid
g. The smelting of zinc oxide
h. The electrode reactions during the charging cycle of the nickel-cadmium storage battery
i. The electrode reactions during silver plating
j. The electrode reactions during copper plating
k. Illustrate the amphiprotism of zinc hydroxide
l. The tarnishing of a silver-plated spoon
m. Silver reacts with concentrated nitric acid
n. An acid solution of potassium permanganate is decolorized by aqueous iron(II) chloride.

24.4 Describe in detail the metallurgy of copper from the mining of the ore to the purified product. Amplify your discussion with chemical equations to describe all chemical changes that occur.

24.5 Criticize the name "rare earths" for the elements having atomic numbers 58–71, inclusive.

24.6 Describe a model to account for the catalytic properties of transition metals and their compounds.

24.7 Write half-reactions for each of the following couples. The acidic or basic nature of each system is indicated in brackets.
a. $MnO_2(s)/MnO_4^{-1}(aq)$ $[H_3O^{+1}(aq)]$
b. $Ti^{+3}(aq)/TiO^{+2}(aq)$ $[H_3O^{+1}(aq)]$
c. $Cr(OH)_4^{-1}(aq)/CrO_4^{-2}(aq)$ $[OH^{-1}(aq)]$
d. $VO^{+1}(aq)/VO_2^{+1}(aq)$ $[H_3O^{+1}(aq)]$
e. $Ir(s)/Ir_2O_3(s)$ $[OH^{-1}(aq)]$
f. $Mn(OH)_2(s)/MnO_2(s)$ $[OH^{-1}(aq)]$
g. $Ag(s)/Ag_2O(s)$ $[OH^{-1}(aq)]$
h. $Fe^{+3}(aq)/FeO_4^{-2}(aq)$ $[H_3O^{+1}(aq)]$

24.8 Identify each of the following by formula.

| | | |
|---|---|---|
| a. ilmenite | e. argentite | i. cinnabar |
| b. chromite | f. chalcopyrite | j. ceria |
| c. molybdenite | g. chalcocite | k. titania |
| d. pyrolusite | h. sphalerite | l. calomel |

24.9 Attempt an explanation for the following on the basis of electron arrangements.
a. Copper(I) chloride is white, copper(II) chloride is colored.
b. Mercury(I) ion dimerizes.
c. Gaseous beryllium atoms are diamagnetic.
d. Liquid oxygen is blue, potassium peroxide and oxide are white, potassium superoxide is orange.
e. Gaseous phosphorus atoms are paramagnetic.

## SUGGESTED READINGS

Moeller, Therald. *Chemistry of the Lanthanides* (paperback). Reinhold, 1963.

Neugebauer, O. G. *The Exact Sciences in Antiquity* (paperback). Harper and Row, 1962.

Prettre, M. *Catalysis and Catalysts* (paperback). Dover, 1961.

SCIENTIFIC AMERICAN

Bachmann, H. G., "The Origin of Ores." June 1960
Boehm, G. A. W., "Titanium." Apr. 1949
Brenner, S. S., "Whiskers." July 1960
Hausman, Eugene A., "The Uses of Nobility." Oct. 1964
Shelton, S. M., "Zirconium." June 1951

# The Story of Steel

Iron, the fourth in abundance of all elements, is the workhorse of the metals.
Annually, nearly 150 million tons of its great alloy—steel—are made
in the United States, greater tonnage than that of any other
metallic substance. In contrast, the *annual* production of steel in the 1860's
would barely meet today's *daily* needs.

## IRON ORE: THE BEGINNING

Large deposits of two high-grade iron ores—brick-red *hematite*, containing $Fe_2O_3$, and black *magnetite*, containing $Fe_3O_4$—are found in the United States. The discovery of these ores, which yield up to 52 per cent iron, has had a profound effect on the growth of this nation.

Iron ore is mined in twenty states. The most important deposits are located in the Lake Superior region of Minnesota, Michigan, and Wisconsin. The Birmingham, Alabama, region is also rich in high-grade ore. Large coal and limestone deposits, raw materials of steelmaking, are also found there.

Vast quantities of *taconite*, a low-grade, vitally important source of iron, surround the high-grade deposits of the Lake Superior region. Taconite consists of very hard rock formations in which iron silicates are imbedded. Use of taconite, which yields up to 32 per cent iron, along with the very high-grade ores yielding up to 67 per cent iron that are imported from Labrador, South America, and even from lands as distant as Liberia and Sweden, gives us a supply of iron sufficient to meet our anticipated needs for many years to come.

The greatest deposits of iron ore in the United States are located in the Mesabi Range of Minnesota. There the ore lies close to the surface, and giant power shovels strip it from the red earth in huge *open-pit* mines. Open-pit iron mining is the most common method used throughout the world. At the left is seen the huge open-pit mine at Cerro Bolívar, Venezuela, owned by the United States Steel Corporation. There a mountain of hematite is being leveled to feed great steel mills in Birmingham, Alabama, and Morrisville and Pittsburgh, Pennsylvania. Above, 4000 tons of ore are being blasted loose at the El Pao, Venezuela, open-pit mine of the Bethlehem Steel Corporation. At the right, the loosened ore is being loaded into a truck for eventual shipment to the huge steel-making facility at Sparrows Point, Maryland, while in the background more blasting holes are being drilled.

When deposits of iron ore are located several hundred feet below the earth's surface, open-pit mining is unfeasible. Then the iron ore is mined through shafts that are sunk into the ground. Major iron ore *shaft-mining* operations are located in Pennsylvania and in upper Michigan.

521

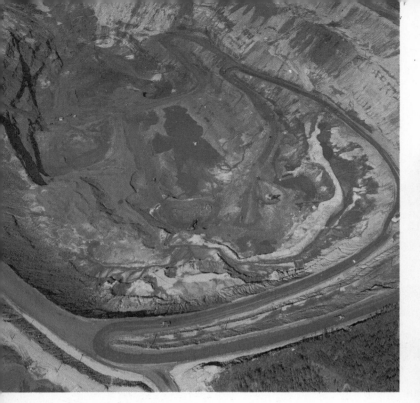

## ORE PREPARATION TECHNIQUES

To increase the efficiency of extracting iron from its ores, important ore-concentrating, or *beneficiation*, methods have been devised. These serve to separate ore-bearing mineral from the waste rock, or *gangue* (GANG), with which it is mined. When the ore differs markedly in specific gravity from the gangue, *gravity separation* is used. Another concentration process is *flotation*. Pulverized, ore-bearing rock is added to a solution that contains a foaming agent and a chemical that selectively coats the ore particles with a water-repellent film. Air is blown through the mixture and vigorous bubbling occurs. The coated ore particles cling to the rising bubbles and become a part of a froth at the surface. This froth is skimmed off for further treatment. A final beneficiation method is *magnetic separation*.

To conserve supplies of high-grade ores, a special ore preparation method known as *sintering* has been developed. With this method, very small ore particles, which may previously have been discarded as waste, are heated to the point at which they fuse into large, more easily handled pellets.

The utilization of taconite deposits requires special mining and ore preparation methods. The low-grade ore, taken from huge open-pit mines (far left), is so hard that it must be prepared for beneficiation by the severest of methods. At the near left, taconite is being pierced with a kerosene-oxygen flame jet. Blasting, crushing, and grinding follow before the ore-bearing mineral is separated magnetically or by flotation from the gangue. Sintering of the ore (below) prepares it for further processing.

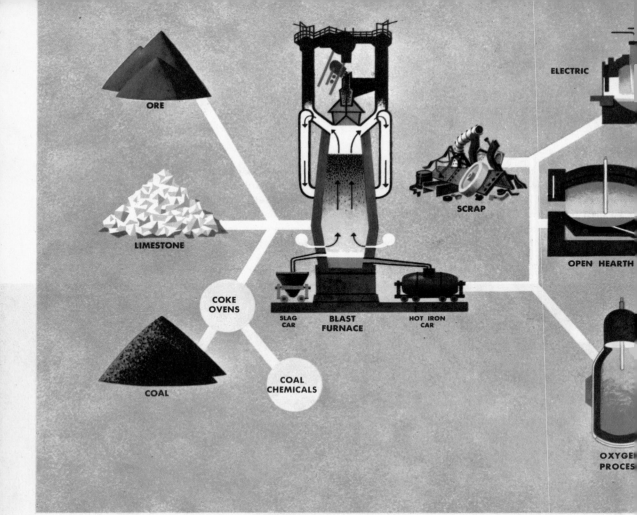

ORE

LIMESTONE

COKE
OVENS

COAL

COAL
CHEMICALS

SLAG
CAR

BLAST
FURNACE

HOT IRON
CAR

SCRAP

ELECTRIC

OPEN HEARTH

OXYGEN
PROCESS

## FROM RED EARTH TO MASTER METAL: The Chemistry of Steelmaking

The flow diagram outlines the steps in the conversion of beneficiated iron ores to steel in its major prefabrication forms. There are two chemical stages involved—*smelting* and *refining*—and relatively simple reactions occur during these.

Smelting, or the reduction of oxides, takes place in the blast furnace. A charge of beneficiated ore, coke, and limestone is fed into the top of the furnace. Hot air is blown through the bottom. Temperatures range from near 200°C at the furnace top to near 1400°C at the bottom. The major reactions leading to the formation of iron are:

$$2C(s) + O_2(g) \overset{\Delta}{=} 2CO(g)$$

$$Fe_2O_3(s) + 3CO(g) \overset{\Delta}{=} 2Fe(l) + 3CO_2(g)$$

$$Fe_3O_4(s) + 4CO(g) \overset{\Delta}{=} 3Fe(l) + 4CO_2(g)$$

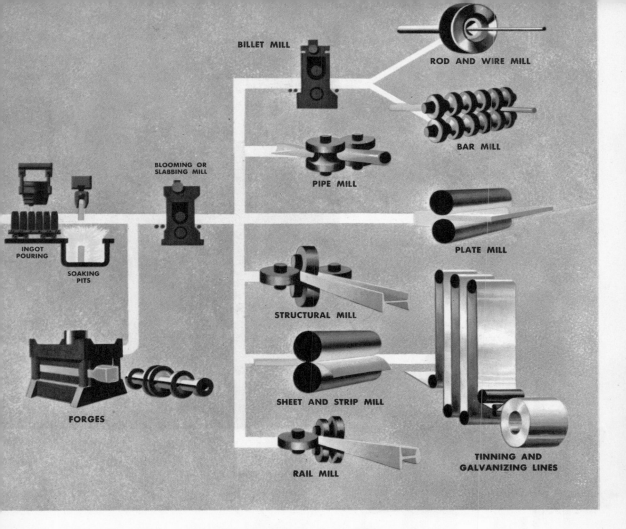

BILLET MILL

ROD AND WIRE MILL

BAR MILL

BLOOMING OR
SLABBING MILL

PIPE MILL

PLATE MILL

INGOT
POURING

SOAKING
PITS

STRUCTURAL MILL

FORGES

SHEET AND STRIP MILL

TINNING AND
GALVANIZING LINES

RAIL MILL

The limestone undergoes thermal decomposition to form lime. The lime acts as a *flux*, ridding the ore of silica impurity by forming a *slag*:

$$CaCO_3(s) \overset{\Delta}{=\!=} CaO(s) + CO_2(g)$$

$$SiO_2(s) + CaO(s) \overset{\Delta}{=\!=} CaSiO_3(l)$$

Molten *pig iron*, containing up to four per cent dissolved carbon and an equal amount of impurities, and the less dense and immiscible silicate slag settle to the furnace bottom, where they are separated.

Pig iron is converted to steel in open-hearth, electric, or basic oxygen furnaces. Since steel is an alloy of iron with up to 1.7 per cent dissolved carbon, the major refinement of pig iron involves burning out excess carbon. Unreacted silica and other acidic oxide impurities are converted to slags with a lime flux.

After refinement and the addition of selected alloying elements, steel is the product tapped from the furnaces and sent on to the mills to be shaped into useful industrial forms.

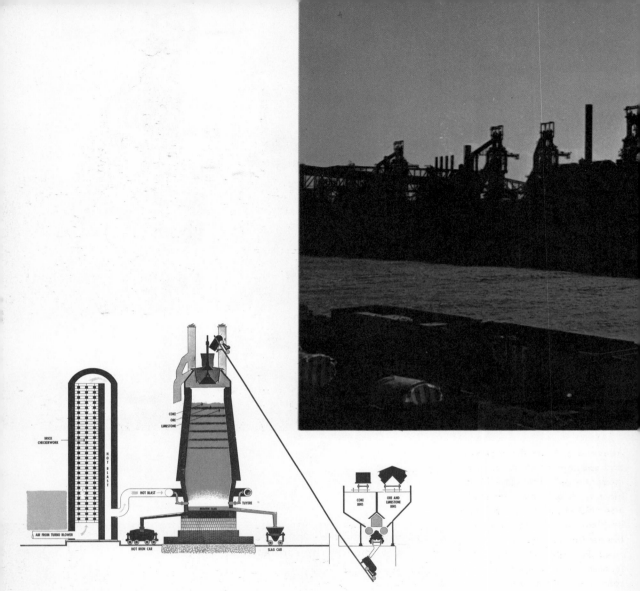

**SMELTING: ORE TO PIG IRON** The modern blast furnace, developed over a period of six centuries, is a huge steel cylinder with an over-all height that may exceed 200 feet. Leading to its top is a *skip hoist* on which *skip cars* travel to unload the furnace charge. The furnace is heavily lined with very high melting, or *refractory*, brick. At the base it is penetrated by several nozzles called *tuyères* (twee AIR). More than 100 tons of air that have been preheated to more than 600°C are forced through the tuyères each hour. A single blast furnace, tapped every six hours, can produce between 800 and 3000 tons of pig iron daily. It may operate continuously for nearly five years before it is closed down for repairs and relining.

Above is pictured the massive and spectacular complex of a modern steel plant. The huge blast furnaces tower over all else. Nearby are the tall cylindrical stoves that preheat the air for the "blast."

At the right, white-hot coke is seen being pushed from a coke oven into a railroad car. The coke is quickly drenched under sprays of water to prevent it from burning in the open air. Fourteen hundred pounds of coke are formed when one ton of soft coal is heated to drive off its volatile components. Coke is ideally suited for the blast furnace. It burns rapidly with intense heat to produce carbon monoxide, the primary ore-reducing agent of the blast furnace.

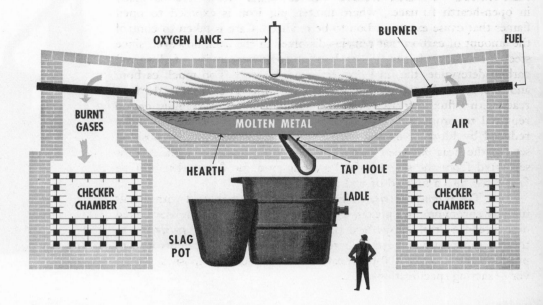

OXYGEN LANCE

BURNER

FUEL

BURNT GASES

MOLTEN METAL

AIR

HEARTH

TAP HOLE

CHECKER CHAMBER

LADLE

CHECKER CHAMBER

SLAG POT

The main components of an *open-hearth furnace* are shown above. The *checker chambers* consist of series of passages made of firebrick. The hot gases from the furnace are exhausted alternately through the two chambers, thereby heating them. The fuel gas that feeds the furnace burners follows the exhaust gases through the chambers and is thus heated prior to combustion. This preheating serves to reduce fuel consumption.

At the left is seen the *furnace-tapping* operation. A heat-resistant clay plug has just been punctured by an explosive charge. The molten steel is gushing into a ladle that is large enough to hold all that was formed in the furnace. The slag, which floats on the surface of the steel, will, however, overflow the ladle into a slag pot, or *thimble.* The ladle, suspended by steel cables from an overhead crane, will be carried to a pouring platform, where the steel is poured, or *teemed,* into molds. After the steel solidifies into *ingots,* the molds are stripped as shown at the right. The solid steel ingots weigh from 5 to 25 tons.

528

## REFINING: FROM IRON TO STEEL

Most steel is made in open-hearth furnaces, where molten pig iron is exposed to open flames that cause excess carbon to be oxidized. Care is taken to control the amount of carbon that remains dissolved in the iron, however, since steel is an alloy of iron and carbon, and the percentage of dissolved carbon determines the final properties of the steel. Too much carbon, and steel is brittle; too little, and it is soft. Other impurities in the iron react with a flux to form a slag. The eight- to ten-hour refining period required to produce a 150- to 375-ton *heat* of carbon steel may be reduced by blowing oxygen into the charge. When the composition set for the heat has been reached, the furnace is tapped. The steel is separated from the slag for final shaping into the forms that will be fabricated into a myriad of end products.

The *stainless steels*, which are carbon steels alloyed with metals such as chromium and nickel, as well as all of the recently developed high-strength steel alloys, are produced in *electric-arc furnaces*. In these, temperature and atmosphere can be very carefully controlled to produce small, 5- to 100-ton heats of steel whose compositions meet very exacting specifications.

**FINAL SHAPING** A red-hot steel ingot is subject to uneven cooling and solidification. Before it can be shaped, or *formed*, the entire ingot must be evenly heated throughout. This is accomplished by placing the ingot in a special type of gas furnace called a *soaking pit*, where it is heated for four to eight hours. After removal from the pit, the ingot is cleaned of all surface oxide scale. The uniformly heated ingot is now soft and plastic enough to be squeezed, or *milled*, into different shapes.

Milling involves passing the hot ingot back and forth between heavy steel rollers. This *hot-rolling* improves the quality of steel by making it denser, tougher, and more workable. In *continuous sheet rolling*, an application of the hot-rolling process, slabs of hot steel are rolled to specified thicknesses in an uninterrupted operation at a rate of more than 1000 feet each minute. In other hot-rolling operations, steel, passed from one milling machine to another, finally emerges as rods, bars, girders, rails, wire, and tubing. Some hot-rolled steel sheets are further processed by *cold-rolling*.

Sheets to be cold-rolled are first cleaned by pickling (see page 125), and then are pressed between rollers until their thickness is reduced tenfold. This sheet steel has a smooth, bright finish to which a protective coating of zinc (galvanization) or tin can be applied.

The newest process of forming steel is called *continuous casting*. In this process, molten steel is cast directly into molds of desired final shape. Cooling is carefully controlled to insure uniform solidification for retention of shape.

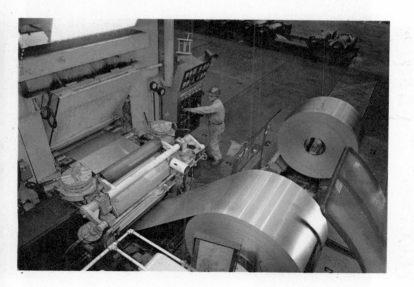

In the photo at the far left, steel ingots are seen in a soaking pit prior to their being sent to rolling mills. At the left center, the preliminary milling of a steel slab is shown. Such hot-processing improves the quality of steel by breaking down any large crystals, or *grains*, in its structure.

Cold-processing leads to steel that is stiff and difficult to work. Two heat-treatment methods that serve to restore malleability and ductility to cold-processed steel are *tempering* and *annealing*. In each of these, the cold-processed steel is uniformly heated. Its rate of cooling is then carefully controlled. The slow cooling results in a product of desired properties, while rapid cooling would lead to hard and brittle steel. Huge annealing towers are shown at the right. Upon leaving such towers, some annealed sheets are then run through a *skin-pass mill* as shown above. In these mills the sheets are again cold-rolled, not to reduce thickness but, rather, to develop a high surface polish. The sheets are then coiled for shipment.

In the top photo, a basic oxygen process furnace is seen in operation. Essentially pure oxygen is being blown through a pipe, or *lance*, into molten pig iron. In only one hour, a heat of 150 to 240 tons of high-quality steel will be produced by such a method. In the photo below, molten steel is being poured into an airless chamber. This vacuum casting leads to ingots free of trapped gaseous impurities that would greatly affect the performance of steel.

An important result of such technological advances in the steel industry as the Basic Oxygen Process and vacuum casting has been the production of *super-alloy steels*. Such steels are used in the manufacture of the giant, two-ton rings shown in the photo that introduces this essay. Those rings eventually become part of huge rockets that must withstand the great stresses of space flight. Such steels are also used for the thin metal skins of defense missiles, such as those seen at the right.

**THE FUTURE** Iron came to be used by man nearly 4000 years ago, somewhat later in his history than the use of gold and copper. It was not until the great industrial revolution of the nineteenth century, however, that man's dependence on iron and steel grew to a great extent. From that time to the present, the world's production of the master metal has grown to staggering proportions. The United States alone has an annual steelmaking capacity in excess of 200 million tons! Yet with emerging nations striving for economic development, with established economies growing to satisfy man's needs, and for the ultimate realization of man's dreams, the future will demand even more.

Modern technological advances in transportation, in space exploration, in nuclear power, and in every facet of daily life increase the demand for stronger, more flexible, lightweight, rust- and heat-resistant steel alloys. The steel industry, through chemical and metallurgical research, responds to these demands. The recently introduced *Basic Oxygen Process* for making steel more quickly and at less expense, and the dramatic *vacuum casting* of steel ingots that leads to the production of impurity-free steel alloys are but two products of research that are changing the steel industry, and the life of this nation and the world.

## QUESTIONS AND PROBLEMS

1. Distinguish among the following terms: mineral, ore, gangue.

2. Name and locate the chief iron ore deposits in the United States. How are these deposits mined?

3. What is meant by ore beneficiation? Describe two methods of such treatment of iron ores.

4. Describe the sintering process. Considering how taconite ore must be mined, why is sintering an important stage in the conversion of taconite to steel?

5. By means of a labeled diagram, describe a typical blast furnace.

6. What constitutes the blast furnace charge? Write equations for the *major* reactions that take place in the blast furnace.

7. **a.** What percentage of iron is present in the iron oxide of hematite ore? **b.** What percentage of iron is present in the iron oxide of magnetite ore?
   ANS.  **b.** 72.4%

8. **a.** What weight of air (assume 20 per cent by weight of oxygen) is required to convert a 900-ton blast furnace charge of coke, containing 85 per cent carbon, to carbon monoxide? **b.** What weight of carbon monoxide gas would be produced? **c.** How many tons of hematite ore, containing 90 per cent iron oxide, could be reduced by the carbon monoxide produced? **d.** What weight of iron would be formed? **e.** What weight of waste carbon dioxide gas would also form?
   ANS.  **b.** 1800 tons   **d.** 2400 tons

9. By means of a labeled diagram, describe an open-hearth furnace equipped with an oxygen lance.

10. Write equations for the major refining reactions that occur during the conversion of pig iron to steel.

11. One of the dissolved impurities in pig iron is tetraphosphorus decoxide. Write an equation showing the formation of the slag formed by this impurity. What general type of reaction is exemplified?

12. Describe the processing of steel from the time it is tapped from an open-hearth furnace to its final shaping.

13. What are meant by annealing and tempering? Why are these steps necessary in the production of industrial steels?

14. Describe hot-rolling versus cold-rolling of steel.

15. Write an equation for the reaction that occurs when steel sheets are pickled prior to cold-rolling.

16. How does galvanized iron corrode? How does tinplate corrode? (Refer to the Table of Standard Oxidation Potentials on pages 402–403 for your answer.)

17. Using independent sources, look up the compositions of various steels and the uses made of them.

18. During an average day, record all the items you use that are made of steel. Compile a class list of such uses.

19. What are the meanings of the following steelmaking terms: blast, thimble, teem, heat, forming, and milling?

20. Describe two recent innovations in steelmaking.

# SUGGESTED READINGS

Beiser, Arthur and Editors of LIFE. *The Earth* (LIFE Nature Library). Time Inc., 1962.

Jaffe, Bernard. *Chemistry Creates a New World* (paperback). Pyramid Publications, 1962. Chapter 6 describes "New Metals for the New Age."

O'Brien, Robert and Editors of LIFE. *Machines* (LIFE Science Library). Time Inc., 1964.

Wolf, A. *A History of Science, Technology, and Philosophy in the 16th and 17th Centuries* (paperback). Harper and Row, 1963.

SCIENTIFIC AMERICAN
Gallagher, L. V. and B. S. Old. "The Continuous Casting of Steel." Dec. 1963.

**CHAPTER 25** | # The Chemistry of

One of the most characteristic features of the transition elements is their reaction to form *complex ions*. We have come across a number of examples of such species in our previous studies—$Fe(SCN)_6^{-3}$, $Cr(OH)_4^{-1}$, $Ag(CN)_2^{-1}$, $Ag(NH_3)_2^{+1}$. These ions, and the compounds in which they are formed, known as *coordination compounds*, have become a major field of experimental and theoretical interest in the past few decades. We now consider some of the experiments and theoretical conclusions that will point up the great fascination that complex ions and coordination compounds hold for the chemist.

## 25.1 The Werner theory of complex ions

Beginning in 1893, and for the next 28 years, a comprehensive and most brilliant theory of complex ion formation was developed by the French-Swiss chemist Alfred Werner. Despite the revolutionary advances in theories of atomic structure and chemical bonding since that time, much of the modern theory of complex ion formation is based on the ideas set forth by Werner. In modern parlance, the Werner theory may be summarized by the following statements:

1. Metals combine chemically in two ways. The first of these is through the formation of ionic, or primary, bonds. The second is through the formation of nonionic, or secondary, bonds.

2. The primary bonds form between cations and anions, either simple or complex. For example, in $K_4[Fe(CN)_6]$, the primary bonds exist between simple $K^{+1}$ ions and the complex $Fe(CN)_6^{-4}$ ion. In $[Co(NH_3)_6]Cl_3$, the primary bonds are between simple $Cl^{-1}$ ions and the complex $Co(NH_3)_6^{+3}$ ion. In $[Co(NH_3)_6]$ $[Cr(CN)_6]$, the primary bond exists between the complex cation, $Co(NH_3)_6^{+3}$, and the complex anion, $Cr(CN)_6^{-3}$.

# Complex Ions

The secondary bonds form between metals, usually in ionic states, and either anions or neutral molecules. For example, in the complex $Fe(CN)_6^{-4}$ ion, secondary bonds exist between an $Fe^{+2}$ ion and six cyanide ions. In the complex cation $Co(NH_3)_6^{+3}$, secondary bonds exist between a $Co^{+3}$ ion and six ammonia molecules. In the neutral *complex molecule* $[Pt(NH_3)_2Cl_2]$, there are no primary bonds present. Secondary bonds exist between the $Pt^{+2}$ ion and two ammonia molecules, and the $Pt^{+2}$ ion and two chloride ions.

Neutral molecules or anions that form secondary bonds with metal ions in the formation of complex ions or molecules are called *ligands*. Any net electrical charge on a complex specie is spread over all the atoms of the specie, including those of the ligands. Thus, in the complex $Co(NH_3)_6^{+3}$ ion, the $+3$ charge is not confined to the cobalt ion, but is spread over the ion as a whole. Thus, the charge density of $Co(NH_3)_6^{+3}$ is considerably less than that of the simple $Co^{+3}$ ion.

3. A metal ion forms a fixed number of secondary bonds with complexing ligands. That fixed number is called the *coordination number* of the metal ion. For example, the coordination numbers for the metal ions in each of the complex species $Ag(NH_3)_2^{+1}$, $CuCl_4^{-2}$, and $Co(CN)_6^{-1}$ are 2, 4, and 6, respectively.*

---

* The coordination number of a metal ion in a complex ion or molecule should not be confused with the coordination number of cations in ionic lattices (Sec. 20.15, p. 434) or of cations in metallic lattices (Sec. 21.4, p. 459). In each of the latter cases, the coordination number is a measure of the number of nearest neighbors that can pack most closely around a central cation.

**Alfred Werner** (1866–1919, French-Swiss). Born out of a dream, the monumental theory of complex ions and coordination compounds created by Werner earned him a Nobel prize in 1913. In retrospect, he is recognized along with Kekulé as one of the founders of modern structural theory.

4. Secondary bonds have specific spatial orientations about the central metal ion, which influence the behavior of complex ions.

We now focus on the experimental observations that led to Werner's theory, and on the theoretical extensions of it that have been made on the basis of the quantum mechanical model of atomic structure and chemical bonding.

## 25.2 Experimental support of the Werner theory

Werner prepared a series of coordination compounds containing different numbers of moles of ammonia molecules per mole of the compound formed. The compounds of the series had the simplest formulas $PtCl_4 \cdot 6NH_3$, $PtCl_4 \cdot 5NH_3$, $PtCl_4 \cdot 4NH_3$, $PtCl_4 \cdot 3NH_3$, $PtCl_4 \cdot 2NH_3$, $PtCl_4 \cdot KCl \cdot 1NH_3$, and $PtCl_4 \cdot 2KCl$, in which no ammonia molecules are present. Werner measured the electrical conductivity of solutions of the solids and calculated the *molar conductivity* for each compound. When he plotted the molar conductivities against the number of moles of ammonia molecules per mole of each compound, he obtained results like those shown in Figure 25.1. He interpreted such results structurally and suggested that the seven species studied had the formulas shown in Figure 25.2. The experimental data could well be explained in terms of the number of ions that would be found in an aqueous solution of each of these compounds.

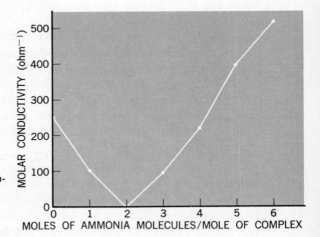

**FIGURE 25.1** Properties of platinum-ammonia coordination compounds as electrolytes

## 25.3 The nomenclature of complex ions and coordination compounds

In our previous studies, and especially in Chapter 24, the names of complex ions were given without further elaboration. At the time, such names as tetrahydroxoaluminate(III) ion for the $Al(OH)_4^{-1}$ ion, diamminesilver(I) ion for the $Ag(NH_3)_2^{+1}$ ion, and tetrachloroaurate(III)

ion for the $AuCl_4^{-1}$ ion may have seemed very complicated. Those names arise from a very systematic nomenclature, however.

1. The names of all anionic ligands end in *-o*. The names of molecular ligands are unchanged, with the exceptions that water is named *aquo* and ammonia is named *ammine*.
2. All complex ions or molecules are named as *single words*, with the names of the ligands present preceding the name of the metal ion. Anionic ligands are named *before* neutral ligands, and, if more than one ligand of either type is present, they are named in *alphabetical order*. Some examples:

$[Pt(NH_3)_4Cl_2]^{+2}$ = dichlorotetrammineplatinum(IV) ion

$[Pt(NH_3)_4(NO_2)(Cl)]^{+2}$ = chloronitrotetrammineplatinum(IV) ion

$[Co(NH_3)_2(NO_2)_2(CN)_2]^{-1}$ = dicyanodinitrodiamminecobaltate(III) ion

3. In complex cations and molecules, the *unchanged* name of the complexed central metal ion follows the names of the ligands. The oxidation state of the metal ion is designated by a roman numeral in parentheses. For complex anions, the same system is followed except that the suffix *-ate* is added to the name or to the stem of the name of the complexed central metal ion. In the cases of iron, copper, silver, and gold, the *Latin* stems are used. Some examples:

$Ni(NH_3)_6^{+2}$ = hexamminenickel(II) ion

$Ni(CN)_4^{-2}$ = tetracyanonickelate(II) ion

$Ag(NH_3)_2^{+1}$ = diamminesilver(I) ion

$Ag(S_2O_3)_2^{-3}$ = dithiosulfatoargentate(I) ion

$HgI_4^{-2}$ = tetraiodomercurate(II) ion

Some examples of coordination compounds are the following:

$[Co(NH_3)_2(NO_2)Cl][Au(CN)_2]$
= chloronitrodiamminecobalt(III) dicyanoaurate(I)

$[Cu(NH_3)_4][CuCl_4]$
= tetramminecopper(II) tetrachlorocuprate(II)

$[Co(NH_3)_5(SO_4)]_2[Zn(OH)_4]$
= sulfatopentamminecobalt(III) tetrahydroxozincate(II)

$[Co(NH_3)_4(CO_3)]_3[Fe(CN)_6]$
= carbonatotetramminecobalt(III) hexacyanoferrate(III)

## 25.4 A model for complex ion formation

One of several modern interpretations of the bonding in complex species involves the concept of orbital hybridization. The interpretation

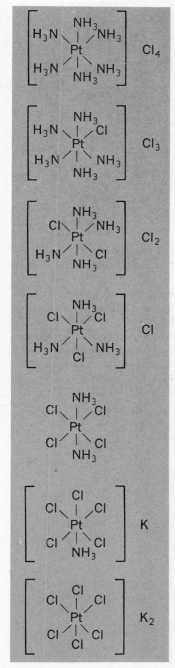

**FIGURE 25.2** Models for platinum-ammonia coordination compounds based on their properties as electrolytes

is somewhat more complicated than our previous considerations of hybrid bonding orbital formation, introduced in Chapters 11 and 20. Then it was only necessary to consider a change in electron configuration within a single atom to arrive at the hybrid bonding orbital model. In dealing with complex species, however, we must consider changes in the electron configurations of both the metal atom and an atom of the ligand. We choose the complex hexamminecobalt(III) ion to begin our interpretation.

The electron configuration of the neutral cobalt atom in the ground state, including the orbitals present in the highest energy shell of that state, is

$$_{27}Co \qquad 1s^2 2s^2 2p^6 3s^2 3p^6 3d^7 4s^2 4p^0.$$

On ionization, this becomes

$$_{27}Co^{+3} \qquad 1s^2 2s^2 2p^6 3s^2 3p^6 3d^6 4s^0 4p^0.$$

Pictorially, the orbital occupancy in the highest energy shell for the simple $Co^{+3}$ ion is

$$Co^{+3} \quad \frac{\uparrow\downarrow}{3d}\,\frac{\uparrow}{3d}\,\frac{\uparrow}{3d}\,\frac{\uparrow}{3d}\,\frac{\uparrow}{3d}\,\Big|\,\frac{}{4s}\,\Big|\,\frac{}{4p}\,\frac{}{4p}\,\frac{}{4p}.$$

This representation is supported by the experimental fact that the simple $Co^{+3}$ ion exhibits paramagnetism indicative of the presence of four unpaired electrons.

Two additional experimental facts—the stable existence of the complex $Co(NH_3)_6^{+3}$ ion, and the *diamagnetic* nature of that ion—must be explained in terms of changes in the orbital occupancy of the simple $Co^{+3}$ ion.

First, the existence of the $Co(NH_3)_6^{+3}$ ion requires a significant change in the electron configuration of the nitrogen atom in the ammonia molecule ligands. Recall that in explaining the structure of the ammonia molecule a covalent bonding model involving the overlap of $s$ bonding orbitals of hydrogen atoms with $sp^3$ hybrid bonding orbitals of nitrogen was successful. (See Fig. 20.15, p. 431.) The remaining $sp^3$ hybrid orbital in the ammonia molecule was occupied by a *lone pair of electrons of coupled spin* and, accordingly, was a *nonbonding orbital*. Therefore, in the formation of the $Co(NH_3)_6^{+3}$ ion, in which ammonia molecules are bonded to a $Co^{+3}$ ion, the nature of the lone pairs of electrons in the ammonia molecules must change from one of nonbonding to one of bonding.

The next point to consider is that of the diamagnetism of the $Co(NH_3)_6^{+3}$ ion. To explain this phenomenon, characteristic of the presence of pairs of electrons with coupled spin, we must first assume that the four unpaired electrons of the simple $Co^{+3}$ ion pair to form an intermediate $(Co^{+3})$ ion:

$$(Co^{+3}) \quad \underset{3d}{\underline{\uparrow\downarrow}}\;\underset{3d}{\underline{\uparrow\downarrow}}\;\underset{3d}{\underline{\uparrow\downarrow}}\;\underset{3d}{\underline{\quad}}\;\underset{3d}{\underline{\quad}}\;\Big|\;\underset{4s}{\underline{\quad}}\;\Big|\;\underset{4p}{\underline{\quad}}\;\underset{4p}{\underline{\quad}}\;\underset{4p}{\underline{\quad}}$$

We note the presence of six orbitals that *could* account for the six covalent bonds implied by the formula $Co(NH_3)_6^{+3}$. There is, however, one more experimental fact to note before we can fit all the pieces of our puzzle together.

In the chemical reactions of the $Co(NH_3)_6^{+3}$ ion, it is not possible to distinguish differences among the six ammonia molecules. They are chemically equivalent. Therefore, they must each be bonded in the same way to the $(Co^{+3})$ ion. At the moment, however, we have six orbitals of slightly different energies available in the $(Co^{+3})$ ion. But we must have six orbitals of exactly the same energy present in the $Co(NH_3)_6^{+3}$ ion. Our model now takes its final form.

We *assume* that in the formation of the $Co(NH_3)_6^{+3}$ ion the following must occur.

1. The lone pairs of electrons in the nonbonding $sp^3$ orbitals of six ammonia molecules become uncoupled.

2. One of the electrons of each of the six uncoupled pairs occupies one of the six bonding orbitals, of equivalent energy, in the $(Co^{+3})$ ion. Each of these orbitals, mathematical combinations of two $d$, one $s$, and three $p$ orbitals, is, therefore, a $d^2sp^3$ orbital:

$$(Co^{+3}) \quad \underset{3d}{\underline{\uparrow\downarrow}}\;\underset{3d}{\underline{\uparrow\downarrow}}\;\underset{3d}{\underline{\uparrow\downarrow}}\;\Big|\;\underset{d^2sp^3}{\underline{\uparrow}}\;\underset{d^2sp^3}{\underline{\uparrow}}\;\underset{d^2sp^3}{\underline{\uparrow}}\;\underset{d^2sp^3}{\underline{\uparrow}}\;\underset{d^2sp^3}{\underline{\uparrow}}\;\underset{d^2sp^3}{\underline{\uparrow}}$$

3. Finally, the remaining uncoupled electron in each of the six ammonia molecules is in an $sp^3$ bonding orbital that overlaps with a $d^2sp^3$ bonding orbital in the $(Co^{+3})$ ion to form the $Co(NH_3)_6^{+3}$ ion. As a result, coupling of electrons occurs and a diamagnetic ion results:

$$Co(NH_3)_6^{+3} \quad \underset{3d}{\underline{\uparrow\downarrow}}\;\underset{3d}{\underline{\uparrow\downarrow}}\;\underset{3d}{\underline{\uparrow\downarrow}}\;\Big|\;\underset{d^2sp^3}{\underline{\uparrow\downarrow}}\;\underset{d^2sp^3}{\underline{\uparrow\downarrow}}\;\underset{d^2sp^3}{\underline{\uparrow\downarrow}}\;\underset{d^2sp^3}{\underline{\uparrow\downarrow}}\;\underset{d^2sp^3}{\underline{\uparrow\downarrow}}\;\underset{d^2sp^3}{\underline{\uparrow\downarrow}}$$

To arrive at this final model, several large creative leaps of the imagination were taken. The validity of any theoretical model, no matter how contrived it may seem, lies in its successful use in the interpretation of experimental fact. The model that we developed is a very successful one. It is not, however, the ultimate model to explain complex ion formation. In fact, it is but one of three different models that are being successfully applied in understanding the nature of complex ions.

### 25.5 A model for the bonding in Ni(CN)₄⁻² ion

In a number of its complex ions, the $Ni^{+2}$ ion exhibits a coordination number of 4. We might analyze one such specie, the tetracyanonickelate(II) ion, to determine another type of orbital hybridization commonly invoked. The electron configuration of a nickel atom is

$$_{28}Ni \qquad 1s^2 2s^2 2p^6 3s^2 3p^6 3d^8 4s^2 4p^0.$$

On ionization, this becomes

$$_{28}Ni^{+2} \qquad 1s^2 2s^2 2p^6 3d^8 4s^0 4p^0 \rightarrow \underset{3d}{\uparrow\downarrow}\ \underset{3d}{\uparrow\downarrow}\ \underset{3d}{\uparrow\downarrow}\ \underset{3d}{\uparrow}\ \underset{3d}{\uparrow}\ \Big|\ \underset{4s}{}\ \Big|\ \underset{4p}{}\ \underset{4p}{}\ \underset{4p}{}\ .$$

The tetracyanonickelate(II) ion is experimentally diamagnetic and contains four equivalent cyanide ligands. Accordingly, the bonding in the $Ni(CN)_4{}^{-2}$ ion may be pictured as

$$Ni(CN)_4{}^{-2} \qquad \underset{3d}{\uparrow\downarrow}\ \underset{3d}{\uparrow\downarrow}\ \underset{3d}{\uparrow\downarrow}\ \underset{3d}{\uparrow\downarrow}\ \Big|\ \underset{(dsp^2)}{\uparrow\downarrow}\ \underset{(dsp^2)}{\uparrow\downarrow}\ \underset{(dsp^2)}{\uparrow\downarrow}\ \underset{(dsp^2)}{\uparrow\downarrow}\ \Big|\ \underset{4p}{}\ .$$

Observe that in this case we assume that the formation of four $dsp^2$ hybrid orbitals occurs, thereby leaving one of the $4p$ orbitals available for further bonding.

### 25.6 A model for the bonding in Zn(NH₃)₄⁺²

Zinc, as a transition metal with a filled $d$ subshell, cannot be expected to form hybrid orbitals involving $d$ orbitals. For the tetramminezinc(II) ion, therefore, in which the zinc ion is exhibiting coordination number 4, hybrid orbitals of a type other than $dsp^2$ will be involved. In considering the orbital occupancy of the simple $Zn^{+2}$ ion,

$$_{30}Zn^{+2} \qquad 1s^2 2s^2 2p^6 3s^2 3p^6 3d^{10} 4s^0 4p^0,$$

and, especially, the highest energy orbitals available for bonding,

$$Zn^{+2} \qquad \underset{3d}{\uparrow\downarrow}\ \underset{3d}{\uparrow\downarrow}\ \underset{3d}{\uparrow\downarrow}\ \underset{3d}{\uparrow\downarrow}\ \underset{3d}{\uparrow\downarrow}\ \Big|\ \underset{4s}{}\ \Big|\ \underset{4p}{}\ \underset{4p}{}\ \underset{4p}{}\ ,$$

it becomes quickly apparent that the familiar $sp^3$ orbital hybridization can be used to explain the properties of the $Zn(NH_3)_4{}^{+2}$ ion:

$$Zn(NH_3)_4{}^{+2} \qquad \underset{3d}{\uparrow\downarrow}\ \underset{3d}{\uparrow\downarrow}\ \underset{3d}{\uparrow\downarrow}\ \underset{3d}{\uparrow\downarrow}\ \underset{3d}{\uparrow\downarrow}\ \Big|\ \underset{(sp^3)}{\uparrow\downarrow}\ \underset{(sp^3)}{\uparrow\downarrow}\ \underset{(sp^3)}{\uparrow\downarrow}\ \underset{(sp^3)}{\uparrow\downarrow}\ $$

Thus, in dealing with metal ions that exhibit coordination number 4 in complex form, two possible orbital hybridizations may present themselves, $dsp^2$ or $sp^3$.

### 25.7 The case of [Pt(NH₃)₂Cl₂] and structural isomerism

The neutral complex molecule dichlorodiammineplatinum(II) can be synthesized in two ways:

$$(PtCl_4)^{-2}(aq) + 2NH_3(aq) = [Pt(NH_3)_2Cl_2](s) + 2Cl^{-1}(aq)$$

$$Pt(NH_3)_4^{+2}(aq) + 2Cl^{-1}(aq) = [Pt(NH_3)_2Cl_2](s) + 2NH_3(aq)$$

The cream-colored solids formed in each reaction appear physically alike, but are found to have different solubilities as well as different chemical properties. Quite obviously, there is a fundamental difference between the two forms of the neutral $[Pt(NH_3)_2Cl_2]$ molecule.

In considering the electron configuration of the platinum atom,

$$_{78}Pt \quad 1s^2 2s^2 2p^6 3s^2 3p^6 3d^{10} 4s^2 4p^6 4d^{10} 4f^{14} 5s^2 5p^6 5d^9 6s^1 6p^0,$$

and, especially, the highest energy orbitals available for bonding in the $Pt^{+2}$ ion,

$$Pt^{+2} \quad \underset{5d}{\uparrow\downarrow}\ \underset{5d}{\uparrow\downarrow}\ \underset{5d}{\uparrow\downarrow}\ \underset{5d}{\uparrow}\ \underset{5d}{\uparrow}\ \bigg|\ \underset{6s}{\quad}\ \bigg|\ \underset{6p}{\quad}\ \underset{6p}{\quad}\ \underset{6p}{\quad},$$

the two possible orbital hybridizations for the $Pt^{+2}$ ion with coordination number 4 in $[Pt(NH_3)_2Cl_2]$ are

$$[Pt(NH_3)_2Cl_2] \quad \underset{5d}{\uparrow\downarrow}\ \underset{5d}{\uparrow\downarrow}\ \underset{5d}{\uparrow\downarrow}\ \underset{5d}{\uparrow\downarrow}\ \bigg|\ \underset{(dsp^2)}{\uparrow\downarrow}\ \underset{(dsp^2)}{\uparrow\downarrow}\ \underset{(dsp^2)}{\uparrow\downarrow}\ \underset{(dsp^2)}{\uparrow\downarrow}\ \bigg|\ \underset{6p}{\quad}$$

and $[Pt(NH_3)_2Cl_2]$

$$\underset{5d}{\uparrow\downarrow}\ \underset{5d}{\uparrow\downarrow}\ \underset{5d}{\uparrow\downarrow}\ \underset{5d}{\uparrow}\ \underset{5d}{\uparrow}\ \bigg|\ \underset{(sp^3)}{\uparrow\downarrow}\ \underset{(sp^3)}{\uparrow\downarrow}\ \underset{(sp^3)}{\uparrow\downarrow}\ \underset{(sp^3)}{\uparrow\downarrow}.$$

The simplest experimental measurement leading to a choice of a bonding model for $[Pt(NH_3)_2Cl_2]$ is that of its magnetic properties. When each of the two forms of $[Pt(NH_3)_2Cl_2]$ is studied, both are found to be *diamagnetic*. Thus, in both cases, it is the $dsp^2$ hybrid orbital model showing no unpaired electrons that must be chosen over the $sp^3$ hybrid orbital model with two unpaired electrons present.

Now we face the problem of determining how the $dsp^2$ hybrid orbital model can account for two different forms of $[Pt(NH_3)_2Cl_2]$. We recall that hybrid bonding orbitals have definite spatial orientations. (Secs. 20.10 and 20.11.) When the probability distributions of four $dsp^2$ hybrid orbitals are calculated, a *square planar* spatial orientation results. (Fig. 25.3.) We may, therefore, arrive at two different structures for complex species involving $dsp^2$ hybrid orbitals. The two possible structures for $[Pt(NH_3)_2Cl_2]$ are shown in Figure 25.4. In the one at the top, the ammonia molecules are farther apart than in the one at the bottom. This would account for differences in chemical properties between the two forms of $[Pt(NH_3)_2Cl_2]$. For example, one form of the molecule reacts with *ethylenediamine*, $H_2NCH_2CH_2NH_2$, to yield the neutral complex molecule, $[Pt(H_2NCH_2CH_2NH_2)Cl_2]$, dichloroethylenediamineplatinum(II). The other form does not react. Each ethylenediamine molecule acts as a donor of *two pairs* of electrons—those available in each nitrogen atom of the molecule—in complex ion

**FIGURE 25.3** $dsp^2$ hybrid orbitals: a model for square planar complex ions

**FIGURE 25.4** Square planar structures for $[Pt(NH_3)_2Cl_2]$

formation. The distance between the two nitrogen atoms is large enough for substitution of two adjacent ammonia molecules in $[Pt(NH_3)_2Cl_2]$ to occur, but not for substitution of two opposite ammonia molecules. Thus, the form of $[Pt(NH_3)_2Cl_2]$ shown at the top of Figure 25.4 must be the one that reacts with ethylenediamine.

$$
\begin{array}{c}
\text{Cl}\diagdown\text{Pt}\diagup\text{NH}_3 \\
\text{Cl}\diagup\quad\diagdown\text{NH}_3
\end{array}
\;+\;
\begin{array}{c}
\text{H}_2\text{N}\diagdown\text{CH}_2 \\
\quad\;\;|\\
\text{H}_2\text{N}\diagup\text{CH}_2
\end{array}
\;\longrightarrow\;
\begin{array}{c}
\text{Cl}\diagdown\text{Pt}\diagup\overset{\text{H}_2}{\text{N}}\diagdown\text{CH}_2 \\
\text{Cl}\diagup\quad\diagdown\underset{\text{H}_2}{\text{N}}\diagup\text{CH}_2
\end{array}
\;+\;2\text{NH}_3
$$

$$
\begin{array}{c}
\text{Cl}\diagdown\text{Pt}\diagup\text{NH}_3 \\
\text{H}_3\text{N}\diagup\quad\diagdown\text{Cl}
\end{array}
\;+\;
\begin{array}{c}
\text{H}_2\text{N}\diagdown\text{CH}_2 \\
\quad\;\;|\\
\text{H}_2\text{N}\diagup\text{CH}_2
\end{array}
\;\longrightarrow\;\text{NO REACTION}
$$

The two compounds shown in Figure 25.4 have the same sets of atoms and the same sets of bonds among those atoms. The difference between the two compounds lies in the spatial orientation of the bonds. The compounds are said to be *geometrical isomers* of each other.* The one in which the ammonia molecules occupy adjacent vertices of the square planar configuration is called the *cis* isomer, from the Latin word meaning "on this side." The structure in which ammonia molecules occupy vertices that are diagonally opposite is called the *trans* isomer, from the Latin word meaning "across."

Each of the bonds in $[Pt(NH_3)_2Cl_2]$ is polar, the Pt-Cl bonds being more so than the Pt-NH$_3$ bonds. In trans-$[Pt(NH_3)_2Cl_2]$, it is apparent that bonds of equal polarity are oriented in opposite directions, thus leading to an over-all nonpolar molecule. Cis-$[Pt(NH_3)_2Cl_2]$, on the other hand, should have a residual dipole moment, with the chlorine side of the molecule being more negative than the ammonia. Dipole moment measurements verify these conclusions which, of themselves, account for the greater solubility in water of the cis isomer compared to the trans isomer.

The existence of geometrical isomers for certain complex species was predicted by Werner. The isolation and characterization of such isomers has been one of the convincing supporting facts of his entire theory. For complexes in which the central metal ion has a coordination number of 6, $d^2sp^3$ hybrid bonds may be shown to be *octahedrally* oriented. For octahedral complexes of the type $Ma_2b_4$,

---

*Isomerism, the existence of compounds having the same molecular formula but different properties, is primarily a feature of organic chemistry, and therefore is described more fully in Chapter 29.

where $a$ and $b$ are different ligands, the existence of cis-trans isomers is predicted. (Fig. 25.5.) There are many examples of such isomers, such as cis- and trans- $[Pt(NH_3)_4Cl_2]^{+2}$, dichlorotetrammineplatinum(IV) ion. (Fig. 25.6.)

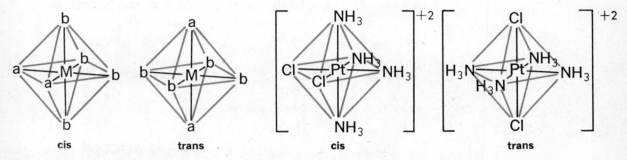

**FIGURE 25.5** *Cis-trans* isomeric forms for octahedral complexes

**FIGURE 25.6** Structural formulas for *cis-* and *trans-* $[Pt(NH_3)_4Cl_2]^{+2}$

## 25.8 Chelates

Ethylenediamine is an example of one of a number of large organic molecules that have more than one atom per molecule that can donate an electron pair in the formation of complex ions. Such ligands are called *multidentate*, from the Latin words meaning "many teeth." In particular, ethylenediamine is a *bidentate* ligand. The complex species formed by multidentate ligands are usually more stable than complexes formed by unidentate ligands. For example, while a solution that is $0.001M$ in tetramminezinc(II) ion is about 8 per cent dissociated at $25.0°C$, a solution that is $0.001M$ in bis(ethylenediamine)zinc(II) ion* is only about 1 per cent dissociated. The large number of quite stable complex species formed from metal ions and multidentate ligands are known as *chelates* (**KEY** lates). The word chelate comes from the Greek word *chelos* meaning "crab's claw." The structures of bis-(ethylenediamine)zinc(II) ion and trans-dichlorobis(ethylenediamine)-cobalt(III) ion indicate the appropriateness of the choice of the word. (Fig. 25.7.)

In recent years, chelation has come to play an important role in analytical chemistry, particularly in the quantitative separation of metal ions of similar chemical properties. In the analytical separation of $Ni^{+2}$ ions, especially in the presence of $Co^{+2}$ ions for example, the final

---

* When a complicated ligand having a polysyllabic name is present more than once in a complex ion or molecule, the *di-, tri-,* and *tetra-* prefixes are replaced by *bis, tris,* and *tetrakis* followed immediately by the name of the ligand in parentheses. Thus, $[Co(H_2NCH_2CH_2NH_2)_3]^{+3}$ is named tris(ethylenediamine)cobalt(III) ion.

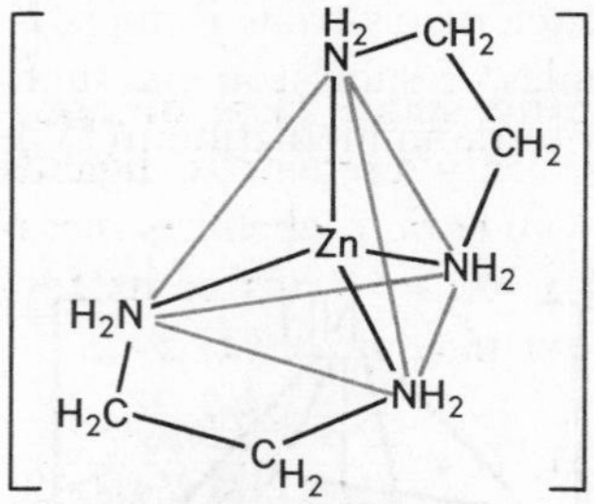

bis(ethylenediamine)zinc(II) ion          trans-dichlorobis(ethylenediamine)cobalt(III) ion

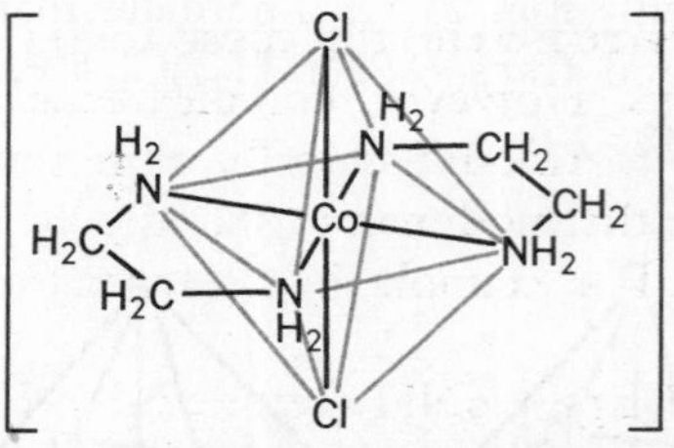

FIGURE 25.7    Structural formulas of two *chelates*

dimethylglyoximonickel (II)

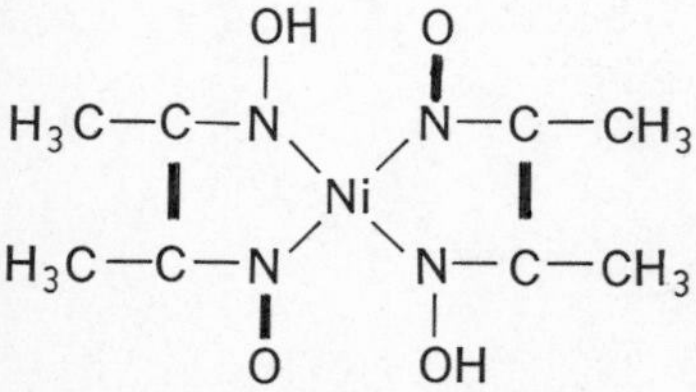

FIGURE 25.8  A  chelate  used
for analysis

step involves the formation of the highly insoluble neutral chelate di-
methylglyoximonickel(II), which is brilliant red in color. (Fig. 25.8.)

It also has been recently recognized that chelation is a phenomenon of widespread and vital biochemical significance. *Chlorophyll*, a
chelate of $Mg^{+2}$ ion, is the catalytic agent of the photosynthetic conversion of carbon dioxide to carbohydrates within the cells of green
plants. *Heme*, a chelate of $Fe^{+3}$ ion, is the biochemically active part of
the hemoglobin molecule, and is involved in the transport of oxygen
molecules in animal cells. The structural similarity between these
chelates of such critical, though diverse, biochemical functions is startling. (Fig. 25.9.)

FIGURE 25.9   Chelates of great biochemical significance

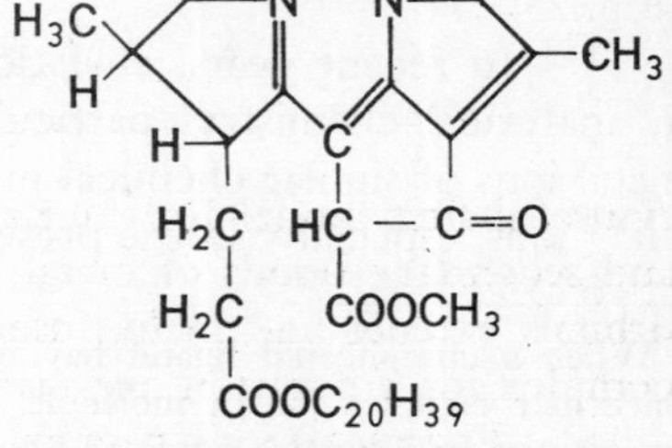

The *Heme* Molecule                    The *Chlorophyll a* Molecule

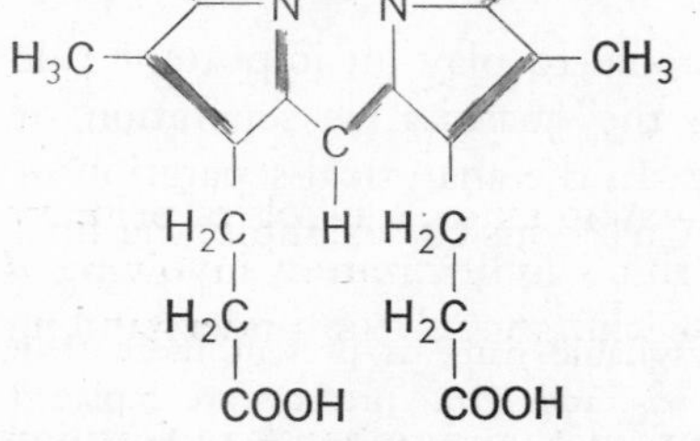

### 25.9 The stability of complex ions

Chelates represent the most thermodynamically stable class of complex ions. However, complex ions involving only unidentate ligands are also thermodynamically quite stable. By convention, chemists measure the thermodynamic stability of a complex ion in terms of its formation. For example, in the formation of hexamminenickel(II) ion,

$$Ni^{+2}(aq) + 6NH_3(aq) \rightleftharpoons Ni(NH_3)_6^{+2}(aq), \quad K = \frac{[Ni(NH_3)_6^{+2}]}{[Ni^{+2}][NH_3]^6}.$$

$K$, the over-all *stability constant* for the $Ni(NH_3)_6^{+2}$ ion, has the experimental value of $1 \times 10^8$ at 25.0°C. By comparison, the over-all stability constant for the formation of the chelate tris(ethylenediamine) nickel(II) ion has the experimental value of $1 \times 10^{18}$.

The thermodynamic stability of complex ions has an important effect on the stabilization of unstable and unusual oxidation states of some elements. The simple, hydrated cations, $Au^{+3}(aq)$ and $Co^{+3}(aq)$, are, as we have seen, very powerful oxidizing agents. ($E^0_{Au/Au^{+3}} = -1.50$ volts, $E^0_{Co/Co^{+3}} = -1.84$ volts.) Both species can be stabilized, however, in the presence of complexing ligands in aqueous solution. [$E^0_{Au/Au(CNS)_4^{-1}} = -0.66$ volt, $E^0_{Co(NH_3)_6^{+2}/Co(NH_3)_6^{+3}} = -0.1$ volt.] Such unusual oxidation states as Ag(II), Ni(III), and Ni(IV) have been formed in the presence of strong complexing ligands. The *carbonyls* are a series of synthesized complex molecules in which bonded elements are present in a most unusual oxidation state. In such volatile species as $Cr(CO)_6$, $Fe(CO)_5$, $Fe_2(CO)_9$, and $Ni(CO)_4$, each of the metal atoms is chemically bonded to neutral carbon monoxide molecules. Since the carbonyls are themselves neutral molecules, the metal atoms in carbonyls must be in the zero oxidation state.

The existence of the metal carbonyls is another long chapter in the intriguing story of complex ions and coordination compounds. There are many other chapters of equal length and fascination to the chemist from the same story. In this chapter, a beginning has been made in an attempt to understand that story.

## SUMMARY

A useful first model for the nature of complex ions involves primary and secondary bonds of metal ions. Orbital hybridization involving $d$ orbitals extends and makes more useful this model for understanding complex ion formation and structure.

For metal ions that exhibit coordination number 4 in forming complex species, a choice between $dsp^2$ and $sp^3$ hybrid orbitals may present itself. In such a case, measurement of the magnetic properties of the species may lead to the proper choice. That choice may then be verified by chemical means. The $dsp^2$ hybrid orbitals can lead to cis and trans structural isomers; the $sp^3$ hybrid cannot. Structural isomerism is also predictable for $d^2sp^3$ hybrid orbitals commonly suggested in the formation of complex species in which the coordination number of the central metal cation is 6.

The complexing agents that react with transition metal ions are called ligands. Many ligands have more than one active site for bonding with the ions. Such polydentate ligands form very stable complex species, known as chelates, with transition metal ions. Chelates find important analytical use for the chemist and are also vital constituents of such natural compounds as chlorophyll and hemoglobin.

## QUESTIONS AND PROBLEMS

**25.1**  List the main features of the Werner theory of complex ion formation.

**25.2**  What is meant by each of the following?
    **a.** coordination compound     **d.** structural isomerism
    **b.** ligand     **e.** chelate
    **c.** coordination number     **f.** tridentate ligand

**25.3**  Name the following species.
    **a.** $Pt(NH_3)_4^{+2}$     **f.** trans-$[Pt(NH_3)_4BrCl]^{+2}$
    **b.** $[Co(C_2O_4)_3]^{-3}$     **g.** $[Co(NH_3)_2(NO_2)Cl]^{+1}$
    **c.** $[Co(NH_3)_4Cl_2]^{+1}$     **h.** $[Mn(CO)_5Br]$
    **d.** $Fe_4[Fe(CN)_6]_3$     **i.** $[Co(H_2NCH_2CH_2NH_2)_2(NH_3)Cl]^{+2}$
    **e.** $[Pt(NH_3)_2Cl_2]$     **j.** $Fe_3[Fe(CN)_6]_2$

**25.4**  Write formulas for the following species.
    **a.** ammonium hexacyanomanganate(II)
    **b.** dichlorotetraaquochromium(III) dicarbonatodiammine-cobaltate(III)
    **c.** tris(ethylenediamine)chromium(III) tetrachloroplatinate(II)
    **d.** oxalatobis (ethylenediamine) chromium (III) dioxalatodiaquo-chromate(III)

**25.5**  What spatial orientations are associated with $sp$, $sp^2$, $sp^3$, $dsp^2$, and $d^2sp^3$ hybrid bonding orbitals?

**25.6**  Draw structural formulas for the following.
    **a.** cis-$[Pt(H_2O)_4Cl_2]$; **b.** $Zn(NH_3)_4^{+2}$; **c.** $Ag(NH_3)_2^{+1}$; **d.** trans-dicarbonatodiamminecobaltate(III) ion

$$\left[ \text{carbonate} = :O-\overset{\displaystyle\overset{O}{\|}}{C}-O: \right]$$

**25.7** Explain and interpret **a.** a physical measurement you might make, and **b.** a chemical procedure you might follow to help you determine which type of orbital hybridization is more plausible for the tetracyanonickelate(II) ion.

**25.8** Explain a chemical procedure that you might follow to determine whether a solution you had contained the cis or the trans isomer of dichlorodiamminecobalt(III) ion.

**25.9** On the basis of Le Chatelier's principle, explain why $E^0_{Au/Au^{+3}}$ = −1.50 volts, but $E^0_{Au/AuCl_4^{-1}}$ = −1.00 volt.

**25.10** The melting point of trans-$[Pt(NH_3)_2Cl_4]$ is about 200°C. The melting point of cis-$[Pt(NH_3)_2Cl_4]$ is about 250°C. Explain these data on the basis of the structures of the two species.

**25.11** The only complex species of its type prepared is the compound $[Pt(C_6H_5N)(NH_3)(NO_2)(Cl)(Br)(I)]$. **a.** Name the compound ($C_6H_5N$: = pyridine). **b.** Draw as many different structural isomers for the compound as you can.

**25.12** Pentacarbonyliron(0) is a diamagnetic molecule. Suggest an orbital hybridization model for its formation that is consistent with this observation.

## SUGGESTED READINGS

Basolo, F., and R. C. Johnson. *Coordination Chemistry* (paperback). W. A. Benjamin, 1965.

Martin, D. F. and B. B. *Coordination Compounds* (paperback). McGraw-Hill, 1964.

*Things perfected by nature are better
than those finished by art.*

*Cicero* (106–43 B.C.)

**CHAPTER 26** | # Carbon, Silicon, and

In moving on in our survey of the elements, we turn now to consider some of the highlights of the chemistry of the elements of Group IV. As we should expect from our look at the Group III elements, the behavior of the elements of Group IV is still less metal-like. Though carbon and silicon, alone among the members of this group, may be considered true nonmetals, even metallic tin and lead, through the amphiprotic nature of their hydroxides, show some behavior not characteristic of metals. Germanium, the middle member of the group, is properly classified as a metalloid.

### 26.1 Some properties of the Group IV elements

Some properties of the Group IV elements are presented in Table 26–1. Since nonmetallic behavior is so pronounced in this group, properties associated with metallic nature, such as ionic radius and ionization energies, are not given as they were for Groups I, II, and III. Observe from Table 26–1 that neither the melting point nor the boiling point for carbon is given. This is because a liquid state for elemental carbon is unknown. At very high temperatures, in excess of 3500°C, graphite, the thermodynamically stable form of carbon, begins to *sublime*. The energy of sublimation of graphite is around 170 kcal/mole. The very strong interatomic bonding in graphite implied by these facts is indicative of covalent bonding and a true nonmetallic nature for the element.

The definite trend of decreasing values in boiling points, melting points, and heats of fusion from silicon to lead clearly indicates a parallel increase in metallicity. The density values found for the elements tend to verify this generalization.

*550*

# Group IV

**TABLE 26–1** PROPERTIES OF THE GROUP IV ELEMENTS

|  | C | Si | Ge | Sn | Pb |
|---|---|---|---|---|---|
| Atomic weight (amu) | 12.01 | 28.09 | 72.60 | 118.70 | 207.21 |
| Boiling point (°C) |  | 2680 | 2830 | 2270 | 1725 |
| Melting point (°C) |  | 1410 | 937 | 232 | 327 |
| Heat of fusion (kcal/mole) |  | 11.1 | 7.6 | 1.72 | 1.22 |
| Heat of vaporization (kcal/mole) |  | (41) | 68 | 70 | 42.4 |
| Density (g/ml) | 2.26*; 3.51† | 2.33 | 5.32 | 7.30 | 11.4 |

* Graphite
† Diamond

## THE INORGANIC CHEMISTRY OF CARBON

In our environment, compounds containing carbon-carbon bonds dominate the living world. The study of such compounds constitutes the science of *organic chemistry*, a science that is introduced in Chapters 29, 30, and 31. There is also a rich variety in the inorganic chemistry of carbon and its compounds, and we touch upon some of that chemistry now.

### 26.2 The allotropes of carbon

As we have seen, elemental carbon exists in two allotropic forms, graphite and diamond. Both forms are giant atomic crystals in which

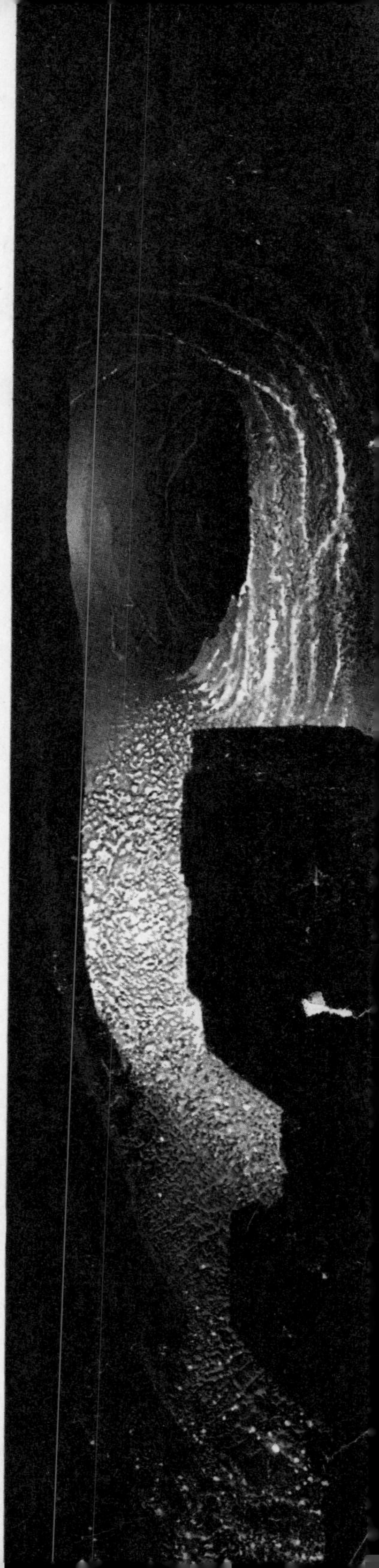

*551*

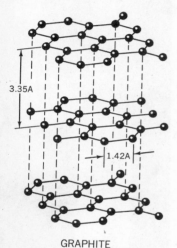

DIAMOND

GRAPHITE

**FIGURE 26.1** Models for allotropes of carbon

strong covalent bonds exist among the carbon atoms. The fundamental difference between the two forms is that the covalent bonding in diamond exists in three dimensions, while in graphite a planar structure is present. (Fig. 26.1.) Thus diamond is a closer packed, denser solid than graphite. Since the planar graphite layers are held together only by weak van der Waals forces, they can move with relative ease. Graphite's soft and slippery nature, as compared with the hard and rigid nature of diamond, can thus be understood.

In diamond, each of the four valence electrons of each carbon atom are involved in strong covalent bonding. The tetrahedral orientation of the bonds may be successfully explained in terms of the formation and overlap of $sp^3$ hybrid orbitals. In graphite, each carbon atom is bonded to *three* neighboring carbon atoms. The implication is that one of the four valence electrons of each carbon atom in graphite has properties different from those of the other three. There is no experimental evidence to indicate that it is a nonbonding electron. Graphite is diamagnetic, for example. There is evidence to indicate that it is a mobile electron, however, since graphite is a good conductor of electricity, while diamond is an insulator.

At ordinary temperatures and pressures, graphite is the thermodynamically stable form of carbon. The stable existence of diamond under such conditions is due, therefore, to the very slow rate of conversion of diamond to graphite. The slow rate can be understood in terms of the great energy requirement necessary to cleave the C-C bonds in diamond.

In 1893, to test the theory that natural diamonds formed under the great heat and pressure within the earth, Henri Moissan (MWAH san), discoverer of fluorine, dissolved pure graphite in molten iron. He plunged the molten mass into cold water, leading to a rapid contraction of the iron. The resultant tremendous internal pressure acted on the dissolved graphite. When Moissan dissolved the iron in acid and examined the residue under a microscope, he was the first to gaze upon synthetic diamonds. It was not until 1955, however, with the development of very high-pressure equipment, capable of building up and maintaining pressures measured in the tens of thousands of atmospheres, that the commercial production of industrial diamonds was begun by the General Electric Company.

Noncrystalline, or *amorphous*, forms of graphite have widespread use in industry. Coke and charcoal are two such forms. *Carbon black*, made by the combustion of natural gas in an insufficient air supply,

$$CH_4(g) + O_2(g) \overset{\Delta}{=} C(s) + 2H_2O(g),$$

is a very important item of commerce and is basic to the manufacture of typewriter ribbons, carbon paper, phonograph records, and black inks and paints. Large quantities of carbon black are consumed by the tire industry as an additive to increase the tire's resistance to wear.

The amorphous forms of carbon characteristically have large surface areas. This has led to their extensive use as adsorbents in the purification of liquids and gases. Polar molecular impurities become bonded to surface sites, or *chemisorbed,* on the carbon, and effectively removed as contaminants.

## 26.3 Chemical properties of carbon

Though relatively inert at ordinary temperatures, carbon becomes the most important industrial reducing agent at high temperatures. As coke, an impure graphite formed from the destructive distillation of soft coal, carbon is used extensively in the smelting of oxide ores. The oxidized form of carbon that results depends upon the temperature required for the reduction of the oxide, which, in turn, depends upon the chemical activity of the metal forming the oxide. For copper oxide reduction, not very high temperatures are required, and carbon dioxide gas is a product:

$$2CuO(s) + C(s) \stackrel{\Delta}{=} 2Cu(l) + CO_2(g)$$

For the reduction of the more stable zinc oxide, the temperature must be so high that any carbon dioxide formed is itself reduced by carbon,

$$2ZnO(s) + C(s) \stackrel{\Delta}{=} 2Zn(g) + CO_2(g)$$

$$CO_2(g) + C(s) \stackrel{\Delta}{=} 2CO(g)$$

With even more stable oxides, such high temperatures are required that *carbide* formation occurs:

$$CaO(s) + 3C(s) \stackrel{\Delta}{=} CaC_2(s) + CO(g)$$

$$2Al_2O_3(s) + 9C(s) \stackrel{\Delta}{=} Al_4C_3(s) + 6CO(g)$$

$$3Fe_2O_3(s) + 11C(s) = 2Fe_3C(s) + 9CO(g)$$

Calcium carbide, $CaC_2$, aluminum carbide, $Al_4C_3$, and iron carbide, or *cementite,* $Fe_3C$, an important constituent of steels, are *saltlike* compounds having ionic lattices. They react in dramatically different ways when treated with water. Treatment of calcium carbide leads to the formation of acetylene gas, $C_2H_2$:

$$CaC_2(s) + 2H_2O(l) = Ca(OH)_2(s) + C_2H_2(g)$$

Treatment of aluminum carbide leads to the formation of *methane* gas, $CH_4$:

$$Al_4C_3(s) + 12H_2O(l) = 4Al(OH)_3(s) + 3CH_4(g)$$

Of more complexity is the reaction of iron carbide with water to yield a gaseous mixture of methane and hydrogen:

$$Fe_3C(s) + 9H_2O(l) = 3Fe(OH)_3(s) + CH_4(g) + \tfrac{5}{2}H_2(g)$$

Another class of carbides is formed by some of the less chemically active transition metals. These are the *interstitial* carbides in which metal atoms are located between very strongly bonded, tightly packed carbon atoms. The interstitial carbides are very hard, have extremely high melting points, and are relatively inert chemically. They find wide use as refractories. Tantalum carbide, TaC, for example, has the highest known melting point of any pure substance—3880°C—and is used in the manufacture of specialized equipment for high temperature use.

Among the most important industrial uses for carbon is the production of hydrogen gas through the catalytic reduction of steam:

$$C(s) + 2H_2O(g) \underset{\text{catalyst}}{\overset{\Delta}{=\!=}} CO_2(g) + 2H_2(g)$$

At one time, the same process, run under noncatalytic conditions, was the source of an important gaseous fuel in this country, the mixture of carbon monoxide and hydrogen gas that is known as *water gas:*

$$C(s) + H_2O(g) \overset{\Delta}{=\!=} CO(g) + H_2(g)$$

With the discovery of vast fuel deposits of *natural gas* in the southwestern United States, the production of water gas for fuel purposes has become far less important.

## 26.4  Fuel cells

For thousands of years the energy released in the burning of carbonaceous fuels has sustained man and has been essential to the progress of civilization. With the industrial revolution of the nineteenth century, and the electrical revolution of this century, conversion of the chemical energy released in the combustion of coal, coke, fuel oils, and fuel gases—all carbonaceous in nature—has led to a mechanical age of almost unbelievable complexity and wonder. In recent times there have been developed other energy conversion processes of major consequence and potential. The production of hydroelectric power and the conversion of nuclear energy to electrical energy are two such processes. Yet the conversion to electrical energy of the potential chemical energy stored in covalent bonds of carbonaceous fuels remains the most important energy conversion of modern times. It is a grossly inefficient conversion, however, generally involving burning the fuel to heat water in a *boiler,* transferring the heat to a *turbine* through the formation of steam, and finally converting the kinetic energy of turbine wheels to electrical energy in a *generator*. At best, usable electrical energy is produced with an efficiency no greater than 40 per cent.

If we consider the chemistry involved, a much more efficient energy conversion process suggests itself. Consider, most simply, the burning of carbon as a fuel:

$$C(s) + O_2(g) \overset{\Delta}{\rightleftharpoons} CO_2(g)$$

Since the oxidation number of carbon changes in this reaction from zero in the element to an apparent value of $+4$ in carbon dioxide, the carbon is *oxidized*. Simultaneously, oxygen gas is reduced by the carbon in the formation of carbon dioxide. On the basis of the principles developed in Chapter 18, we can write two half-reactions leading to the over-all reaction:

$$
\begin{array}{lr}
\text{Reduction:} & O_2(g) + \quad 4e^{-1} \rightleftharpoons 2O^{-2} \\
\text{Oxidation:} & C(s) + \quad 2O^{-2} \rightleftharpoons CO_2(g) + 4e^{-1} \\
\hline
& C(s) + O_2(g) \rightleftharpoons CO_2(g)
\end{array}
$$

If the two half-reactions that constitute the over-all combustion reaction involving carbon as a fuel could be made component half-cells of a galvanic cell, then the possibility of the *direct* conversion of the chemical potential energy of carbonaceous fuels into electrical energy should be possible, and with a theoretical efficiency of 100 per cent.

Today, in research and development laboratories throughout the world, major efforts are being made to create galvanic cells that will efficiently and inexpensively convert the potential chemical energy of basic fuels directly into electric current. Such cells are known as *fuel cells*, and it is already clear that, under practical operation, conversion efficiencies of at least 70 per cent can be obtained from them. Thus, fuel cells offer great promise for the inexpensive production of electrical energy and hope for the efforts to conserve the fuel resources of the earth.

One of a number of modern fuel cells. In this one, which is portable, oxidation of liquid hydrocarbon fuels is the basis for the direct conversion of potential chemical energy into electrical energy.

Aside from complex engineering problems, the successful development of fuel cells lies in finding appropriate catalysts for the
electrode half-reactions as well as suitable electrolytes for the cell.
Symbolic of the new era of energy supply that will be ushered in with
the development of economically feasible fuel cells is the fact that the
Apollo spacecraft, which will carry Americans to the moon, will have
its electric power supplied by a fuel cell using hydrogen and oxygen
gases as fuels.

### 26.5  The oxides of carbons

Three gaseous oxides of carbon are known. *Carbon suboxide*, $C_3O_2$,
least common of the oxides of carbon, behaves as the anhydride of
*malonic acid*, $HOOCCH_2COOH$, and can be obtained reversibly
through the dehydration of the acid by tetraphosphorus decoxide:

$$HOOCCH_2COOH(l) \overset{P_4O_{10}}{\rightleftharpoons} C_3O_2(g) + 2H_2O(l)$$

Though the existence of $C_3O_2$ is not commonly known, its chemistry
has been widely studied. Much more commonly known are *carbon
monoxide* and *carbon dioxide*.

Carbon monoxide—a colorless, odorless, polar, diamagnetic gas
—is the product of the catalytic dehydration of *formic acid*, $HCOOH$,
by concentrated sulfuric acid:

$$HCOOH(l) \overset{H_2SO_4}{=} CO(g) + H_2O(l)$$

Since the gas is so water-insoluble, the reverse reaction does not occur.
Thus, carbon monoxide is not considered to be the anhydride of formic
acid.

Chemically, carbon monoxide is first and foremost very toxic.
Preferentially over oxygen, it combines with the hemoglobin of the
blood to form carboxyhemoglobin, and thus interferes with the oxygen
transport mechanism necessary to the sustenance of life. Since carbon
monoxide is a constituent of gasoline-engine combustion exhaust fumes,
the use of catalytic "after-burners" in the exhaust systems of automobiles is being actively urged by doctors and air pollution experts. In
such devices, the carbon monoxide is oxidized to carbon dioxide.

Carbon monoxide is used in the preparation of very pure nickel.
In the *Mond process*, impure nickel is treated with carbon monoxide
gas at 50–100°C to form tetracarbonylnickel(0), which is distilled.
When this extremely toxic substance is heated above 180°C, it decomposes to reform pure, elemental nickel and carbon monoxide:

$$Ni(s) + 4CO(g) \underset{180°C}{\overset{50-100°C}{\rightleftharpoons}} Ni(CO)_4(g)$$

The largest use of carbon monoxide is in the synthesis of methyl alcohol, or methanol. Approximately two and a half million pounds of this vital industrial solvent are produced annually from the catalytic reaction between carbon monoxide and hydrogen gases. (See Sec. 30.4, p. 620.) For such industrial use, the gases are produced via the water gas reaction.

Carbon dioxide is a dense, colorless gas, used in immense quantities to prepare "carbonated" drinks. The weakly acidic nature of an aqueous solution of the gas, often called *carbonic acid*, gives carbonated water its unique taste. Commercially, the gas is obtained as a by-product in the production of "alcoholic" beverages (Sec. 30.4), and in the production of lime (Sec. 22.7, p. 479). In the laboratory, it is released in the reaction between carbonates and acids:

$$CO_3^{-2}(aq) + 2H_3O^{+1}(aq) = CO_2(g) + 3H_2O(l)$$

The major chemical reaction involving carbon dioxide occurs in the photosynthetic process in green plants, the net reaction being the conversion of the gas and water into *carbohydrates*:

$$CO_2(g) + H_2O(l) \xrightarrow[\text{chlorophyll}]{\text{light energy}} [CH_2O](aq) + O_2(g)$$

We have previously seen the role carbon dioxide plays in the formation of natural caves. (Sec. 22.6, p. 478.) The fact that the gas is, generally, not very reactive has led to its use in providing an inert atmosphere for welding and, especially, as a fire extinguisher.

## SILICON AND THE MINERAL WORLD

As compounds containing carbon-to-carbon bonds dominate our living world, so, too, do compounds with silicon-to-oxygen bonds dominate the mineral world most familiar to man. The existence of a bewildering array of silicates in the earth's crust accounts for silicon's status as the second most abundant element in that crust. Before considering the silicates, we turn first to a brief study of silicon itself.

### 26.6 Silicon and carbon: their chemical differences

Somewhat unexpectedly, perhaps, there are major differences between the chemical properties of elemental silicon and those of carbon. While C–C and C–H bonds are formed preferentially in carbon compounds, it is the Si–O bond, and not the Si–Si and Si–H bonds, that is thermodynamically favored in silicon compounds. Thus, while methane gas, $CH_4$, is thermodynamically stable in air at room temperature, *silane gas*, $SiH_4$, is not, and undergoes spontaneous combustion under the same conditions:

$$SiH_4(g) + 2O_2(g) = SiO_2(s) + 2H_2O(g)$$

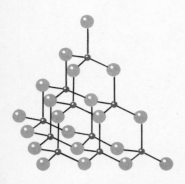

**FIGURE 26.2** A model for cristobalite, the "diamond form" of silica

A second difference between the behavior of silicon and that of carbon is that compounds containing *double* covalent bonds between carbon and oxygen are quite prevalent among organic compounds, while few have been characterized for silicon-oxygen compounds. Thus, in silicon chemistry there are no *analogs* of *aldehydes, ketones, organic acids,* and *esters,* all of which contain a $\diagup \text{C}=\text{O}$ group. (See Secs. 30.6–30.8, pp. 622–624.) This difference is most strikingly noted in the simple dioxides of carbon and silicon. Carbon dioxide is a nonpolar, linear gas molecule under ordinary conditions, in which two C=O bonds are present. Silicon dioxide, or *silica,* under the same conditions, is a nonpolar, giant molecular solid appearing naturally as *sand, quartz,* and *flint,* or, when colored by impurities, as *agate, opal, amethyst,* and *onyx.* One of the three different crystalline modifications of silicon dioxide has the "diamond structure." (Fig. 26.2.) Elemental silicon, itself, also has that structure.

### 26.7 Some chemistry of silicon

Except for its slow reaction at room temperature with strong bases to liberate hydrogen gas,

$$\text{Si}(s) + 4\text{OH}^{-1}(aq) = 2\text{H}_2(g) + \text{SiO}_4^{-4}(aq),$$

silicon is relatively inert under such conditions. At the very high temperatures obtained in the electric resistance furnace, silicon and its dioxide each reacts with metals to form both saltlike and interstitial *silicides.* The saltlike silicides are a source of silicon hydrides, analogous to the reaction of saltlike carbides to form carbon hydrides:

$$2\text{Mg}(s) + \text{Si}(s) \overset{\Delta}{=} \text{Mg}_2\text{Si}(s)$$

or

$$4\text{Mg}(s) + \text{SiO}_2(s) \overset{\Delta}{=} \text{Mg}_2\text{Si}(s) + 2\text{MgO}(s),$$

then

$$\text{Mg}_2\text{Si}(s) + 4\text{H}_3\text{O}^{+1}(aq) = \text{SiH}_4(g) + 2\text{Mg}^{+2}(aq) + 4\text{H}_2\text{O}(l).$$

Silicon reacts directly with fluorine:

$$\text{Si}(s) + 2\text{F}_2(g) \overset{\Delta}{=} \text{SiF}_4(g)$$

Corresponding tetrahalides are obtained by reducing silica with coke at high temperatures in the presence of the halogen:

$$\text{SiO}_2(s) + 2\text{C}(s) + 2\text{X}_2(g) \overset{\Delta}{=} \text{SiX}_4(g) + 2\text{CO}(g)$$
$$\text{where } X = \text{Cl, Br, or I.}$$

Silicon tetrachloride (bp = 58°C), unlike carbon tetrachloride, reacts with water:

$$\text{SiCl}_4(l) + 4\text{H}_2\text{O}(l) = \text{Si(OH)}_4(s) + 4\text{HCl}(aq)$$

The white solid formed in the reaction is *orthosilicic acid*, $Si(OH)_4$ or $H_4SiO_4$, and is the main constituent of smoke screens and "sky-writing."

The chemical reactivity of the silicon tetrahalides, when compared with the relative inertness of the analogous carbon compounds, along with the previous differences we noted between silicon and carbon require theoretical understanding. It is currently felt that the availability of empty $3d$ orbitals, not very much higher in energy than the $3p$ orbitals that are occupied in silicon, may serve to explain many of the differences observed. For carbon, the next available energy states beyond the $2p$ orbitals being occupied are the $3s$ orbitals, which are very much higher in energy.

## 26.8 Silica

While silicon monoxide, SiO, is known as an unstable gaseous molecule, it is silica that is the more important and chemically interesting oxide of silicon.

As an acidic oxide, silica will fuse and react with metal oxides. The products of such reactions are *glasses*, noncrystalline *supercooled liquids* of variable composition. Soft glass, made by fusing silica, sodium carbonate as a source of $Na_2O$, and calcium carbonate as a source of CaO, is characterized by a high coefficient of thermal expansion and shatters when subjected to thermal shock. Heat-resistant glasses, such as Pyrex and Kimax, are made with $Al_2O_3$ and $B_2O_3$. For special purposes, pure quartz and Vycor (96 per cent $SiO_2$ and 4 per cent $B_2O_3$), with extremely low coefficients of thermal expansion, are used for high-temperature laboratory ware.

Pure quartz has additional properties that make it very useful. Unlike ordinary glass, quartz transmits ultraviolet radiation and, thus, is used in sun lamps. Quartz is a *piezoelectric* substance. That is, it has the property of reversibly converting mechanical energy into electrical energy. Thus, quartz fibers and crystals find a wide application in electronic instruments.

Two chemical properties of silica attain special significance in light of the presence of silica in glass. The oxide *slowly* reacts with strong alkalies to form *metasilicates:*

$$SiO_2(s) + 2OH^{-1}(aq) = SiO_3^{-2}(aq) + H_2O(l)$$

This leads to a slow etching of the interior of glass containers that are used to store alkalies. The second reaction, of silica with hydrofluoric acid,

$$SiO_2(s) + 4HF(aq) = SiF_4(g) + 2H_2O(l),$$

is the basis of the industrial etching of glass.

Hydrofluoric acid will etch the glass exposed by the scratches being made in the wax-coated cylinder.

◀ Pure quartz being pulled from a crystal-growing chamber

When silica and sodium carbonate alone are fused, a complex mixture of sodium silicates forms:

$$xSiO_2(s) + Na_2CO_3(s) \stackrel{\Delta}{=} Na_2O \cdot xSiO_2(s) + CO_2(g)$$

A solution of these soluble silicates is known as *water glass*. When acidified, water glass solutions lead to the formation of a very gelatinous, hydrated silica. When this is dehydrated, a spongy, highly adsorptive form of silica known as *silica gel* results, which finds extensive use as a dessicant in industry. Silica gel also finds use as the filtering component of some cigarette and cigar holders.

At the very high temperatures of the electric furnace silica undergoes two additional reactions, which yield impure silicon and silicon carbide:

$$SiO_2(s) + 2C(s) \stackrel{\Delta}{=} Si(s) + 2CO(g)$$

$$SiO_2(s) + 3C(s) \stackrel{\Delta}{=} SiC(s) + 2CO(g)$$

The impure silicon is refined by a process known as *zone refining*, in which impurities are melted out of the silicon. The refined silicon, which is very costly, is used widely in semiconductor devices. (See p. 565.) Silicon carbide, SiC, a covalent carbide, is the very important industrial abrasive known as *Carborundum*.

### 26.9 The silicates

The principal structural materials in the earth's crust are silicates, especially those of aluminum, iron, and magnesium. Essentially, all the clays, rocks, and soils of the earth are composed mainly of these complex substances. Basic to each is a tetrahedral structural unit consisting of a silicon atom and four oxygen atoms that comprise the *orthosilicate ion.*

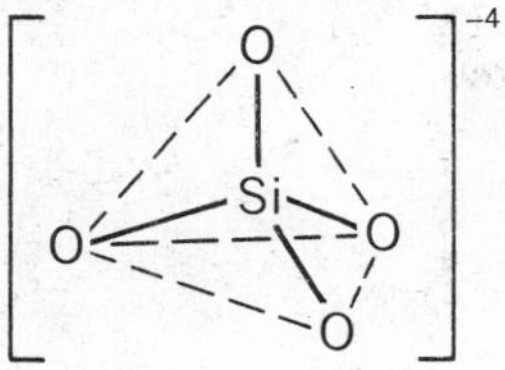

$$\left[ \begin{array}{c} O \\ | \\ O\!-\!Si\!-\!O \\ | \\ O \end{array} \right]^{-4}$$

From all experimental evidence it is apparent that these tetrahedra bond to each other to form a bewildering variety of mineral species. Most simply, mineral species containing discrete anions are known. (Fig. 26.3.) Also, silicate minerals exist in which tetrahedra are bonded in indefinite, extended, chains. (Fig. 26.4.) The giant anions in the *pyroxenes* and *amphiboles* are held together by the cations present in the crystal. When the anions are oriented in parallel layers, fibrous minerals of the *asbestos* type result.

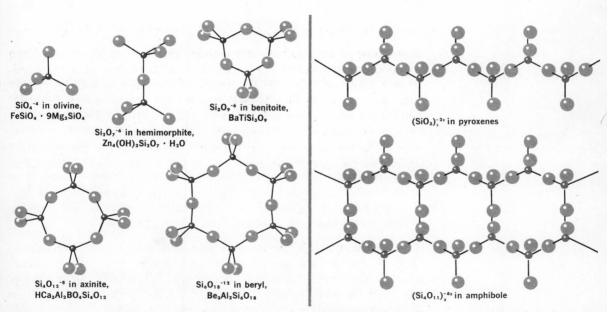

$SiO_4^{-4}$ in olivine,
$FeSiO_4 \cdot 9Mg_2SiO_4$

$Si_2O_7^{-6}$ in hemimorphite,
$Zn_4(OH)_2Si_2O_7 \cdot H_2O$

$Si_3O_9^{-6}$ in benitoite,
$BaTiSi_3O_9$

$Si_4O_{12}^{-8}$ in axinite,
$HCa_3Al_2BO_4Si_4O_{12}$

$Si_6O_{18}^{-12}$ in beryl,
$Be_3Al_2Si_6O_{18}$

$(SiO_3)_x^{-2x}$ in pyroxenes

$(Si_4O_{11})_x^{-6x}$ in amphibole

**FIGURE 26.3** Discrete silicate anions found in some silicate minerals

**FIGURE 26.4** Giant silicate anion chains found in some silicate minerals

There are soft, layered silicate minerals, like *mica* and *talc*, in which parallel layers of extended silicate anion sheets are a unique structural feature. (Fig. 26.5.) Finally, there are silicate minerals in which endless chaining of tetrahedra occurs in three dimensions to

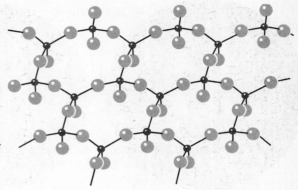

**FIGURE 26.5** Giant silicate anion sheets typical of soft silicate minerals

form giant *framework* minerals. Quartz, itself, is such a mineral. (Fig. 26.2, p. 558.) There are naturally occurring minerals having the quartz structure, in which silicon atoms are replaced by aluminum atoms. The result is that the frameworks of such minerals are, in reality, giant three-dimensional anions. Thus, cations such as $Na^{+1}$, $K^{+1}$, and $Ca^{+2}$ are associated with these minerals. The *feldspars, clays,* and *zeolites* are such *alumino-silicate* minerals.

### 26.10 Hard water, zeolites, and ion exchange

In many parts of this country, water used in home and industry contains a high content of $Ca^{+2}$ ion. Such water is known as *hard water* and can present great problems. Since the $Ca^{+2}$ ion forms an insoluble solid with soaps, the annoyance of *soap scum* is a common problem associated with hard water. More importantly, over periods of time an insoluble lime deposit may build up inside boilers and the pipes that carry the heated hard water. These deposits will not only cause a great decrease in heating efficiency, but also may result in a boiler explosion as steam pressure builds up within constricted pipelines. The buildup of lime results from the reaction

$$Ca^{+2}(aq) + 2HCO_3^{-1}(aq) \stackrel{\Delta}{=} CaO(s) + 2CO_2(g) + H_2O(l).$$

One of the ways of solving the hard-water problem is to pass the water through natural zeolites. Within the myriad channels existing in the open structure of the mineral, the $Ca^{+2}$ ions of the hard water preferentially replace the $Na^{+1}$ ions of the zeolite. Such *ion exchange* results in the generation of *soft water*, water with a greatly reduced $Ca^{+2}$ ion concentration. The zeolite may be *regenerated* into its original form by flushing it with a brine solution. The whole process may be summarized thusly:

$$2Na^{+1}(zeolite) + Ca^{+2}(aq) \rightleftharpoons 2Na^{+1}(aq) + Ca^{+2}(zeolite)$$

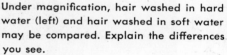

Under magnification, hair washed in hard water (left) and hair washed in soft water may be compared. Explain the differences you see.

The major problem caused by hard water. It is of interest to compare this photograph of a boiler pipe caked with lime with the photographs on page 652.

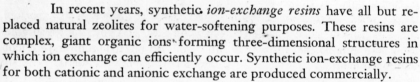

In recent years, synthetic *ion-exchange resins* have all but replaced natural zeolites for water-softening purposes. These resins are complex, giant organic ions forming three-dimensional structures in which ion exchange can efficiently occur. Synthetic ion-exchange resins for both cationic and anionic exchange are produced commercially.

Ion-exchange resins play a vital role in modern chemical research. The first quantitative separation of the lanthanide ions was accomplished through ion exchange. When a solution containing lanthanide ions is poured into an *ion-exchange column*, the ions become bonded to the anionic resin in exchange for hydronium ions. If citric acid is then poured through the column, complex lanthanide-citrate ions form. Each lanthanide ion forms a complex citrate of slightly different stability, so that the lanthanide ions become unbonded from the resin and bonded to the citrate ions in a different order. As the citrate complexes trickle through the column, they become involved in countless lanthanide ion exchanges with the column resin. Thus, though stability differences among the complexes are small, by the time the complex citrates are distributed throughout the column length, large separation factors result. The net result is that the complex lanthanide citrates come off the column at different times, and can be effectively and quantitatively separated from each other. (Fig. 26.6.)

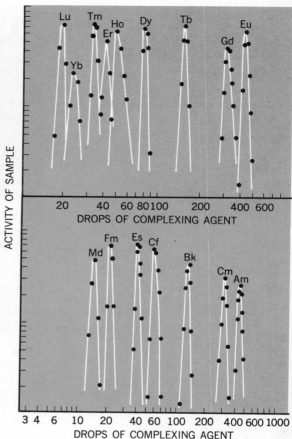

**FIGURE 26.6** Ion-exchange separation of the lanthanides (top), and of the homologous actinides. Note that in each series the elements come off the column in reverse order of atomic number. Shown in the photograph are ion-exchange columns used to produce kilogram quantities of the separated lanthanides.

Ion exchange is used industrially, particularly in the separation and purification of some pharmaceuticals such as vitamins, penicillin, and streptomycin. In some sugar mills, the final refining stages involve ion exchange. The major industrial use of ion exchange remains, however, the softening of water.

## GERMANIUM, TIN, AND LEAD

The last three elements of Group IV, while not as vitally important as carbon and silicon, find significant use in modern life. Tin-plating for ordinary "tin cans" and the continued use of the lead storage battery and tetraethyl and tetramethyl lead as antiknock gasoline additives should provide a substantial market for tin and lead metals for many years to come. Though of less importance, the use of the metals in their special alloys should also provide a continuing need for the metals. Thus, bronze, a structural alloy of copper and tin known to the ancients, still finds use in modern times. *Babbitt metal*, containing 4–8 per cent of both copper and antimony, is still widely used in lining sleeve bearings. The low-melting alloys of lead play familiar and useful roles in modern society. These alloys include *solder* (lead with tin) and *type metal* used in printing (lead with tin and antimony).

Until 1948, germanium, rarest member of Group IV, remained a laboratory curiosity. In that year, after ten years of basic research, a Nobel-prize-winning team of physicists at the Bell Telephone Laboratories developed the *transistor*, and germanium became a vital element in the progress of science and technology. Pure germanium, like pure silicon, is essentially a nonconducting material. When crystals of pure germanium or pure silicon are "doped" with traces of impurities they become *semiconductors* and, as such, can be used to replace larger, and more fragile, vacuum tubes in many types of electronic circuits. The development of transistorized devices—from the pocket radio to the modern computer—has been one of the outstanding technological feats of recent years.

Aside from the industrial value of germanium, tin, and lead, these elements have interesting structural and chemical properties, which we now consider.

## 26.11 Structural considerations

Germanium, like diamond, silicon, and *gray tin*, forms a crystal of interlocking tetrahedra. At temperatures of 13.2°C or below, tin exists in the nonmetallic, stable allotropic form gray tin. Under more usual conditions, tin exists in an allotropic form that is decidedly metallic in properties. This form, known as *white tin*, is characterized by a deformed octahedral or a close-packed cubic metallic lattice. (Fig. 21.2, p. 460.) The thermodynamic conversion of white tin to gray tin—from a soft, malleable metallic form to a hard, brittle nonmetallic form—occurs slowly in cold climates, and is a process that has long been called "tin disease." Lead forms a close-packed cubic metallic lattice in which experimental evidence indicates that $Pb^{+2}$, rather than $Pb^{+4}$, cations exist.

## 26.12 Some chemistry

Germanium and tin show similar chemical properties, which differ from those of lead. For example, germanium and tin react with concentrated nitric acid to form insoluble oxides in their higher oxidation states,

$$3M(s) + 4NO_3^{-1}(aq) + 4H_3O^{+1}(aq) = 3MO_2(s) + 4NO(g) + 6H_2O(l),$$

while lead reacts to form a soluble nitrate in its *lower* oxidation state:

$$3Pb(s) + 2NO_3^{-1}(aq) + 8H_3O^{+1}(aq) = 3Pb^{+2}(aq) + 2NO(g) + 12H_2O(l)$$

From other chemical evidence, the +2 oxidation state is most stable for lead, while only the +4 oxidation state is known for germanium. Stable compounds containing tin in both the +2 and +4 oxidation states are known. This behavior parallels previous behavior among the Group III elements where we observed stabilization of the +1 oxidation state for thallium, the last member of the group.

Both hydroxides of tin, and lead(II) hydroxide are amphiprotic:

$$Sn(OH)_2(s) + 2OH^{-1}(aq) \rightleftharpoons Sn(OH)_4^{-2}(aq)$$

$$Sn(OH)_4(s) + 2OH^{-1}(aq) \rightleftharpoons Sn(OH)_6^{-2}(aq)$$

$$Pb(OH)_2(s) + 2OH^{-1}(aq) \rightleftharpoons Pb(OH)_4^{-2}(aq)$$

Lead forms a series of strikingly colored oxides. Lead(II) oxide, PbO, exists in both a yellow and a red form. *Red lead*, or *litharge*, is $Pb_3O_4$, while lead(IV) oxide is maroon in color. The color of these oxides of nontransition elements would imply some complex bonding within them in which unpaired electrons are present. Red lead is an interesting compound in which lead is present in both of its oxidation states and may be represented as $2PbO \cdot PbO_2$. It is the important component of the standard protective paint for structural iron and steel. And thus we end our survey of the Group IV elements and turn to the elements of Group V.

## SUMMARY

The inorganic chemistry of carbon centers about its reactions with metal oxides and the reactions of its three oxides. The inorganic chemistry of silicon revolves about the Si–O–Si linkage, the most fundamental one found in the mineral world. The zeolite aluminosilicates are naturally occurring ion-exchange materials useful for softening hard water. Synthetic ion-exchange resins, functioning in basically the same way, are now major industrial products.

## QUESTIONS AND PROBLEMS

26.1  Write chemical equations for each of the following. Where appropriate, net ionic equations should be used. a. Silver(I) oxide smelted with coke; b. calcium carbide added to water; c. hydrolysis of sodium carbonate; d. spontaneous combustion of silane; e. industrial production of carbon black; f. industrial etching of glass; g. the water gas reaction; h. alumina and coke heated in an electric furnace; i. reaction of silicon with a strong base; j. alkaline etching of glass; k. the production of carborundum;

l. amphiprotism of tin(IV) hydroxide; m. germanium added to concentrated nitric acid; n. carbon dioxide gas bubbled through aqueous sodium hydroxide; o. combustion of stannane; p. formation of magnesium silicide; q. generation of silane.

26.2 Contrast and discuss the physical properties of the allotropes of carbon in terms of their structures.

26.3 Applying Le Chatelier's principle, what conditions would you establish for the industrial synthesis of diamonds from graphite: C(graphite) $\rightleftharpoons$ C(diamond), $\Delta H = +0.5$ kcal/mole?

26.4 Draw Lewis structures for a. malonic acid; b. carbon suboxide; c. carbon dioxide; d. germane; e. silicon carbide.

26.5 Draw the laboratory setup you would use for the generation and collection of carbon dioxide gas.

26.6 Explain the operation of a fuel cell that would use natural gas, mainly methane, $CH_4$, and air as consumable reactants.

26.7 Relate the properties of asbestos, talc, and quartz to their structures.

26.8 a. Describe the hard-water problem. b. Describe the softening of hard water using ion-exchange resins.

26.9 Write formulas for the *ortho* and *meta* forms of boric acid, silicic acid, and phosphoric acid.

26.10 What is meant by each of the following: a. chemisorption; b. glass; c. amorphous carbon; d. interstitial carbide; e. silica gel; f. transistor; g. piezoelectricity; h. water glass; i. fuel cell; j. zeolite; k. tin disease?

## SUGGESTED READINGS

Diamond, F. *The Story of Glass*. Harcourt, Brace and World, Inc., 1953.

Landsberg, H. H., and F. Fischman. *Resources in America's Future* (paperback). The Johns Hopkins Press, 1963.

Mitchell, Lane. *Ceramics: Stone Age to Space Age* (paperback). Scholastic Book Services, 1953.

SCIENTIFIC AMERICAN

Greene, Charles H., "Glass." Jan. 1961

Kuenen, Ph. H., "Sand." Apr. 1960

*For nitrogen plays a double role
in human economy. It appears like Brahma
in two aspects, Vishnu the Preserver
and Siva the Destroyer.*

*Edwin E. Slosson* (1865–1929)

**CHAPTER 27** | # The Elements of

The elements of Group V—nitrogen, phosphorus, arsenic, antimony, and bismuth—reflect in their properties the trends that we noted in Groups III and IV. The first member, nitrogen, is very nonmetallic in nature, its properties differing somewhat from those of the other members of the group. In this we are reminded of boron in Group III, as well as of carbon in Group IV. Bismuth, the last member of Group V, is metallic in nature, again showing the tendency for increasing metallic character in going down a group.

The increase in metallic nature in going down a chemical group is presumed to be due to the greater distance between the nucleus and the valence electrons, that is, the increase in atomic radius. This results in lower ionization energies and, hence, greater ease of metallic bonding. As we progress from left to right along a period, however, the radius may not change greatly as the number of outer electrons increases. This is reflected in an increase in the degree of covalency in the bonding, consequently lessening the metallic character. Both the brittleness and the relatively low electrical conductivity of metallic bismuth attest to the presence of some covalency that prevents the atoms and electrons from being easily moved from their positions.

The increase in metallic character going from nitrogen to bismuth in Group V is one of many interesting features of the group. We turn now to consider others.

### 27.1 Some properties of the Group V elements

A number of the properties of the Group V elements are presented in Table 27–1.

*568*

# Group V

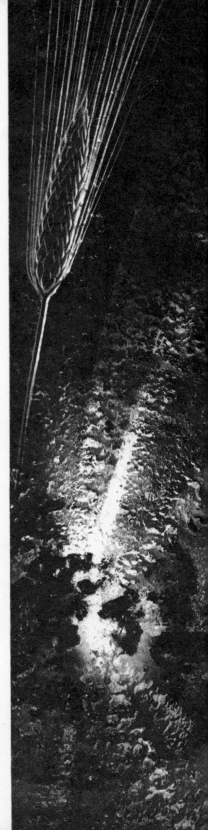

**TABLE 27–1** PROPERTIES OF THE GROUP V ELEMENTS

|  | N | P | As | Sb | Bi |
|---|---|---|---|---|---|
| Atomic weight (amu) | 14.01 | 30.98 | 74.91 | 121.76 | 209.00 |
| Melting point (°C) | −210.10 | 44.1 | 817 | 630.5 | 271.3 |
| Boiling point (°C) | −195.8 | 280 | 613 | 1637 | 1559 |
| Heat of fusion (kcal/mole) | 0.086 | 0.15 | 6.62 | 4.74 | 2.6 |
| Heat of vaporization (kcal/mole) | 0.67 | 2.97 | 34.5 | 16.2 | 36.2 |
| Density (g/ml) | 0.96 | 1.82 | 5.72 | 6.69 | 9.80 |

In the elemental state, nitrogen exists as the diatomic gas $N_2$. Phosphorus, arsenic, and antimony each form tetratomic solid species —$P_4$, $As_4$, and $Sb_4$—as one of several allotropic forms. Bismuth exists only as a metal.

## 27.2 Nitrogen: the destroyer

In Table 27–2 are given the molar heats of dissociation of a number of common diatomic molecules. Note that elemental nitrogen is, therefore, the second most stable diatomic molecular specie known. This can be attributed to the presence of a very strong triple covalent bond in $N_2$.

**TABLE 27–2** Heats of Dissociation of Diatomic Molecules

| (kcal/mole) | | | (kcal/mole) | |
|---|---|---|---|---|
| CO | 256.7 | | $Cl_2$ | 57.9 |
| $N_2$ | 225.9 | | $Br_2$ | 46.1 |
| $O_2$ | 118.9 | | $F_2$ | 37 |
| $H_2$ | 104.2 | | $I_2$ | 36.1 |

The great thermodynamic stability of $N_2$ is the reason why so many nitrogen-containing compounds react explosively. *Gunpowder,* a mixture of potassium nitrate, charcoal, and sulfur, first made thousands of years ago in China, explodes to yield $N_2$ gas:

$$2KNO_3(s) + 3C(s) + S(s) \overset{\Delta}{=} K_2S(s) + N_2(g) + 3CO_2(g)$$

The reaction is very rapid, and highly exothermic. Thus there is an immediate expansion of the gaseous products that form, which accounts for the characteristic properties of explosions.

Practically all nonnuclear explosives are nitrogen-based. Nitrocellulose and nitroglycerin, invented in the middle of the nineteenth century, are far more powerful explosives than the "black powder" of the Chinese. Since they both are also much more sensitive to shock, they are quite dangerous to handle. In 1888, Alfred Nobel, a Swedish inventor, found a way to handle nitroglycerin more safely by absorbing it in a fine clay, or *diatomaceous earth.* The resultant mixture (and all similar concoctions) is known as *dynamite* and has been one of the most important inventions in the technological progress of man.

Nitrogen explosives are often detonated by the shock waves produced when even more unstable nitrogen compounds explode. *Fulminate of mercury,* or mercury(II) cyanate, $Hg(OCN)_2$, and lead(II) *azide,* $Pb(N_3)_2$, containing the linear $N_3^{-1}$ ion, are commonly used detonators.

## 27.3 Nitrogen: the preserver

More significant than the nitrogen-containing compounds that are explosives are those that are essential to life. Among the myriad chemical substances of biological significance are many that contain nitrogen. Animal and plant growth and reproduction are dependent on such major classes of compounds as the *proteins* and the *nucleic acids*—both containing bonded nitrogen atoms whose presence in these compounds determines their biochemical activities. (See Secs. 31.8–31.9, pp. 655–656, and Secs. 31.12–31.14, pp. 661–665.)

Although nitrogen is the most abundant element in the earth's atmosphere, it is present in a generally unusable form. In order for plants and animals to build proteins, they must have nitrogen present in soluble and chemically reactive compounds. Diatomic nitrogen molecules possess neither property. The conversion of stable, molecular

Well-nodulated pea roots. Each nodule contains many nitrogen-fixing bacteria.

nitrogen to useful nitrogen compounds—the process known as *nitrogen fixation*—occurs naturally through the *nitrifying* action of certain bacteria present in nodules on the roots of *leguminous*, or pealike, green plants. These bacteria have the ability to change molecular nitrogen, present in porous soil, into soluble nitrogen compounds, particularly nitrates. Farmers will plant crops of peas or alfalfa and plow them under as *fertilizers* to replenish the usable nitrogen of depleted soils.

In nature, nitrogen fixation also takes place during electrical storms when sufficient energy is available for the endothermic production of nitrogen monoxide, NO, in the atmosphere:

$$\tfrac{1}{2}N_2(g) + \tfrac{1}{2}O_2(g) = NO(g) \qquad \Delta H_f = 21.6 \text{ kcal/mole}$$

The nitrogen monoxide gas reacts with oxygen in the air to form nitrogen dioxide, $NO_2$, which reacts, in turn, with water to form nitric acid:

$$NO(g) + \tfrac{1}{2}O_2(g) = NO_2(g)$$
$$3NO_2(g) + H_2O(l) = 2HNO_3(aq) + NO(g)$$

The rapidly increasing human population has required man to assist nature through the synthesis of nitrogen fertilizers to increase food crop production. Chief among such fertilizers is ammonia.

## 27.4 Ammonia

The synthetic fixation of atmospheric nitrogen occurs through the Haber process. (Sec. 15.9, p. 342.) Most of the eight million tons of ammonia produced annually by this method in the United States is used directly as a fertilizer and, also, to synthesize nitrate and ammonium compounds that are themselves used extensively as fertilizers. Urea, $OC(NH_2)_2$, is synthesized from ammonia and carbon dioxide gases,

$$CO_2(g) + 2NH_3(g) \overset{150°C}{\underset{35\,atm}{=}} OC(NH_2)_2(l) + H_2O(g),$$

and is widely used as a fertilizer.

Ammonia, to be used as a fertilizer, may be directly administered to nitrogen-deficient soils (left) or fed through irrigation systems.

More than 75 per cent of all chemical nitrogen products are produced from synthetic ammonia. This includes annually some five million tons of nitric acid, nearly two million tons of ammonium sulfate fertilizer, and over four million tons of ammonium nitrate, used mainly as a fertilizer and also as an explosive. We have seen how ammonia is also an essential ingredient in the synthesis of sodium carbonate through the Solvay process. (Sec. 21.14, p. 467.)

Ammonia is readily prepared in the laboratory by heating an ammonium compound in the presence of a strong base:

$$NH_4^{+1}(aq) + OH^{-1}(aq) \overset{\Delta}{\rightleftharpoons} NH_3(g) + H_2O(l)$$

Most conveniently, a paste of $NH_4Cl$ and $CaO$ is heated to serve as a source of the gas:

$$2NH_4Cl(s) + CaO(s) \overset{\Delta}{\underset{H_2O}{\rightleftharpoons}} 2NH_3(g) + CaCl_2(s) + H_2O(l)$$

Aqueous solutions of the very soluble gas are sources of both $NH_3$ molecules and $OH^{-1}$ ions:

$$Cu^{+2}(aq) + 2NH_3(aq) + 2H_2O(l) \rightleftharpoons Cu(OH)_2(s) + 2NH_4^{+1}(aq)$$
$$Cu(OH)_2(s) + 4NH_3(aq) \rightleftharpoons Cu(NH_3)_4^{+2}(aq) + 2OH^{-1}(aq)$$

## 27.5 The oxides of nitrogen

Six well characterized oxides of nitrogen are known. Two years prior to his discovery of oxygen, Priestley was the first to produce *dinitrogen monoxide,* or nitrous oxide, $N_2O$, a colorless, heavy gas, slightly sweetish in odor, that is somewhat soluble in water. He learned that it supported the burning of a candle better than ordinary air did, which is *now* recognized to be due to the fact that it decomposes rather easily into nitrogen and combustion-supporting oxygen.

Just before the close of the eighteenth century, Humphry Davy achieved fame overnight by his discovery of the physiological effects of $N_2O$ gas. He breathed four gallons of it and noticed its power to produce a peculiar intoxication, which included laughing.

An anonymous cartoon of the 19th century showing "the effects of breathing nitrous oxyd"

The poet Samuel Coleridge, as well as other distinguished persons, came to Davy's London laboratory to experience the thrill of inhaling this gas. Nitrous oxide, known familiarly as *laughing gas*, is still prepared as Davy made it, by *gently* heating ammonium nitrate:

$$NH_4NO_3(s) \stackrel{\Delta}{=} N_2O(g) + 2H_2O(g)$$

Today the gas is used as an anesthetic, especially in dentistry. Easily liquefied, it is sold in cylinders and finds wide use as a propellant in the aerosol packaging of foods such as whipped cream.

*Nitrogen monoxide*, or nitric oxide, NO, is a poisonous, colorless gas, very slightly soluble in water and about as heavy as air. As we have seen, it is formed directly from atmospheric nitrogen and oxygen in the presence of a sufficiently high energy source. Cavendish discovered this gas in 1770 while conducting experiments in which an electric spark was passed through a gaseous mixture of hydrogen and air in an attempt to synthesize water.

Priestley, after his discovery of oxygen, made a thorough study of NO gas formed directly from the elements. He also prepared the gas by the action of *dilute* nitric acid on copper, still a useful laboratory preparation:

$$3Cu(s) + 2NO_3^{-1}(aq) + 8H_3O^{+1}(aq) = 3Cu^{+2}(aq) + 2NO(g) + 12H_2O(l)$$

Nitric oxide is chemically very active, and reacts immediately with atmospheric oxygen to form the brown, paramagnetic, water-soluble gas *nitrogen dioxide*, $NO_2$. Nitrogen dioxide dimerizes to form a fourth oxide of nitrogen—the colorless, diamagnetic *dinitrogen tetroxide*, $N_2O_4$.

*Dinitrogen trioxide*, $N_2O_3$, the anhydride of nitrous acid, $HNO_2$, exists only in the solid state (mp = $-102°C$). *Dinitrogen pentoxide*, $N_2O_5$, the anhydride of nitric acid, $HNO_3$, exists as a stable solid at temperatures below $8°C$ in the absence of sunlight. It is prepared by the dehydration of the acid with tetraphosphorus decoxide, $P_4O_{10}$. There is experimental evidence to indicate that $N_2O_5$ is, in reality, better considered to be *nitronium nitrate*, $(NO_2)^{+1}(NO_3)^{-1}$.

### 27.6 Nitric acid

Soon after Haber's successful synthesis of ammonia, Wilhelm Ostwald, a brilliant German chemist who had helped Arrhenius establish the validity of the theory of electrolytic dissociation and ionization, showed how ammonia gas could be converted into nitric acid on an industrial scale.

The basic step of the Ostwald process involves the catalytic oxidation of ammonia in air:

$$4NH_3(g) + 5O_2(g) \overset{800°C}{\underset{Pt}{\rightleftharpoons}} 4NO(g) + 6H_2O(g)$$

The nitric oxide product is cooled and then mixed with oxygen, with which it spontaneously reacts to form nitrogen dioxide. The nitrogen dioxide is passed into warm water with which it reacts to form nitric acid:

$$3NO_2(g) + 3H_2O(l) = 2NO_3^{-1}(aq) + 2H_3O^{+1}(aq) + NO(g)$$

Historically, nitric acid was largely prepared from natural supplies of Chilean *saltpeter*, $NaNO_3$. A small amount of nitric acid is still made from saltpeter by heating it *carefully* in the presence of concentrated sulfuric acid:

$$NaNO_3(s) + H_2SO_4(aq) \overset{\Delta}{=} NaHSO_4(aq) + HNO_3(g)$$

The more volatile nitric acid may be distilled from the reaction mixture and condensed. This reaction serves as the basis of the laboratory preparation of nitric acid, which is carried out in a glass retort since the acid and its fumes are very corrosive. (Fig. 27.1.) Care must be taken not to overheat the reaction mixture since nitric acid thermally decomposes:

$$4HNO_3(g) \overset{\Delta}{=} 4NO_2(g) + O_2(g) + 2H_2O(g)$$

Sunlight will also bring about the decomposition of the acid.

Besides being a strong acid, nitric acid is an excellent oxidizing agent. ($E^0_{NO/NO_3^{-1}} = -0.96$ volt) As such it finds major use in the research laboratory and in industry. Industrially, it is used most extensively in the *nitration* of organic compounds to form explosives and *nitrobenzene*, $C_6H_5NO_2$, a chemical precursor of the major industrial chemical intermediate *aniline*, $C_6H_5NH_2$. Aniline, produced by the

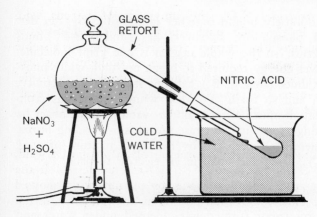

GLASS
RETORT

NITRIC ACID

NaNO$_3$
+
H$_2$SO$_4$

COLD
WATER

**FIGURE 27.1** Laboratory preparation of nitric acid

reduction of nitrobenzene, is used extensively to form important products used in the manufacture of rubber tires, and it is still used in the synthesis of the well-known aniline dyes.

With this brief overview of the properties of elemental nitrogen and its major compounds, ammonia and nitric acid, we move on to consider the chemistry of phosphorus.

### 27.7 Properties of phosphorus

Phosphorus is the only element in Group V not found free in nature. It is the eleventh most abundant element in the earth's crust, being widely distributed in rocks and soils, usually as phosphates. It is a major element of living matter. Bones, for example, are about 60 per cent calcium phosphate. Along with nitrogen and potassium, phosphorus is one of three essential food elements frequently missing in soil. Thus, the phosphorus fertilizer industry is a major one.

Elemental phosphorus exists mainly in white and red allotropic forms, some of whose properties are listed in Table 27–3.

**TABLE 27–3**  THE ALLOTROPES OF PHOSPHORUS

|  | Red Phosphorus | White Phosphorus |
|---|---|---|
| Melting point (°C) | 593 | 44 |
| Boiling point (°C) | sublimes at 1431 | 280 |
| Solubility in CS$_2$ | insoluble | soluble |
| Relative toxicity | nontoxic | highly toxic |
| Reaction in air | ignites at 260°C | ignites spontaneously at room temperature |

In all of the properties listed, the consistent behavior is one of lower reactivity for the red form of phosphorus. X-ray studies have shown that white phosphorus is composed of separate molecules of P$_4$

WHITE PHOSPHORUS, $P_4$

RED PHOSPHORUS, $P_x$

**FIGURE 27.2** The allotropes of phosphorus

tetrahedra which are loosely bound together in the solid by van der Waals forces. Red phosphorus, however, has similar P–P bonds throughout its structure, so the whole crystal is one giant molecule. (Fig. 27.2.) The lower energy required to break up solid, white phosphorus into smaller units (that is, $P_4$) explains its greater reactivity, solubility, volatility, and so forth. To keep white phosphorus from igniting spontaneously, it must be stored under water. It must never be touched with bare fingers, for it will cause severe, slow-healing burns.

The pure element is prepared by heating a mixture of *rock phosphate*, $Ca_3(PO_4)_2$, sand, and coke in an electric furnace:

$$2Ca_3(PO_4)_2(s) + 6SiO_2(s) + 10C(s) \overset{\Delta}{=\!=} 6CaSiO_3(l) + 10CO(g) + P_4(g)$$

The white phosphorus vapor formed is condensed under water and cast in molds. Most of this phosphorus is burned in dry air to form tetraphosphorus decoxide, $P_4O_{10}$, which is used to make phosphates including phosphoric acid:

$$P_4O_{10}(s) + 6H_2O(l) = 4H_3PO_4(aq)$$

This weak acid is used in soft drinks, jellies, and preserves, and in synthesizing phosphate fertilizers.

## 27.8 Phosphate fertilizers

About 90 per cent of the phosphate rock mined is converted into fertilizers, the rest is used to prepare elementary phosphorus, phosphorus compounds, and alloys such as phosphor bronze. In the manufacture of fertilizers, insoluble rock phosphate is finely ground and treated either with concentrated sulfuric acid or with phosphoric acid to form soluble calcium dihydrogen phosphate, $Ca(H_2PO_4)_2$. In the former case,

$$Ca_3(PO_4)_2(s) + 2H_2SO_4(aq) = 2CaSO_4(s) + Ca(H_2PO_4)_2(s),$$

the resulting solid mixture is used directly as "superphosphate" fertilizer. In the latter case,

$$Ca_3(PO_4)_2(s) + 4H_3PO_4(aq) = 3Ca(H_2PO_4)_2(s),$$

the final product is known as "triple superphosphate" fertilizer. Soluble nitrogen-based compounds and soluble phosphorus-based compounds, along with soluble potassium-based compounds are the important constituents of some thirty million tons (!) of fertilizer mixtures and materials used annually in the United States alone.

## 27.9 Arsenic

The stable allotrope of arsenic is a steel-gray, brittle, metallic-looking solid that is found in both free and combined forms. Like bismuth, it is seldom used as the pure element and is a minor, but important, constituent of many alloys. Lead, for example, alloyed with a trace of arsenic, is hardened sufficiently to be formed into nearly perfect spherical shot.

When heated in air, arsenic forms *white arsenic*, or tetrarsenic hexoxide, $As_4O_6$, exhibiting, like bismuth and antimony, an oxidation state of $+3$ in its stable oxide. As might be expected, arsenic also exhibits the $+5$ oxidation state, in species such as arsenic acid, $H_3AsO_4$. The $+5$ oxidation state is shown to a lesser degree by antimony, though the $Sb(OH)_6^{-1}$ ion is a common specie. Bismuth exhibits this state only in the *bismuthate* ion, $BiO_3^{-1}$, a very powerful oxidizing agent.

White arsenic is a powder that is used in glassmaking and as a preservative in the mounting of skins. The poisonous nature of the compounds of arsenic is used in man's battle against the insect pests that, by attacking his cattle and crops, cause losses of billions of dollars yearly. Insects destroy approximately 10 per cent of man's food and fiber crops each year. Suspensions of *lead*(II) *arsenate*, $Pb_3(AsO_4)_2$, and *calcium arsenate*, $Ca_3(AsO_4)_2$, are widely used agricultural insecticides for spraying.

## 27.10 Antimony

The stable allotrope of antimony is silvery, brittle, and crystalline. Its chief use is in alloys, such as type metal and Babbitt metal, and in lead storage battery plates. When molten type metal solidifies, it *expands* slightly, thus spreading into the sharp corners of the mold, producing a sharply defined cast. Antimony, like most metals, shrinks when solidified and cannot be cast but must be die-stamped, or struck. It is fascinating that the behavior of the alloy of antimony, tin, and lead, however, is contrary to normal metallic behavior.

## 27.11 Bismuth

Bismuth, a white, lustrous, brittle metal with slightly reddish tinge, occurs in both free and combined forms. In that it contracts on melting, it is an abnormal metal.

Bismuth is used chiefly in making low-melting-point alloys such as *Wood's metal* (mp 71°C), which contains 40 per cent bismuth in addition to lead, tin, and cadmium. Electric fuses, safety plugs in boilers, and other automatic devices for protection against fire or explosion contain this metal. For example, if a fire breaks out in a building equipped with an automatic sprinkler system, a temperature of 71°C is reached quickly. The bismuth alloy in the sprinkler plugs then melts, setting streams of water loose and at the same time breaking an electric circuit to set off a fire alarm. On that note, we end our survey of the elements of Group V and turn to a brief study of the versatile nonmetal *sulfur*, and the other elements of Group VI.

## SUMMARY

By virtue of the vital role they play in life processes, nitrogen and phosphorus compounds dominate any technical consideration of the Group V elements. The fixation of atmospheric nitrogen into useful nitrogen-containing compounds is the outstanding technological reaction of concern. The solubilization of insoluble phosphates through reaction with sulfuric acid is only slightly less important.

Aside from their use in the fertilization of croplands, the elements of Group V offer a wide variety of interesting properties, ranging from the explosive nature of many nitrogen compounds to the unique properties of antimony and bismuth alloys. The chemistry of nitrogen and its compounds, especially, is a study in versatility. The element can exist in a large number of oxidation states. Its compounds often behave in a variety of ways. Ammonia, for example, is a Brønsted-Lowry base and a complexing ligand. Another example is nitric acid, both a strong acid and a strong oxidant.

As the group is descended, the expected decrease in non-metallic nature among the heavier elements is found. Thus, while arsenic and antimony are metalloids, bismuth is a metal. While the +5 oxidation state exists commonly for nitrogen, phosphorus, and arsenic, it is uncommon for antimony, and very unstable for bismuth.

## QUESTIONS AND PROBLEMS

**27.1**  Interpret the quotation that appears at the head of this chapter.

**27.2**  What similar role do lightning, *rhizobium*, and *azotobacter* play in nature?

**27.3**  Write net ionic equations illustrating reactions of aqueous ammonia as a Brønsted-Lowry base and as a ligand.

**27.4**  Write net ionic equations illustrating reactions of aqueous nitric acid as a Brønsted-Lowry acid and as an oxidizing agent.

**27.5**  Describe in detail, with equations, each of the following: a. the Haber process; b. the Solvay process; c. the Ostwald process.

**27.6**  What is the thermodynamic basis for nitrogen explosives?

**27.7**  Determine the effect that the Haber and Ostwald processes had on World War I.

**27.8**  Draw a laboratory setup you might use for the generation and collection of ammonia gas.

**27.9**  Write chemical equations for each of the following. Use net ionic equations where appropriate.

a. The synthesis of superphosphate fertilizer
b. The thermal decomposition of nitric acid
c. The commercial synthesis of urea, $OC(NH_2)_2$
d. The industrial production of white phosphorus
e. Magnesium nitride, $Mg_3N_2$, is added to water
f. The amphiprotic nature of the monohydrogen phosphate ion
g. The hydrolysis of sodium dihydrogenarsenate
h. The oxidation of $Mn^{+2}(aq)$ to $MnO_4^{-1}(aq)$ by $BiO_3^{-1}(aq)$ in acid solution. [$Bi^{+3}(aq)$ is a product of the reaction.]

**27.10** What is the oxidation number of nitrogen in each of the following: a. ammonia; b. hydrazine, $N_2H_4$; c. hydroxylamine, $NH_2OH$; d. hydrazoic acid, $HN_3$; e. nitrosyliron(II) ion, $Fe(NO)^{+2}$?

**27.11** How many pounds of white phosphorus can be extracted from 1.50 tons of rock phosphate containing 85.0 per cent $Ca_3(PO_4)_2$?

**27.12** Draw Lewis structures for a. $N_2$; b. $N_2O_4$; c. $HONO_2$; d. $OC(NH_2)_2$; e. $NaN_3$; f. $(OH)_3PO$; g. $(OH)_2PH$.

**27.13** Based on the tetrahedral structure of white phosphorus, suggest structural formulas for a. $P_4O_6$; b. $P_4O_{10}$.

**27.14** A 0.10 $M$ $H_3AsO_4$ solution has a pH of 1.7. Calculate $K_{H_3AsO_4}$.
ANS.  $K_{H_3AsO_4} = 5 \times 10^{-3}$

**27.15** Suggest an experiment in which you might determine whether dinitrogen pentoxide, $N_2O_5$, is better formulated as nitronium nitrate, $(NO_2)(NO_3)$.

**27.16** Refer to Table 17–2, page 373, and explain why it is not possible to obtain pure sodium orthophosphate, $Na_3PO_4$, by titration of an orthophosphoric acid solution with aqueous sodium hydroxide.

## SUGGESTED READINGS

Asimov, Isaac. *The World of Nitrogen* (paperback). Collier, 1962.

CHEMISTRY
Fullmer, June Z., "The Great Laughing Gas Experiment." Apr. 1964

*Quickly, O! Dame, bring fire that I may burn sulfur, the cure of ills.*

*Homer* (c. 1100–900 B.C.)

# CHAPTER 28 | Sulfur and the

The final family of elements we shall consider in our survey of the periodic classification of the elements is Group VI. Having previously studied the lead element of the group, oxygen, in Chapter 5, our present concern will center mainly on sulfur, since relatively few experimental investigations into the chemistry of selenium, tellurium, and polonium, which comprise the remainder of Group VI, have been made.

## 28.1 Some properties of the Group VI elements

A number of the properties of the Group VI elements are presented in Table 28–1. From the table, the familiar trends of properties within a family of elements are clearly evident. Thus, we note the rising melting points, heats of fusion, densities, and so forth, with the increasing atomic weights of the elements as the group is descended.

In Group VI, oxygen and sulfur are typical nonmetallic elements, whereas selenium and tellurium are metalloids. All the isotopes of polonium are radioactive, and only small quantities have been isolated. As a consequence, only a meager amount of information is available on its chemistry. However, indications are that polonium, as expected, is the most metallic of the Group VI elements, though it is probably more nonmetallic than metallic in its properties. Thus, experimental evidence indicates that polonium seems to form oxyanions rather than cations. In one of its allotropic forms, however, polonium does have a metallic structure.

## 28.2 Elemental sulfur

Sulfur, the *brimstone* of the Bible, usually is found as a pale-yellow, soft, but brittle solid with a very faint odor and no marked taste. It is

# Group VI Elements

TABLE 28-1 Properties of the Group VI Elements

|                                | O      | S     | Se    | Te    | Po    |
| ------------------------------ | ------ | ----- | ----- | ----- | ----- |
| Atomic weight (amu)            | 16.00  | 32.07 | 78.96 | 127.6 | 210   |
| Melting point (°C)             | −219   | 119   | 217   | 450   | 254   |
| Boiling point (°C)             | −183   | 445   | 685   | 990   | 962   |
| Heat of fusion (kcal/mole)     | 0.053  | 0.34  | 1.25  | 4.28  |       |
| Heat of vaporization (kcal/mole) | 0.815 | 2.3   | 3.34  | 11.9  | (29)  |
| Density (g/ml)                 | 1.14   | 2.07  | 4.79  | 6.24  | (9.2) |
| Radius of $X^{-2}$ (A)         | 1.40   | 1.84  | 1.98  | 2.21  |       |

practically insoluble in water, more soluble in carbon tetrachloride, $CCl_4$, and very soluble in carbon disulfide, $CS_2$.

Sulfur is a poor conductor of heat. It melts, forming a pale-yellow liquid, which on further heating darkens and thickens, becoming almost black at 235°C. At still higher temperatures, it becomes less viscous again, and finally boils off, as a yellow vapor, at 445°C.

## 28.3 The allotropic forms of sulfur

Sulfur occurs in two common crystalline forms and one noncrystalline, or *amorphous*, form. Each has different properties because of the differences in their structures.

Sulfur is found naturally in the form of *rhombic* crystals, the most stable allotropic form under normal conditions. (Fig. 28.1.) Sulfur molecules within the crystal consist of puckered rings of eight sulfur atoms linked by single covalent bonds. (Fig. 28.2.) Rhombic sulfur may be prepared by dissolving sulfur in carbon disulfide and allowing the

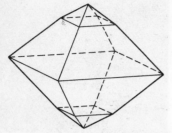

FIGURE 28.1 A rhombic crystal of sulfur, represented diagrammatically

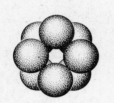

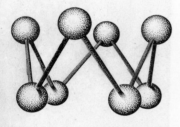

FIGURE 28.2 Two structural models for the octatomic sulfur molecule

FIGURE 28.3 A monoclinic crystal of sulfur, represented diagrammatically

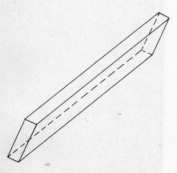

solvent to evaporate slowly. *Roll sulfur,* made by cooling molten sulfur in cylindrical molds, is almost entirely rhombic.

When sulfur is heated until it just melts and is then allowed to cool slowly, it forms long needle-shaped *monoclinic* crystals, whose density is somewhat less than that of rhombic sulfur. (Fig. 28.3.) Evidence indicates that $S_8$ molecules also exist in monoclinic sulfur, though the orientation of the eight sulfur atoms is not yet known.

When molten sulfur above 160°C is suddenly cooled by pouring it into cold water, a dark-amber, somewhat elastic solid forms. This amorphous sulfur, unlike the crystalline modifications, is insoluble in carbon disulfide. On standing, amorphous sulfur loses its elasticity and becomes quite brittle. Eventually it reverts to the thermodynamically stable rhombic form at room temperature. A common commercial form of sulfur known as *flowers of sulfur* is a powdered mixture of rhombic and amorphous sulfur.

X-ray studies of amorphous sulfur indicate the existence of intertwined long chains of sulfur atoms. Apparently, when sulfur is heated beyond its melting point, the octatomic ringlike molecules break open to form linear molecules, which at first tend to link and crosslink. This is evidenced by the increasing viscosity and deepening color of the melt. At higher temperatures, near the boiling point, the added thermal energy is apparently sufficient to cause breaking of the giant, intertwined sulfur chains into smaller, simpler groupings. This is evidenced by the decreasing viscosity and lighter color of the melt near the boiling point.

Experimental evidence indicates that sulfur vapor consists primarily of diatomic molecules. When the sulfur vapor containing this $S_2$ species is cooled rapidly to −196°C, a purple, paramagnetic solid forms. In this respect, sulfur behaves like oxygen, which forms a blue, paramagnetic solid.

## 28.4 An American pharmacist creates a new industry.

The discovery of petroleum in Pennsylvania in 1859 led at once to a wide search for other stores of oil. Only six years later, oil prospectors stumbled upon huge deposits of sulfur about 500 feet below the earth's surface in western Louisiana not far from the Gulf of Mexico. Here, geologists believe, a vast geyser spouted ages ago, leaving sulfur—formed perhaps by the bacterial decomposition of calcium sulfate—within and about its crater. The sulfur was covered with layers of clay, limestone, and, worst of all, gas, and quicksand. Thus, it was impossible to sink mine shafts to reach the deposits. Many companies were formed to exploit these deposits, but because of the many mining difficulties they all failed.

In 1891, Herman Frasch, a German-born Philadelphia druggist, heard about this Louisiana sulfur. Chemistry had long fascinated Frasch and he had carried on many researches on petroleum products in the back of his drugstore. He had later sold his store and devoted all his time to the study of chemical engineering. This led him to the problem of extracting sulfur from the Louisiana deposits. He devised an ingenious extraction process that many thought to be a foolish and impossible one. But Frasch kept improving his method and ultimately he succeeded in founding a new American industry based on his process.

Frasch's plan was to sink a well by means of an oil-drilling rig, and lower three concentric pipes inside a casing down to the sulfur deposit. Through an outermost six-inch pipe, superheated water was to be pumped to melt the sulfur. Through an innermost one-inch pipe, compressed air was to be forced down to the sulfur deposit. The result was to be a flood of molten, foamy sulfur gushing under pressure from the three-inch pipe between the other two. (Fig. 28.4.)

Frasch's method worked. Indeed, it has worked so well that mountains of sulfur, 99.5 per cent pure, have been pumped from the vast supply of native sulfur near and under the Gulf of Mexico. These mountains, added to at a rate of more than five million tons annually, stand ready to be blasted into smaller pieces to be loaded and shipped to many locations in the United States and throughout the world.

In recent years, the United States has become not only the world's largest producer and consumer of sulfur, but also the largest exporter of this very basic element.

## 28.5 Chemical properties and uses of sulfur

As oxygen forms ionic, metallic oxides, so sulfur unites with most metals to form ionic, metallic sulfides. Since sulfur is a larger, less electronegative atom than oxygen is, metallic sulfides have a higher degree of covalency than corresponding oxides have. For the same reason, when sulfur reacts with oxygen or chlorine to form covalent oxides and chlorides, sulfur exists in positive oxidation states.

Much sulfur is used in the industrial preparation of *disulfur dichloride*, $S_2Cl_2$, long known more familiarly as sulfur monochloride. This amber, unstable liquid with an irritating odor is used in the vulcanizing of rubber (see p. 641), and in the industrial preparation of *carbon tetrachloride*, an important industrial solvent:

$$2S_2Cl_2(l) + C(s) = CCl_4(l) + 4S(s)$$

*Carbon disulfide*, $CS_2$, a heavy, colorless liquid, is prepared by passing sulfur vapor over hot coke in an electric furnace:

$$2S(g) + C(s) \stackrel{\Delta}{=} CS_2(g)$$

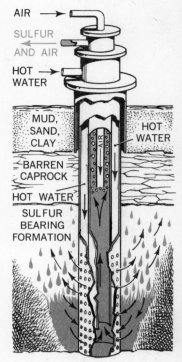

AIR →
SULFUR AND AIR
HOT WATER →

MUD, SAND, CLAY
HOT WATER
BARREN CAPROCK
HOT WATER
SULFUR BEARING FORMATION
AIR

BARREN ROCK
ROCK SALT

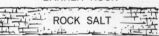

**FIGURE 28.4** Diagram of the Frasch process for extracting sulfur

The highly flammable, liquid $CS_2$, which has a very disagreeable odor due to the presence of impurities, finds use, as sulfur monochloride does, in the manufacture of carbon tetrachloride:

$$CS_2(l) + 3Cl_2(g) = CCl_4(l) + S_2Cl_2(l)$$

Carbon disulfide finds its widest application in the manufacture of viscose rayon, vulcanized rubber, and fungicides. The liquid and its vapor are not only toxic to certain fungi and molds, but are also used in the extermination of rodents, particularly rats and prairie dogs.

Elemental sulfur itself is a fungicide familiar to the rose grower. Dusting rose bushes with finely powdered sulfur is an effective preventive against many rose diseases. Aside from this use and very many other industrial uses, most elemental sulfur is used in the vulcanization process and, especially, in the synthesis of sulfuric acid.

### 28.6 Hydrogen sulfide and the sulfides

Sulfur is a very versatile nonmetal, exhibiting a variety of oxidation states. In its lowest oxidation state, $-2$, sulfur is found in the noxious, foul-smelling gas hydrogen sulfide, $H_2S$, and its derivatives, the sulfides.

Hydrogen sulfide is prepared industrially and on a laboratory scale by treating iron(II) sulfide, a common, black iron ore, with sulfuric acid:

$$FeS(s) + H_2SO_4(aq) = H_2S(g) + FeSO_4(aq)$$

Industrially, this reaction serves to produce not only $H_2S$ gas, but also solid hydrated iron(II) sulfate, $FeSO_4 \cdot 7H_2O$, known as *copperas* or *green vitriol*, used in the manufacture of blue-black inks. The salt is reacted with the tannic acid obtained from oak *nutgalls*, abnormal growths caused indirectly by parasitic insects. Essentially colorless, soluble iron(II) tannate forms. This is colloidally suspended in an aqueous solution of *gum arabic* and colored with a blue dye, such as *indigo*. On exposure to air, the iron(II) tannate oxidizes to black iron(III) tannate, whose color obscures the pale-blue shade of the unoxidized ink.

Hydrogen sulfide is colorless, slightly heavier than air, easily liquefied, and fairly soluble in water, a saturated aqueous solution being about $0.1M$ in $H_2S$. Upon being decomposed, natural "sulfur waters," which contain hydrogen sulfide in solution, leave a deposit of free sulfur. The most characteristic physical property of hydrogen sulfide is its odor.

Due to bacterial decomposition of matter, hydrogen sulfide forms in marshes, oil wells, and mines, and in coal piles, manure pits, and sewers. Mild exposure to the gas results in inflamed throat, headache, a heavy feeling in the stomach, and dizziness. When breathed in larger quantities, it causes death.

In sufficient air, $H_2S$ gas burns with a pale-blue flame to form water vapor and sulfur dioxide gas, which is responsible for an irritating odor:

$$2H_2S(g) + 3O_2(g) = 2SO_2(g) + 2H_2O(g)$$

The *incomplete combustion* of $H_2S$ gas leads to the formation of water as before, but free sulfur is produced instead of sulfur dioxide:

$$2H_2S(g) + O_2(g) = 2S(s) + 2H_2O(g)$$

The fact that sulfur forms in this reaction probably accounts for its presence around volcanoes, which emit hydrogen sulfide gas.

Hydrogen sulfide gas reacts with certain metals and also with some metallic salts to form sulfides. The tarnishing of silverware is caused by the formation of brownish-black silver sulfide. The blackening of "lead paints," paints based on *white lead*, $Pb(OH)_2 \cdot 2PbCO_3$, is caused by the formation of black lead(II) sulfide. *Lithopone*, a widely used base for white paint consisting of a mixture of barium sulfate and zinc sulfide, and titanium dioxide–based paints do not lose their color by the action of $H_2S$. The salts of *hydrosulfuric acid*, the aqueous solution of $H_2S$ gas, form an important class of compounds called *sulfides*. Many of these occur in nature and constitute important ores such as *galena*, $PbS$; *zinc blende*, $ZnS$; *cinnabar*, $HgS$; and *chalcocite*, $Cu_2S$. Some colored sulfides are used as mineral pigments in the coloring of paints.

Since the colors of the sulfides of many metals differ, chemists can use these differences in color in detecting the presence of these metals. For example, zinc sulfide is white, arsenic(III) sulfide is yellow, antimony(III) sulfide is orange, and copper(II) sulfide is brownish-black. The pH-controlled precipitation of these and other colored heavy metal sulfides can be used as a method of qualitatively analyzing a mixture of metal compounds.

$H_2S$ gas and hydrosulfuric acid are excellent reducing agents ($E^0_{H_2S/S} = -0.14$ volt) and find use as such in laboratory and industry. The acid is extremely weak:

$$H_2S(aq) + H_2O(l) \rightleftharpoons H_3O^{+1}(aq) + HS^{-1}(aq) \qquad K = 1.0 \times 10^{-7}$$
$$HS^{-1}(aq) + H_2O(l) \rightleftharpoons H_3O^{+1}(aq) + S^{-2}(aq) \qquad K = 1.0 \times 10^{-13}$$

Thus, soluble sulfides hydrolyze extensively to form strongly alkaline solutions. Such solutions serve as solvents for elemental sulfur:

$$xS(s) + S^{-2}(aq) = (S_{x+1})^{-2}$$

The resultant solutions are known as *polysulfides* and have an intense yellow color. Metal polysulfides exist naturally, particularly $FeS_2$, iron(II) disulfide, or *iron pyrites*. The golden sheen of this mineral has led to its common name—one that evokes an image of shattered dreams of great wealth—*fool's gold*.

## 28.7 The oxides of sulfur

When sulfur is burned or an oxide ore is roasted, a dense, colorless gas of suffocating odor forms. This gas, sulfur dioxide, $SO_2$, is highly soluble in water, forty volumes of the gas at one atmosphere dissolving in one volume of water at room temperature. The resulting solution is, as we have seen, a moderately weak acid:

$$SO_2(aq) + 2H_2O(l) \rightleftharpoons H_3O^{+1}(aq) + HSO_3^{-1}(aq) \quad K = 1.7 \times 10^{-2}$$

$$HSO_3^{-1}(aq) + H_2O(l) \rightleftharpoons H_3O^{+1}(aq) + SO_3^{-2}(aq) \quad K = 6.2 \times 10^{-8}$$

Though reaction of such a solution yields a series of hydrogen sulfite and sulfite salts, it must be remembered that the existence of sulfurous acid, $H_2SO_3$, itself has never been experimentally proven.

Aqueous solutions of sulfur dioxide are mild reducing agents ($E^0_{SO_2(aq)/SO_4^{-2}} = -0.17$ volt); hence, solutions of sulfites are readily oxidized in air ($E^0_{H_2O/O_2} = -0.82$ volt):

$$2SO_2(aq) + O_2(g) + 6H_2O(l) = 2SO_4^{-2}(aq) + 4H_3O^{+1}(aq)$$

Sulfite solutions find major industrial application in the bleaching *by reduction* of straw, silk, dried fruits, flour, molasses, and canned corn —all of which would be partially destroyed by stronger oxidative bleaching agents.

In addition to being reducing agents, aqueous solutions of sulfur dioxide are also mild oxidants ($E^0_{S/SO_2(aq)} = -0.45$ volt). From the $E^0$ values of the half-reactions involving aqueous $SO_2$ as a reducing agent and as an oxidizing agent, it becomes apparent that a solution of the gas is unstable with respect to *auto-oxidation*:

$$3SO_2(aq) + 6H_2O(l) = 2SO_4^{-2}(aq) + 2S(s) + 4H_3O^{+1}(aq)$$

Sulfite and hydrogen sulfite solutions are also unstable to heat,

$$HSO_3^{-1}(aq) + H_3O^{+1}(aq) \overset{\Delta}{=} SO_2(g) + 2H_2O(l),$$

and to acid,

$$SO_3^{-2}(aq) + 2H_3O^{+1}(aq) = SO_2(g) + 3H_2O(l),$$

as well as to reduction, and to oxidation.

Sulfur dioxide gas is easily liquefied and is shipped in metal cylinders or in tank cars. The major consumer of this chemical is the paper industry. Cellulose fibers are separated from the less useful components of wood by *digesting* the wood in sulfite baths. This process is known as *pulping* and is a necessary step in the conversion of certain woods to paper. Sulfite pulps are light in color because of the bleaching property of aqueous sulfur dioxide. A more extensively used pulping process employs a strongly alkaline solution of sodium sulfide and sodium hydroxide as the pulping agent. Almost any wood can be pulped by this *kraft process*. The resultant pulp, however, is dark and difficult to bleach. In the unbleached state, the kraft pulps are converted directly to the dark kraft paper used for paper bags and boxes.

Under normal conditions, sulfur forms a trioxide, $SO_3$, only in the presence of a catalyst. Below room temperature this oxide exists as a sublimable solid in one of three polymeric forms. In the absence of water, the least complex form exists as a trimer. (Fig. 28.5.) Each of the three forms boils at 45°C to form simple, planar molecules that fume in moist air as they exothermically react with water vapor to form sulfuric acid droplets:

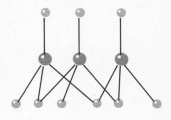

**FIGURE 28.5** A model for the cyclic trimeric form of $SO_3$

$$SO_3(g) + H_2O(g) = H_2SO_4(l)$$

Sulfur trioxide is, therefore, the anhydride of sulfuric acid, and sulfuric acid is the most important synthetic inorganic chemical.

## 28.8 Sulfuric acid and the contact process

The equivalent of more than 22 million tons of 100 per cent sulfuric acid is synthesized and *used* industrially in the United States alone each year. So important is this versatile compound to the economy of this and all nations that its production and consumption are used as economic barometers.

Well over 90 per cent of the sulfuric acid produced annually is synthesized by a catalytic process known as the *contact process*. In the first step of the process, molten sulfur is sprayed into combustion furnaces, where it burns in an atmosphere of dry air. The sulfur dioxide gas that forms passes into a huge *converter*, a large chamber in which the catalytic conversion of $SO_2$ gas to $SO_3$ gas occurs. The converter consists of many perforated shelves covered with platinized asbestos or vanadium pentoxide, either of which can serve as a heterogeneous catalyst. At a carefully regulated temperature of 450°C, the equilibrium reaction

$$2SO_2(g) + O_2(g) \underset{\text{catalyst}}{\overset{450°C}{\rightleftharpoons}} 2SO_3(g) \qquad \Delta H = -45 \text{ kcal}$$

proceeds to yield $SO_3(g)$ in excess of 95 per cent. The $SO_3$ gas passes from the converter into a cooler, and then into a series of absorption towers. Since $SO_3$ gas is more soluble in sulfuric acid than in water, the gas bubbles up through quartz pebbles or acid-resistant packing rings over which 98 per cent by weight sulfuric acid is circulated. The concentrated acid dissolves the $SO_3$ gas to form *oleum*, or pyrosulfuric acid, $H_2S_2O_7$, which is then *added to water* to produce sulfuric acid of any concentration. A final tower is filled with coke, which serves as an adsorption filter to prevent the escape of any undissolved $SO_3$ gas and unreacted $SO_2$ gas into the atmosphere as pollutants.

### 28.9 The lead chamber process

More than a million and a half tons of sulfuric acid are produced annually in this country by a process that is more than two centuries old. In the *lead chamber process*, the conversion of $SO_2$ gas to $SO_3$ is homogeneously catalyzed by $NO_2$ gas in enormous lead-lined reaction chambers. Still not completely understood, the reaction probably occurs in the following sequence:

$$2NO(g) + O_2(g) \rightleftharpoons 2NO_2(g)$$

$$3NO_2(g) + 2SO_2(g) + H_2O(g) \overset{\Delta}{\rightleftharpoons} NO(g) + 2ONOSO_3H(g)$$

$$2ONOSO_3H(g) + H_2O(g) \overset{\Delta}{\rightleftharpoons} 2HOSO_3H(aq) + NO_2(g) + NO(g)$$

The compound $ONOSO_3H$, *nitrosyl sulfuric acid*, is an intermediate that is stable enough to be isolated. The formulas for the intermediate and for the sulfuric acid end product are given as they are in order to indicate the structural similarities between the two.

A disadvantage of the lead chamber process is that only dilute sulfuric acid—of not more than 78 per cent concentration and often impure—results. However, there is still sufficient demand for such a product—especially in the production of fertilizers and in the pickling of iron and steel—so that the small amount produced is profitable.

### 28.10 The properties and uses of sulfuric acid

Sulfuric acid is at the same time a strong acid,

$$H_2SO_4(1M) + H_2O(l) \rightarrow H_3O^{+1}(aq) + HSO_4^{-1}(aq)$$
$$HSO_4^{-1}(1M) + H_2O(l) \rightleftharpoons H_3O^{+1}(aq) + SO_4^{-2}(aq) \qquad K = 1.3 \times 10^{-2},$$

and a good oxidizing agent,

$$SO_2(g) + 6H_2O(l) \rightleftharpoons SO_4^{-2}(aq) + 4H_3O^{+1}(aq) + 2e^{-1} \quad E^0 = -0.17 \text{ volt.}$$

As expected, it becomes a much more powerful oxidant in more concentrated solutions. When concentrated, it has the additional property of exhibiting a great affinity for water. It forms four crystalline hydrates, $H_2SO_4 \cdot XH_2O$, where X has the values 1, 2, 3, or 4. Alone, or in concert, the properties of sulfuric acid as an acid, as an oxidizing agent, and as a dehydrating agent account for the vast industrial consumption of this giant among chemicals.

More than 30 per cent of the sulfuric acid used is in the production of superphosphate fertilizers. Other major uses are in the production of other inorganic chemicals, such as sodium sulfate and, especially, ammonium sulfate. Since sulfuric acid is an oxidizing agent, it finds use only in the production of nonreducing acids such as hydrochloric acid and nitric acid.

The industrial preparation of hydrochloric acid is instructive in that it is representative of a general industrial method employed in the synthesis of a number of widely used acids. When rock salt, impure NaCl, is heated in the presence of a moderately concentrated solution of sulfuric acid, $H_2SO_4$, hydrogen chloride gas is evolved. This gas is dissolved in water to form hydrochloric acid. The complete equation for the reaction is:

$$NaCl(s) + H_2SO_4(aq) \overset{\Delta}{\rightleftharpoons} HCl(g) + NaHSO_4(aq)$$

The low volatility of the sulfuric acid is the basis for its use in this economically vital, general preparation method. In each case, the product acid formed is not chemically pure. These low-cost *technical-grade* acids, are nonetheless widely used. Technical-grade hydrochloric acid, usually called *muriatic acid*, and yellow in color, finds its largest use in the iron and steel industry for the pickling of oxide scale. (See page 125 and 530.)

When bromides and iodides are treated with sulfuric acid they react vigorously as reducing agents, thereby precluding the use of $H_2SO_4$ in the synthesis of HBr and HI:

$$2NaBr(s) + SO_4^{-2}(aq) + 4H_3O^{+1}(aq)$$
$$= Br_2(l) + SO_2(g) + 2Na^{+1}(aq) + 6H_2O(l)$$
$$8NaI(s) + SO_4^{-2}(aq) + 10H_3O^{+1}(aq)$$
$$= 4I_2(s) + H_2S(g) + 8Na^{+1}(aq) + 14H_2O(l)$$

More than a million tons of sulfuric acid are used in the pickling of iron and steel and more than a half million tons are needed for the processing of nonferrous metals. The manufacture of rayon depends upon sulfuric acid, as does the production of petroleum fuels. The electrolyte in the lead storage battery is sulfuric acid. This list could go on to touch upon uses of this remarkable compound in processes that affect every phase of modern life.

## 28.11 Selenium, tellurium, and polonium

We end our tour of the periodic classification of the elements with a brief look at the properties and uses of the last three members of Group VI.

Selenium and tellurium are quite nonmetallic in nature, though their behavior deviates sufficiently from that of true nonmetals to result in their being classified as metalloids by some chemists. Selenium has a number of allotropic forms. The gray, metallic, hexagonal form is the only stable one at ordinary conditions, and evidence indicates the presence of "zig-zag" chains of selenium atoms in the solid state. (Fig. 28.6.) A red, monoclinic form of selenium appears to consist of puckered $Se_8$ rings analogous to those of rhombic sulfur. Gray selenium has the unusual property of sharply increasing its electrical conductivity upon exposure to light. As a result, in recent years it has found widespread use in *photoelectric cells.*

Only one crystalline form of tellurium is well characterized. This is a metallic form consisting of gray, hexagonal crystals with low electrical conductivity, which, unlike that of selenium, is unaffected by light.

The chemistry of selenium is like that of sulfur. Tellurium's chemistry is somewhat more complex, while that of polonium has been little studied. Each forms a dihydride. The more metallic properties of polonium suggest a formula of $PoH_2$ for its hydride, while the hydride formulas for selenium and tellurium are definitely more correctly written as $H_2Se$ and $H_2Te$, respectively. The gases hydrogen selenide and hydrogen telluride are toxic and among the most vile-smelling substances known. Both form weakly acid aqueous solutions, among whose metallic derivatives are some highly colored selenides and tellurides.

Thus, we complete eight chapters in which an understanding of the principles developed in the first twenty chapters of this book bring meaning to the facts of nature presented. We move on from this survey of all the elements to refocus upon one of them—carbon. In the next three chapters we consider carbon as it appears in organic compounds and we will note how such compounds dominate the living world.

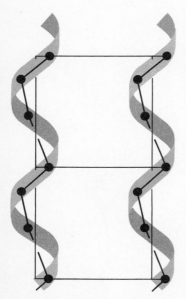

**FIGURE 28.6** A model for the solid state of selenium. The color band is present to indicate the spiral configuration of the atoms in the crystal.

## SUMMARY

With oxygen, previously studied in Chapter 5, sulfur constitutes the major topic of interest among the elements of Group VI. This very versatile nonmetallic element exhibits a number of oxidation states in its compounds and is the precursor of the major industrial compound sulfuric acid. The latter finds such widespread use in so many diverse processes that its production and consumption on a national scale serve to indicate the state of the over-all economy.

## QUESTIONS AND PROBLEMS

**28.1** Describe the behavior of sulfur as it is continuously heated from its melting point to its boiling point. Explain the behavior in terms of a model for the changing structure of liquid sulfur.

**28.2** Write chemical equations for each of the following. Use net ionic equations where appropriate.

   **a.** The self-oxidation of aqueous $SO_2$

   **b.** The hydrolysis of sodium hydrogen sulfide

   **c.** The complete combustion of hydrogen sulfide

   **d.** The blackening of white lead-based paints

   **e.** Sulfur is boiled in aqueous sodium sulfide.

   **f.** Concentrated sulfuric acid is added to solid sodium iodide.

   **g.** Concentrated sulfuric acid is used in the synthesis of muriatic acid (HCl), nitric acid, and hydrofluoric acid.

**28.3** Draw a laboratory setup you might use for the generation and collection of hydrogen sulfide gas.

**28.4** Write net ionic equations illustrating the role of aqueous $H_2S$ as a Brønsted-Lowry acid, as a reducing agent, and as a precipitant.

**28.5** Write net ionic equations illustrating the role of aqueous $H_2SO_4$ as a Brønsted-Lowry acid and as an oxidant.

**28.6** **a.** Describe the contact process for the manufacture of sulfuric acid. **b.** List major uses for sulfuric acid and, where possible, the chemical basis for these uses.

**28.7** Draw Lewis structures for **a.** $SO_4^{-2}$; **b.** $S_2O_3^{-2}$; **c.** $S_2$; **d.** $O_2$.

**28.8** $K_{hydrolysis}$ for the $HSO_3^{-1}(aq)$ ion equals $K_W/K_{H_2SO_3}$. Using data from Table 17–2, page 373, predict whether a solution of sodium hydrogen sulfite will be acidic or alkaline.

**28.9** Show by equation which equilibrium systems are present in a saturated solution of copper(II) sulfide.

**28.10** **a.** Calculate the molar solubility of copper(II) sulfide from its $K_{sp}$ value of $8.5 \times 10^{-45}$. **b.** Compare this value with its measured solubility of $3.3 \times 10^{-5}$ g/100 ml of water. Explain any difference.

**28.11** **a.** Determine the simplest formula for a compound consisting of 1.03 per cent hydrogen, 33.0 per cent sulfur, and 66.0 per cent oxygen by weight.

   **b.** What is the oxidation state of sulfur in the compound?

   **c.** The compound in question has a molecular weight of 194 amu and is called *peroxydisulfuric acid*. What is its true formula?

   **d.** Draw a Lewis structure for the compound.

## SUGGESTED READING

MCA (Washington, D.C.). *The Chemical Industry Fact Book* (paperback). Manufacturing Chemists' Association, 1965.

*Let us dream, then perhaps we shall find the truth . . . but let us beware of publishing our dreams before they have been put to the proof by the waking understanding.*

*Friedrich August Kekulé* (1829–1896)

<table>
<tr><td>CHAPTER 29</td><td># Carbon, the Chain</td></tr>
</table>

Carbon is unique among the elements. It is the only element capable of forming long chains from atoms of the same type. These long-chain carbon compounds play the basic role in the structure and control of living things. Whole industries have developed and now flourish as new knowledge of the chemistry of carbon chain compounds has increased. This knowledge has provided man with the opportunity to improve himself and his life through the synthesis of medicines, plastics, dyes, and numerous other types of materials. New fields will continue to open, with man and his world the beneficiaries.

## COMPOUNDS: ORGANIC OR INORGANIC

The alchemists and early chemists studied the substances that they could isolate from rocks and from other inanimate objects found in nature. They also investigated some of the chemical substances found in animal and vegetable materials. These substances derived from living matter often differed greatly from those derived from inanimate materials. Whether liquid or solid, they were rather easily destroyed by heat. On the other hand, many substances from inanimate objects were either crystalline solids with very high melting points or simple gases such as nitrogen and oxygen. To differentiate between these two distinct classes of compounds, the substances derived from animal or vegetable materials were called *organic compounds*, while those from inanimate materials were termed *inorganic compounds*.

As chemists learned more about compounds by analyzing for their constituent elements, another difference between inorganic and organic compounds became obvious. Inorganic compounds were found

# Former

to be composed of any of all the known elements. Organic compounds, on the other hand, were found to consist of relatively few of the known elements. Some organic compounds, like the paraffin waxes, contained only carbon and hydrogen. Others, like alcohol, contained oxygen in addition to carbon and hydrogen; while a few others, such as urea, also contained nitrogen. Moreover, there had developed a firm belief that all these differences reflected the fact that organic compounds could be made only within living things and not without the intervention of a *vital force*. This was not essential to the formation of inorganic compounds, many of which could, even then, be synthesized by man in his laboratory.

### 29.1 Wöhler's synthesis of urea: the era of organic chemistry begins.

The belief in the vital force theory for the formation of organic compounds persisted until 1828, when Friedrich Wöhler (VER ler) synthesized urea, the first organic compound made outside the living body. He did this by heating the inorganic compound ammonium cyanate:

$$\underset{\text{ammonium cyanate}}{NH_4NCO} \overset{\Delta}{=} \underset{\text{urea}}{(NH_2)_2CO}$$

This synthesis was nothing more than a simple rearrangement of the atoms of the ammonium cyanate. But it was one that destroyed the old idea that organic compounds could be formed only within living matter, and a new era in chemistry was ushered in giving witness to "the great tragedy of science, the slaying of a beautiful hypothesis by an ugly fact."

**Friedrich Wöhler** (1800–1882, German). A student and lifelong friend of Berzelius, Wöhler made many contributions to experimental inorganic chemistry. He was the first to isolate elemental aluminum, boron, and silicon, and he discovered elemental beryllium and yttrium. Of the more than 300 research papers he wrote, Wöhler is remembered most for the one in which he announced the synthesis of urea, which destroyed the false notion that "nothing but the texture of living vegetables, nothing but their vegetating organs, could form the matter extracted from them; and no instrument invented by man could imitate the compositions found in the organic machines of plants."

One hundred thirty years after Wöhler's achievement, penicillin was synthesized from its elements. What enormous accomplishments in organic chemical research occurred between Wöhler's synthesis of urea and synthetic penicillin! A glance at some of the epic discoveries of the years just following Wöhler's urea synthesis will underscore the effect on man's total life that organic chemical research has had.

In 1846 Dr. John C. Warren performed the first major surgical operation in which an anesthetic was employed. The operation took place in the Massachusetts General Hospital, where the patient was put under the influence of *ether*. This incident ushered in a new era in medicine, for it banished overnight the dreadful pains of surgery without anesthesia. The first use of *chloroform* as an anesthetic was made the following year by James Simpson, an Edinburgh surgeon. Berthollet studied the sting of the red ant and, in 1855, learned the secret of preparing *formic acid*, the liquid responsible for the sting of not only the ant but also the bee, the hornet, and the wasp. Thus, quite early in the development of organic chemistry, its role in the service of medicine was clearly established.

In 1856 William Perkin, while washing bottles in a London laboratory, accidentally mixed the contents of two bottles and discovered a method of synthesizing *mauve*—the first of a series of organic dyes that rival the colors of nature. Within three decades of Perkin's discovery, Joseph Swan in England synthesized the first artificial fiber —*rayon*. Today, synthetic fibers of all kinds clothe humanity. Synthetic dyes color those fibers to delight the eye.

It is not surprising to learn that only seven years after the synthesis of urea, Wöhler wrote to Berzelius, his teacher:

> "Organic chemistry nowadays almost drives me mad.
> To me it appears like a primeval tropical forest full of
> the most remarkable things, a dreadful endless jungle
> into which one does not dare enter, for there seems no
> way out."

We can well wonder what Wöhler would say today if he could see the enormous garden of abundance that has been created out of this primeval forest.

### 29.2 Paths in the organic jungle

Two men may be singled out for the key importance of their contributions to our present knowledge of organic chemistry. The first of these, Friedrich Kekulé, had been considering the riddle of the existence of the multitude of hydrocarbons, those organic compounds containing only carbon and hydrogen. After a long period of intensive thought, Kekulé, in 1858, conceived the idea that carbon atoms formed four

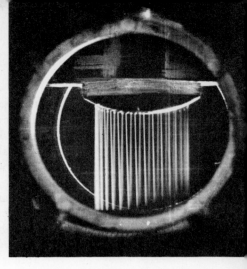

Flame-retardant *urethane foam,* derived from urea, being applied to the walls of a coal mine: another product of creative organic chemical research, developed for the well-being of mankind

*Cellulose acetate* being forced through fine holes of a *spinneret*—rayon, the first synthetic fiber, results.

chemical bonds and, furthermore, that they joined together to form long chains consisting of carbon atoms only.

The second man of key importance, Jacobus van't Hoff, interested himself in another facet of organic chemistry. It was known that if the simplest organic compound methane, $CH_4$, was reacted with bromine, a compound called *bromomethane* was always formed:

$$CH_4(g) + Br_2(l) = HBr(g) + CH_3Br(g)$$

The formation of the same compound in all cases had to be interpreted to mean that all four of the hydrogen atoms in methane *were equivalent*; that is, they all had the same chemical relationship to the carbon atom. This could occur only if the methane molecule had only one of three possible structures. (Fig. 29.1.)

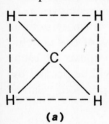 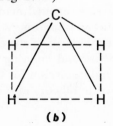 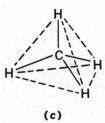

**(a)**          **(b)**          **(c)**

**FIGURE 29.1** Possible structures of methane: a. planar rectangle or square with carbon at the center; b. pyramid with carbon at the apex; c. tetrahedron with carbon at the center

Van't Hoff postulated, in 1874, that the tetrahedral structure was the correct one and that it was inherent to carbon atoms to have their four bonds directed to the corners of a tetrahedron. This was a daring idea and in direct contradiction to the accepted theory of the time, which held that the orientation of chemical bonds was a result of the attached atoms. According to that theory, the orientation of bonds about a carbon atom could be different in $CH_4$ than in $CH_3Br$, whereas van't Hoff held that it should remain unchanged. Voluminous experimental evidence has since shown the correctness of van't Hoff's idea.

Let us consider only one experiment which proves that structure *c* (Fig. 29.1) is correct whereas structures *a* and *b* cannot exist. If methane is reacted with bromine to form bromomethane, $CH_3Br$, and this is treated further with bromine, a *single* compound called *dibromomethane*, $CH_2Br_2$, is always formed. If either structure *a* or structure *b* were correct, the product would contain *two* compounds having different properties. For structure *a*, there are two possible compounds with different arrangements of the atoms of $CH_2Br_2$ (Fig. 29.2a) and for structure *b*, there are two possible arrangements (Fig. 29.2b).

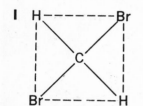 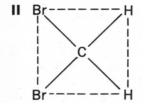    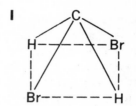 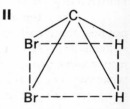

FIGURE 29.2a Possible planar structures of dibromomethane, $CH_2Br_2$ (Fig. 29.1a.)

FIGURE 29.2b Possible pyramidal structures of dibromomethane, $CH_2Br_2$ (Fig. 29.1b.)

In both figures, 29.2a and 29.2b, the distance between bromine atoms is different in I and II, and this difference would result in slightly different chemical properties for each. *Two or more compounds having exactly the same molecular formula but different properties are called isomers.* In agreement with experimental evidence, for structures *a*, *b*, and *c*, only structure *c*, the tetrahedron, would not form structural isomers of $CH_2Br_2$. Convince yourself of the correctness of this conclusion by making two tetrahedra and coloring any two apexes of each. The impossibility of structural isomerism for $CH_2Br_2$ will be proved by your ability to orient the two tetrahedra into identical positions relative to the two colored apexes.

### 29.3  The bonding in carbon: a modern view

One of the successes of the quantum mechanical model of the atom is its ability to account for the tetrahedral orientation of the bonds about carbon. Recall from Chapters 11 and 20 that carbon may form four $sp^3$ hybrid bonds that orient themselves toward the corners of a tetrahedron with carbon at the center. (Fig. 20.13, page 429.) The wisdom of van't Hoff is thus reflected in a theory that arose more than six decades after he made his important contribution.

We also recall, from Chapter 11, that the C—H bond is quite covalent because of the small difference in electronegativity between these two atoms. Furthermore, we find that the C—O and the C—N bonds are also covalent, but more polar than the C—H bonds. (See Table 11–2, page 281.) As a consequence, organic chemistry is primarily concerned with covalent bonds in contrast to inorganic chemistry, which is concerned with all types of bonds.

## THE ALIPHATIC HYDROCARBONS

As a result of the ability of carbon to bond to itself in chains and even in rings, an almost infinite variety of organic compounds is possible. It has been estimated that more than two million different organic compounds have been studied and this figure is being increased at the rate of several thousand new ones each year. In contrast, the number of known inorganic compounds is only about 250,000.

Since there is such a vast number of known organic compounds, the classification of them into major groups is necessary for a systematic study of them. The first breakdown of organic compounds into smaller groups of compounds with similar properties is based on what atoms other than carbon are present in them. Thus, we shall begin our systematic study of organic compounds by considering the hydrocarbons. These are the simplest organic compounds in composition, consisting only of carbon and hydrogen. On the basis of structure, the hydrocarbons are further divided into two main classes, and then into families:

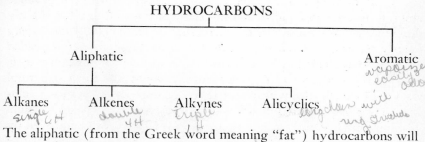

The aliphatic (from the Greek word meaning "fat") hydrocarbons will be our first concern.

### 29.4 The alkanes

The first few members of the related series of hydrocarbons known as the *alkanes* are shown in Figure 29.3. Notice that beginning with methane, each succeeding member of the series is formed by addition of a *methylene* group (—CH$_2$—). Such a series, where each succeeding member is formed by addition of the same group, is known as a *homologous series*. The homologous series of alkanes can be represented by the general formula C$_n$H$_{2n+2}$.

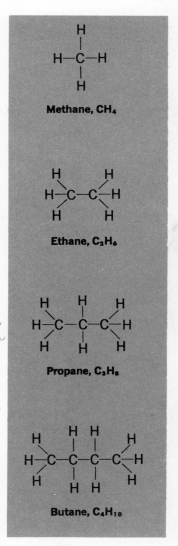

**FIGURE 29.3** Alkanes

The formulas shown for the first four members of the alkane series are known as *extended structural formulas* and clearly show which atoms are bonded to each other. In order to conserve space and time in writing structural formulas, organic chemists often use the *condensed structural formula*. The condensed structural formulas corresponding to the extended structural formulas in Figure 29.3 are: $CH_4$, $CH_3CH_3$, $CH_3CH_2CH_3$, $CH_3(CH_2)_2CH_3$.

Since each of the four valence electrons of carbon are bonded to four other atoms in the alkane molecules, the maximum bonding capacity of the carbon atom has been achieved in them. For this reason, the alkanes are known also as the *saturated* hydrocarbons. The fact that the bonding capacity of carbon in the alkane molecules is saturated underlies their relative chemical inactivity. It is that relative inactivity that gave rise to the older name for this family of hydrocarbons—the *paraffins*, from the Latin words meaning "little affinity." Table 29–1 lists a number of the members of the alkane series with their boiling points and some uses for them.

### TABLE 29–1    The Alkanes

| Compound | Molecular Formula | Boiling Point (°C) | Use |
|---|---|---|---|
| methane | $CH_4$ | $-161.4$ | natural gas ($C_1$—$C_4$) |
| ethane | $C_2H_6$ | $-88.6$ | |
| propane | $C_3H_8$ | $-41.1$ | high grade fuel |
| butane | $C_4H_{10}$ | $-0.5$ | naphtha ($C_4$—$C_6$) |
| *pentane* | $C_5H_{12}$ | 36.0 | |
| *hexane* | $C_6H_{14}$ | 68.7 | |
| *heptane* | $C_7H_{16}$ | 98.4 | gasoline ($C_7$—$C_{10}$) |
| *octane* | $C_8H_{18}$ | 125.7 | |
| *nonane* | $C_9H_{20}$ | 151 | |
| *decane* | $C_{10}H_{22}$ | 174 | |
| *dodecane* | $C_{12}H_{26}$ | 214 | kerosene ($C_{12}$—$C_{15}$) |
| *octadecane* | $C_{18}H_{38}$ | Melts at 28°C | lubricant ($C_{16}$—$C_{25}$) |
| *triacontane* | $C_{30}H_{62}$ | Melts at 66.1°C | paraffin ($C_{20}$—$C_{30}$) |

Beginning with pentane, the names in Table 29–1 were obtained by adding the proper Greek numerical prefix to *-ane*, the suffix that is used to indicate the alkane series.

### 29.5 Branched chains and isomers

Nature, in all its aspects, seems to have a wonderful variety, while at the same time retaining a beautiful underlying simplicity. It is the variety that makes for scientific adventure. It is the simplicity that makes for scientific understanding. This is well illustrated in the alkanes, where not only compounds with straight chains of carbon atoms are found, but also *branched-chain structural isomers* of such compounds. For example, two isomers exist for butane, $C_4H_{10}$:

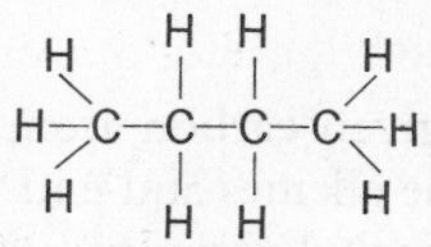

H H
| |
H—C—C—C—C—H
| | | |
H H H H

normal or n-butane,
(bp −0.5°C)

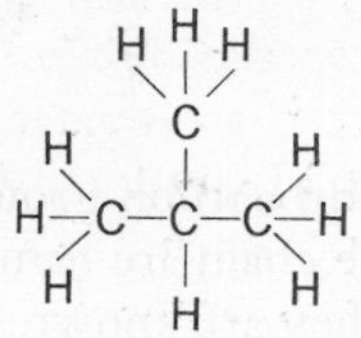

H H H
\ | /
C
/ \
H H
| |
H—C—C—C—H
| | |
H H H

isobutane,
(bp −10°C)

For pentane, $C_5H_{12}$, three isomeric forms are possible. (Fig. 29.4.)

The number of possible isomeric forms increases rapidly with the number of carbon atoms in the molecule. For example, it may be calculated that there are 35 isomers of nonane, 75 isomers of decane, and $7 \times 10^{13}$ isomers of tetracontane, $C_{40}H_{82}$.

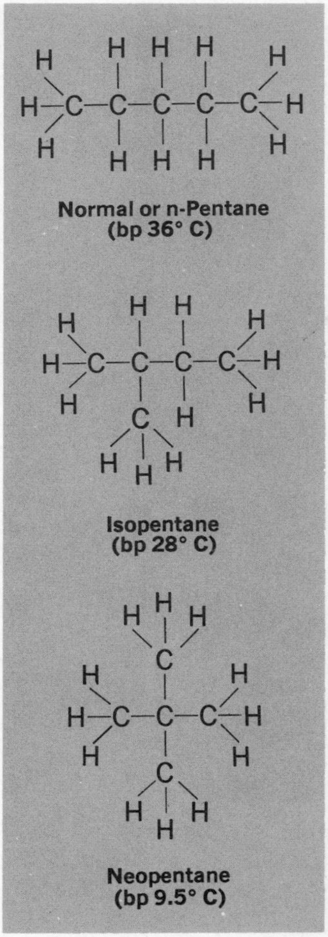

## 29.6 Nomenclature of the alkanes and their derivatives

As we have noted, the normal, or straight-chain, alkanes are named on the basis of the number of carbon atoms in the molecule. In naming the thousands upon thousands of isomeric variations and chemical derivatives of the alkanes, it becomes imperative to establish a nomenclature that is equally logical and systematic. Chemists have agreed on such a nomenclature. Its *essentials* are now given.

1. For branched-chain hydrocarbons and hydrocarbon derivatives, the longest chain of *unbranched* carbon atoms in the molecule is used as the basis for the name. Examples:

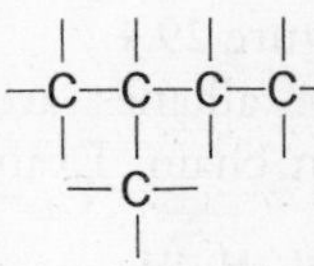

| | | |
—C—C—C—C—
| | | |
—C—
|

a *butane* derivative

| | | | | |
—C—C—C—C—C—C—
| | | | | |
—C—
|
—C—
|

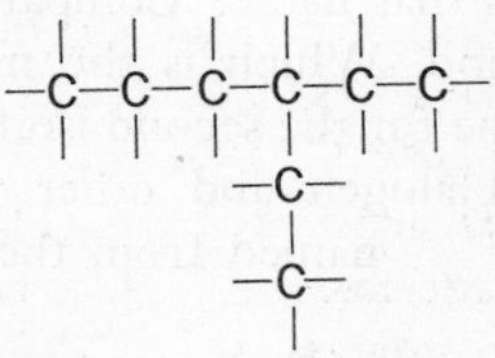

a *hexane* derivative

2. Each carbon of the unbranched chain is given a number to locate its position along that chain. The carbons are numbered so that those positions at which branching or substitution for hydrogen atoms take place have the lowest possible numbers. Examples:

a.

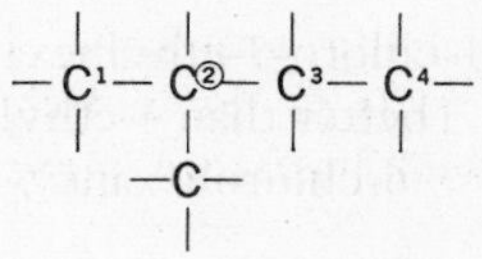

| | | |
—C¹—C²—C³—C⁴—     and not     —C⁴—C³—C²—C¹—
| | | |                        | | | |
—C—                              —C—
|                                |

**FIGURE 29.4** The isomers of pentane

Normal or n-Pentane
(bp 36° C)

Isopentane
(bp 28° C)

Neopentane
(bp 9.5° C)

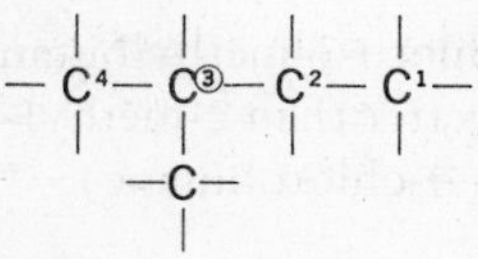

b.

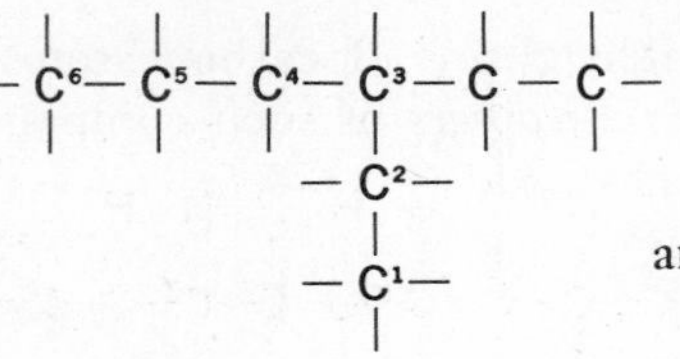

$$- C^6 - C^5 - C^4 - C^3 - C - C -$$
$$- C^2 -$$
$$- C^1 -$$

and not

$$- C^1 - C^2 - C^3 - C^4 - C - C -$$
$$- C^5 -$$
$$- C^6 -$$

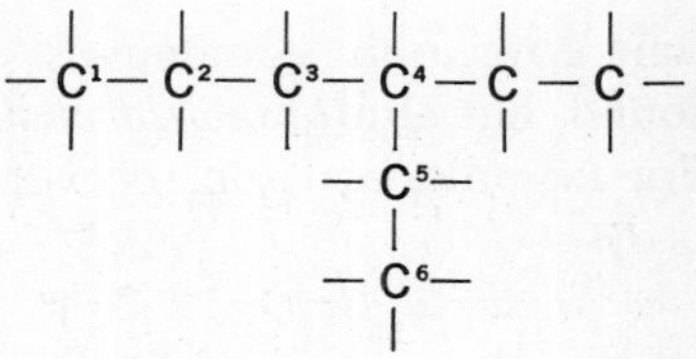

3. The hydrocarbon groups that branch off a given carbon atom along the chain are named as derivatives of the alkanes and end in *-yl*. They are known as *alkyl groups* or *radicals*. Examples:

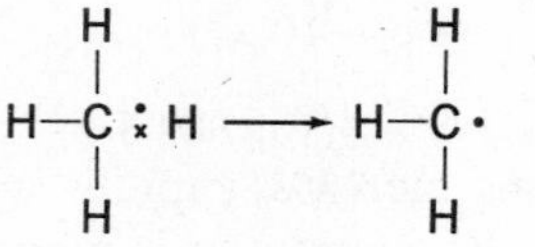

methane     methyl

ethane     ethyl

as in:

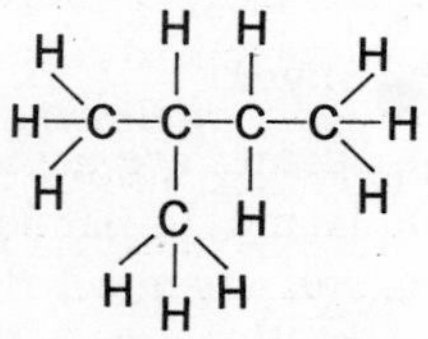

2-methylbutane

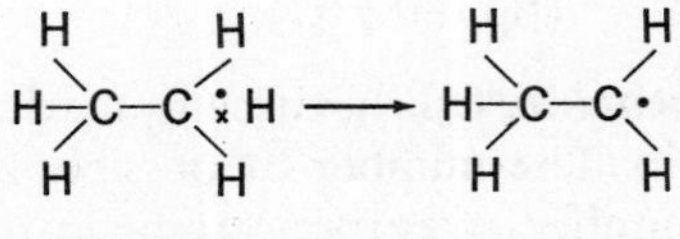

as in:

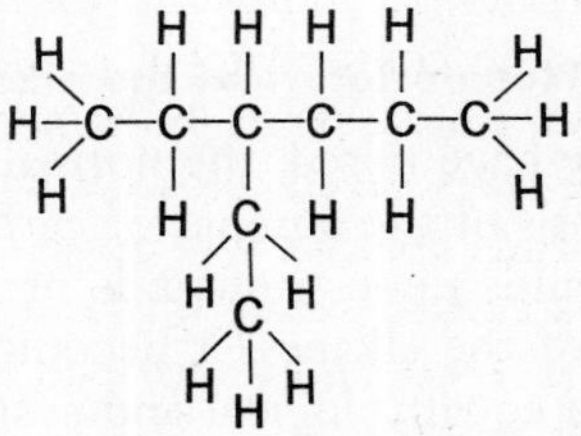

3-ethylhexane

In Figure 29.4, 2-methylbutane appeared under a different name. What was that name? Compare the two names you now have for the compound. Which is the more informative? Give the more informative name for the second isomer of n-pentane given in Figure 29.4.

4. Halogen and other nonalkyl derivatives of the alkanes are also named from their position along the carbon chain. Examples:

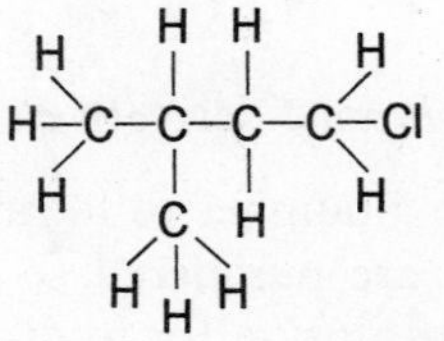

1-chloro-3-methylbutane
(better than 2-methyl-
4-chlorobutane)

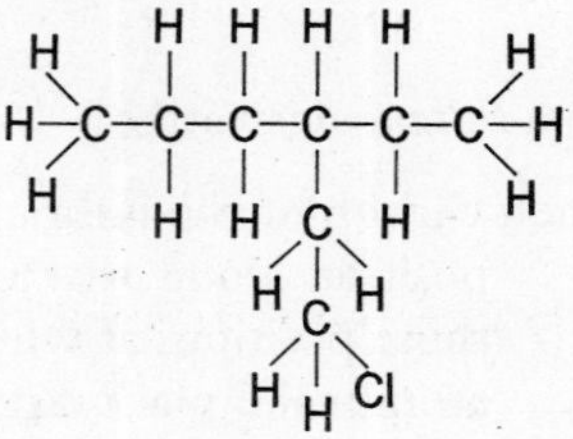

1-chloro-3-ethylhexane
(better than 4-ethyl-
6-chlorohexane)

```
        H                              H
      H | H                          H | H
  H   H H C H H      H         H   H C H H H H H      H
   \  | | | | |  /            \  | | | | | | | |  /
  H—C—C—C—C—C—C—C—H           H—C—C—C—C—C—C—C—C—C—H
   /  | | | | |  \            /  | | | | | | | |  \
  H   H H C H H   H          H   H H H C H H H H   H
        H | H                          H | H
        H C H                          H C H
       / | \                          / | \
      H  H  H                        H  H Cl
                                        H C H
                                       / | \
                                      H  H  H
```

| 4-ethyl-4-methylheptane (alphabetical preference for ethyl over methyl) | 3-methyl-5(2-chloropropyl)- nonane |
|---|---|

Consideration of the last examples given indicates that an increasing complexity in molecular constitution is accompanied by a necessary increase in complexity of nomenclature. Organic nomenclature is a tool and not a focal point in the systematic study of organic chemistry. The simple rules given, plus the few that will arise later, are useful in the brief study that we will make. Moreover, their systematic nature mirrors the systematic nature of the study of organic chemistry today.

To see how well you are able to apply the rules, try the following exercises.*

1. Refer back to Section 29.5. Give systematic names for isobutane and isobutyl chloride.

2. Name the following:

```
a.    H   H H   H            b.    H   H H   H
      |   | |   |                  |   | |   |
    H—C—C—C—C—H                  H—C—C—C—C—H
      |   | |   |                  |   | |   |
      H   H C   H                  H   H C   H
          / | \                        / | \
         H  H  H                      H  H  H
            H                            Br
```

c. CH₃CHClCH₃     d. CH₃C(CH₃)₂CH₂CH(CH₃)CH₂Br

c. $CH_3CHClCH_3$     d. $CH_3C(CH_3)_2CH_2CH(CH_3)CH_2Br$

3. Draw extended structural formulas for:

   a. 2, 3-dimethylbutane

   b. 1-bromo-3,4-dimethyl-4-ethylheptane

---

* Confucius is purported to have said: "In case of crisis, we must reform the nomenclature." This, unfortunately, does not apply here *for you*.

### 29.7 Cyclic alkane hydrocarbons: the alicyclics

We may briefly note that *closed-chain* saturated aliphatic hydrocarbons exist. In this case, the end carbons of an open chain bond to form a *ring*, or *cyclic, compound*. Essentially, the chemistry of these alicyclic hydrocarbons is the same as that of their open-chain relatives; certain differences in physical properties, such as higher boiling points and densities of the cyclic compounds, may be noted.

These *alicyclic* hydrocarbons, which are derived from petroleum, are named by adding the prefix *cyclo-* to the name of the corresponding open-chain hydrocarbons. (Fig. 29.5.)

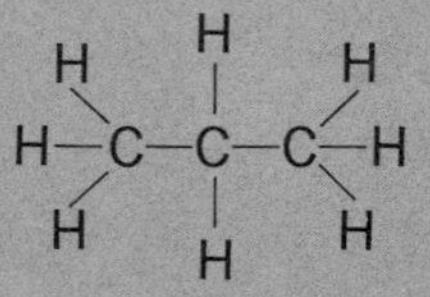

### 29.8 Reactions of the alkanes

As we noted in Chapter 14, it is a general characteristic of covalent bonds that reactions involving breaking and forming such bonds proceed relatively slowly when compared to the rate at which ionic reactions take place. However, at elevated temperatures hydrogen atoms may be replaced by other atoms such as halogen atoms at a relatively rapid rate:

$$RCH_3 + X_2 \xrightarrow{\Delta} RCH_2X + HX$$

This type of reaction is known as a *substitution reaction*. The $R$ in $RCH_3$ and $RCH_2X$ is the symbol generally used for an alkyl group. If, for example, $R$ symbolized a methyl group, $-CH_3$, then the general equation describing the halogenation of an alkane by substitution would become more specific for ethane:

$$\underset{\text{ethane}}{CH_3CH_3} + X_2 \xrightarrow{\Delta} \underset{\substack{\text{haloethane} \\ \text{(ethyl halide)}}}{CH_3CH_2X} + HX$$

The simplest halogen substitution that we may consider involves methane, $CH_4$, however. One or more hydrogen atoms of methane may be replaced by chlorine atoms. The completeness of this substitution will depend on the conditions under which the reaction takes place. The greater the chlorine to methane ratio, the more complete will be the substitution.

$$\underset{\text{methane}}{CH_4(g)} \xrightarrow{Cl_2(g)} \underset{\substack{\text{chloro-} \\ \text{methane}}}{CH_3Cl(g)} \xrightarrow{Cl_2(g)} \underset{\substack{\text{dichloro-} \\ \text{methane}}}{CH_2Cl_2(l)} \xrightarrow{Cl_2(g)} \underset{\substack{\text{trichloro-} \\ \text{methane}}}{CHCl_3(l)} \xrightarrow{Cl_2(g)} \underset{\substack{\text{tetra-} \\ \text{chloro-} \\ \text{methane}}}{CCl_4(l)}$$

Each of the colorless, nonflammable chloromethanes is a useful industrial product. Table 29–2 summarizes some of their properties and uses.

Propane, $C_3H_8$
(bp $-41°C$)

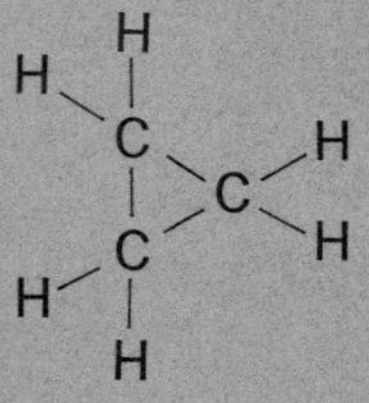

Cyclopropane, $C_3H_6$
(bp $33°C$)

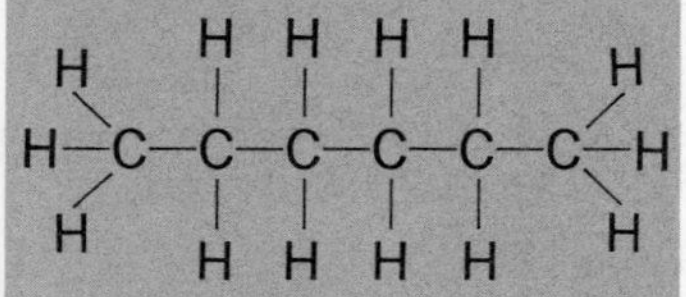

Hexane, $C_6H_{14}$
(bp $69°C$)

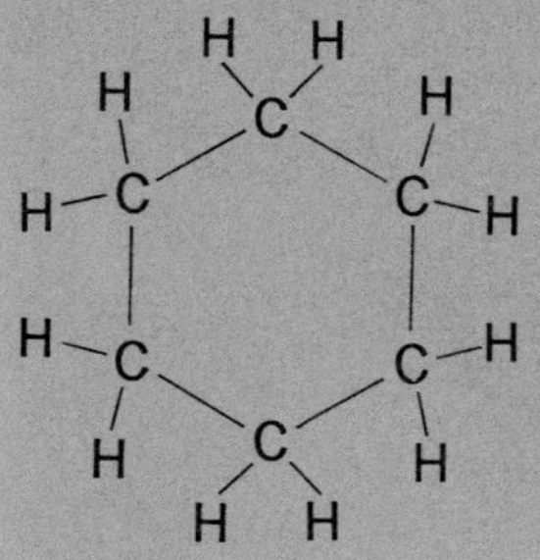

Cyclohexane, $C_6H_{12}$
(bp $81°C$)

**FIGURE 29.5** Alicyclic hydrocarbons and related alkanes

**TABLE 29–2**   CHLORINE SUBSTITUTION PRODUCTS OF METHANE

| Compound | Boiling Point (°C) | Uses |
|---|---|---|
| $CH_3Cl$<br>chloromethane<br>(methyl chloride) | −24 | low temperature solvent; refrigerant |
| $CH_2Cl_2$<br>dichloromethane<br>(methylene chloride) | 40 | solvent in the manufacture of acetate film and fiber |
| $CHCl_3$<br>trichloromethane<br>(chloroform) | 61 | solvent used for extraction of penicillin |
| $CCl_4$<br>tetrachloromethane<br>(carbon tetrachloride) | 77 | smothering-action fire extinguisher, especially around electrical equipment; solvent in "dry cleaning"* |

Bromination of methane takes place somewhat less readily than chlorination, and iodine will not react at all with it. On the other hand, fluorine reacts so vigorously with methane that only one substitution product is formed, tetrafluoromethane, or carbon tetrafluoride, $CF_4$.

Another alkane reaction is called *dehydrogenation*. It is usually brought about catalytically in the absence of oxygen, and leads to the formation of the more reactive *unsaturated* hydrocarbons:

ethane  ⟶  ethylene + hydrogen

The unsaturated hydrocarbons will be considered more fully beginning in Section 29.9.

One of the most significant of all industrial reactions is known as *cracking.* This type of reaction involves chain breaking in alkane molecules and will occur spontaneously at very high temperatures (pyrolysis) in the absence of oxygen. Industrially, cracking is a catalytic process:

propane  ⟶  ethylene   +   methane

---

* Dry cleaning is now done chiefly with nonflammable perchloroethylene (Perchlor), $C_2Cl_4$, which is less toxic than $CCl_4$.

Methyl bromide, an *alkyl halide*, used as a grain fumigant   The catalytic cracking tower: a modern cornucopia

In the petroleum industry, large alkane molecules found in crude oil are cracked into the smaller, more volatile molecular components of high-grade gasolines.

Finally, *oxidation* of the alkanes is an important and versatile reaction type. The oxidation products will vary depending on the conditions under which the reaction occurs. For example, oxidation of ethane can yield any one of three useful products:

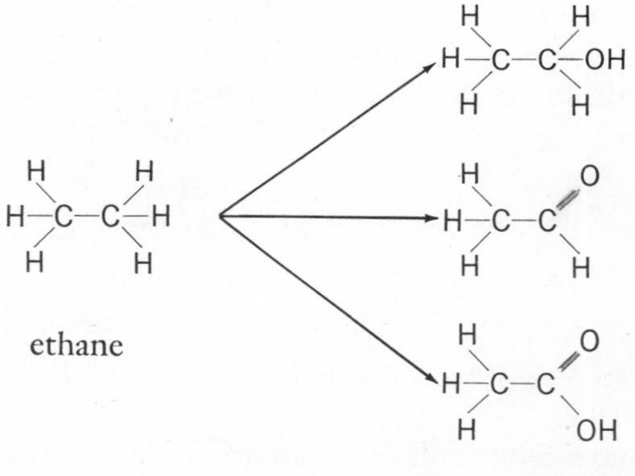

ethane

ethyl alcohol

acetaldehyde

acetic acid

Which product results depends on the temperature and pressure conditions of the reaction, as well as on the oxidizing agent or catalyst used. Of course, under the most extreme condition, *combustion*, the most complete oxidation reaction, occurs:

$$C_2H_6(g) + 3\tfrac{1}{2}O_2(g) \longrightarrow 2CO_2(g) + 3H_2O(g)$$

The combustion of alkanes in the internal combustion engine is a chemical reaction whose social and economic impact is so great as to be immeasurable.

With this brief overview of the alkane and alicyclic hydrocarbons, we turn next to two families of aliphatic hydrocarbons that are structurally and chemically more unique.

## 29.9 The alkenes

Ethylene, $C_2H_4$, produced from alkanes by dehydrogenation and by cracking, serves as the first of a new homologous series of compounds called the *alkenes*. The alkenes are represented by the general formula $C_nH_{2n}$. An older name for ethylene, *olefiant gas* (from the Latin words meaning "oil making"), led to the traditional name for this series of compounds—the *olefins*.

Unlike the alkanes, the maximum bonding capacity of the carbon atoms in the alkenes is not fully satisfied by hydrogen atoms bonded to them. At least one carbon-to-carbon double covalent bond exists within an alkene molecule. For this reason, the alkenes are also known as *unsaturated* hydrocarbons. Table 29–3 lists seven simple alkenes.

**TABLE 29–3** THE ALKENES

| Compound | Molecular Formula | Boiling Point (°C) | Use |
|---|---|---|---|
| ethene (ethylene) | $C_2H_4$ | −102.0 | polyethylene plastics |
| | | | ethylene glycol antifreeze |
| propene (propylene) | $C_3H_6$ | −48.0 | polypropylene plastics |
| 1-butene (butylene) | $C_4H_8$ | −6.5 | polybutylene tires |
| 1-pentene | $C_5H_{10}$ | 30.0 | |
| 1-hexene | $C_6H_{12}$ | 63.5 | |
| 1-octene | $C_8H_{16}$ | 123.0 | |
| 1-decene | $C_{10}H_{20}$ | 171.0 | |

## 29.10 Nomenclature of the alkenes and their derivatives

As you might have guessed, the basic name of an alkene is obtained by using the Greek prefix appropriate to the number of carbon atoms in the chain and adding the suffix *-ene*. However, in the alkenes, nomenclature becomes more complex, since the double bond may exist at different places in the molecule. That is, *double bond structural isomerism* occurs. We now start with the longest carbon chain that contains the double bond, and name the compound as we did with the alkanes—substituting the ending *-ene* for *-ane*. For convenience, we begin numbering our carbon atoms from the end of the chain nearest the double bond.

$$CH_3CH_2CH=CH_2$$
1-but*ene*

$$CH_3CH=CHCH_3$$
2-but*ene*

Alkyl and other derivatives of the alkenes are named as they were in the case of the alkanes. The double bond of the alkenes, however, establishes the numerical order given to the carbon atoms.

$(CH_3)_2CHCH_2CH_3$
2-methylbutane

$CH_2$=$C(CH_3)CH_2CH_3$
2-methyl-1-butene

$CH_3CH$=$C(CH_3)CH_2Cl$
1-chloro-2-methyl-2-butene

$CH_2$=$CHC(CH_3)_3$
3,3-dimethyl-1-butene

To instill self-confidence, attempt the following exercises.
1. Name the following:

a.

b.

c. $CH_2$=$CHCH_2Cl$    d. $CH_3C(CH_3)_2CH$=$C(CH_3)_2$

2. Draw extended structural formulas for:
   a. chloroethene
   b. 4,4-dimethyl-1-pentene
   c. 1,4-dichloro-2-butene
   d. 1,3-butadiene

## 29.11 The alkenes and cis-trans isomerism

The existence of the double bond in the alkenes leads to another interesting type of isomerism. Thus far we have considered isomerism brought about by *different bonding combinations among the same atoms*. Thus, two compounds of the same formula could have different structures and different properties. Such compounds, as we have learned, are known as *structural isomers*.

With the alkenes, however, a second type of isomerism arises. Two compounds having the same formula and the *same chemical bonding*, but different spatial orientation, may exist. These *geometrical isomers* would have different properties as a result of the different spatial orientation of their atoms. The simplest case of geometrical isomerism in the alkenes occurs with 2-butene. (See Fig. 29.6.)

The double bond between the two carbon atoms prevents those atoms from rotating with respect to each other. Thus, the planar molecule can and experimentally does have the two *cis-trans* structural isomers shown. As before for complex ions, we again note that cis-trans isomerism is one of the most dramatic examples of how molecular structure underlies and gives meaning to molecular behavior.

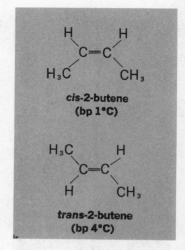

FIGURE 29.6 Geometrical isomers of 2-butene

## 29.12 The alkynes

Acetylene, $C_2H_2$, is the first compound of a third homologous series of aliphatic hydrocarbons, the *alkynes*. The general formula for this series is $C_nH_{2n-2}$. The alkynes are named in identically the same manner as are the alkenes except that the ending *-yne* is added rather than the ending *-ene*. Two examples of alkyne molecules are:

ethyne (acetylene), $C_2H_2$     or     H—C≡C—H

propyne, $C_3H_4$     or     H—C≡C—C—H

As you may see from these structural formulas, the characteristic feature of the alkynes is the presence of a *triple covalent bond*; that is, three pairs of bonding electrons between adjacent carbon atoms. Thus, the alkynes are, like the alkenes, unsaturated hydrocarbons.

## 29.13 Reactions of the unsaturated aliphatic hydrocarbons

The presence of the double bond in the alkenes and of the triple bond in the alkynes causes these compounds to be more reactive than the corresponding alkanes. Their most characteristic reaction is *addition*, whereby an atom is added to each of the adjacent unsaturated carbon atoms. When hydrogen is added, the process is known as *hydrogenation*. Many liquid vegetable oils, such as those used in cooking or in salad dressings, are unsaturated, having many double bonds in their long chains. Upon saturation with hydrogen, these oils become solid fats of the type used in cooking. Examples of addition reactions of unsaturated hydrocarbons are:

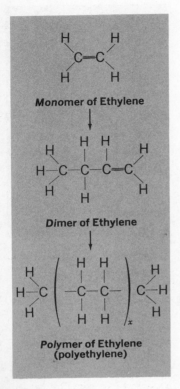

**Monomer of Ethylene**

↓

**Dimer of Ethylene**

↓

**Polymer of Ethylene (polyethylene)**

**FIGURE 29.7** Polymerization of ethylene

1. *Hydrogenation*

$$CH_2{=}CH_2(g) + H_2(g) \longrightarrow CH_3CH_3(g)$$
　　　ethene　　　　　　　　　　　　ethane

2. *Halogen addition*

$$CH_2{=}CH_2(g) + Cl_2(g) \longrightarrow CH_2ClCH_2Cl(l)$$
　　　ethene　　　　　　　　　　　　1,2-dichloroethane

3. *Hydrogen halide addition*

$$CH_2{=}CH_2(g) + HCl(g) \longrightarrow CH_3CH_2Cl(g)$$
　　　ethene　　　　　　　　　　　　chloroethane

Another important type of reaction of these unsaturated molecules is *polymerization*. This is a self-addition reaction in which a very large molecule is built up from many small, identical molecules (*monomers*). Ethylene polymerizes to form polyethylene, a substance very familiar to us in our daily life but almost unknown not too many years ago. (Fig. 29.7.) (Polymers and mechanisms of polymerization are discussed more fully in the photographic essay on Giant Molecules that begins on page 631.) Acetylene can be polymerized to form benzene, a cyclic, unsaturated hydrocarbon:

$$3\ HC{\equiv}CH(g) \xrightarrow[\text{quartz tube}]{550°C} C_6H_6(l)$$

## BENZENE AND THE AROMATIC HYDROCARBONS

The last reaction given in Section 29.13 indicated the synthesis of a new type of chemical compound with which we are unfamiliar. Thus far, we have considered only the members of the aliphatic class of organic compounds—the alkanes, the alkenes, the alkynes and the alicyclics. The alicyclics, you will recall, were closed-chain saturated hydrocarbons. Now we shall consider the closed-chain *unsaturated* hydrocarbon class of compounds known as the aromatic hydrocarbons. *Benzene and all the hydrocarbon compounds that resemble benzene in chemical behavior or are derivatives of benzene are known as the aromatic hydrocarbons.*

### 29.14 The structure of benzene

The structural and chemical nature of this second major class of hydrocarbons was not so apparent to the chemists who first considered the problems of organic substances after the overthrow of the vital force theory. For some forty years the structure of benzene, first obtained from whale and codfish oil in 1825 by Faraday, remained undetermined. Based on Kekulé's suggested four chemical bonds for the carbon atom, and the known molecular formula for benzene, $C_6H_6$, a number of possible structural arrangements for the compound were proposed, among them:

$$CH_3—C≡C—C≡C—CH_3$$

and

$$CH_2=CH—C≡C—CH=CH_2$$

In 1865, after a strenuous day in his laboratory, Kekulé fell asleep in a chair before his fireplace. He began to dream of snakes and atoms whirling round and round him. The old problem of the structure of benzene still haunted him. "All at once," he reported, "I saw one of the snakes seize hold of its own tail, and the form whirled mockingly before my eyes. As if by a flash of lightning, I awoke." Kekulé had solved the knotty problem. He gave the benzene molecule a hexagonal ring structure (Figure 29.8a.), which he followed a year later by a space model (Figure 29.8b.) with single and double bonds equivalent to a more modern formula. (Fig. 29.8c.)

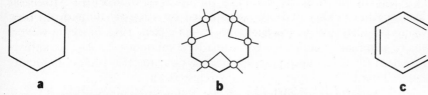

**a**            **b**            **c**

**FIGURE 29.8** Evolution of a model for the structure of benzene

**Friedrich Kekulé** (1829–1896, German). Undoubtedly, his early training in architecture had a great influence on Kekulé's profound contributions to structural theories in organic chemistry. Though he shared the honor accorded to the theory of carbon quadrivalency with the Scottish chemist A. S. Couper, who proposed it simultaneously, Kekulé, alone, proposed the theory on the hexagonal structure of benzene. That work has been called "the most brilliant piece of prediction to be found in the whole range of organic chemistry" and remains a lasting monument in honor of its discoverer.

If the alternating single bond–double bond structural formula for benzene is correct, it should be possible to prepare two structural isomers of $C_6H_4Br_2$, in which the two bromine atoms are bonded to adjacent carbon atoms:

However, only one compound of $C_6H_4Br_2$ has ever been isolated in which the two bromine atoms are on adjacent carbons. Furthermore, bond measurements on alkanes and alkenes have shown that the normal C—C single bond distance is 1.54 A, while the normal C—C double bond distance is 1.34 A. For benzene, each of the six carbon atoms is at a distance of 1.39 A from each of its two neighbors. This constant distance could not exist if the molecule in reality had a structure in which single and double bonds alternated. Other clues to the

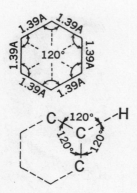

**FIGURE 29.9** The experimentally determined arrangement of atoms in benzene

**FIGURE 29.10** A modern structural formula for benzene

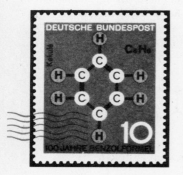

A nation's tribute to a man's dream

true nature of the structure of benzene are that all the angles between the C—C bonds are 120°C (compared to the 109° for tetrahedral structure), and that benzene is a planar molecule. (Fig. 29.9.)

The application of the quantum mechanical theory of chemical bonding has led to a model for the benzene molecule that satisfactorily accounts for much of the experimental knowledge that we have of that molecule. The model is quite complex and will not be considered here. In our consideration of benzene and other aromatic hydrocarbons, we shall use the most commonly used modern structural formula for benzene derived from that complex model. (Fig. 29.10.) From that formula, the equality of the bond lengths and the equality of the bond angles in benzene are evident. The inner circle suggests the unsaturatedness of all the C—C bonds as being intermediate between single and double bonds.

### 29.15 Nomenclature of benzene derivatives

A systematic nomenclature for the hundreds of thousands of aromatic hydrocarbons exists. It is a system based on a logical numerical order being assigned to the carbon atoms of the benzene ring. Since, however, many commonly encountered aromatic compounds have been known and used for many years, the less systematic names for such compounds are still used. These will be given parenthetically.

Careful study of each of the following examples should lead you to discover some simple rules for naming simple aromatic hydrocarbons:

1,4-dichlorobenzene
(*p*-dichlorobenzene)*

1,3,5-trinitrobenzene

2,4,6-trinitrotoluene
(trinitrotoluene, TNT)

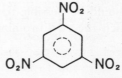

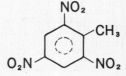

hydroxybenzene
(phenol, carbolic acid)

bromobenzene
(phenyl bromide)

1-bromo, 2-nitrobenzene
(*o*-bromonitrobenzene)

---

* An older, but acceptable, nomenclature for substituted benzene compounds uses the prefixes *ortho* (*o*-), *meta* (*m*-), and *para* (*p*-), for substituents in the 1,2-, 1,3-, and 1,4-positions, respectively. Thus, 1,2-dichlorobenzene, 1,3-dichlorobenzene, and 1,4-dichlorobenzene are also named *o*-dichlorobenzene, *m*-dichlorobenzene, and *p*-dichlorobenzene, respectively.

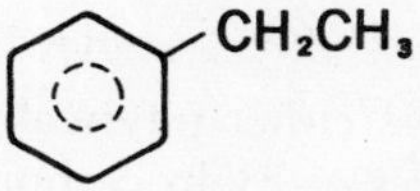

ethylbenzene or phenylethane

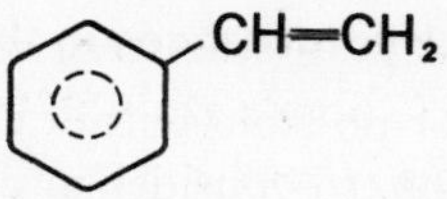

phenylethene or
vinylbenzene (styrene)

The last two compounds chosen as examples contain both aliphatic and aromatic units. Hydrocarbons of this kind are known collectively as *arenes*. Apply the nomenclature rules you discovered to the following exercises.

1. Name the aromatic hydrocarbons shown at the right.
2. Draw structural formulas for the following:
   a. *o*-chlorobromobenzene
   b. 2,4-dinitrotoluene
   c. 2,3,5,-trinitromethylbenzene
   d. butylbenzene

a.

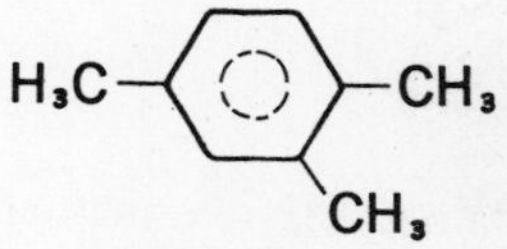

b.

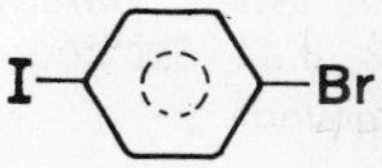

c.

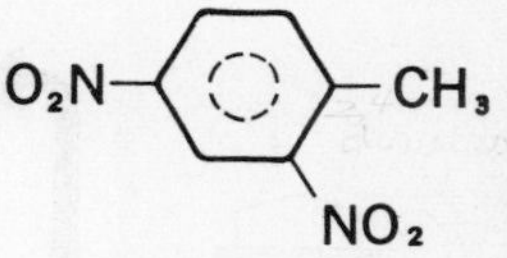

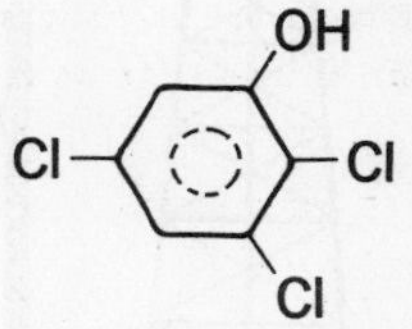

## 29.16 Some reactions of benzene

A further indication that benzene lacks the definite double bond character of a true alkene is the fact that it reacts by substitution more readily than by addition. For example:

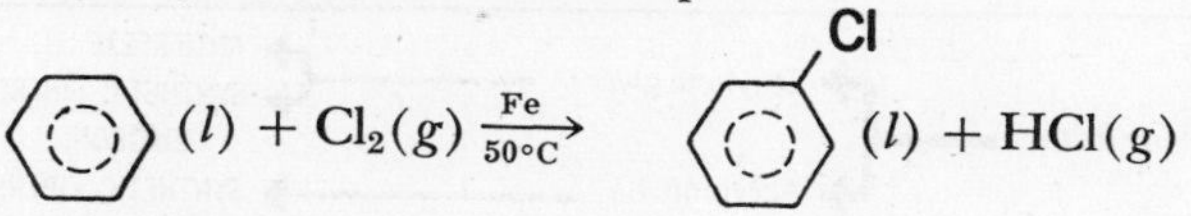

d.

An indication that benzene lacks the properties of a true alkane is the vital fact that benzene is much more chemically reactive than the alkanes. Benzene is used as the starting material for the synthesis of many organic compounds whose own practical value reflects even more importance to benzene as a major industrial chemical. For example, when benzene is treated with nitric acid, one of its hydrogen atoms may be substituted for a *nitro* group ($-NO_2$), forming *nitrobenzene*, $C_6H_5NO_2$. The nitro group may then be reduced with hydrogen, forming $C_6H_5NH_2$, *aniline*, a colorless liquid that is the basis of many coal-tar or aniline dyes. The sequence of reactions,

coal $\longrightarrow$ benzene $\longrightarrow$ nitrobenzene $\longrightarrow$ aniline $\longrightarrow$ an aniline dye,

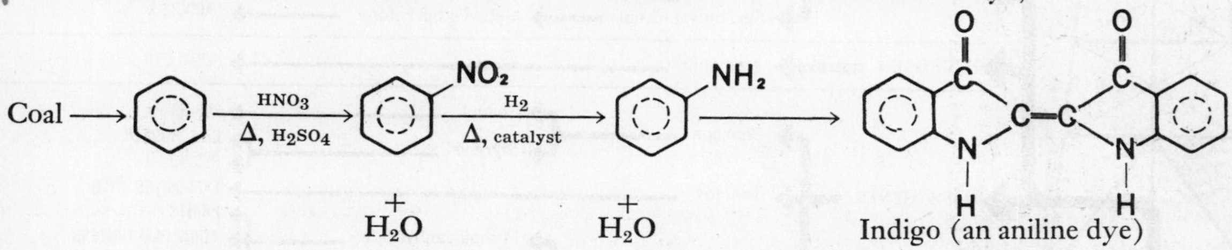

is representative of the great creativity associated with organic chemical syntheses.

### 29.17 Hydrocarbons in the service of man

It is not possible within the scope of this book, either physically or by intention, to consider in detail the manifold uses of hydrocarbons in the service of man. Figure 29.11 gives a brief indication of the vast creative wealth that the petrochemicals industry, alone, has bestowed upon mankind. Surely, not a day in each of your lives passes that has not been made healthier, safer, and more pleasant through the products of organic chemical research. If there is a lesson to be learned from this very brief introduction to the hydrocarbons, it is that only through a systematic study of such compounds has it been possible for the countless products of the organic chemical industry to have been synthesized. Despite the almost bewildering array of compounds within his research interest, the organic chemist has learned to bring order to the seeming chaos through an understanding and application of the principles of atomic structure, chemical bonding, thermodynamics, and chemical kinetics that you have begun to understand.

**FIGURE 29.11** Petrochemicals: more than 650,000 possible compounds

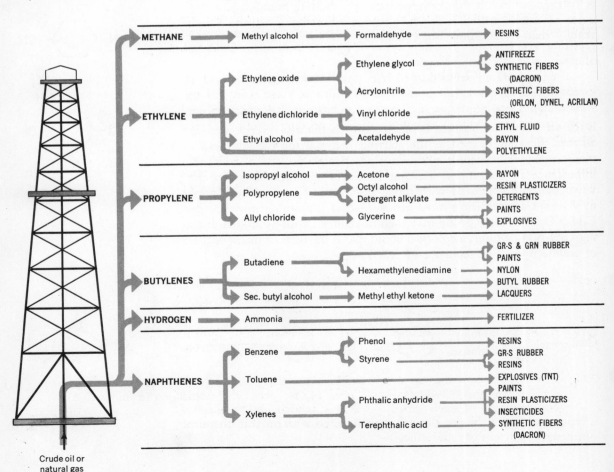

Crude oil or natural gas

# SUMMARY

With Wöhler's rearrangement of ammonium cyanate, the science of organic chemistry began. Van't Hoff showed the way to a better understanding of the structure of organic compounds by proving that the tetravalent carbon atom formed equivalent, tetrahedrally oriented bonds. The ability of carbon to bond covalently to itself in chains and rings explains the fact that more organic compounds have been identified than inorganic ones.

The hydrocarbons are the simplest organic compounds. Consisting only of hydrogen and carbon, they form two major groups: the aliphatics and the aromatics. The close relationships of compounds in homologous series are typical of the aliphatic hydrocarbons, as is structural isomerism. Important to the study of the hydrocarbons is a system of specific and unambiguous nomenclature.

Reactions involving the saturated hydrocarbons, or alkanes, are relatively slow. Halogen substitution reactions, dehydrogenations, and cracking are common reaction types for such molecules. Oxidation of them yields a variety of products.

Unsaturated carbon-to-carbon bonds in the alkenes and alkynes introduce geometric isomerism. In addition, these points of unsaturation lead to reactions such as hydrogenation, halogenation, and hydrogen halide addition. Another very important reaction of the unsaturated hydrocarbons is polymerization.

Kekulé's dream and the modern concept of the benzene structure are really not too different. The aromatic series of compounds based on benzene include tremendous numbers of ring molecules of great practical importance.

# QUESTIONS AND PROBLEMS

**29.1**   Why may Wöhler's synthesis of urea from ammonium cyanate be considered solely as a rearrangement of atoms?

**29.2**   a. What is a hydrocarbon? b. Name the two major hydrocarbon groups. c. Give formulas for specific compounds from each group.

**29.3**   a. What is a homologous series? b. Name the three homologous series of aliphatic hydrocarbons. c. Give the general formula for members of each series. d. Give extended and condensed structural formulas for a member of each series that has four carbon atoms per molecule.

29.4 Describe and explain the relationship between boiling point and molecular weight in a homologous series of hydrocarbons.

29.5 a. What is meant by structural isomerism? b. Give extended structural formulas for the structural isomers having the formula $C_6H_{14}$. c. Name each of the isomers.

29.6 Describe and explain the relationship between the boiling point and structure of straight-chain and branched-chain isomers.

29.7 Name each of the following:

a. $CH_3(CH_2)_5CH_3$

b. $(CH_3)_2CHC(CH_3)(C_2H_5)_2$

c. $BrCH_2C(CH_3)_2CH_2CH_3$

d. $CH_3CH(CH_2CH_2CH_3)_2$

e. $(CH_3)_3CCH_2CH(CH_3)_2$

f. $CH_3C(CH_3)_2CH_2CH_2Cl$

29.8 Write equations for the complete combustion of the compounds in parts a., b., d., e., of Problem 29.7.

29.9 Give condensed and extended structural formulas for the following: a. 3,3-dichloro-4-methylheptane; b. 2,2,4-trimethylpentane; c. 2,4,6-trimethyl-3,5-dichloroheptane; d. 2-methylbutane.

29.10 Criticize the names of the following and suggest correct names for them: a. 2-ethyl-4-methylhexane; b. 2-bromo-4-ethylpentane.

29.11 Give structural formulas for the following: a. methylcyclohexane; b. cyclobutane; c. 1,3-dimethylcyclopentane; d. cyclopropane.

29.12 What is meant by the term "cracking"? Of what industrial significance is the cracking process?

29.13 Give extended structural formulas for each of the following: a. 1-butene; b. 1,2-butadiene; c. 3-heptyne; d. 4,4-dimethyl-2-pentene; e. 3-methyl-1-hexyne; f. 4-bromo-1-butene.

29.14 a. What is meant by geometric isomerism? b. Give extended structural formulas for the geometric isomers having the formula $C_2H_2Cl_2$. c. Name each of the isomers.

29.15 The boiling point of cis-dichloroethene is 60.1°C; that of trans-dichloroethene is 48.4°C. Explain.

29.16 Write equations for the following: a. bromine addition to 1-butene; b. hydrogen chloride addition to propene; c. hydrogenation of 2-pentene.

29.17 Describe the general properties of aromatic hydrocarbons in terms of those of aliphatic hydrocarbons.

29.18 Give structural formulas for the following: a. 1,3-dibromobenzene; b. *o*-dinitrobenzene; c. hexamethylbenzene; d. *p*-dichlorobenzene; e. phenyl iodide; f. 2-bromo-1,3-dimethylbenzene; g. 1,3,4-trichlorobenzene.

29.19 Determine the percentage compositions of: **a.** hexacontane (Table 29–1); **b.** 2-undecene (Table 29–3); **c.** 6-dodecyne; **d.** benzene.

ANS.  **b.** 85.7% C; **d.** 92.3% C

29.20 What volume of oxygen gas (STP) is necessary for the complete combustion of 15.5 l of propane gas stored at 23.0°C and 745 torrs?

29.21 What volume of hydrogen gas (STP) is required for the complete hydrogenation of $5.41 \times 10^5$ g of 1,3-butadiene?

ANS.  $4.48 \times 10^5$ l

29.22 When solid anthracene is completely burned to form carbon dioxide and water vapor, 1,700.4 kcal/mole are liberated. Using data in Table 13–1, calculate the heat of formation of solid anthracene. (Anthracene = $C_{14}H_{10}$)

# SUGGESTED READINGS

Asimov, Isaac. *The World of Carbon* (paperback). Crowell-Collier, 1962.

Benfey, Otto, T. *From Vital Force to Structural Formulas* (paperback). Houghton Mifflin, 1964.

Herz, Werner. *The Shape of Carbon Compounds: An Introduction to Organic Chemistry* (paperback). W. A. Benjamin, 1963.

Lessing, Lawrence P. *Understanding Chemistry* (paperback). New American Library, 1959.

CHEMISTRY
"A Concatenation of Rings." Oct. 1964
Tamelen, E. van, "Benzene—the Story of its Formulas." Jan. 1965

SCIENTIFIC AMERICAN
Brown, J. F., "Inclusion Compounds." July, 1962
Wasserman, E., "Chemical Topology." Nov. 1962

*The contributions to science
of academic research supply the food
for the applied scientist....*

*Roger Adams* (1889–      )

**CHAPTER 30**

# Functional Groups

In his systematic study of organic compounds, the chemist has observed that a further simplified classification of those compounds is possible. It is a classification that is based on similar chemical properties among compounds having the same chemically reactive atom or group of atoms in addition to their hydrocarbon cores. We might first examine the properties of the group of compounds known as *alcohols* to make clearer the basis of that kind of classification.

### 30.1 Some properties of the alcohols

Table 30–1 lists a few alcohols with their structural formulas and some of their physical properties. As in the homologous series of alkanes and alkenes (Tables 29–1 and 29–3, respectively), a regular change can be observed in the properties of these alcohols. The first four members of this series are water soluble and each has a higher boiling point than the corresponding simple alkane from which it is derived. Their solubility in water, in contrast with the insolubility of the alkanes, must reflect the existence of a degree of chemical similarity to water. This can be seen if we look upon an alcohol molecule as a water molecule in which an alkyl group, such as $CH_3-$, has replaced one of the two hydrogen atoms. (Fig. 30.1.)

Viewing the structure of the alcohols in this way also explains their elevated boiling points. In Chapter 12 we saw that water has a boiling point that is much higher than expected. This fact was explained on the basis of the strong attraction between the $H_2O$ molecules in liquid water that was due to hydrogen bonding. From the structure of methanol, we can see that hydrogen bonding can also occur between

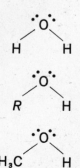

**FIGURE 30.1** Alcohols as derivatives of water

616

# and Organic Chemistry

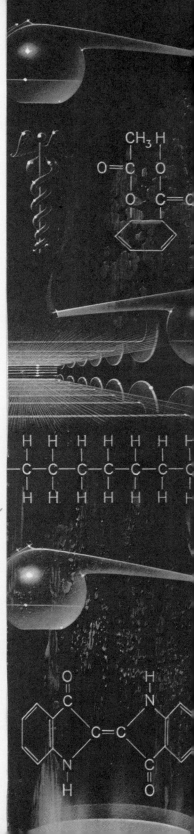

alcohol molecules. Although the alkyl group does not participate, the hydroxyl group in the molecule does. (Fig. 30.2.)

### TABLE 30–1  ALCOHOLS

| Name | Structural Formula | mp (°C) | bp (°C) | Density at 20°C (g/ml) | Solubility (g/100 g H₂O) |
|---|---|---|---|---|---|
| Methanol | H–C–OH | −97 | 64.5 | 0.793 | ∞ |
| Ethanol | H–C–C–OH | −115 | 78.3 | 0.789 | ∞ |
| 1-Propanol | H–C–C–C–OH | −126 | 97 | 0.804 | ∞ |
| 1-Butanol | H–C–C–C–C–OH | −90 | 118 | 0.810 | 7.9 |

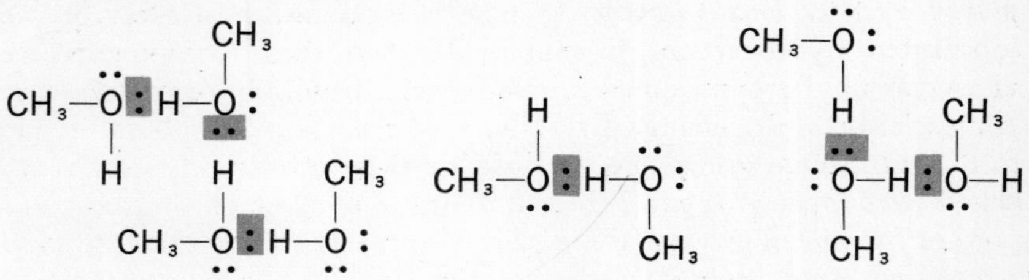

**FIGURE 30.2** Hydrogen bonding between alcohol molecules. Note that the alkyl hydrogen atoms do not participate.

### 30.2 What are functional groups?

From what has just been said, it is seen that there is some logic in considering *alcohols as hydrocarbons in which a hydrogen has been re-*

**TABLE 30–2** ORGANIC FUNCTIONAL GROUPS AND COMPOUND TYPES

| *Functional Group* | *Compound Type* | *Compound Formula* |
|---|---|---|
| —*X** | halide | *RX** |
| —OH | alcohol | *R*OH |
| —C(=O)—H | aldehyde | *R*CHO |
| —C(=O)—*R′* | ketone | *R*(CO)*R′*† |
| —C(=O)—OH | acid | *R*COOH |
| —O—*R′* | ether | *R*O*R′* |
| —C(=O)—O—*R′* | ester | *R*COO*R′* |
| —N(H)—H | amine | $RNH_2$ |
| —N(=O)—O | nitro | $RNO_2$ |

* where *X* = F, Cl, Br, I
† The alkyl groups *R* and *R′* *may* be the same.

*placed by a hydroxyl group.* In fact, the chemistry of most of the substituted hydrocarbons is simplified when those compounds are viewed as alkyl groups joined to some other, chemically reactive group. Almost always, the chemical reactivity of the alkyl compound is due to this substituted group. Because of this, these substituting groups are called *functional groups.* Table 30–2 lists a number of the most important functional groups. Remember that *the basic chemistry of alkyl compounds is determined by the functional group portion of the molecule.* It is this classification of organic compounds by functional grouping that has led to the further simplification of organic chemistry.

In a hydrocarbon derivative, the alkyl group retains its entity in most reactions. This is a reflection of the chemical stability of C—H bonds. (The low chemical reactivity of the alkane hydrocarbons was the first evidence of that stability.) While the functional group determines the basic chemistry of the compound, the alkyl group does affect the physical properties. We may thus interpret the data in Table 30–1. We now see that the polar —OH functional group produces solubility in water. The nonpolar alkyl group opposes such solubility. For all alkyl groups larger than $C_4H_9$—, the solubility opposition effect is sufficient to lead to measurable limits of solubility. Thus, we see that the physical properties especially and, to a certain extent, the chemical properties of hydrocarbon derivatives are the sum of the effects contributed by the alkyl *and* the functional groups.

## 30.3  Chemical reactions of the alcohols

From our structural viewpoint that an alcohol molecule, *ROH*, may be considered as a derivative of a water molecule, HOH, alcohols might be expected to undergo reactions analogous to those of water. In many cases, this is true.

Corresponding to the crystal hydrate, $MgCl_2 \cdot 6H_2O$, for example, are the crystal *alcoholates,* $MgCl_2 \cdot 6CH_3OH$ and $MgCl_2 \cdot 6C_2H_5OH$. Reaction of active metals with alcohols parallels the behavior of those metals with water:

$$CH_3OH(l) + Na(s) = (CH_3O)^{-1}Na^{+1}(soln) + \tfrac{1}{2}H_2(g)$$
sodium methoxide

$$ROH(l) + Na(s) = (RO)^{-1}Na^{+1}(soln) + \tfrac{1}{2}H_2(g)$$
sodium alkoxide

$$HOH(l) + Na(s) = (HO)^{-1}Na^{+1}(aq) + \tfrac{1}{2}H_2(g)$$
sodium hydroxide

The rate of *alkoxide* formation, however, is much slower than that of hydroxide formation.

Alcohols, of course, also show chemical behavior that is uniquely theirs. Two important reactions are:

1. Reaction with hydrogen halides:

$$ROH + HX = RX + HOH$$
$$\text{alkyl halide}$$

2. Oxidation or dehydrogenation to aldehydes and ketones:

$$
\underset{\text{a \textit{primary} alcohol}}{R-\overset{\displaystyle H}{\underset{\displaystyle H}{C}}-OH}
\xrightarrow[\text{via oxidation}]{\text{dehydrogenation}}
\underset{\text{an aldehyde}}{R-C\overset{\displaystyle O}{\big\langle}_{H}}
$$

$$
\underset{\text{a \textit{secondary} alcohol}}{R-\overset{\displaystyle H}{\underset{\displaystyle OH}{C}}-R'}
\xrightarrow[\text{via oxidation}]{\text{dehydrogenation}}
\underset{\text{a ketone}}{R-\overset{\displaystyle O}{\underset{\displaystyle \|}{C}}-R'}
$$

If the dehydrogenation reaction is not carefully controlled, complete oxidation to $CO_2$ and $H_2O$ occurs. For example:

$$CH_3OH(l) + \tfrac{3}{2}O_2(g) \overset{\Delta}{=} CO_2(g) + 2H_2O(g)$$

## 30.4 Three important alcohols

Of the many different alcohols that exist or that have been synthesized, three may be singled out for their particular value—methanol, ethanol, and glycerol.

*Methanol* (methyl or wood alcohol) was originally obtained from the *destructive distillation* of wood.* Among the products of this process are charcoal, wood tar, and a brownish liquid called *pyroligneous acid.* Fractional distillation of this liquid yields acetic acid, acetone, and methanol. A more efficient and less expensive way to produce the alcohol is to synthesize it from carbon monoxide and hydrogen:

$$CO(g) + 2H_2(g) \xrightarrow[\text{ZnO; Cr}_2\text{O}_3]{\Delta,\ \text{pressure}} CH_3OH(g)$$

Methanol is the main reactant used in the manufacture of many important organic compounds and is widely used as a solvent for lacquers, varnishes, and polishes. Because of its low freezing point, methanol was

---

* Complex organic materials, heated in a limited supply of air, will decompose into simpler substances without undergoing combustion.

once used extensively as an antifreeze in automobile radiators. Since it evaporated out of the system too quickly, substitutes for it were sought. *Ethylene glycol*, or 1,2-dihydroxyethane, a dihydroxy alcohol, was the main substitute found.

Human consumption of methanol or breathing of its fumes often causes blindness and even death. Tragic deaths of people addicted to alcohol who inadvertently have drunk methanol-based liquids because of that addiction are recorded each year.

*Ethanol* (ethyl or grain alcohol), $C_2H_5OH$, a flammable, colorless liquid, is prepared today, as it was thousands of years ago, by *fermentation*. Fermentation is a chemical action brought about by bacteria, yeasts, or molds. The bacteria, yeasts, or molds produce complex organic compounds called *enzymes*, which act as catalysts in the chemical breakdown of molecules. When yeast cells, for example, are placed in a sugar solution and kept warm, the enzyme *zymase* is produced by the living yeast plant. The zymase acts catalytically, helping to increase the rate of the chemical breakdown of the glucose molecule into ethanol and carbon dioxide. The over-all equation is:

$$C_6H_{12}O_6(aq) \xrightarrow{\text{zymase}} 2C_2H_5OH(l) + 2CO_2(g)$$

When the concentration of the alcoholic solution reaches between 8 and 12 per cent, the yeast plants are killed and the reaction ceases. The concentration of the alcoholic solution may be increased to 95 per cent by volume (190 proof) by fractional distillation.*

Immense quantities of *synthetic* ethanol are being manufactured today from ethylene, obtained from petroleum and natural gas:

$$CH_2{=}CH_2(g) + (HO)_2SO_2(aq) = CH_3CH_2O(HO)SO_2(aq)$$
ethylene     98% sulfuric acid     ethyl hydrogen sulfate

$$C_2H_5O(HO)SO_2(aq) + H_2O(l) \overset{\Delta}{=} C_2H_5OH(aq) + (HO)_2SO_2(aq)$$
ethyl hydrogen sulfate               ethanol

Ethanol is the alcohol base of "alcoholic" beverages. For this purpose (a very major one indeed in terms of amount produced), the alcohol is prepared only by fermentation of sugar from a wide variety of plant sources. Ethanol produced for beverage purposes is heavily

---

* This concentration limit exists because a *mixture* of 5 per cent water and 95 per cent ethyl alcohol has a lower boiling point (78.15°C) than either water (100°C) or ethyl alcohol (78.3°C). Therefore, some water is always distilled over with the alcohol. *Absolute*, or 100 per cent, ethanol may be prepared by a related, but different, distillation.

taxed. Since most of the ethanol that is produced is intended for industrial use, it must be made available in a form that is unfit to drink and thus not subject to taxation. This is accomplished by the addition of a *denaturant*, a substance that makes the ethanol unpotable and even in some cases toxic while not interfering greatly with its industrially important properties. Methanol is used as a denaturant, as are many other legally approved substances. Ethanol is the most important industrial solvent next to water. This compound is also a chemical intermediate in the industrial synthesis of hundreds of different organic compounds.

During the fermentation of sugar, a small amount of still another alcohol is produced. This is called *glycerin*, or *glycerol*, from a Greek word meaning "sweet." Glycerol is a trihydroxy alcohol and may be considered as a derivative of propane, three of whose hydrogen atoms have been replaced by three hydroxyl groups. (Fig. 30.3.)

Glycerol is largely obtained commercially as a by-product of the manufacture of soap. (Sec. 30.9.) It has also been synthesized from natural gas. Glycerine's most familiar uses are as a lubricant and a humectant. Its chief use, however, is in the manufacture of nitroglycerin and dynamite.

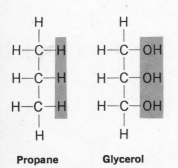

**Propane          Glycerol**

**FIGURE 30.3** Glycerol is the trihydroxy derivative of propane.

**FIGURE 30.4** Water, alcohols, ethers

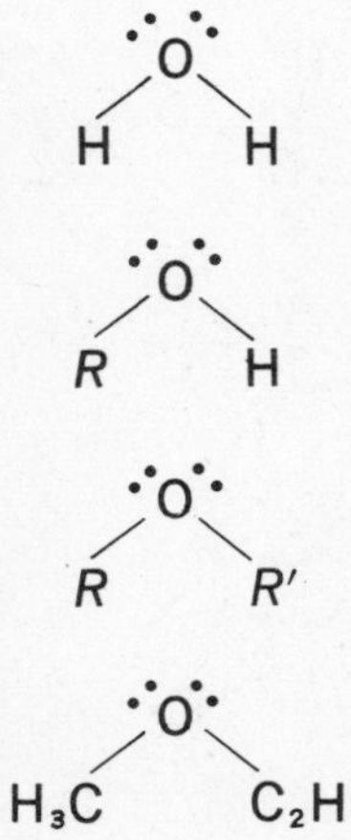

### 30.5 Ethers: derivatives of alcohols

The ethers, *R—O—R′*, can be considered as dialkyl derivatives of water, as monoalkyl derivatives of alcohols, and as isomers of alcohols. (Fig. 30.4.) However, since there are no hydrogen atoms bonded to the oxygen in ethers, hydrogen bonding between molecules does not occur. As a consequence, ethers, with little intermolecular attraction, have lower boiling points than the alcohols with which they may be considered isomeric. This illustrates the fact that structural differences between compounds are reflected by large differences in properties.

The ethers, sometimes called organic oxides, are chemically less active than alcohols. They do not react with acids, bases, or mild oxidizing agents. *Diethyl ether*, $C_2H_5OC_2H_5$, a flammable, colorless liquid, is the common anesthetic. It is an excellent solvent for fats and waxes and is prepared commercially by the action of sulfuric acid on ethyl alcohol:

$$2C_2H_5OH(l) \xrightarrow{\text{H}_2\text{SO}_4} H_2O(l) + C_2H_5\text{—}O\text{—}C_2H_5(l)$$
$$\text{ethanol} \qquad\qquad\qquad \text{diethyl ether (bp 35°C)}$$

### 30.6 Aldehydes and ketones: oxidation products of alcohols

When methanol is reacted with acidic solutions of potassium dichromate or some other oxidizing agent of similar strength, a rather sharp odor becomes noticeable. For anyone familiar with biology laboratories, the odor is recognized as that of *formaldehyde*, HCHO, simplest of all the aldehydes. The reaction is:

$$3CH_3OH(aq) + Cr_2O_7^{-2}(aq) + 8H_3O^{+1}(aq)$$
$$= 3HCHO(g) + 2Cr^{+3}(aq) + 15H_2O(l)$$

Industrially, formaldehyde is prepared by the catalytic air oxidation of methanol:

$$CH_3OH(g) + O_2(g) \overset{\Delta}{\underset{\text{catalyst}}{=}} HCHO(g) + H_2O(g)$$

Formaldehyde finds its largest use in the synthesis of *phenol-formalde-hyde* plastics. (See p. 634.)

Formaldehyde is a gas (bp −21°C), and it is usually handled in aqueous solution (*Formalin*) or as one of its solid polymers. (Fig. 30.5.) Polymerization of *acetaldehyde*, CH₃CHO, next most simple of aldehydes, also occurs, and the volatile monomer of this compound is safely obtained from this solid form. (Fig. 30.6.)

You recall that when a secondary alcohol is oxidized under mild conditions, a ketone results. (Sec. 30.3.) The formation of *acetone* (dimethyl ketone), simplest of the ketones, from 2-propanol (isopropyl alcohol) is a good example of such a reaction:

$$3 \; H_3C\overset{\overset{\displaystyle H}{|}}{\underset{\underset{\displaystyle OH}{|}}{C}}CH_3(aq) + Cr_2O_7^{-2}(aq) + 8H_3O^{+1}(aq) \overset{\Delta}{=}$$

$$3 \; H_3C\overset{}{\underset{\underset{\displaystyle O}{\|}}{C}}CH_3 \; (g) + 2Cr^{+3}(aq) + 15H_2O(l)$$

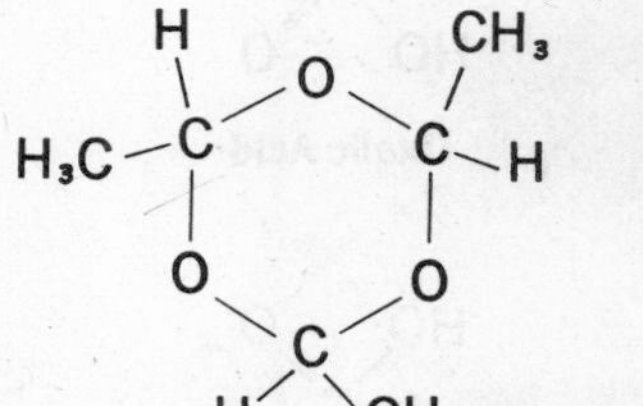

Acetone is the most important industrial ketone. This highly flammable, fragrant liquid is used as a solvent.

The physical properties of aldehydes and ketones are greatly influenced by the high polarity of the *carbonyl* functional group, $\text{C=O}$, in them. In general, aldehydes and ketones have high dipole moments, and higher boiling points than the alcohols from which they are derived. The polarity of the low molecular weight carbonyl compounds accounts for their unusual solubility in water.

## 30.7 The carboxylic acids: organic acids

If the oxidation of alcohols is carried out under stronger oxidizing conditions, the reaction proceeds beyond the aldehyde or ketone stage to produce an organic acid.

$$\left[ \; CH_2\,OCH_2\,OCH_2O \; \right]_x$$

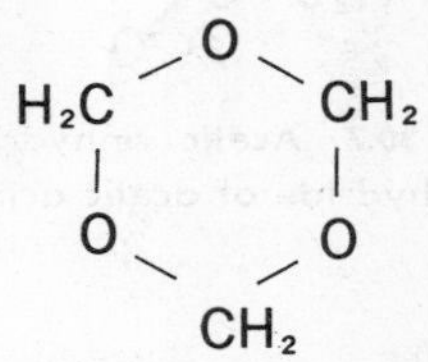

FIGURE 30.5 The solid polymers of formaldehyde: *para-formaldehyde* (top) and *trioxane* (bottom)

FIGURE 30.6 The solid trimer of acetaldehyde: *paraldehyde*

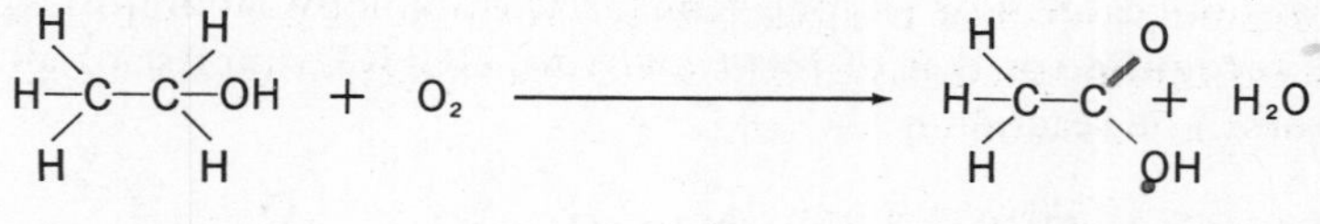

$$H-\overset{\overset{\displaystyle H}{|}}{\underset{\underset{\displaystyle H}{|}}{C}}-\overset{\overset{\displaystyle H}{|}}{\underset{\underset{\displaystyle H}{|}}{C}}-OH \ + \ O_2 \quad\longrightarrow\quad H-\overset{\overset{\displaystyle H}{|}}{\underset{\underset{\displaystyle H}{|}}{C}}-C\overset{\displaystyle O}{\underset{\displaystyle OH}{}} \ + \ H_2O$$

ethanol                          acetic acid (CH₃COOH)

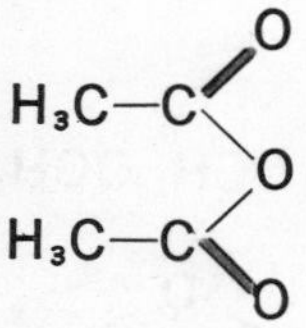

**FIGURE 30.7** Acetic anhydride: the anhydride of acetic acid

The $-C\overset{\displaystyle O}{\underset{\displaystyle OH}{}}$ functional group is called the *carboxyl* group and organic acids are, therefore, *carboxylic acids*. The hydrogen atom that is attached to the carboxyl group is replaceable in the same manner as the hydrogen in inorganic acids such as HCl and $H_2SO_4$. However, the carboxylic acids are weak acids, since they are only slightly ionized in aqueous solutions.

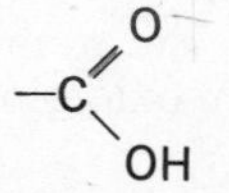

Acetic acid is the most important of all carboxylic acids. It is produced by the catalytic oxidation of acetaldehyde,

$$CH_3CHO(aq) + \tfrac{1}{2}O_2(g) \overset{catalyst}{=} CH_3COOH(aq),$$

as well as by the fractional distillation of pyroligneous acid, and is used in many industrial processes. The dilute solution of acetic acid (about 5 per cent in strength) that is known as *vinegar* is produced by the very slow, enzyme-catalyzed air oxidation of the ethanol produced by fermenting wine, cider, or malt:

$$CH_3CH_2OH(aq) + O_2(g) \overset{enzyme}{=} CH_3COOH(aq) + H_2O(l)$$

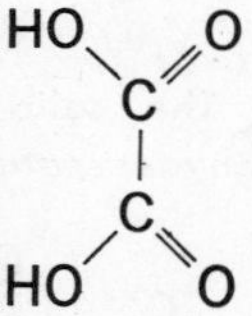

Pure, anhydrous acetic acid is an oily liquid which solidifies to icelike crystals at 16.6°C. It is known as glacial acetic acid. The anhydride of acetic acid may also be prepared. (Fig. 30.7.)

Just as polyhydroxy alcohols exist, such as ethylene glycol and glycerol, so, too, do polycarboxylic acids. The simplest of these is oxalic acid, in which two carboxyl groups are bonded together. A more complex case is that of citric acid, which is found in citrus fruits. (Fig. 30.8.)

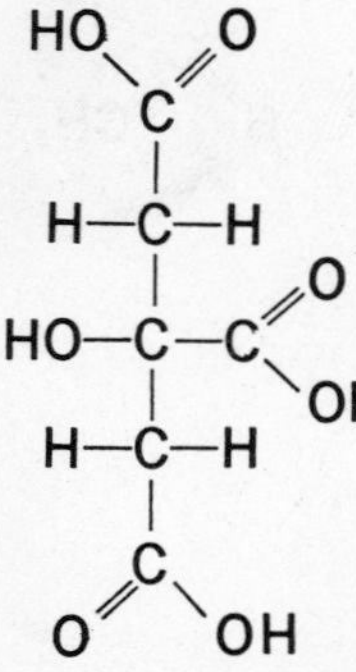

**Oxalic Acid**

**Citric Acid**

**FIGURE 30.8** Polycarboxylic acids

### 30.8 Esters: derivatives of organic acids

When alcohols are mixed with carboxylic acids in the presence of either hydronium or hydroxyl ion as a catalyst, the important reaction known as *esterification* takes place:

$$ROH(aq) + HOOCR'(aq) \underset{\text{or base}}{\overset{acid}{\rightleftharpoons}} ROOCR'(l) + H_2O(l)$$

The organic product of this reaction is known as an *ester*. Superficially, the esterification reaction resembles the neutralization reaction between an inorganic base and an inorganic acid:

$$MOH(aq) + HX(aq) \rightleftharpoons MX(aq) + H_2O(l)$$

The latter reaction, however, occurs at a much faster rate and via a relatively simple mechanism. There can be no doubt that the hydrogen atom of the inorganic acid and the hydroxyl group of the base form the water molecule product. In the case of esterification, however, two mechanisms are possible:

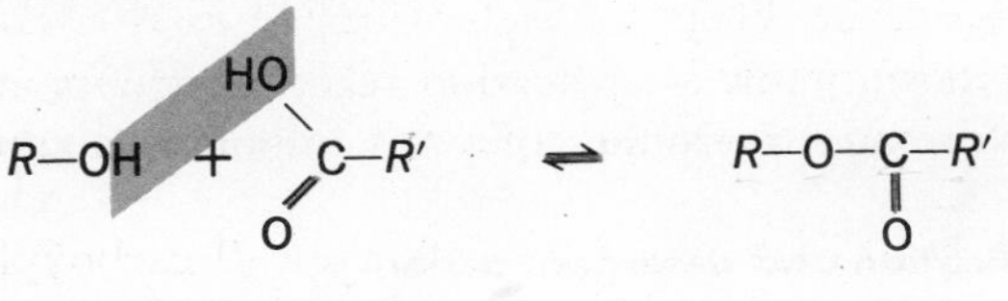

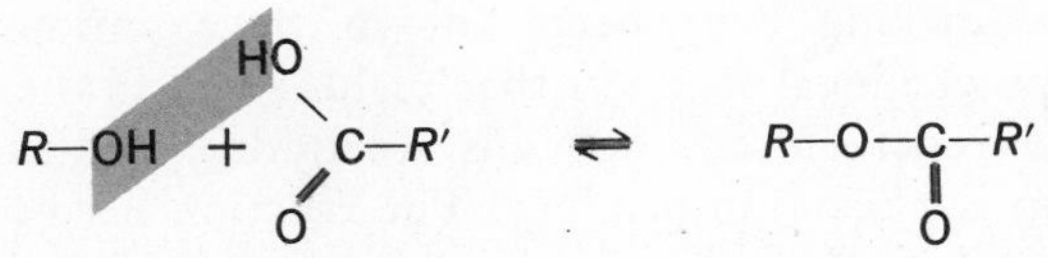

It is interesting to note that using compounds tagged with heavy oxygen atoms, $^{18}_{8}O$ rather than $^{16}_{8}O$, and following the path of those heavy atoms, both possible mechanisms have been found for different combinations of alcohols and acids.

Most esters are colorless liquids, soluble in alcohol, with fragrant, fruity odors. Examples of esters used as food flavoring are listed in Table 30–3.

**TABLE 30–3** Some Esters Used as Flavoring in Foods

| Ester* | Derivation | Flavor |
|---|---|---|
| $HCOOC_2H_5$<br>ethyl formate<br>ethyl methanoate | ethanol and formic (methanoic) acid | rum |
| $CH_3COOC_5H_{11}$<br>amyl acetate<br>n-pentyl ethanoate | amyl alcohol (n-pentanol) and acetic (ethanoic) acid | banana |
| $CH_3(CH_2)_2COOC_2H_5$<br>ethyl butyrate<br>ethyl butanoate | ethanol and butyric (butanoic) acid | pineapple |
| $HOC_6H_4COOCH_3$<br>methyl salicylate<br>methyl o-hydroxybenzoate | methanol and salicylic (o-hydroxybenzoic) acid | wintergreen (synthetic oil) |

* We note the unpleasant state of affairs that to name esters properly, their structural formulas must be read backwards.

Many waxes and animal and vegetable fats and oils are esters or mixtures of esters. In these natural products, high molecular weight alcohols and acids have combined to form solid esters of high weight. Beeswax, for example, contains the ester whose formula is $C_{15}H_{31}COOC_{31}H_{63}$. A common ester found in beef fat is glycerol tristearate, or *stearin*, which may also be synthesized in the laboratory:

$$C_3H_5(OH)_3(l) + 3C_{17}H_{35}COOH(s) \rightleftharpoons$$
$$\text{glycerol} \qquad\qquad \text{stearic acid}$$

$$(C_{17}H_{35}COO)_3C_3H_5(s) + 3H_2O(l)$$
$$\text{stearin}$$

When the reverse of this esterification reaction occurs in the presence of sodium hydroxide, a product of great importance results—soap.

### 30.9 Saponification and detergent action

Soap and soapmaking have been known since antiquity. We now understand the chemical reaction that yields soap. If the esters present in animal and vegetable fats and oils are hydrolyzed in the presence of a base, soap is a reaction product. The reaction between stearin and sodium hydroxide will serve as an example of *saponification*:

$$(C_{17}H_{35}COO)_3C_3H_5(s) + 3NaOH(aq) \rightleftharpoons$$
$$\text{stearin, a fat}$$

$$3(C_{17}H_{35}COO)^{-1}Na^{+1}(aq) + C_3H_5(OH)_3(l)$$
$$\text{sodium stearate, a soap} \qquad \text{glycerol}$$

Soaps then are the metallic salts of high molecular weight fatty acids.

On the basis of modern concepts of molecular structure, we are also now able to suggest a plausible mechanism for the cleansing, or *detergent*, action of soap. This action can most simply be considered in terms of the electrical properties of the fatty acid anion part of a soap molecule. As Figure 30.9 indicates, the anion, by virtue of its unusual structure, serves to bind together two usually immiscible substances—grease and water.

In recent years, synthetic detergents, or *syndets*, have largely replaced soaps as cleansing agents, particularly in industrial use. Syndets have structural features similar to soap that impart cleansing action. They have the added virtue of not forming insoluble products with heavy metal ions. (Sec. 26.10.) They have disadvantages, too. The tons of syndets poured into our waters as waste are not broken down by natural bacterial action as readily as are soaps. Accordingly, much contamination and foaming in water supplies has become evident. The syndet industry has met the challenge by developing a *biodegradable* series of detergents whose use will *completely* supplant older, contaminating detergents.

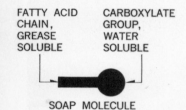

FATTY ACID CHAIN, GREASE SOLUBLE    CARBOXYLATE GROUP, WATER SOLUBLE

SOAP MOLECULE

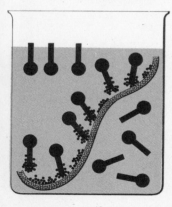

**FIGURE 30.9** Detergent action of soap

A sewage disposal unit. What is the problem? What is the solution?

## 30.10 Functional groups and aromatic hydrocarbons

Again, the physical limitations and scope of this book preclude a more detailed study of functional groups. We have limited our brief view to aliphatic hydrocarbons and functional groups. It will not surprise you to learn that alcohols, aldehydes, ketones, carboxylic acids, and esters also exist in the sprawling domain of the aromatic hydrocarbons. Figure 30.10 shows a number of these and hints at the importance and familiar use of some of them.

**FIGURE 30.10** Aromatic hydrocarbon derivatives

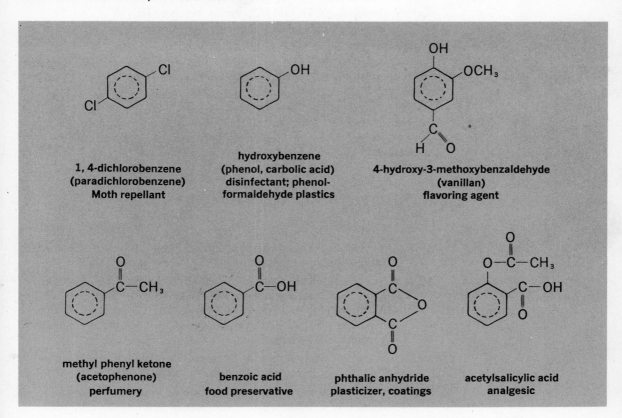

1, 4-dichlorobenzene
(paradichlorobenzene)
Moth repellant

hydroxybenzene
(phenol, carbolic acid)
disinfectant; phenol-
formaldehyde plastics

4-hydroxy-3-methoxybenzaldehyde
(vanillan)
flavoring agent

methyl phenyl ketone
(acetophenone)
perfumery

benzoic acid
food preservative

phthalic anhydride
plasticizer, coatings

acetylsalicylic acid
analgesic

The field of organic chemistry is so fertile for study and so fraught with practical implications that no one book or article can reflect all the facets of its many wonders. Selected readings from the literature on organic chemistry and its applications should lead you to a sounder understanding of the structure of, and a warmer feeling for the romance of, organic chemistry.

## SUMMARY

A most important classification for organic compounds is one that brings together compounds containing the same functional group. In alcohols, the functional group is —OH, and the properties of alcohols, *ROH*, can be compared with the properties of water, *HOH*.

Controlled, mild oxidation of alcohols leads to the formation of two different classes of organic compounds, in which the carbonyl group, $\text{C}=\text{O}$ , is part of the functional group. Oxidation of primary alcohols, $RCH_2OH$, yields aldehydes, *RCHO*. Oxidation of secondary alcohols, *RCH(OH)R′*, yields ketones, *RCOR′*.

Organic acids, *RCOOH*, also containing the carbonyl group as part of the functional group, result when alcohols undergo controlled oxidation under more severe conditions. Organic acids, weakly ionized in aqueous solution, react with alcohols to form esters, *RCOOR′*, in a reversible reaction. The alkaline hydrolysis of the glycerol esters of fatty acids leads to the formation of soaps. The mechanism for the detergent action of soaps and synthetic detergents is based on the different electrical properties of opposite ends of very long ions.

## QUESTIONS AND PROBLEMS

**30.1**  Account for the relatively high boiling points of alcohols of low molecular weight.

**30.2**  Give extended structural formulas for the following: **a.** 1-butanol (1-hydroxybutane or *n*-butyl alcohol); **b.** 2-butanol (2-hydroxybutane); **c.** 2-methyl-2-propanol (2-methyl-2-hydroxypropane); **d.** 2,2-dimethylpropanol; **e.** 2-methyl-2-butanol; **f.** 3-methyl-2-butanol.

**30.3**  Of the alcohols noted in Problem 30.2, which are **a.** primary alcohols; **b.** secondary alcohols; **c.** tertiary alcohols?

**30.4**  Write equations for the following: **a.** complete combustion of 2-butanol; **b.** dichromate oxidation of ethanol to acetaldehyde;

**c.** dichromate oxidation of 2-butanol to methyl ethyl ketone (2-butanone); **d.** formation of sodium ethoxide.

**30.5** Give structural formulas for 1,2-ethanediol (1,2-dihydroxy-ethane or ethylene glycol) and for 1,2,3-propanetriol. What commercial uses are made of these compounds?

**30.6** Give structural formulas for the different types of benzene derivatives that contain the carbonyl group, $>C=O$. Choose the simplest compound representative of each possible type.

**30.7** Phthalic acid is 1,2-benzenedicarboxylic acid. Give the structural formula for phthalic anhydride.

**30.8** Write equations for the esterification reaction that occurs between the following pairs of compounds and name the ester formed in each case: **a.** methanol and acetic acid; **b.** ethanol and formic acid; **c.** propanol and benzoic acid.

**30.9** Maleic acid and fumaric acid are the *cis* and *trans* isomers of 1,2-ethylenedicarboxylic acid, respectively. **a.** Give structural formulas for each of the two acids. **b.** Which of the two acids do you think has the higher melting point? Explain your answer and determine whether it is correct. **c.** Give the structural formula for maleic anhydride.

**30.10** $K_A$ for phenol is $1.3 \times 10^{-10}$. $K_A$ for benzoic acid is $6.5 \times 10^{-5}$. Explain the difference in acid strengths on the basis of molecular structures.

**30.11** Salicylic acid is *o*-hydroxybenzoic acid. Which functional group in salicylic acid do you think will be involved in esterification? Explain your answer.

**30.12** Why does a solution of an inorganic base feel slippery to the touch?

**30.13** Describe a mechanism for the detergent action of a soap.

**30.14** In what ways are syndets superior to soaps?

**30.15** A 25.0-ml sample of diethyl ether, of density equal to 0.714 g/ml, is burned completely in air. **a.** What volume of dry $CO_2$ gas, measured at 750 torrs and 27.0°C, will the reaction yield? **b.** How many molecules of steam will be produced?
ANS. **b.** $7.28 \times 10^{23}$ molecules

**30.16** Given the following data at 25.0°C and 1.0 atm:

$$C_2H_5OH(l) \quad \Delta H_f = -66.4 \text{ kcal/mole}$$
$$C_2H_5OH(g) \quad \Delta H_f = -56.2 \text{ kcal/mole}$$

**a.** Calculate the heat of vaporization per mole of ethanol at 25.0°C and 1.0 atm. **b.** Calculate the heat of combustion per mole of liquid ethanol at 25.0°C and 1.0 atm. (See Table 13–1, p. 309, for other data needed.)
ANS. **b.** $-295$ kcal/mole

**30.17** What is the pH of a 0.20M $C_6H_5COOH$ solution? ($K_A$ of $C_6H_5COOH$ is $6.5 \times 10^{-5}$.)

**30.18** The solubility of calcium stearate, $Ca(C_{18}H_{35}O_2)_2$, is $4.00 \times 10^{-2}$ gram per liter of solution. **a.** Calculate $K_{sp}$ of calcium stearate. **b.** What is the practical significance of this compound?

## SUGGESTED READINGS

Carson, Rachel. *Silent Spring* (paperback). Fawcett, 1964.

Jaffe, Bernard. *Chemistry Creates a New World* (paperback). Pyramid Publications, 1961.

Read, John. *A Direct Entry into Organic Chemistry* (paperback). Harper, 1960.

Rochow, E. G. *Organometallic Chemistry* (paperback). Reinhold, 1964.

CHEMISTRY

Jaffe, E. E. and W. J. Marshall, "Origin of Color in Organic Compounds." Dec. 1964

SCIENTIFIC AMERICAN

Braidwood, R. J., "The Agricultural Revolution." Sept. 1960

Collier, H. O. J., "Aspirin." Nov. 1963

De Bruyne, N. A., "The Action of Adhesives." Apr. 1962

Mason, Brian, "Organic Matter from Space." Mar. 1963

# Giant Molecules

## PLASTICS, FIBERS, FILMS, AND FEATHERS

The story of giant molecules is one as old as life itself.  Nearly sixty
million years ago, a living insect was entombed in the sticky, natural
*resin* exuded by a coniferous tree. As long years passed, organic
molecules in the resin linked together, or *polymerized,* to form the giant
molecules that constitute *amber,* the jewel-like crypt for this fossil fly.

## FEATHERS, BEAKS,

Nature, itself, is the domain of the *high polymer*. As we have seen, the nonliving world is dominated by silicate minerals. Many of these are giant molecules in which $SiO_4$ tetrahedra are linked in a variety of spatial orientations (Sec. 26.9).

In the living world, it is the self-bonding, or *catenation*, of carbon atoms that results in the polymeric species that constitute living matter. As we shall see, such essential molecular constituents of life as *carbohydrates*, *proteins*, and *nucleic*

The protein *keratin* is the basis of myriad forms of great beauty—the peacock's feathers (above), the toucan's beak (far right)—and of great strength—the rhinoceros' horn, the eagle's claw. *Fibroin* is the basis of silk and the gossamer beauty of the spider's web.

Out of the polymeric, resinous secretions of *Laccifer lacca*, the oriental *lac bug* (near right), comes shellac.

Cellulose is woven into patterns of symmetrical beauty in the great woody plants that we call trees (center).

632

## AND SPIDER WEBS

*acids* are all high polymers. (See Secs. 31.7–31.10, 31.12–31.14.)

*Cellulose*, a carbohydrate, is the main structuring molecule of the plant kingdom. The proteins *keratin* and *fibroin* are important structuring molecules in the physiology of animals. *Deoxyribonucleic acid, DNA*, a giant *polyester*, appears to be the molecular component of plants and animals that bears genetic information. There are literally tens upon tens of thousands of giant molecules that Nature weaves into the variegated fabric of life. And with what wonder and beauty does that fabric emerge.

## PLASTICS AND FIBERS: A History in Brief

The era of *synthetic plastics* began in 1868 with the efforts of an inventive American printer, John Wesley Hyatt. Previously, a few discoveries had been made that led to alterations in the structure and composition of natural polymers. Among these were the *tanning* of leather, the *mercerization* of natural fibers, the *vulcanization* of rubber, and the synthesis of *cellulose nitrate*, or *pyroxylin (collodion)*. In his search to find a substitute for ivory—then in too short supply to be used in the manufacture of billiard balls—Hyatt hit upon the idea of treating pyroxylin with solid camphor. The result of his work was *Celluloid* and the American plastics industry was born. It was, however, another four decades before the industry saw its next advance.

In 1909, Dr. Leo Hendrik Baekeland, a Belgian-born American, introduced *phenol-formaldehyde* plastics, and techniques for converting them to commercial use. In his honor the first commercial *phenolic* was given the trade name *Bakelite*. Since Baekeland's pioneering efforts, there has been created a whole spectrum of plastics—giant molecular materials that are solids in a finished form, but fluid at some stage during processing.

Another milestone in the history of synthetic polymers occurred in the laboratory of Dr. Wallace Hume Carothers of the E. I. du Pont de Nemours & Company, in 1930, with the discovery of *nylon*. Though not the first man-made fiber—that honor goes to *rayon*, a reconstituted cellulose derived from nitrocellulose—nylon was the first synthetic polymer derived from simple chemicals that could be spun into yarn. It was soon followed by a host of other fibers that were products of the test tube, and that have changed the clothing habits of this nation and much of the world.

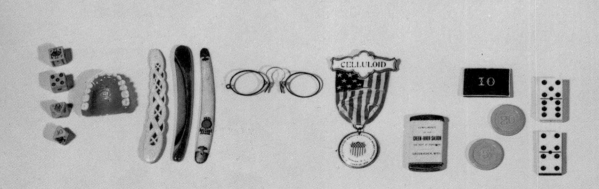

In the bottom photograph are some examples of early products made from the highly flammable, easily discolored *Celluloid*. The most famous product of all, the Celluloid collar, is shown at the right in the top photograph. Two examples of early products manufactured from *phenolic resins* may also be seen in the top photograph—the billiard balls and the agitator of a washing machine. At the center of this photograph is pictured one of the first pairs of hose made from *nylon* fiber.

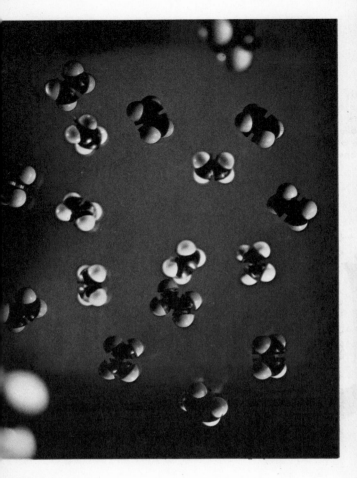

In the above photograph are models representing gaseous ethylene monomers. Under reaction conditions, 250°C and pressures above 300 atm, the ethylene molecules are induced to form free radicals by the catalyst, represented by the large orange spheres shown in the photograph at the top center. In this same photograph, an ethylene monomer is about to react with the four-carbon free radical shown in the foreground. In the right center photograph, the noted addition has occurred, resulting in the formation of a six-carbon free radical. Other, shorter radicals are depicted being formed catalytically. In the photograph at the near right, additional polymerizations are represented. In the photograph at the far right, chains of polyethylene are illustrated in a crystalline orientation. Note that while some of the chains may double back or may be discontinuous, almost no *cross-linking* or *branching* has occurred.

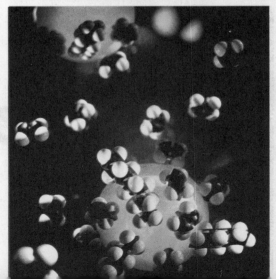

## ADDITION POLYMERIZATION

As we have seen, a characteristic property of alkenes is self-polymerization at the site of the double bond. (Sec. 29.13.) The classic example of such an *addition polymerization* is the case of the formation of polyethylene:

$$n\ H_2C{=}CH_2 \xrightarrow[\text{catalyst}]{\Delta} H\left[-\underset{\underset{H}{|}}{\overset{\overset{H}{|}}{C}}-\underset{\underset{H}{|}}{\overset{\overset{H}{|}}{C}}-\right]_n H \quad \Delta H = -22\ \text{kcal/mole}\ C_2H_4$$

This highly exothermic reaction proceeds via a free radical mechanism. (Sec. 14.6.) The catalyst used, therefore, is one that leads to free radical formation. The resultant product, a *homopolymer*, derived from monomers of the same kind, is a solid with molecular weight generally between 10,000 and 40,000 amu, though forms of higher molecular weight can also be made. Some two billion pounds of polyethylene were produced in the United States in 1963.

Derivatives of ethylene lead to a second great class of addition polymers—the *vinyls*. In 1963, vinyl chloride, $C_2H_3Cl$, vinyl alcohol, $C_2H_3OH$, and vinyl acetate, $C_2H_3OOCCH_3$, were formed into more than 1.5 billion pounds of homopolymers and *copolymers* of widespread use. Vinyl benzene, or styrene, $C_6H_5C_2H_3$, is the monomer from which 1.5 billion pounds of *polystyrene*, another major class of addition polymers, were synthesized in 1963. Of growing commercial importance is *polypropylene*, a *polyolefin* that can be formed into fibers.

## CONDENSATION POLYMERIZATION

When hexamethylenediamine, $H_2N(CH_2)_6NH_2$, is reacted under appropriate conditions with *adipic acid*, $HOOC(CH_2)_4COOH$, a giant chainlike molecule forms:

$$n \; H-\underset{\underset{H}{|}}{N}(CH_2)_6\underset{\underset{H}{|}}{N}-H \; + \; n \; HO-\overset{\overset{O}{\parallel}}{C}(CH_2)_4\overset{\overset{O}{\parallel}}{C}-OH$$

$$H\left[-\underset{\underset{H}{|}}{N}(CH_2)_6\underset{\underset{H}{|}}{N}-\overset{\overset{O}{\parallel}}{C}(CH_2)_4\overset{\overset{O}{\parallel}}{C}-\right]_n OH \; + \; (2n-1)H_2O$$

This *polyamide*, characterized by the presence of the $-\underset{\underset{H}{|}}{N}-\overset{\overset{O}{\parallel}}{C}-$ , *amide*, functional group, is nylon. The process in which monomer molecules combine with the loss of some small, simple molecule—water, in this case—is called *condensation polymerization*.

Organic acids containing more than one carboxyl group will undergo condensation polymerization with *amines* containing more than one $-NH_2$ group, or with alcohols containing more than one hydroxyl group, to form polyamide and polyester products, respectively. Some of these have become so widely used that their trade names have become household words. The table on the next page summarizes the polymeric nature of these and other familiar polymeric items of commerce in this golden age of synthetic organic chemistry.

At the far left are seen models of hexamethylenediamine and adipic acid. These react to form the dimer *nylon salt* (near left). When heated, the nylon salt dimers undergo condensation polymerization to form *nylon-6,6* chains (above). Hydrogen bonding, shown as green bands in the above right photograph, occurs between the polyamide chains. This imparts an axis of orientation to the polymer, which allows it to be pulled into fibers.

## POLYMERS IN THE SERVICE OF MAN

### ADDITION POLYMERS

| Basic Monomeric Unit | Familiar Trade Products |
|---|---|
| $H_2C=CHC\equiv N$<br>acrylonitrile | *Acrilan; Creslan; Dynel; Orlon* |
| $H_2C=C(CH_3)COOCH_3$<br>methyl methacrylate | *Lucite; Plexiglas* |
| $H_2C=CCl_2$<br>vinylidene chloride | *Saran* |
| $H_2C=CHC=CH_2$<br>1,3-butadiene | *Buna S* [*] and *Buna N* [†]<br>synthetic rubbers; *Neoprene* [‡] |

### CONDENSATION POLYMERS

| General Polymeric Type | Familiar Trade Products |
|---|---|
| Polyamides | *Antron; Caprolan; Nylon; Zytel*<br>Urea-formaldehyde resins<br>Polyurethane "foam rubber" |
| Polyesters | *Dacron; Fortrel; Kodel;*<br>*Lexan; Mylar* |

[*] Copolymer with styrene
[†] Copolymer with acrylonitrile
[‡] A homopolymer formed from the 2-chloro-substituted monomer

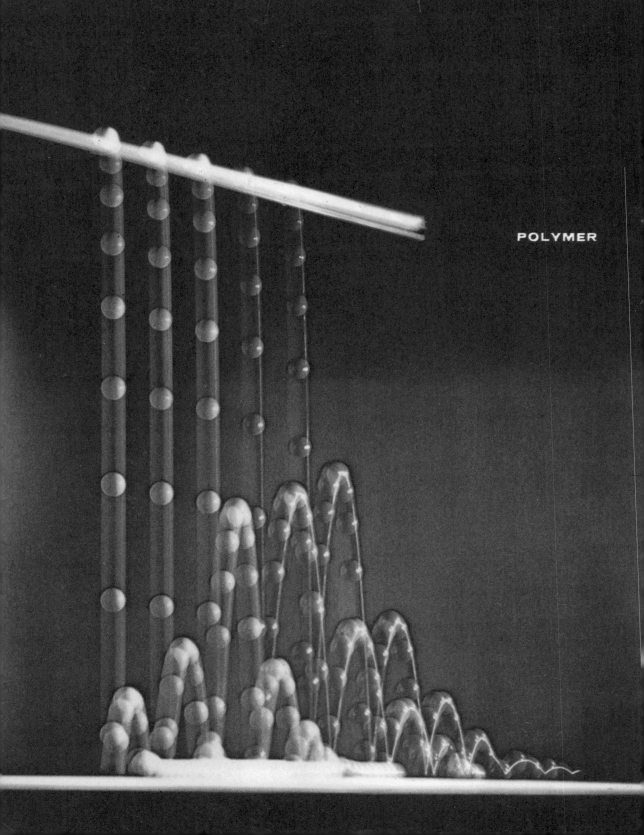

POLYMER

## STRUCTURE AND PROPERTIES

Generally, the behavioral properties of a high polymer are determined by the structure and interaction of the giant molecular chains comprising it, as shown dramatically in the photograph.* Under tension, polymeric chains tend to "slip" past one another. In most cases, however, *cross-linking* between chains tends to limit such elastic motion. Natural rubber is a tacky and difficult-to-handle material that lacks temperature stability. When heated in the presence of some sulfur, it forms a product that contains *sulfur bridge* cross-links. The product, *vulcanized rubber*, was accidentally discovered by the American Charles Goodyear in 1839 and, though less elastic, is stronger, harder, and more easily worked than natural rubber.

Most synthetic fibers contain cross-linked chains, mainly through hydrogen bonding. As a result, the fibers are strong, but lack elasticity. Recently, fiber polymers have been synthesized that have "hard" and "soft" segments along the molecular chain in regions where cross-linkings are strong or nonexistent, respectively. The hard segments impart strength to the fiber; the soft segments impart elasticity. The resulting class of *spandex fibers* is finding widespread use in the clothing industry (*Duraspan, Lycra, Vyrene*).

A significant development in polymer science has been the discovery of *stereospecific catalysts* for addition polymerizations. These induce a specific spatial orientation to a growing polymer chain, thereby building in its physical properties. Already the promise of this great discovery is being fulfilled with the stereospecifically controlled synthesis of "polyolefin fibers" made from propylene.

* From left to right the "rubber" balls are composed purely of: 1. 2-poly-methylpropene, or *butyl rubber;* 2. *trans*-1,3-polybutadiene; 3. *cis*-polyiso-prene, or *natural rubber;* 4. *cis*-1,3-polybutadiene; 5. ethylene-propylene copolymer.

**FORMING AND SHAPING** Plastics can be divided into two groups based on their behavior when heated—those that are *thermoplastic*, and those that are *thermosetting*. Thermoplastics characteristically are composed of linear molecules with few, if any, cross-linkings. As their name implies, they may be melted, shaped, and hardened any number of times. In contrast are the thermosetting materials; these consist initially of linear molecules that, upon heating, irreversibly form a network of cross-linked chains, leading to a finished product that is hard and strong and, in general, more heat resistant than a thermoplastic.

In the forming of finished products, a pure plastic itself may be processed, as in the cases of polystyrene, polymethylmethacrylate, and transparent polyethylene film. More frequently, however, plastics are modified in an early stage of their processing by the addition of *plasticizers*, *fillers*, *dyes*, and *pigments*. These give them desired properties for specific use or serve to aid in later processing.

Plasticizers are usually added to improve processing capabilities, to increase plasticity and flexibility, and to render the finished product inactive to moisture and chemical degradation.

Fillers are usually added to improve mechanical and physical properties. Among others, asbestos, mica, cork, wood fibers, cotton and glass fibers, metallic carbides, and graphite are used in this capacity.

Dyes and pigments are added to give color to the final product. Often, pigments may be filler materials as well.

BLOW MOLDING

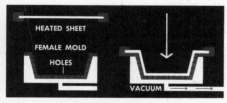

INJECTION MOLDING

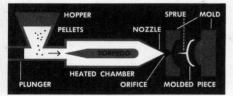

VACUUM FORMING

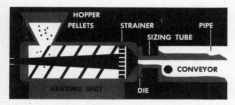

EXTRUSION

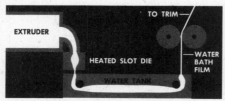

SHEET FILM EXTRUSION

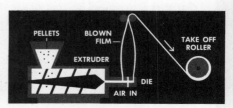

TUBE FILM EXTRUSION

At the left are seen diagrams illustrating six common methods for forming plastics into useful end products.

In the *blow-molding* process, a heated plastic tube is enclosed in a mold and inflated with air until it conforms to the shape of the mold.

In *injection molding*, raw pellets are heated until they soften. The molten material is forced by high pressure into a closed, cool mold.

The *thermo-forming*, or *vacuum-forming*, process begins with sheets of plastic that are heated until softened, then placed on a mold and "vacuum-pulled" against the mold until the plastic conforms to the mold design.

In the *extrusion* process, which is a continuous one, molten plastic is fed continuously through a die of a desired shape. Two variations of the extrusion process are shown at the bottom of the facing page. At the left, is a diagram of the *transparent film* process; at the right, the *blowtube* process.

In the photograph at the right, a huge continuous polyethylene film tube is seen emerging from a blow-film die.

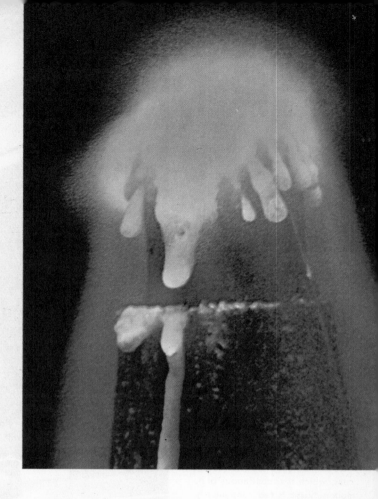

**NEW HORIZONS**   With the technological translation of giant molecule research into major industrial processes, man is now able to use his natural chemical resources in synthesizing materials that have never existed before.  The test tube has become a modern cornucopia into which are poured tons of coal, oil, salt, water, natural gas, cotton, and wood, and out of which flow products that shelter, clothe, and give comfort to man.  And in what torrents do the technological products of polymer science pour forth —30 million polyethylene bags and nearly 2 billion blow-molded plastic bottles, more than 200 million pounds of polyester fiber and nearly 2 million tons of synthetic rubber—a total tonnage of synthetic resins and rubber more than half that of steel, all in one year!

Giant molecules are helping to clothe man. They are helping to feed him and to house him. They are being used to repair and replace diseased or damaged parts of him. They are helping to carry him into the far reaches of our universe.

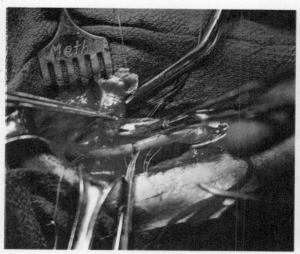

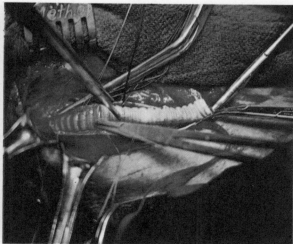

At the far left is seen an *ablative* plastic nose cone for a space vehicle, being tested for re-entry properties. Above, the plastic blood shunt (left) and *Dacron* patch (right) are shown in use in the surgical removal of fatty deposits from an artery wall. Below, the use of polyethylene in *plasticulture*, a new farming technique, is shown.

# QUESTIONS AND PROBLEMS

1. What is meant by each of the following?

   a. catenation
   b. phenolics
   c. vinyls
   d. nylon salt
   e. homopolymer
   f. copolymer
   g. free radical
   h. polyamide

   i. polyester
   j. addition polymerization
   k. vulcanized rubber
   l. spandex fibers
   m. stereospecific catalysts
   n. plasticizer
   o. ablative plastic

2. Using polyethylene, distinguish between branching and cross-linking of polymer chains.

3. Determine what is meant by, and describe, the tanning of leather and the mercerization of cotton.

4. Why is the polymer formed from hexamethylenediamine and adipic acid called nylon-6,6?

5. Distinguish between thermoplastics and thermosetting plastics.

6. Interpret the lower photograph on page 645.

7. Describe methods for shaping plastics into desired end products.

8. Draw structural formulas for a. 2-methylpropene; b. *cis*-1,3-butadiene; c. styrene; d. vinyl chloride.

9. Draw structural formulas for the following polymers, showing the repeating unit of the polymer once: a. polyvinyl chloride; b. polystyrene; c. butyl rubber.

10. The monomer of natural rubber is *isoprene*, or 2-methyl-1,3-butadiene. Addition polymerization occurs *at $C^1$ and $C^4$, resulting in a remaining double bond between $C^2$ and $C^3$.* The only product formed naturally is *cis*-polyisoprene. a. Draw the structural formula for isoprene. b. Draw two parallel chains of natural rubber showing only four repeating units in each chain. c. On the basis of the structures drawn in b, explain why natural rubber tires become chemically degraded relatively quickly in smoggy atmospheres. d. Using the structures drawn in b as a basis, draw parallel chains of vulcanized rubber.

# SUGGESTED READINGS

Melville, H. *Big Molecules.* Macmillan, 1958.

O'Driscoll, K. F. *The Nature and Chemistry of High Polymers* (paperback). Reinhold, 1964.

## Chemistry

Flory, Paul J., "Understanding Unruly Molecules." May 1964
Morton, M., "Big Molecules." Jan. 1964
Morton, M., "Design and Formation of Long-chain Molecules." Mar. 1964
"Nylon's First 25 Years." Feb. 1964
"Nylon—From Test Tube to Counter." Sept. 1964
Speier, J. L., "The Si-C Bond and Silicones." July 1964

## Scientific American

Natta, G., "Precisely Constructed Polymers." Aug. 1961
Williams, Simon. "Synthetic Fibers." July 1951

*What a piece of work is man.*

*Shakespeare* (1564–1616) *from* Hamlet

**CHAPTER 31** | # Biochemistry

In previous chapters, the chemistry of many familiar materials has been discussed. However, until now, little mention has been made of that group of chemicals with which you are most intimately associated —those of which you are constructed. It is perhaps comforting to our ego to learn that we, as well as all living systems, represent almost unbelievable chemical complexity. Nevertheless, the study of the chemistry of living organisms, both plant and animal, is intensively pursued today by biochemists. This activity has been richly rewarded by an increasing knowledge about the chemical processes of life. In this chapter, a few aspects of biochemistry—the chemistry of life—will be discussed to show some of the scope and progress in this exciting area of science.

### 31.1 The elements of life

Of the known chemical elements, only a few are involved in the chemistry of living material. As with the large organic molecules, the ability of carbon atoms to combine in long chains and rings is responsible for carbon forming the skeletal framework for the large biochemical molecules. Carbon, oxygen, nitrogen, and hydrogen constitute more than 97 per cent of the atoms in the human being. Despite their low abundance, the remaining elements are, however, extremely important. The elements vital to human life are listed in Table 31–1 along with their biological significance. It is noteworthy that only two of these elements have atomic numbers greater than 30.

648

## 31.2 Major categories of biological compounds

The fundamental biological unit is the cell. The structure of the cell is based on three kinds of very large polymer-type molecules known as *carbohydrates*, *nucleic acids*, and *proteins*. In addition to these three kinds of structural units, animal and plant cells also contain *fats and lipids*, *water*, and a small amount of *inorganic material*. Table 31–2 shows the composition of a variety of biological substances.

## 31.3 Inorganic material

Although only a small amount of biological material is inorganic in nature, it nevertheless is of great importance. The fact that the alkali chlorides are the chief soluble electrolytes dissolved in the body has been a contributing factor to the theory that organic life originated in the oceans of the primordial earth, between one and two billion years ago. According to this theory, these biological solutions of sodium and potassium chloride are remnants of a past when primitive cells first appeared immersed in the saline oceans.

## 31.4 The biological importance of water

All living matter has water as its most abundant compound. In the human, the tissue with the lowest concentration is the dentine of the teeth (10%); the greatest concentration is in the gray matter of the brain (85%). Generally, the younger and more active the tissue, the

## TABLE 31-1 ELEMENTS IN THE HUMAN BODY

| Element | Atomic Number | % of Total Body Weight | % of Total Body Atoms | Biological Significance |
|---|---|---|---|---|
| Hydrogen | 1 | 10 | 63.0 | These four elements are the fundamental constituents of carbohydrates, fats, and proteins. |
| Oxygen | 8 | 65 | 23.5 | |
| Carbon | 6 | 18 | 9.5 | |
| Nitrogen | 7 | 3.0 | 1.4 | |
| Calcium | 20 | 2.0 | 0.31 | 99% of body calcium is found as $Ca_3(PO_4)_2$, the major structural component of bone and teeth; also essential for blood coagulation and rhythmic activity of the heart. |
| Phosphorus | 15 | 1.1 | 0.22 | Indispensable for biochemical synthesis and energy transfer. |
| Potassium | 19 | 0.35 | 0.057 | Principal intracellular cation essential for transport of nerve impulses, muscle contraction. |
| Sulfur | 16 | 0.25 | 0.049 | Constituent of some proteins and many other important biological compounds. |
| Sodium | 11 | 0.15 | 0.041 | Principal extracellular cation; proper balance and distribution of water in the body. |
| Chlorine | 17 | 0.15 | 0.026 | Principal intracellular and extracellular anion. |
| Magnesium | 12 | 0.05 | 0.013 | Required for the activity of many enzymes. |
| Iron | 26 | 0.004 | 0.0039 | Most important metal ion; found in hemoglobin; concerned with oxygen transport and utilization. |
| *Trace elements* | | | | |
| Zinc | 30 | 0.0002 | 0.00015 | Required for certain enzyme activity. |
| Manganese | 25 | 0.00013 | 0.00002 | Required for the activity of a number of enzymes; functions in animal reproduction. |
| Copper | 29 | 0.0001 | 0.00002 | Essential constituent of vital oxidative enzymes; used in synthesis of hemoglobin. |
| Fluorine | 9 | 0.0001 | 0.00001 | Minor constituent of some body structures, such as teeth. |
| Iodine | 53 | 0.0001 | 0.00001 | Essential constituent of the thyroid hormone. |
| Molybdenum | 42 | 0.0001 | 0.00001 | Required for certain enzyme activity. |
| Cobalt | 27 | 0.0001 | 0.00001 | Structural component of vitamin $B_{12}$; deficiency results in anemia.* |

---

* The Nobel Prize in Chemistry was awarded in 1964 to Dr. Dorothy C. Hodgkin, Oxford University, England, for her determination of the structure of vitamin $B_{12}$ by X-ray techniques. Dr. Hodgkin became the third woman in history to be so honored.

**TABLE 31–2** Per Cent Composition of Some Biological Materials

| Material | Water | Carbohydrates | Lipids | Proteins | Inorganic Material |
|---|---|---|---|---|---|
| Blood | 79 | 1.1 | 1 | 19 | 0.9 |
| Bone | 20–25 | — | trace | 20 | 60 |
| Brain | 78 | 0.1 | 12–15 | 8 | 1.0 |
| Muscle | 70 | 0.6 | 7 | 22 | 1.1 |
| Liver | 60–80 | 1–15 | 3–20 | 15 | 2 |
| Milk | 88 | 4.7 | 3.4 | 3.4 | 0.8 |
| Yeast | 70–75 | 10 | 0–5 | 15 | 1.2 |
| Cabbage | 88 | 0.9 | 0.7 | 2.7 | 3.9 |
| Potato | 75 | 21 | 0.1 | 2 | 0.7 |
| Peas | 14 | 52 | 2 | 23 | 3 |
| Honey | 19 | 80 | — | 0.3 | 0.3 |

greater is the concentration of water. Of the water in the human body, some 37% is extracellular (plasma and tissue fluid) and the remaining 63% is intracellular. Nearly all of the water (85%) serves as a solvent to provide a medium for movement and interaction of ions and compounds within cells, between cells, and between the organism and the environment. The remaining water is found bound as water of hydration in proteins.

## 31.5 The lipids

The lipids are a broad class of long-chain aliphatic esters that yield fatty acid components when they are broken down. Lipids are classified into three groups based upon their chemical make-up. The first of these are the *simple fats*, which are the glycerol esters of fatty acids. The fatty acids usually found in humans are:

$$CH_3(CH_2)_{16}COOH \qquad CH_3(CH_2)_{14}COOH$$
$$\text{stearic acid} \qquad\qquad \text{palmitic acid}$$

$$CH_3(CH_2)_7CH{=}CH(CH_2)_7COOH$$
$$\text{oleic acid}$$

The simple fats are valuable in that they, unlike proteins and carbohydrates, are capable of being stored and then later utilized as an energy source. Oxidation of a simple fat yields more than twice the energy yielded by an equal weight of either protein or carbohydrate.

The second class of lipids is known as the *phospholipids*. These result when one of the fatty acid groups of a simple fat is replaced by a phosphate group and a nitrogenous base. (Fig. 31.1.) The phospholipids are important constituents of cell membranes and affect the selective permeability of those membranes.

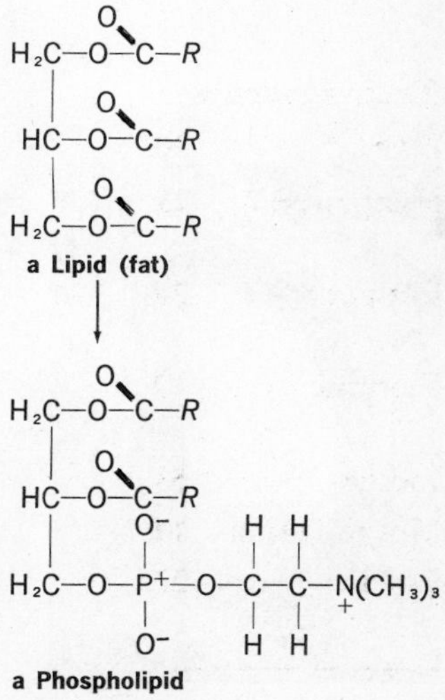

a Lipid (fat)

a Phospholipid

**FIGURE 31.1** Relationship between a lipid and a phospholipid

The final class of lipids are called the *steroids*. These are lipids with a ring structure and are all derivatives of *phenanthrene*. (Fig. 31.2.) The lipid *cholesterol* has been the subject of intensive study, since it is believed to be a contributing cause of the heart disease *atherosclerosis*. *Estrone* and *testosterone* are hormones of the type that are responsible for secondary sex characteristics, female and male, respectively. It is remarkable that these two molecules differ basically by only one extra methyl group in the male hormone.

**FIGURE 31.2**   Steroids are derivatives of phenanthrene

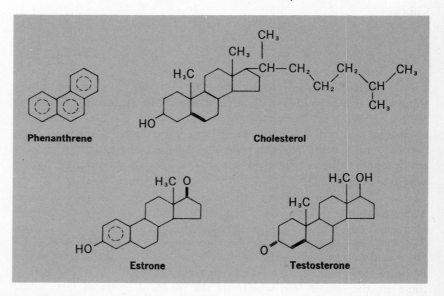

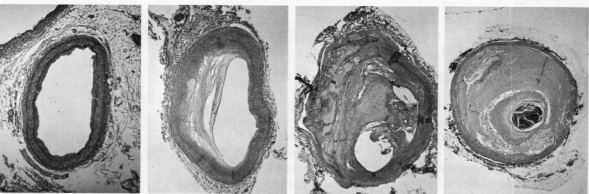

Atherosclerosis, a type of arteriosclerosis. The gradual buildup of fatty deposits in the coronary arteries is followed by the formation of hard tissue. If the blood channel has been narrowed enough and a blood clot forms, the channel is closed completely and a heart attack ensues.

### 31.6 Sugars are carbohydrates.

A carbohydrate is a compound of carbon, hydrogen, and oxygen, in which the H and O are present in the same ratio as in water. Examples are the simple sugars, such as *ribose* ($C_5H_{10}O_5$), and *glucose* ($C_6H_{12}O_6$) and *fructose* ($C_6H_{12}O_6$), which are manufactured by green plants in the photosynthetic process. (Fig. 31.3.)

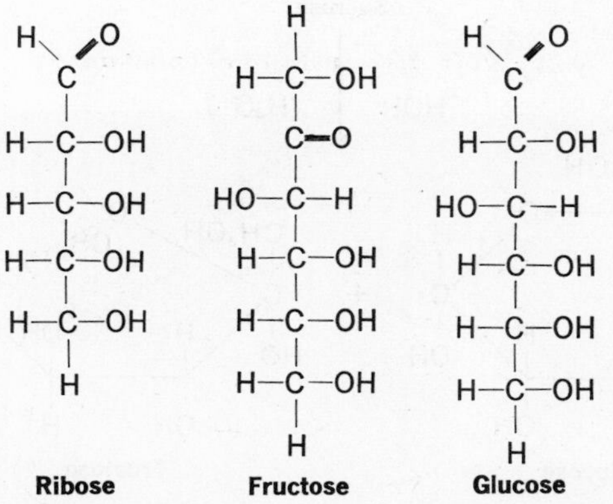

**FIGURE 31.3 Simple sugars**

**Ribose      Fructose      Glucose**

Brief consideration of the sugar structures shows us that glucose and ribose are polyhydroxyaldehydes, whereas fructose is a polyhydroxyketone. The carbonyl group reacts with one of the alcohol groups to form a more stable, cyclic structure. (Fig. 31.4.)

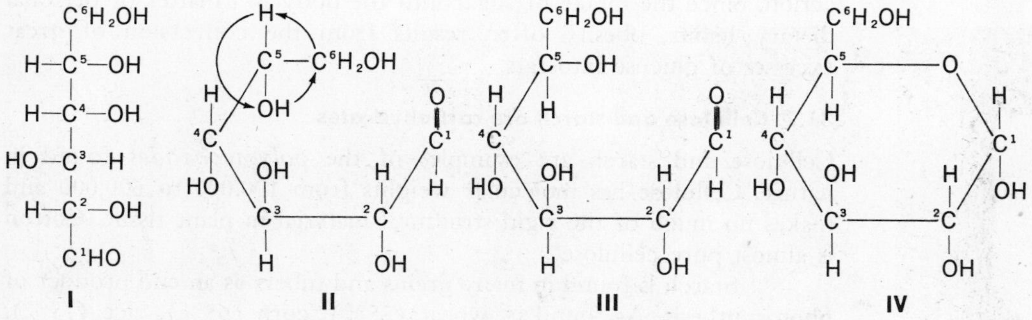

**FIGURE 31.4 The cyclic structure of glucose**

The simple monomeric sugars are known as *monosaccharides*. Sucrose, common table sugar, is a *disaccharide* that can be hydrolyzed in dilute acid to the monosaccharides glucose and fructose, which are isomers. This process is called *inversion*. (Fig. 31.5.)

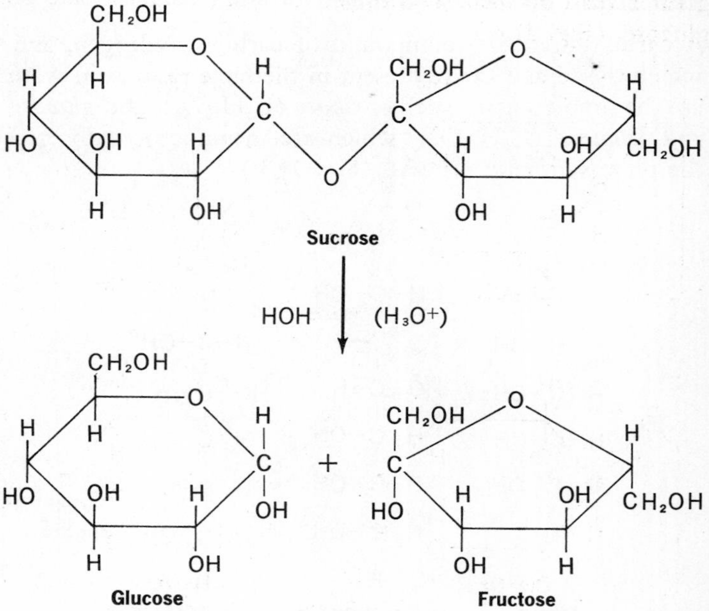

**FIGURE 31.5** The inversion of sucrose

Glucose is a most essential body chemical. Its oxidation supplies the energy for muscle and gland activity and for body heat. The soluble glucose is maintained in the blood stream at a concentration of 0.1 per cent by the liver, which converts excess quantities of glucose reversibly to animal starch, *glycogen*, $(C_6H_{10}O_5)_n$, a high polymer of glucose. Conversion of excess glucose to fatty acids and fat for more permanent storage in *adipose* tissue is an important biochemical reaction. Since the intake of sugar into the body is a matter of personal dietary habits, obesity often results from the conversion of great excesses of glucose into fats.

### 31.7 Cellulose and starch are carbohydrates.

Cellulose and starch are examples of the *polysaccharides* found in nature. Cellulose has molecular weights from 100,000 to 600,000 and makes up much of the rigid structural material in plant tissue. Cotton is almost pure cellulose.

Starch is found in many grains and tubers as an end product of photosynthesis. As found in wheat (55%), corn (65%), rice (75%), and potatoes (15%), starch is a common source of carbohydrates in the diets of all nations.

There are two types of starch polymers. Approximately 20 per cent of starch is a water-soluble fraction known as *amylose*, with molecular weights of 4000 to 50,000. The remaining 80 per cent, known as *amylopectin*, a water-insoluble material, has molecular weights of greater than 500,000. Hydrolysis of both cellulose and starch yields glucose. (Fig. 31.6.)

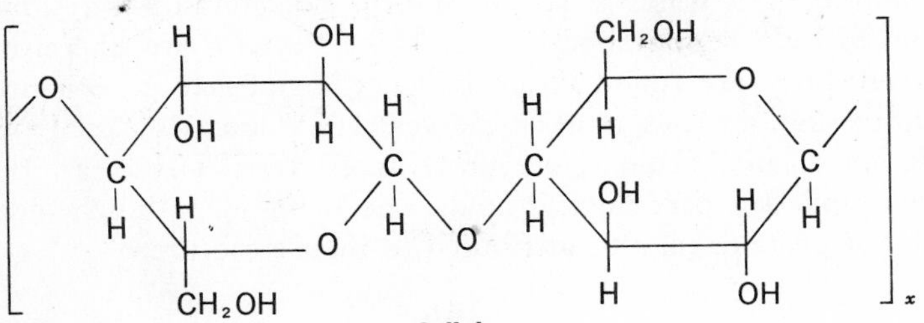

**Cellulose**

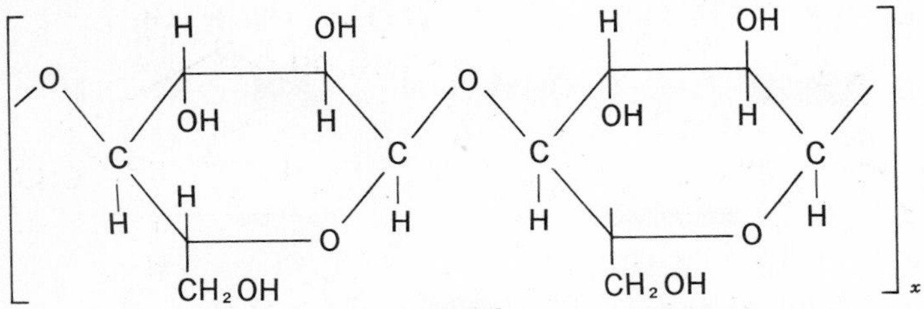

**Starch**

**FIGURE 31.6** Cellulose and starch are polymers of what sugar?

## 31.8 The proteins

The name *protein* is derived from the Greek word meaning "first" and is quite appropriate since, as we shall see, proteins are the underlying structure of all living organisms. Proteins are distinguished from carbohydrates and fats by the presence of nitrogen in their structure. In addition to carbon, hydrogen, and oxygen, proteins contain about 16 per cent nitrogen, and in some cases some sulfur and phosphorus as well. Just as glucose is the monomeric building block in the polymeric carbohydrate structures of starch and cellulose, the *amino acids* are the basic building blocks of the proteins. (Fig. 31.7.)

**FIGURE 31.7** Some amino acids found in man

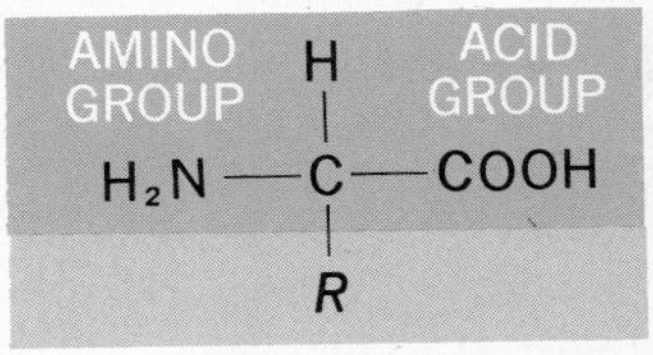

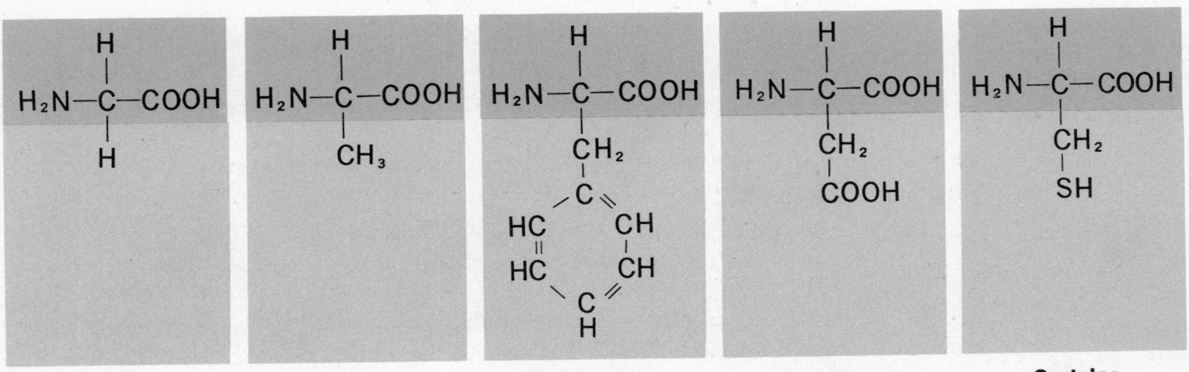

**Glycine**     **Alanine**     **Phenylalanine**     **Aspartic Acid**     **Cysteine**

Proteins are giant molecules formed by the condensation of amino acids. As the amino group of one acid reacts with the carboxyl group of another acid, water is split off and the two amino acid residues become linked by a *peptide* bond. (Fig. 31.8.) Proteins are, therefore, *polypeptides*. They are found in all living cells and are the principal constituent of skin, muscles, tendons, nerves, and blood. Most enzymes, antibodies, and many hormones are proteins. Bacterial viruses are one part protein and one part nucleic acid. The preeminent biochemical significance of proteins may be attributed to their structure.

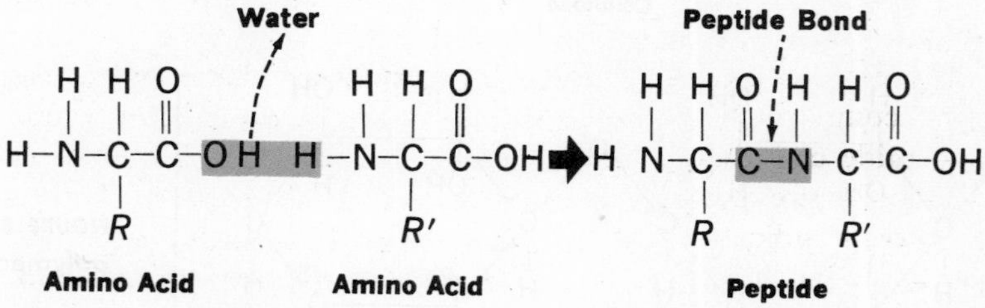

**FIGURE 31.8** Formation of a dipeptide

## 31.9 Structure and the function of proteins

There are three related aspects of structure in protein chemistry. Conveniently, we may talk about the *primary, secondary,* and *tertiary* structures of these polypeptides.

The primary structure of a protein refers to the sequence of amino acid residues in the polypeptide. Any variation in the sequence leads to a different protein of different biochemical significance. Painstaking biochemical research is making slow but steady progress in determining primary structures of proteins. (Fig. 31.9.)

**FIGURE 31.9** The amino acid sequence in insulin

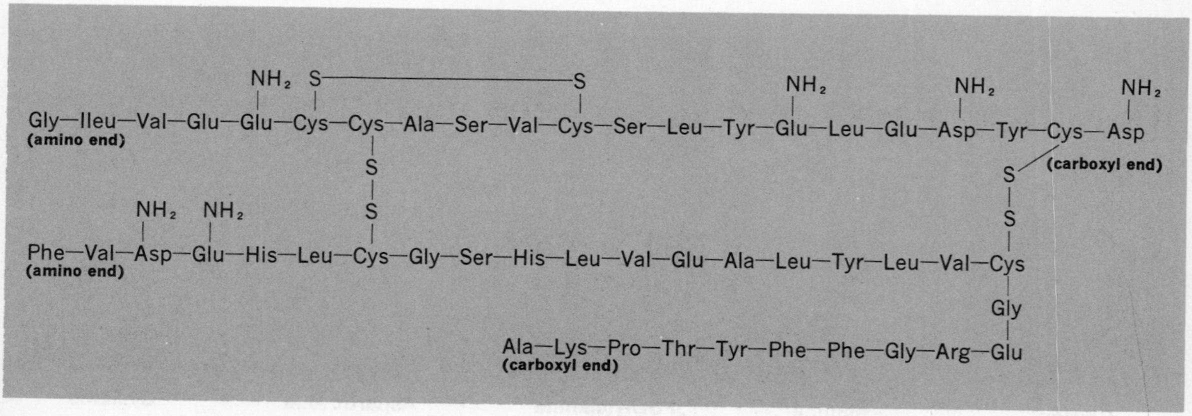

From the complex X-ray diffraction patterns yielded by crystalline proteins, Professor Pauling and his co-workers at the California Institute of Technology were able to deduce in 1951 that certain proteins had a secondary structure, relative to their orientation in space. That secondary structure is depicted as a helical shape made possible by intramolecular hydrogen bonding. (Fig. 31.10.) The linearity implied by such a model correlates well with the properties of the *fibrous proteins*. These long, threadlike polypeptides that arrange themselves in hydrogen-bonded layers form water-insoluble fibers. Examples of fibrous proteins are *keratin*, found in skin, hair, nails, wool, horn, and feathers; *collagen*, found in tendons; *myosin*, the contractile protein of muscles; and *fibroin*, the structural basis of silk.

More recent structural studies of certain proteins indicate that some very complicated tertiary structure must be present, in which the polypeptide chain wraps around itself. The net result is that there is one particular site along the chain that is especially exposed. It is at this site, theory indicates, that the biochemical function of a protein may take place. In Figure 31.11 is a model for the tertiary structure of hemoglobin deduced by Professors Kendrew and Perutz, at Cambridge University in England, from their patterns of the crystalline protein. It would appear that the extraordinarily complex convolution of the polypeptide chain is necessary to provide a site for the iron atom in hemoglobin. It is at this site that an oxygen molecule is bound for its transport to body cells. The tertiary structure implies a spheroidal shape for certain proteins. Indeed, a whole class of *globular* proteins is known. These contain such proteins as, the vital hormones, insulin, thyroglobulin, and ACTH, and albumin, gamma globulin, and fibrinogen—three major constituents of blood. Perhaps the mechanism of the specific biochemical activity of each of these globular proteins will some day be understood in terms of their tertiary structure. It seems clear already, for example, that the uncoiling of the fibrinogen tertiary structure to form the fibrous protein *fibrin* is responsible for the clotting of the blood.

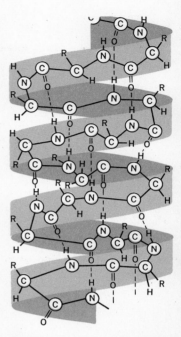

**FIGURE 31.10** The alpha helix protein structure proposed by Pauling and others

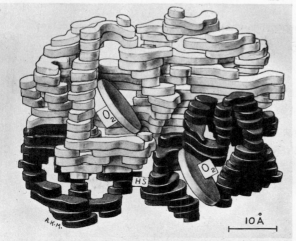

**FIGURE 31.11** A model for the tertiary structure of hemoglobin. What is the function of this molecule?

It is apparent, therefore, that sequence of amino acid residues alone does not determine the biochemical function of a protein. Spatial orientation of the chain is also vital. That orientation is brought about by the formation of intramolecular hydrogen bonding. Recalling that the hydrogen bond is relatively weak, it is not surprising that proteins are very heat-sensitive. Heating, or changing the chemical environment that supports the formation of hydrogen bonds, causes hydrogen bonds in proteins to break. The spatial structure of the protein becomes undone, and the protein loses its biological activity. This generally irreversible process is known as protein *denaturation*. It is most familiarly

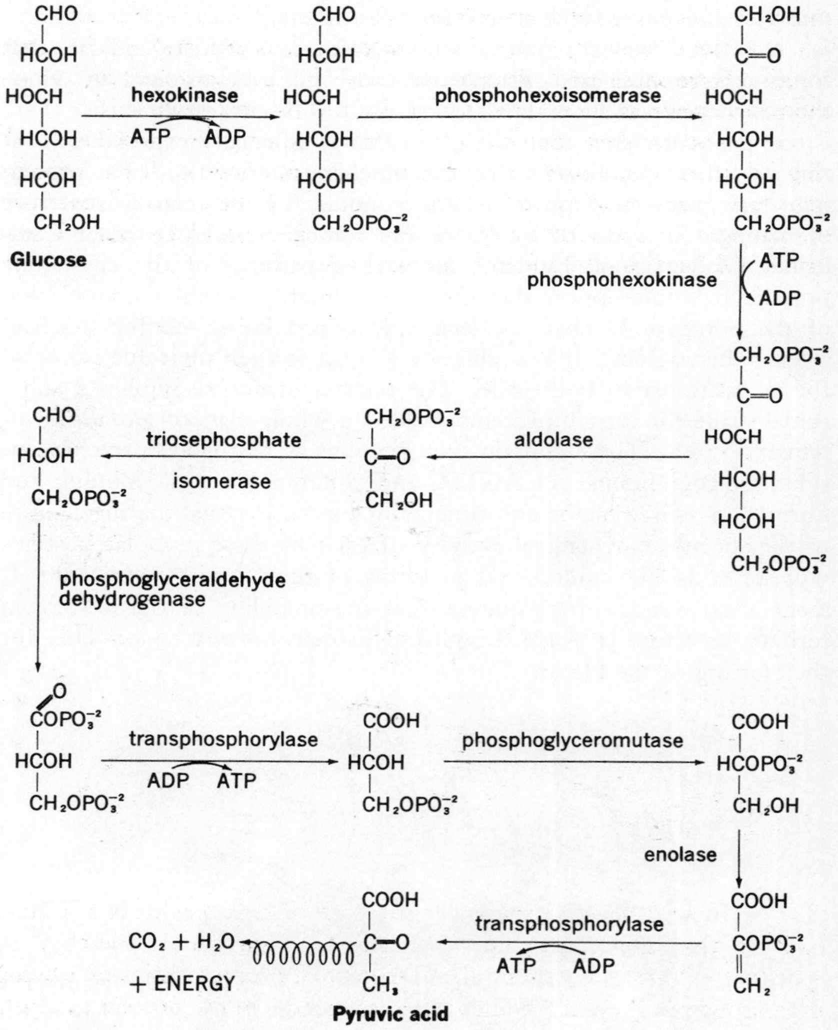

**FIGURE 31.12** The metabolism of glucose

Glucose

$$
\begin{array}{c}
CHO \\
HCOH \\
HOCH \\
HCOH \\
HCOH \\
CH_2OH
\end{array}
\xrightarrow[\text{ATP} \quad \text{ADP}]{\text{hexokinase}}
\begin{array}{c}
CHO \\
HCOH \\
HOCH \\
HCOH \\
HCOH \\
CH_2OPO_3^{-2}
\end{array}
\xrightarrow{\text{phosphohexoisomerase}}
\begin{array}{c}
CH_2OH \\
C=O \\
HOCH \\
HCOH \\
HCOH \\
CH_2OPO_3^{-2}
\end{array}
$$

phosphohexokinase $\begin{cases} \text{ATP} \\ \text{ADP} \end{cases}$

$$
\begin{array}{c}
CHO \\
HCOH \\
CH_2OPO_3^{-2}
\end{array}
\xleftarrow[\text{isomerase}]{\text{triosephosphate}}
\begin{array}{c}
CH_2OPO_3^{-2} \\
C=O \\
CH_2OH
\end{array}
\xleftarrow{\text{aldolase}}
\begin{array}{c}
CH_2OPO_3^{-2} \\
C=O \\
HOCH \\
HCOH \\
HCOH \\
CH_2OPO_3^{-2}
\end{array}
$$

phosphoglyceraldehyde dehydrogenase

$$
\begin{array}{c}
COPO_3^{-2} \\
HCOH \\
CH_2OPO_3^{-2}
\end{array}
\xrightarrow[\text{ADP} \quad \text{ATP}]{\text{transphosphorylase}}
\begin{array}{c}
COOH \\
HCOH \\
CH_2OPO_3^{-2}
\end{array}
\xrightarrow{\text{phosphoglyceromutase}}
\begin{array}{c}
COOH \\
HCOPO_3^{-2} \\
CH_2OH
\end{array}
$$

enolase

$$
CO_2 + H_2O + \text{ENERGY} \longleftarrow
\begin{array}{c}
COOH \\
C=O \\
CH_3
\end{array}
\xleftarrow[\text{ATP} \quad \text{ADP}]{\text{transphosphorylase}}
\begin{array}{c}
COOH \\
COPO_3^{-2} \\
CH_2
\end{array}
$$

**Pyruvic acid**

observed in the cooking of an egg. A raw egg is water-soluble. The cooked egg, in which protein denaturation has occurred, is insoluble.

### 31.10 Enzymes and metabolism

The whole of biochemistry may be summed up as the study of *metabolism*—the chemical fate of all substances used by living matter. Over the years the metabolic fates of many substances have been experimentally determined in exquisite detail. (Fig. 31.12.) A striking observation concerning these metabolic processes is that they occur within a narrow, and relatively low, range of temperatures. From test-tube experimentation, it has become apparent that at biological temperatures, biochemical reactants lack the energy of activation required for reaction. Obviously, since these reactions do occur, and usually quite rapidly, there must exist biochemical catalysts. The large protein molecules that serve as such catalysts of life are the *enzymes*.

The number and kinds of reactions that take place in a cell depend upon which particular enzymes the cell contains. It has become apparent from biochemical research that *each* biochemical reaction is catalyzed by a specific enzyme. This enzyme specificity has led to a "lock and key" model for enzyme catalysis. (Fig. 31.13.)

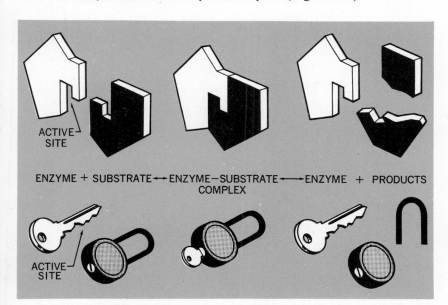

ENZYME + SUBSTRATE ←→ ENZYME—SUBSTRATE ←→ ENZYME + PRODUCTS
COMPLEX

ACTIVE SITE

**FIGURE 31.13** A "lock and key" model for enzyme specificity

In actuality, it is the linear sequence of amino acids in a protein catalyst that determines its biochemical activity and, thereby, its specificity. Thus, the structural and metabolic characteristics of a living organism depend upon the amino acid sequences in the protein catalysts contained in the cells of that organism.

### 31.11 Energy and metabolism

Many biochemical reactions are endothermic and require a source of energy. Biochemists have learned that a remarkably simple substance, *adenosine triphosphate*, or ATP, is quite commonly involved in supplying the necessary energy to allow such reactions to occur. (Fig. 31.14.)

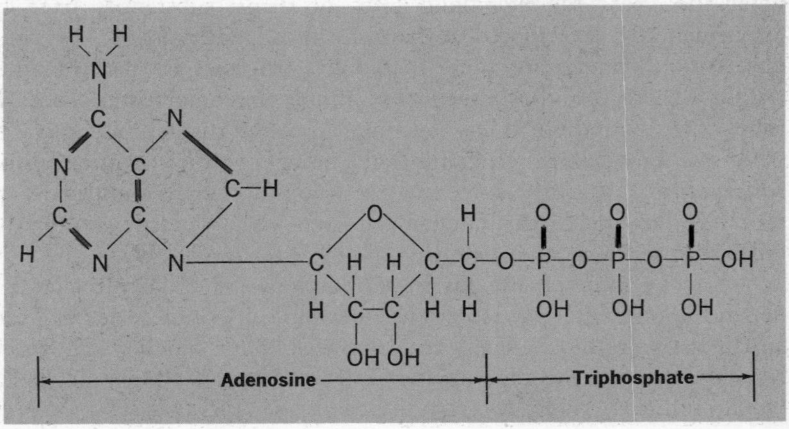

FIGURE 31.14  Adenosine triphosphate

Most simply, hydrolysis of the end *phosphate anhydride* group occurs in ATP, leading to *adenosine diphosphate*, or ADP, phosphoric acid, and 8 kcal/mole:

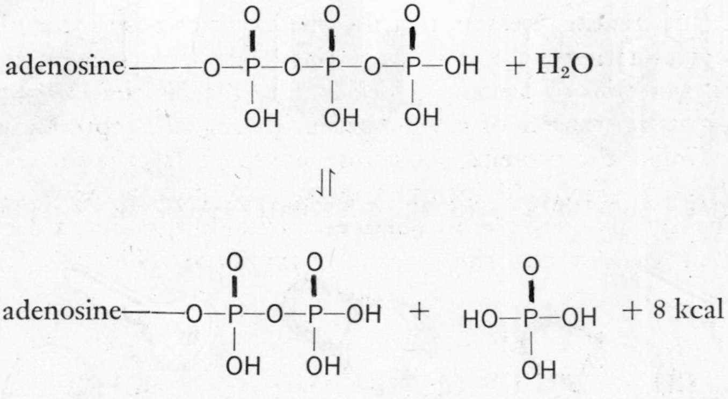

$$\text{adenosine} - \text{O}-\overset{\overset{\text{O}}{\|}}{\underset{\underset{\text{OH}}{|}}{\text{P}}}-\text{O}-\overset{\overset{\text{O}}{\|}}{\underset{\underset{\text{OH}}{|}}{\text{P}}}-\text{O}-\overset{\overset{\text{O}}{\|}}{\underset{\underset{\text{OH}}{|}}{\text{P}}}-\text{OH} \;+\; \text{H}_2\text{O}$$

$$\Updownarrow$$

$$\text{adenosine} - \text{O}-\overset{\overset{\text{O}}{\|}}{\underset{\underset{\text{OH}}{|}}{\text{P}}}-\text{O}-\overset{\overset{\text{O}}{\|}}{\underset{\underset{\text{OH}}{|}}{\text{P}}}-\text{OH} \;+\; \text{HO}-\overset{\overset{\text{O}}{\|}}{\underset{\underset{\text{OH}}{|}}{\text{P}}}-\text{OH} \;+\; 8 \text{ kcal}$$

The reversibility of this reaction is very important, for energy is stored when ADP is converted to ATP at the site of exothermic biochemical reaction. Thus, the formation of ATP in energy-rich reactions allows the storage of energy that may then be used for energy-deficient reactions. How vital is ATP, the so-called *energy currency* of biochemical reactions? Besides its general use in supplying energy to endothermic biochemical reactions, ATP energy currency is involved in muscular contraction and in the motion of cilia and flagella in single-celled animals. The energy it yields is converted to the bioelectric shock of the electric eel, and the bioluminescent glow of the firefly.

An illuminating experiment: two grams of ATP added to five grams of dehydrated fire-fly tails

## 31.12 The nucleic acids

Rivaling the proteins for preeminence in biochemical significance are the giant molecules known as the *nucleic acids*. It would appear, on the basis of quite recent research, that the nucleic acids possess the ultimate in biological activity, for it is a certainty that they control the biochemical synthesis of proteins and, thus, are the molecules responsible for the genetic transfer of characteristics during cell reproduction.

Unlike the proteins, which are polypeptides, the nucleic acids are *polyesters*. The acid involved in the esterification is phosphoric acid. The hydroxy compound is not an alcohol but, rather, a derivative of one of two sugars, ribose or 2-deoxyribose. (Fig. 31.15.) The

**FIGURE 31.15** The sugars of nucleic acids

Ribose

Deoxyribose

derivatives arise from the substitution of one of five organic bases on the carbon atom in the number 1 position in the sugar ring. (Fig. 31.16.)

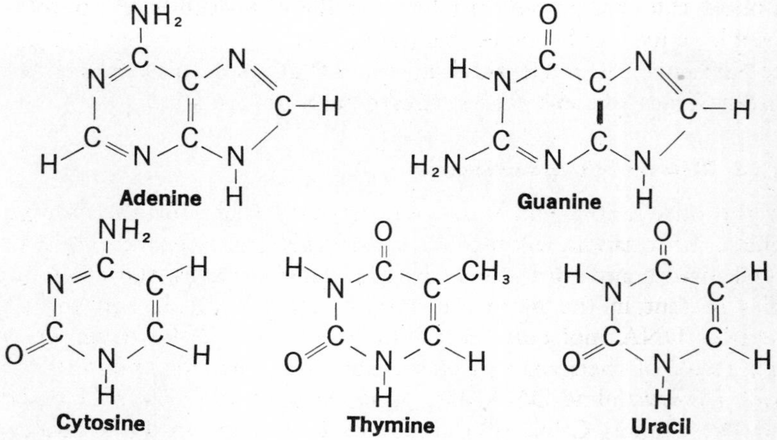

**FIGURE 31.16** The organic bases of nucleic acids

The monomeric species that consist of acid, sugar, and base are called *nucleotides.* (Fig. 31.17.) It is important to note that upon polymerization of the nucleotides two families of nucleic acids arise. *Deoxyribonucleic acids* (DNA) consist of nucleotides containing the bases adenine (*A*), thymine (*T*), guanine (*G*), and cytosine (*C*). In the *ribonucleic acids* (RNA), uracil (*U*), and not thymine, is found in one of the nucleotides. (The letters *A*, *T*, *G*, *C*, and *U* are conveniently used to represent a whole nucleotide unit.)

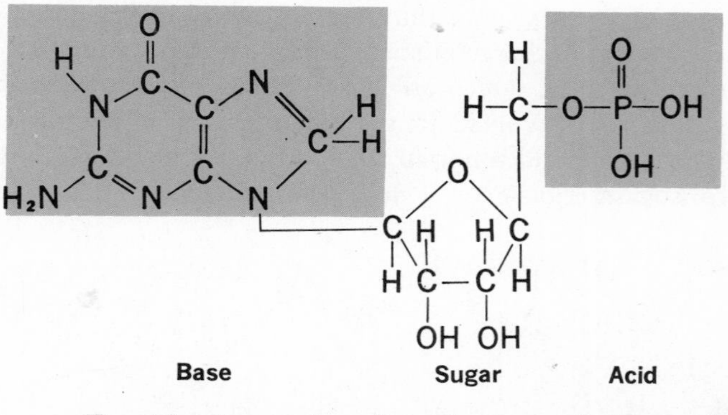

**FIGURE 31.17** A ribonucleotide

Base            Sugar            Acid

Esterification and polymerization of the nucleotides occurs with the hydroxyl groups on carbon atoms at positions 3 and 5 of the sugar rings. Giant *polynucleotides* result. (Fig. 31.18.) It should be apparent that DNA and RNA are truly families of compounds. The number of times a given base appears in a chain and the sequence of bases along the chain differ from one nucleic acid to another.

Consider a tetranucleotide to be made up of one or more of the four different nucleotides *A*, *T*, *C*, and *G*. There are $4^4$, or 196, possible sequences for those four nucleotides. When it is realized that thousands of nucleotides are present in DNA and RNA molecules, the number of possible sequences becomes staggering. Yet it is now believed that it is the sequence of nucleotides in the DNA molecules found in the chromosomes of cells that carries genetic information.

### 31.13 DNA and the genetic code

At the outset, if a DNA molecule is responsible for the storage of genetic information, it must be a self-replicating molecule. Thus, when a cell divides and forms two identical daughter cells, the DNA molecules present in the mother cell must likewise divide and form two identical DNA molecules that will be present in the daughter cells. As a result of their analysis of the complex X-ray diffraction patterns made by crystalline DNA, Dr. James Watson of Harvard University and Dr. Francis Crick of Cambridge University in 1954 deduced a three-dimensional structure for DNA that could account for its self-replication. (Fig. 31.19.) The significant feature of the Watson-Crick model is that the double helix comes about only by virtue of intermolecular hydrogen bonding, between pairs of *complementary bases*. *A* on one helix is always hydrogen-bonded to a *T* on the second. *C* is always hydrogen-bonded to *G*. This is the key to the self-replication

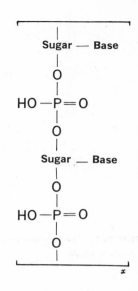

**FIGURE 31.18** A nucleic acid is a polynucleotide.

**FIGURE 31.19** The Watson-Crick model of DNA

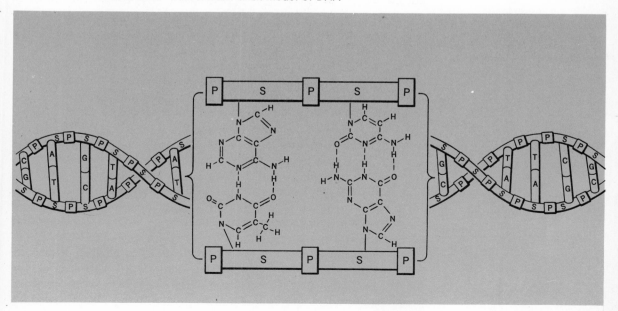

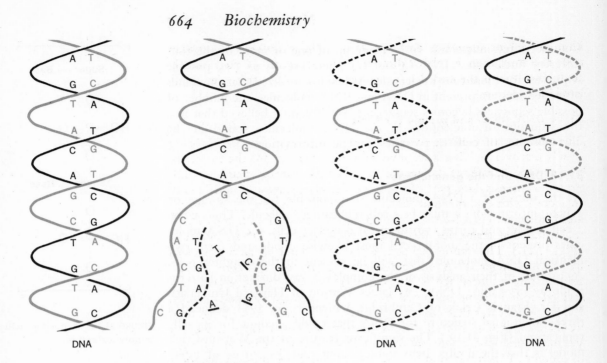

**FIGURE 31.20**  The Watson-Crick model for DNA replication

of DNA, which is shown in Figure 31.20. The Nobel Prize in Medicine was awarded to the youthful scientists, Dr. Watson and Dr. Crick in 1962.

The next question concerning DNA as bearer of the genetic code concerns the number of letters involved in such a code. The ultimate transcription of the genetic code lies in the synthesis of proteins from the twenty amino acids present in cell fluids. Thus, the code must be able to account for specific amino acids to be bound in a specific sequence. How many of the four letters $A$, $T$, $G$, and $C$ are required for encoding the amino acids? There cannot be a 1:1 correspondence between a letter and an acid, for such would lead only to the utilization of four amino acids. If a combination of two letters corresponded to a given amino acid, only $4^2$, or 16, acids could be accounted for. Since use of all four letters would encode $4^4$, or 196, acids, molecular biologists feel that a three-letter code, with a possibility of $4^3$, or 64, combinations, is the simplest to work with. There has been significant experimental evidence to support the supposition of a three-letter code. (See bibliographic references.)

The linear sequence of the nucleotides in a DNA molecule, then, must contain enough three-letter "code words" to arrange the amino acids in a particular sequence within a protein. These proteins become involved in metabolic reactions in such a way that a particular kind of cell or organism develops. The cellular difference between mice and men, then, is related directly to the structure of their nucleic acids. But how is the coded information of the DNA molecules translated into proteins?

### 31.14 DNA, RNA, and protein synthesis

The complex story of the genetic ordering of protein synthesis is being slowly discovered. That story involves the mechanism for the transcription and the transfer of the genetic code and its ultimate translation into protein synthesis. One part of the story already seems well understood. In accord with experimental evidence, one of the features of the mechanism appears to involve the intermediate formation of *messenger* RNA molecules that transcribe the genetic code from the DNA molecule. (Fig. 31.21.) The transcribed code is transferred out of the cell nucleus by the messenger RNA molecules into the *ribosomes*. There, aminoacid-bearing *transfer* RNA molecules "read" and translate the transcribed code in some unknown manner, and protein synthesis results. Evidence indicates that enzymes are involved in each step of the total mechanism, though not all the details are yet known. Indeed, there is yet much unknown about the roles of DNA and RNA in the synthesis of proteins. This is as it must be in an area of concern at the very frontiers of scientific research.

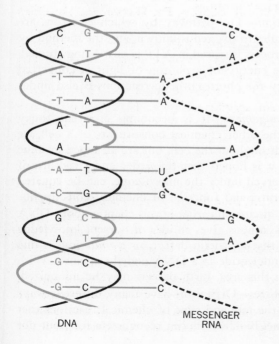

DNA

MESSENGER
RNA

**FIGURE 31.21** A model for genetic code transcription and transfer

### 31.15 Biochemical horizons

It is the ultimate goal of biochemists to understand completely the chemistry of living organisms. Great strides have been made in the last few years, but the distance yet to go and the knowledge yet to be gained remain almost overwhelming. Perhaps a brief list of several areas of current and future interest will serve to show how much is still not understood.

a. *Chemical Constituents*—Most of the quantitatively important compounds found in living organisms, such as the cellular constituents previously mentioned, the vitamins, and the hormones manufactured by the glands of internal secretion (endocrine glands), are known. Because of continuing advancement in the sensitivity of methods for detecting trace amounts of compounds, however, new, naturally occurring compounds are still being discovered. In some cases, the function of these compounds is completely unknown.

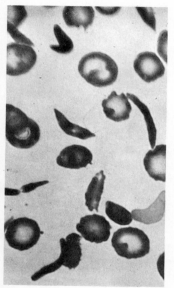

One alteration in the sequence of the 287 amino acids of hemoglobin results in human *sickle-cell anemia.*

b. *Metabolic Reactions*—The major reaction sequences, or metabolic pathways, are known in considerable detail. These include the paths of conversion of glucose into $CO_2$ and $H_2O$ (Fig. 31.12), the conversion of $CO_2$ and $H_2O$ into glucose (by photosynthesis), the synthetic and degradative reactions of major constituent compounds (fatty acids, sterols, amino acids, purines, pyrimidines, sugars, and so forth), and a number of other important processes. There are still unknown reaction sequences, however, particularly those involving the compounds found in trace quantities.

c. *Energy Utilization*—The pathway by which electrons are passed from organic molecules to oxygen is known, and the method by which the energy of this process is stored in ATP is now being studied. The process by which the energy of a photon of light is converted into useful chemical energy for photosynthetic reactions is also under intensive investigation.

d. *Structural Arrangement*—It is becoming apparent today that the enzymes and all the other chemical constituents of a cell are not randomly distributed throughout the cell, but are arranged in some specific order. Eventually it is hoped that the order and structure of the cell, which can be observed under the microscope, can be equated in detail with order, structure, and function of chemical constituents.

e. *Heredity*—The discussion earlier in this chapter about DNA and its relation to protein synthesis gives an idea of current knowledge in this area. It is now felt that a genetic defect, or a *mutation*, is due to a misplaced or missing nucleotide in a DNA coded sequence. With increased understanding in this area, birth defects may be minimized.

f. *Control Mechanisms*—Organisms have many different ways of exercising control over the rate and type of chemical reactions that will occur at any given time. Biochemists can recognize a few, but not all, of these control mechanisms. A rather unusual control mechanism, about which little is known, is the phenomenon of the "biological clock." Some organisms are responsive to time sequence, and their chemistry runs in definite cycles.

g. *Chemotherapy*—Since the time of Paracelsus, chemistry has given to mankind priceless information about foods, vitamins, and hormones. Chemistry has still much to contribute in the service of health. Chemotherapy is the attack on disease by certain chemical compounds known as *specifics*. When Paul Ehrlich (AIR lik), a German scientist, after trying 605 different arsenic compounds finally introduced 606, or *Salvarsan*, in 1910, he gave mankind a magic bullet which could destroy the agent that causes that scourge of mankind, the disease *syphilis*. Today, chemists are attempting to make a direct attack upon specific diseases by plotting the molecular structure of a desired drug in such a way that it will interact with some abnormal molecule that causes some disease and neutralize its harmful effects. This is "molecular medicine," which according to Professor Pauling is the medicine of the future.

h. *Brain Functions*—Certain of the chemical aspects of nerve transmission are understood, but the chemical basis of reasoning and memory are completely obscure.

i. *Evolution*—A comparative study of what chemicals, reactions, and enzymes are found in different species should eventually provide a chemical basis for the theory of evolution. It is also possible that we will one day understand how complicated molecules were first formed and how they were arranged to form living organisms.

j. *Unknown Problems*—As our knowledge of biochemistry expands, we will no doubt come across problems whose existence we cannot even suspect today. To the dominion of chemistry, there is no end.

## SUMMARY

The chemistry of living organisms is one of tremendous complexity, yet only a relatively few elements constitute most of the compounds of biological significance.

Though the cell with its carbohydrates, proteins, nucleic acids, fats, lipids, salts, and water may be microscopic in size, it would take an entire industrial complex to synthesize cellular products.

Modern biochemical research has clearly shown that the structure of molecules has a profound effect on their biochemical activity. This is especially true in the case of proteins, the underlying structure of all living organisms, and in the case of nucleic acids, the bearers, transmitters, and executors of the genetic code.

The metabolic fate of all substances used by living matter depends on the enzymatic control of the biochemical reactions involving those substances. In addition, most metabolic reactions depend on adenosine triphosphate, ATP, the biochemical energy currency.

## QUESTIONS AND PROBLEMS

**31.1**   Briefly discuss the following terms:
a. polypeptide    g. denaturation    m. messenger RNA
b. chemotherapy    h. bioluminescence    n. sucrose inversion
c. steroids    i. mutation    o. polysaccharide
d. metabolism    j. energy currency    p. hormones
e. polynucleotide    k. lipids    q. complementary base pairing
f. enzymes    l. alpha helix    r. photosynthesis

**31.2**   What evidence lends support to the theory that organic life began in the oceans of primordial earth?

**31.3**   a. Give the extended formula for the amino acid valine (2-amino-3-methylbutanoic acid or 2-amino-3-methylbutyric acid).
b. Give a structural equation showing the formation of the dipeptide from two valine molecules.

**31.4**   Defend the statement: "The amino acids are the building blocks of animate nature."

**31.5**   Briefly discuss the primary, secondary, and tertiary structures of proteins and how they relate to protein function.

**31.6**   Defend the statement: "DNA is the molecule of life."

**31.7**   Discuss the role hydrogen bonding plays in life processes.

**31.8**   Briefly describe the "lock and key" mechanism for enzymatic catalysis.

**31.9**   a. What are the component parts of a nucleotide? b. In what ways can nucleotides differ from each other?

**31.10**   Diagrammatically describe a model for DNA replication.

**31.11**   Diagrammatically describe a model for the role of the nucleic acids in protein synthesis.

**31.12**   What similar structural property of the compounds adenine, thymine, guanine, and cytosine causes each of them to behave chemically alike.

## SUGGESTED READINGS

Asimov, Isaac. *The Chemicals of Life* (paperback). New American Library, 1962.

Asimov, Isaac. *The Genetic Code* (paperback). New American Library, 1963.

Baldwin, E. *The Nature of Biochemistry* (paperback). Cambridge University Press, 1962.

Borek, Ernest. *The Atoms Within Us* (paperback). Columbia University Press, 1963.

Calder, Ritchie. *Profile of Science* (paperback). Macmillan, 1951. Contains an excellent account of penicillin and other modern drugs.

Cheldelin, V. H., and R. W. Newburgh. *The Chemistry of Some Life Processes* (paperback). Reinhold, 1962.

Farb, Peter. *Living Earth* (paperback). Pyramid Publications, 1962.

Harrison, K. *A Guidebook to Biochemistry* (paperback). Cambridge University Press, 1959.

Hoffman, Katherine. *Chemistry of Life* (paperback). Scholastic Book Services, 1964.

Keosian, J. *The Origin of Life* (paperback). Reinhold, 1964.

Pfeiffer, John, and the Editors of LIFE. *The Cell* (LIFE Science Library). Time Inc., 1964.

White, E. H. *Chemical Background for the Biological Sciences* (paperback). Prentice-Hall, 1964.

## CHEMISTRY

Alexander, Leroy E., "X-rays, Crystals, and Life. Unraveling Structures of Large Molecules." Part 1, Aug. 1964; Part 2, Sept. 1964

Axelrod, Bernard, and L. E. Trachtman, "The World's Smallest Chemical Factory." May 1964

Bjorksten, Johan, "Why Grow Old?" June 1964

Wise, Louis E., "Wood—a Renewable Natural Resource." Oct. 1964

## SCIENTIFIC AMERICAN

Amoore, J. E., J. W. Johnston, Jr., and M. Rubin, "The Stereochemical Theory of Odor." Feb. 1964

Arnon, Daniel I., "The Role of Light in Photosynthesis." Nov. 1960

Bassham, J. A., "The Path of Carbon in Photosynthesis." June 1962

Crick, F. H. C., "The Genetic Code." Oct. 1962

Deering, R. A., "Ultraviolet Radiation and Nucleic Acid." Dec. 1962

Fisher, A. E., "Chemical Stimulation of the Brain." June 1964

Fraenkel-Conrat, H., "The Genetic Code of a Virus." Oct. 1964

Green, David E., "The Synthesis of Fat." Feb. 1960

Hao Li, Choh, "The ACTH Molecule." July 1963

Horne, R. W., "The Structure of Viruses." Jan. 1963

Hurwitz, Jerard, and J. J. Furth, "Messenger RNA." Feb. 1962

Kendrew, John C., "The Three-dimensional Structure of a Protein Molecule." Dec. 1961

McElroy, Wm. D., and H. H. Seliger, "Biological Luminescence." Dec. 1962

Nirenberg, M. W., "The Genetic Code: II." Mar. 1963

Perutz, M. F., "The Hemoglobin Molecule." Nov. 1964

Sinsheimer, R. L., "Single-stranded DNA." July 1962

Spiegelman, S., "Hybrid Nucleic Acids." May 1964

Stein, William H., and S. Moore, "The Chemical Structure of Proteins." Feb. 1961

*"The Italian navigator has landed in the New World."*
*"How were the natives?"*
*"Very friendly."*

Arthur H. Compton to James B. Conant
December 2, 1942

CHAPTER 32 | # Nuclear Chemistry

Until 1942, elemental uranium was an unfamiliar metal with limited use in some glass, glazes, and steel. Then on a cold winter's afternoon in Chicago, this obscure element became the basis of a new era—the nuclear age. You have grown up in this era. You have become aware of the awesome responsibilities for both good and evil that characterize it. In this chapter, we shall consider some of the scientific discoveries and principles that gave rise to the nuclear age and that bring order and understanding to it.

### 32.1 The nature of radioactivity

The nuclear age really began forty-six winters before that of 1942, with Becquerel's chance discovery of the radioactive nature of uranium.* Painstaking research that followed, particularly that of Rutherford, led to the startling and revolutionary concept that radioactivity was a nuclear effect. Some atomic nuclei undergo a sudden and spontaneous change, releasing any one of three energetic, charged particles and accompanying radiant energy in the form of penetrating gamma rays.

As a result of the spontaneous emission of charged particles, radioactive nuclei are transformed, or *decay*, into nuclei of different elements. The two most common types of radioactive decay are characterized by the emission of alpha and of beta particles. The alpha particle is identical with the nucleus of the helium-4 atom, $^4_2$He.† Consequently, when a nucleus emits an alpha particle, the new nucleus has

---

* Review of Chapter 8 is recommended as a basis for fuller understanding of this chapter.

† For exactness, the full symbol for an $\alpha$ particle is $^4_2$He$^{+2}$. Since, however, radioactivity is a nuclear phenomenon, it is common practice in this case to symbolize only the nuclear make-up.

an *atomic number* that is *two less* than that of the decaying nucleus, and an *atomic mass* that is *four units less*.

When a nucleus of specific atomic number and atomic mass is considered, the nuclear scientist refers to such a nucleus as a *nuclide*. Thus, the alpha decay of the uranium-238 nuclide leads to the formation of the thorium-234 nuclide. This *nuclear reaction* can be written in equation form:

$$^{238}_{92}U \rightarrow \,^{234}_{90}Th + \,^{4}_{2}He$$

Balancing nuclear equations is a simple task. Both nuclear charge and atomic mass must be conserved. Thus, the sums of atomic numbers and atomic masses before and after a nuclear reaction must be the same.

Negative beta particles are identical with electrons. They are symbolized best as $_{-1}^{0}e$. Thus, when a nucleus emits a beta particle, the new nucleus has an *atomic number one greater* than that of the decaying nucleus, but the *same atomic mass*. For example, the beta decay of the uranium-239 nuclide yields neptunium-239:

$$^{239}_{92}U \rightarrow \,^{239}_{93}Np + \,^{0}_{-1}e$$

Observe that the conservation of atomic number in this nuclear equation involves the addition of a positive and a negative number.

Though the negative beta particle is identical with the electron, electrons themselves *do not* exist within the nucleus. In some manner still poorly understood, a neutron in the nucleus changes into a proton with the simultaneous creation and emission of an electron. Decay by beta emission occurs for nuclides located throughout the periodic table, whereas only the heaviest elements have isotopes that undergo alpha decay.

The third mode of nuclear decay is by positive beta particle, or *positron*, emission. The positron is a positively charged particle having the same mass that the electron has. It was originally discovered in 1932 by C. D. Anderson of the California Institute of Technology as a constituent of the *cosmic radiation* that reaches the earth from outer space. It is symbolized $_{+1}^{0}e$ and, when emitted by an unstable nuclide, results in a new nuclide of the *same atomic mass* but *one lower in atomic number*. This may be exemplified by the radioactive decay of antimony-120:

$$_{51}^{120}Sb \rightarrow {}_{50}^{120}Sn + {}_{+1}^{0}e$$

In this process a proton changes into a neutron in the nucleus with the simultaneous creation and emission of a positron.

The gamma rays, which are usually emitted immediately after one of the other forms of radioactive decay, are very high-energy electromagnetic radiations. They are emitted as a result of rearrangements of the neutrons and protons in a nucleus into new nuclear energy states. *Neither the mass number nor the atomic number is changed by gamma ray emission.*

## 32.2 Nuclear instability and the neutron-proton ratio (n/p)

Nuclear scientists have learned that a two-part pattern exists with respect to the stability of nuclei to radioactive decay. Nuclei may be grouped for stability on the basis of whether they have an even or odd number of protons and neutrons. When all the nonradioactive, or stable, isotopes of the elements are considered, those in which the nuclei have an even number of protons and of neutrons are by far the most abundant. Approximately equal in abundance are those with nuclei having an even number of protons but an odd number of neutrons, and those having an odd number of protons but an even number of neutrons. By far the least abundant stable isotopes are those in which the nuclei have odd numbers of protons and of neutrons, there being only nine of these out of some 300 known stable isotopes. These facts are understood in terms of pairing of the spins of protons and of neutrons within the nucleus. Such pairing, which leads to nuclear stability just as electron pairing leads to stable chemical bonds within molecules, is at a maximum when even numbers of protons and of neutrons are present. The pairing is at a minimum when odd numbers of both are present.

Nuclear stability also appears to be greatest when the number of neutrons is equal to or slightly greater than the number of protons. When the number of neutrons in the nuclei of the stable isotopes is plotted against the number of protons, Figure 32.1 results. The numerical value, or quotient, obtained by dividing the number of neutrons, n, by the number of protons, p, can be indicated by n/p and is often referred to as the n/p ratio. For a nucleus that lies outside of the stability

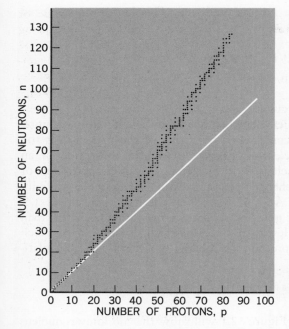

**FIGURE 32.1** Stable isotopes of the elements. What is the significance of the white line?

zone, radioactive decay leads to a change in the n/p ratio that brings that ratio closer to the stability zone. Several radioactive decays may occur before the n/p ratio reaches a value in the zone of stability.

We may use the neutron-proton curve to predict the type of radioactive decay an unstable nucleus is most likely to undergo. For a nucleus whose n/p ratio *is high* relative to the n/p ratio of a stable nucleus of same atomic number, a radioactive decay that will decrease the n/p ratio is predicted. This is achieved during beta decay. Figure 32.1 indicates that stable nuclei exist for elements of low atomic number only when the n/p ratio is near 1.0. For example, the n/p ratio for the stable carbon nuclide, C-12, is 1.0. Accordingly, we might predict that C-14 with an n/p ratio of 1.3 would be radioactive and that it would be a beta emitter. That is, we would predict that

$$^{14}_{6}C \rightarrow ^{14}_{7}N + ^{0}_{-1}e$$

should occur. Experimentally, we find that *it does*.

The only stable isotope of iodine is I-127, for which the n/p ratio equals 1.4. For I-133, the n/p ratio equals 1.5, and we would predict that

$$^{133}_{53}I \rightarrow ^{133}_{54}Xe + ^{0}_{-1}e$$

should occur, and it does.

For a nucleus whose n/p ratio *is low* with respect to the n/p ratio of the stable nucleus of same atomic number, a radioactive decay that will increase the n/p ratio is predicted. This increase is achieved by positron decay. Thus,

$$^{10}_{6}C \text{ (n/p = 0.67)} \rightarrow {}^{10}_{5}B + {}_{+1}^{0}e$$

$$^{121}_{53}I \text{ (n/p = 1.3)} \rightarrow {}^{121}_{52}Te + {}_{+1}^{0}e$$

are predictable, and do occur.

Among the heavier elements, a nuclear event more common than positron emission occurs when the value of the n/p ratio is too low. This event, called *electron capture*, results in absorption of an orbital electron by the nucleus. With the simultaneous disappearance of the electron, a proton is changed into a neutron. For example, the only stable nuclide of gold is Au-197, for which the n/p ratio equals 1.5. Therefore, all isotopes of gold for which the mass number is less than 197 will have n/p ratios less than 1.5. Almost all of some fifteen such isotopes decay by electron capture. Gold-194 decays to stable platinum-194 in this manner:

$$^{194}_{79}Au + {}_{-1}^{0}e \rightarrow {}^{194}_{78}Pt$$

Careful study of Figure 32.1 will show that no known nucleus heavier than bismuth-209 is stable. Thus, it would appear that among the heaviest nuclei, the total repulsion among the protons is too large for stability. In the case of such nuclei, alpha particle emission is a common mode of decay. Three examples of such nuclear decay are:

$$^{232}_{90}Th \rightarrow {}^{228}_{88}Ra + {}^{4}_{2}He$$

$$^{235}_{92}U \rightarrow {}^{231}_{90}Th + {}^{4}_{2}He$$

$$^{238}_{92}U \rightarrow {}^{234}_{90}Th + {}^{4}_{2}He$$

The three isotopes Th-232, U-235, and U-238 are parent members of three naturally occurring radioactive families, or series. Each of the three series ends in a stable isotope of lead, after as many as fourteen radioactive transformations. It is a remarkable achievement of nuclear scientists that the details of each of the naturally occurring radioactive families are known with great certainty. (Fig. 32.2.)

## 32.3 Half-life: rate of radioactive decay

The more frequently radioactive decay occurs, the more unstable are the nuclei that are decaying. The experimentally determined rate of decay is expressed in terms of *half-life*, $t_{\frac{1}{2}}$. *The half-life of a radioactive nuclide is the length of time required for a sample of the nuclide to become half as radioactive as it was at any given point in time.* Half-lives, as measured by nuclear scientists, vary enormously from billions

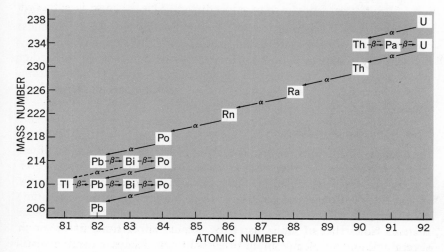

**FIGURE 32.2** Uranium-238 to stable lead-206, a naturally occurring transformation series

of years for some nuclides to infinitesimal fractions of a second for very unstable ones. In fact, we cannot be certain that some nuclides we now call stable are not actually unstable to radioactive decay, with half-lives too long to allow observation of the decay by present experimental techniques.

Figure 32.3 shows the experimental curve obtained when the radioactivity or, simply, the *activity* of a sample of I-131 is measured as a function of time. The curve indicates that the half-life of the beta emitter is 8.1 days. Further, it shows that after intervals of 8.1, 16.2, 24.3, and 32.4 days, the activity of the sample will be $\frac{1}{2}$, $\frac{1}{4}$, $\frac{1}{8}$, and $\frac{1}{16}$ of its initial value. That is, the activity, $A$, of the isotope can be determined by the formula

$$A = A_0 \left(\tfrac{1}{2}\right)^n$$

where $A_0$ is the initial activity and $n$ is the number of half-life intervals since the initial activity was measured.

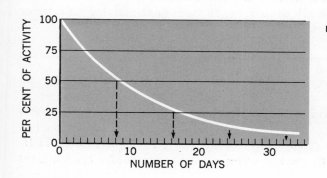

**FIGURE 32.3** Half-life curve for iodine-131

It is important to note that radioactive decay, being a nuclear phenomenon, is independent of the factors that usually affect chemical changes, such as temperature and pressure. Further, radioactive decay is essentially a statistical process, in which it is not possible to predict when a particular nucleus will undergo radioactive transformation. Thus, the decay properties of an unstable isotope are measured from studies of large numbers of atoms of the isotope.

## 32.4 Detection of radiation

As nuclear emanations from radioactive decay travel through matter, they transfer some of their kinetic energy to the matter. Alpha particles, which travel at 10,000–20,000 miles/sec, are the least penetrating. About five centimeters of air, a sheet of paper, or a thin sheet (0.1 mm) of aluminum will stop them. Beta particles, liberated at speeds more than six times that of alpha particles, require several meters of air or several millimeters of aluminum to absorb them. Gamma rays have still greater penetrating power—tens of centimeters of aluminum are often required to stop them. The dissipation of kinetic energy as the emanations penetrate matter results in the formation of ions from neutral atoms or molecules. This ionization is the basis for most of the detectors utilized by nuclear scientists in their study of unstable nuclei.

One category of detectors translates the ionization caused by decay radiations directly into an electrical signal. In this category are the Geiger-Müller counter, the proportional counter, and the ionization chamber. A common type of Geiger-Müller tube (Fig. 32.4.) consists of an argon-filled tube that has a central wire as anode and an outer cylinder as cathode. A very high voltage is maintained between the two electrodes. When a beta particle or gamma ray penetrates the thin

**FIGURE 32.4**   A model of a Geiger-Müller tube

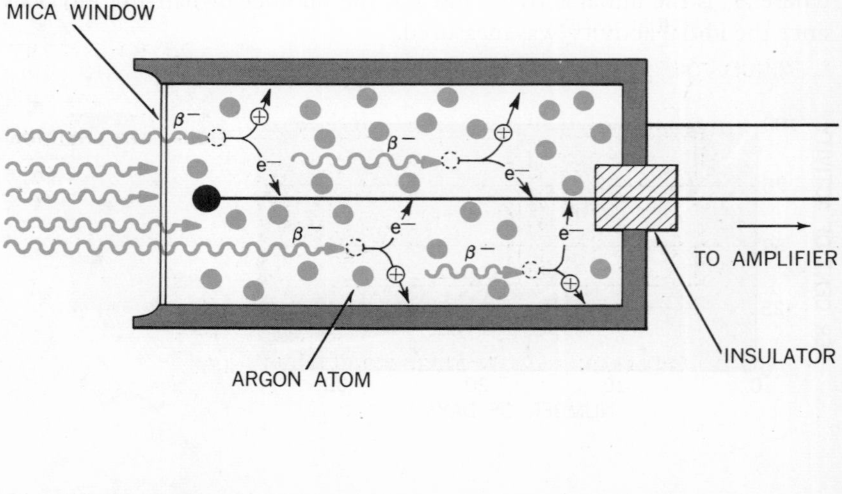

window and enters the tube, it causes ionization of a large number of gas atoms. Electrons are attracted to the anode wire and the argon cations to the cathode. The tube is discharged and a flow of current results. Each discharge is amplified and registered as a loud click or a flash of light.

A second category of detectors, now the most used in high-energy nuclear research, consists of the *cloud chamber* and *bubble chamber*. In the cloud chamber, whose principle was discovered by the English physicist C. T. R. Wilson in 1896, an incoming particle leads to condensation. A visible vapor trail of droplets appears along its ionization path in an atmosphere supersaturated with alcohol or some other vapor. In the bubble chamber, which was conceived in 1952 by the American physicist Donald Glaser, the ionization produced in a superheated liquid leads to boiling of the liquid and formation of visible bubbles along the path of the ionizing radiation.

A third category of detectors consists of photographic emulsions. Similar to but of higher density than regular photographic emulsions, these emulsions are "exposed" by charged particles passing through them. They are then developed by ordinary means. Often these emulsions are "stacked," so that penetrating power and effect of radiation may be studied.

A final class of detectors does not depend upon ionization but rather on the emission of light by certain substances, called *phosphors,* when they are struck by radiation. In the *scintillation counter*, a light flash is emitted each time a nuclear particle or gamma ray photon strikes and energizes a phosphor molecule. (Fig. 32.5.) Each flash, or scintillation, leads to the production of a photoelectron which leads, in turn, to the production of a pulse of current in the counter.

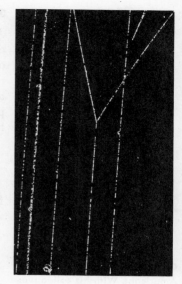

Entering from the bottom, a very high-energy proton collides with a stationary proton in a liquid hydrogen bubble chamber. (See page 215.) Two new elementary particles are produced.

**FIGURE 32.5** A scintillation counter. The scintillation-induced photoelectron shower leads to a pulse of current.

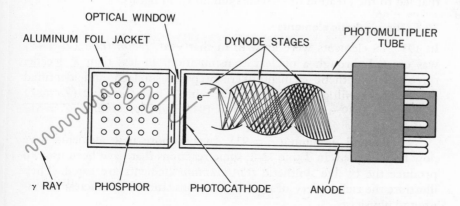

OPTICAL WINDOW

ALUMINUM FOIL JACKET

DYNODE STAGES

PHOTOMULTIPLIER TUBE

e⁻

γ RAY        PHOSPHOR        PHOTOCATHODE        ANODE

**Glenn T. Seaborg** (1912– American). With his colleagues and students at the Radiation Laboratory at the University of California at Berkeley, he discovered nine of the twelve transuranium elements. In 1951, he was honored with the Nobel Prize in Chemistry and in 1961 became chairman of the United States Atomic Energy Commission. In addition to his great scientific accomplishments and generous public service, Professor Seaborg is noted for his contributions toward educational reforms at the high school and college levels.

### 32.5  Nuclear transmutations and artificial radioactivity

As you recall, one of the chief goals of the ancient alchemists was to change the base metals, such as lead and iron, into gold. The alchemists, of course, failed to reach that goal. Today, however, this dream of transmutation has come true. The first *induced* transmutation was achieved in 1919 by Rutherford, who bombarded nitrogen with alpha particles. The nitrogen nucleus emitted a proton, changing into the heavy isotope of oxygen, O-17:

$$^{14}_{7}N + ^{4}_{2}He \rightarrow ^{17}_{8}O + ^{1}_{1}H$$

Later experiments showed that other elements could be built up from lighter elements. For example, when powdered beryllium is mixed with a trace of an alpha-emitting radium salt, the following neutron-yielding reaction occurs:

$$^{9}_{4}Be + ^{4}_{2}He \rightarrow ^{12}_{6}C + ^{1}_{0}n$$

This is an important source of energetic neutrons for nuclear research.

There are more than 300 naturally occurring nuclides, most of which are stable. Although a number of radioactive nuclides are found in nature, a very great many more have been prepared by scientists by nuclear transmutation. "Artificial radioactivity" was discovered in 1934 by Frédéric and Irène Joliot-Curie. The Joliot-Curies bombarded boron with alpha particles, leading to the formation of a radioactive nitrogen isotope:

$$^{10}_{5}B + ^{4}_{2}He \rightarrow ^{13}_{7}N + ^{1}_{0}n$$

Well over 1000 new radioactive nuclides have been produced and studied in the years since this example of modern alchemy. Among the most exciting transmutations that have been accomplished are those that led to the creation of elements unknown in nature.

### 32.6  The synthetic elements

In 1937, 88 elements were known. In that year, *technetium* ($Z = 43$) was created through a nuclear transmutation. In less than a decade, three other synthetic elements were prepared similarly and identified by chemists to fill gaps in the periodic table. Thus, *francium* ($Z = 87$) followed in 1939, *astatine* ($Z = 85$) in 1940, and *promethium* ($Z = 61$) in 1945.

Beyond uranium ($Z = 92$), twelve more new elements have now been created. In Table 32–1, some reactions that have been used to produce the twelve synthetic *transuranium* elements are listed. They illustrate the rich variety of nuclear reactions studied by nuclear chemists and physicists.

**TABLE 32-1** SYNTHESIS OF THE TRANSURANIUM ELEMENTS

| Target | | Projectile | | Products | | |
|---|---|---|---|---|---|---|
| $^{238}_{92}U$ | + | $^{2}_{1}H$ | $\rightarrow$ | $^{238}_{93}Np$ (neptunium) | + | $2\,^{1}_{0}n$ |
| $^{238}_{92}U$ | + | $^{4}_{2}He$ | $\rightarrow$ | $^{240}_{94}Pu$ (plutonium) | + | $2\,^{1}_{0}n$ |
| $^{239}_{94}Pu$ | + | $^{4}_{2}He$ | $\rightarrow$ | $^{241}_{95}Am$ (americium) | + | $^{1}_{1}H + \,^{1}_{0}n$ |
| $^{239}_{94}Pu$ | + | $^{4}_{2}He$ | $\rightarrow$ | $^{240}_{96}Cm$ (curium) | + | $3\,^{1}_{0}n$ |
| $^{244}_{96}Cm$ | + | $^{4}_{2}He$ | $\rightarrow$ | $^{245}_{97}Bk$ (berkelium) | + | $^{1}_{1}H + 2\,^{1}_{0}n$ |
| $^{238}_{92}U$ | + | $^{12}_{6}C$ | $\rightarrow$ | $^{245}_{98}Cf$ (californium) | + | $5\,^{1}_{0}n$ |
| $^{238}_{92}U$ | + | $^{14}_{7}N$ | $\rightarrow$ | $^{247}_{99}Es$ (einsteinium) | + | $5\,^{1}_{0}n$ |
| $^{238}_{92}U$ | + | $^{16}_{8}O$ | $\rightarrow$ | $^{250}_{100}Fm$ (fermium) | + | $4\,^{1}_{0}n$ |
| $^{253}_{99}Es$ | + | $^{4}_{2}H$ | $\rightarrow$ | $^{256}_{101}Md$ (mendelevium)* | + | $^{1}_{0}n$ |
| $^{246}_{96}Cm$ | + | $^{13}_{6}C$ | $\rightarrow$ | $^{251}_{102}No$ (nobelium)† | + | $8\,^{1}_{0}n$ |
| $^{252}_{98}Cf$ | + | $^{10}_{5}B$ | $\rightarrow$ | $^{257}_{103}Lw$ (lawrencium) | + | $5\,^{1}_{0}n$ |
| $^{242}_{94}Pu$ | + | $^{22}_{10}Ne$ | $\rightarrow$ | $^{260}_{104}?$ (unnamed) | + | $4\,^{1}_{0}n$ |

* Only eight atoms of mendelevium were produced in the discovery experiments by bombardment of an invisible amount (several billion atoms) of einsteinium. Professor Choppin, coauthor of this book, was one of the members of the team that discovered mendelevium.

† The honor of naming an element goes to its discoverer. Since the discovery of element 102 is a matter of dispute with some nuclear scientists, they do not accept the name nobelium, but consider the element unnamed.

## 32.7 Barrier to charged particle reactions

All the projectiles listed in Table 32-1 are positive ions ranging in charge from +1 for the *deuteron*, $^{2}_{1}H$, to +6 for the $^{16}_{8}O$ ion. It is found that no reaction occurs unless the positive projectiles have a certain minimum kinetic energy. This "activation energy" is approximately twice as large for alpha particles as for protons for the same target. Also, it increases as the atomic number of the target increases. This behavior is consistent with an electrostatic model in which activation energy is necessary to overcome the mutual repulsion existing between an approaching positively charged projectile and a positively charged target nucleus. An alpha particle with a +2 charge has approximately twice as great a repulsion to overcome as a proton with a +1 charge. For the target, the larger the atomic number—the number of protons—the greater the repulsive effect on an approaching positive particle. This hypothesis of a repulsive barrier to reaction by charged particles is strengthened by the observation that neutrons, bearing no charge, react with target nuclei even when the kinetic energy of the neutrons is almost zero.

### 32.8 Particle accelerators: atom smashers

In order to impart high enough kinetic energies to nuclear projectiles, particle accelerators have had to be devised. The *linear accelerator* consists of a series of tubular electrodes. By rapidly alternating the polarity of these electrodes, a charged particle is simultaneously repelled by the tube through which it has just drifted and is attracted to the next. Acceleration, therefore, of the charged particle occurs only in each successive gap between the tubes. (Fig. 32.6.)

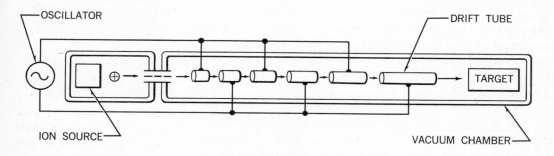

**FIGURE 32.6** A model of a linear accelerator. Of what significance is the vacuum chamber?

A 110-foot-long linear accelerator nears completion.

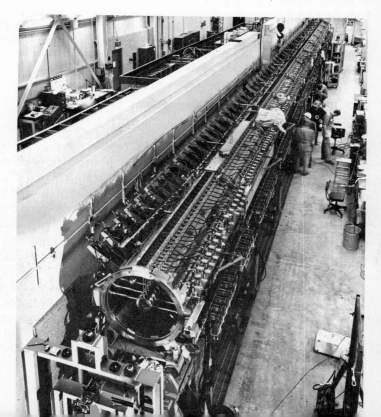

In *cyclotrons* and *synchrotrons*, whose principle was first proposed by the American Ernest O. Lawrence in 1929, the particles are passed through a magnetic field at the same time they are being accelerated. This causes the path of the charged particles to be bent. (Fig. 32.7.) The magnetic field does *not* increase the energy of the particles, but causes them to pass repeatedly through the same voltage-gap. Thus, very high particle energies such as 30 billion electron volts (Bev), which corresponds to 690 trillion calories per mole, can be obtained without resorting to linear accelerators that are several miles in length.

It is very difficult to achieve the simultaneous acceleration and bending of the path of high-energy electrons. Thus, in order to obtain electrons of extremely high energies, it is necessary to use a linear accelerator. At present, an electron accelerator two miles in length is under construction at Stanford University in California which will produce 100-billion-electron-volt beams of electrons. The electrons in such beams will have kinetic energies in excess of $2 \times 10^{15}$, or two quadrillion, calories per mole.

As enormous as are the projectile energies required to bring about some nuclear transformations, the energy that lies within an atom's nucleus is even greater. The first clue of just how much energy is locked within atomic nuclei came in the early years of this century.

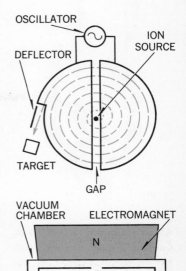

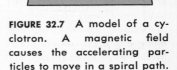

**FIGURE 32.7** A model of a cyclotron. A magnetic field causes the accelerating particles to move in a spiral path.

The *Cosmotron*, a 70-foot-diameter synchrotron. A million million protons, their path a small channel in a fixed circle of magnets, are accelerated to speeds approaching the velocity of light and energies of 3.1 Bev. The cylinder at the rear of the synchrotron is a Van de Graaff accelerator, which injects 3.6 million electron volt (Mev) protons into the accelerating channel.

## 32.9 Energy and mass are the same.

As we learned in Chapter 1, Albert Einstein, in 1905, advanced the revolutionary idea that matter and energy were really different forms of the same thing, and that matter could be changed into energy—at least theoretically. He developed a mathematical equation to express the conversion of matter into energy:

$$E = mc^2$$

where $E$ is energy expressed in *ergs*,* $m$ is mass expressed in grams, and $c$ is the speed of light expressed in centimeters per second.

According to this equation, if it were possible to convert one pound of carbon *completely* into energy, about 11 billion kilowatt-hours would be released. This is about double the amount of electric energy produced in an entire year by the largest generating plant in this country that uses coal as a fuel. In *burning* the same amount of carbon to carbon dioxide, only about four kilowatt-hours of energy are released.

Burning involves destruction and formation of chemical bonds. Nuclear reactions, however, involve forming and breaking "bonds" between nuclear particles. Chemical bond energy is measured in kilo-calories, while "nuclear bond energy" is measured in millions of kilo-calories. The change in mass corresponding to the energy released in a chemical reaction is too small to be detectable by the most sensitive balances available to scientists today. However, the changes in mass associated with the much larger energy changes are measured easily for nuclear reactions.

The idea of the interconversion of mass and energy had no experimental substantiation until 1932. In that year, two British scientists, J. D. Cockcroft and E. T. S. Walton, working in Rutherford's laboratory, bombarded lithium with high-speed protons. As products they obtained alpha particles with energies almost 100 times as great as the energy that was used to break the lithium atom. This extra energy was the *binding energy* that held the lithium nucleus together and came from the conversion of matter into energy:

$$^7_3\text{Li} + {}^1_1\text{H} \rightarrow 2\,{}^4_2\text{He} + 396 \times 10^6 \text{ calories/mole}$$

$$7.0182 \text{ amu} + 1.0081 \text{ amu} \rightarrow 2(4.0039) \text{ amu}$$

$$8.0263 \text{ amu} \rightarrow 8.0078 \text{ amu}$$

$$\text{Loss of mass} = 0.0185 \text{ amu}$$

---

* One erg is approximately the energy required to lift a postage stamp to a height equal to five times its thickness.

**Albert Einstein** (1879–1955, German). Einstein was the greatest theoretical physicist of our century. In 1905 he published his *Special Theory of Relativity*, and in 1916 his *General Theory of Relativity*. These treatises put forth revolutionary ideas relating to absolute motion, time, and space, and a new science—relativistic physics—emerged. Einstein made many other contributions in theoretical physics and chemistry throughout his life. His genius was recognized early with a Nobel Prize, awarded in 1921. In 1933 he was driven out of Germany and became a naturalized American citizen. In 1939 Einstein wrote a letter that changed the course of history. In it, he apprised President Roosevelt of the possibilities of the development of an "atomic bomb." Six years later, the bomb was a reality. In his last years, Einstein was a fervent advocate of nuclear disarmament.

The clue to unleashing nuclear energy is found in a detailed consideration of the binding energy of nuclei.

## 32.10 Nuclear binding energy

From the known masses of protons and neutrons, it is possible to calculate the expected mass of any nucleus. When the calculated mass of a nucleus is compared with its experimentally determined mass, the latter is always less. A *mass deficit* is always observed. This mass deficit may be translated through the Einstein equation into the binding energy of the nucleus. The binding energy of a nucleus may be considered to be the energy released in the formation of the nucleus from elementary particles. To break up a nucleus into the elementary particles of which it is composed requires, therefore, the input of energy equal to the binding energy.

Binding energies vary greatly with nuclear make-up. Thus, the binding energy of the neon-20 nucleus is calculated to be four billion calories per mole of nuclei; that for the bismuth-209 nucleus is forty billion calories per mole. If, however, the binding energy is divided by the number of nuclear particles, or *nucleons*, in the given nucleus, we find that the binding energy per nucleon for neon-20 (20 nucleons) and for bismuth-209 (209 nucleons) is essentially the same, 200 million calories per mole. Despite the fact that the two nuclides lie at extremes of the atomic weight scale, nearly the same energy is required in order to remove a nucleon from either of them. In fact, when the binding energies per nucleon ratios for all stable nuclei are calculated, a remarkable regularity is observed. (Fig. 32.8.)

Examination of Figure 32.8 leads us to conclude that nuclei with an atomic mass around 60 are most stable, since they have the largest binding energy per nucleon. We would predict then that if nuclei with masses greater than 60 could be broken down, great amounts of energy would be released. From the shape of Figure 32.8 we would

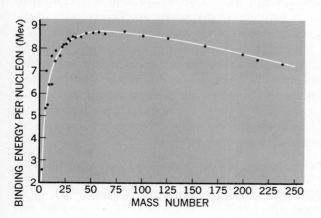

**FIGURE 32.8** Binding energy curve for stable nuclei

further predict that if nuclei with masses lower than 60 could be combined, then even greater amounts of nuclear energy would be unleashed. Figure 32.8, then, gives meaning to the two terms that fill the nuclear age with fear and with hope—nuclear fission and nuclear fusion.

### 32.11 Nuclear fission

In 1934, a young Italian physicist, Enrico Fermi, bombarded uranium with neutrons. He had slowed them down by passing them through paraffin. Earlier, he had discovered that such *slow* neutrons have a better chance of hitting and reacting with nuclei than do high-speed neutrons. Recall that there is no repulsive barrier to the approach of neutrons to a nucleus. Thus, no minimum kinetic energy is required for neutron bombardment. The radioactive properties of the bombardment products from uranium led Fermi to believe, incorrectly, that he had created a new element ($Z = 93$), and he turned to other research problems. Four years later, news came from Berlin that Otto Hahn and Fritz Strassmann in repeating Fermi's experiments had obtained a variety of known elements, with atomic numbers between those of krypton ($Z = 36$) and barium ($Z = 56$), and a great deal of energy. Uncertain as to the complete explanation of what had happened, they published their findings.

In Denmark, Dr. Lise Meitner, an eminent woman scientist who had shortly before fled from Nazi Germany, learned of the experiments and discussed them with Niels Bohr and her nephew Otto R. Frisch. Drs. Meitner and Frisch suggested that when the uranium is bombarded with slow neutrons, the uranium splits, or *fissions*, into more or less equal parts, forming a mixture of lighter nuclei.

### 32.12 Nuclear chain reactions

A few weeks later, at a conference held in Washington, D.C., Niels Bohr related these findings to a number of famous American and European nuclear physicists. Included in the group was Fermi, who, in the meantime, having gone with his family to Sweden in December 1938 to receive a Nobel Prize, refused to return to Fascist Italy. Instead, he had proceeded to London and then to America, where he was continuing his work at Columbia University. At the Washington meeting, Fermi and Bohr exchanged information and discussed the problem of fission. Bohr suggested that it was the uranium-235 nuclide that was fissionable. Fermi mentioned the possibility that neutrons might be emitted in the fission process as, for example:

$$^{235}_{92}U + {}^{1}_{0}n \rightarrow {}^{143}_{56}Ba + {}^{90}_{36}Kr + 3{}^{1}_{0}n + 4.6 \times 10^{12} \text{ cal/mole}$$

These product neutrons could collide with other uranium nuclei, yielding still more neutrons. The possibility of a *chain*, or self-propagating,

**Enrico Fermi** (1901–1954, Italian). Among the most outstanding scientists in history, Fermi was one of the architects of the so-called Atomic Age. He left Fascist Italy, and in 1939 became professor of physics at Columbia University. Later, he directed construction of the first nuclear reactor to achieve controlled nuclear fission. In 1938 Fermi won the Nobel Prize for his early experimental and theoretical contributions in physics. Two days before his untimely death from cancer in late 1954, Fermi was awarded a special prize of $25,000 by the Atomic Energy Commission for his outstanding later achievements in the field of nuclear physics and chemistry. That prize, now awarded annually, has been named in honor of Fermi, as has been element 100—fermium.

*reaction* began to crystallize, and experimental work was started even before the meeting was concluded.

By midsummer of 1940, the important facts regarding the emission of neutrons in nuclear fission had been discovered. For five years, while war raged in Europe, Asia, and Africa, nuclear fission research was carried out in utmost secrecy. Then in late summer, 1945, the world obtained its first knowledge of the success of that research and the beginning of a frightening new era in the history of man as Hiroshima, Japan, was destroyed by a nuclear fission weapon. Three days later, the similar destruction of Nagasaki ended World War II.

### 32.13 The Manhattan Project: the nuclear age dawns.

The story of the making of the first nuclear weapon is one unprecedented in human history. Early in 1940, Franklin Roosevelt and Winston Churchill pooled the efforts of American and British scientists on a research program called the Manhattan Project. Its goal was the release of nuclear energy through a weapon with which the war against the Axis nations might be won more quickly. Knowledge that research on such a weapon was being carried on by the enemy compelled quick, cooperative action. The race was on—the prize, victory. The people of the United States invested two billion dollars in ". . . the greatest scientific gamble in history"—and won.

The triumph and tragedy of uncontrolled nuclear fission: Nagasaki—August 9, 1945

Facts indicated that if a sufficient quantity of the fissionable U-235 could be brought together under the proper conditions, a self-sustaining nuclear reaction would result. Since the rate of fission is related to the number of neutrons captured by U-235 nuclei, it was important to determine the *critical mass* and *critical size* of the fissionable material. For a self-sustaining nuclear reaction, the proper mass-to-surface-area ratio had to be calculated, since the number of neutrons that escape from fissioning material depends on the *surface area*, while the number of neutrons captured to sustain the fission process depends upon *volume*.

By the winter of 1942, enough pure uranium, mostly in the form of oxide, had been painstakingly prepared to test the theories behind a self-sustaining fission reaction. On December 2, under the brilliant leadership of Fermi, theory was put to the test of experiment. In a squash court under the stands of Stagg Field at the University of Chicago stood a latticework of 285 tons of the purest graphite ever prepared. Interspersed among the graphite layers were layers containing some 40 tons of uranium and its oxide. Near the bottom of the uranium-graphite *pile* was a radium-beryllium neutron source that would serve to initiate fission. To assure control of the entire process, cadmium strips were inserted in the pile. These acted as neutron absorbers and prevented a chain reaction. Finally, under Fermi's direction, the cadmium

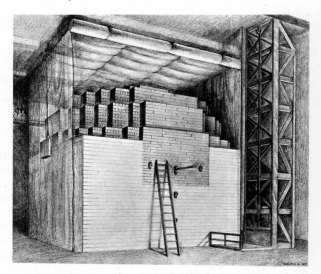

The first nuclear reactor: Chicago Pile 1. No photographs of the completed reactor exist. This drawing is based on physical measurements of the reactor and recollections of the group of scientists who built it.

strips were carefully withdrawn from the pile. The neutron intensity within the pile slowly increased until, exactly according to calculations, a *controlled*, sustained nuclear fission reaction resulted. The "Italian navigator" had indeed landed in the New World and the world would never be the same again.*

### 32.14  Uncontrolled chain reactions and nuclear weapons

Heartened by the successful demonstration of a self-sustaining fission reaction, scientists of the Manhattan Project continued their efforts to develop a fission weapon that would end the war. To make such a device, a large amount of pure U-235 was essential, and unless the fissionable isotope could be isolated from the isotopic mixture found in natural uranium, a weapon could not be made.

The problem was a very difficult one. In the first place, of the three isotopes present in naturally occurring uranium, U-235 was present only to the extent of 0.7 per cent. Along with a negligible amount of U-234, U-238 constituted nearly all of the natural uranium. Then, since isotopes of an element have nearly identical chemical properties, nonchemical separation techniques had to be devised. Of a number of complex procedures tried, two proved most useful—electromagnetic separation (Fig. 32.9) and separation by gaseous diffusion (Fig. 32.10). Major separation facilities based on these processes were built in Oak Ridge, Tennessee.

---

* The cryptic dialogue that opens this chapter occurred spontaneously between two scientists who had important administrative roles in the Manhattan Project. Dr. Compton also played an important scientific role in this project.

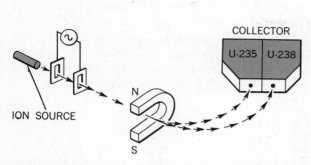

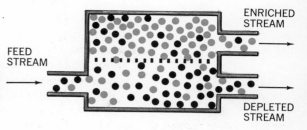

**FIGURE 32.9** A mass spectrometer. A beam of accelerated uranium ions is separated in a magnetic field. Ions of U-235 are deflected from their initial path to a slightly greater extent than are those of the heavier U-238. Proper placement of collectors permits isolation of the isotopes. This method was found to be uneconomical for large-scale separation, but is still used for research purposes.

**FIGURE 32.10** A gaseous diffusion stage for the separation of the isotopes of uranium. The feed stream contains gaseous $UF_6$ with a natural abundance of 0.71 per cent U-235. Slightly more $^{235}UF_6$ molecules (yellow) than $^{238}UF_6$ molecules (black) diffuse through the barrier. Continued enrichment through thousands of stages yields a final product that contains more than 90 per cent U-235.

While work proceeded on the very difficult and expensive process of separating the isotopes of uranium, a new process was developed to take advantage of an important property of U-238, the very abundant, but nonfissionable, uranium isotope. U-238 absorbs slow neutrons and undergoes transmutation:

$$^{238}_{92}U + ^1_0n \rightarrow ^{239}_{92}U$$

The artificially produced U-239 isotope decays in a reaction that first led to the synthesis of *neptunium*,

$$^{239}_{92}U \rightarrow ^{239}_{93}Np + ^0_{-1}e \ (t_{\frac{1}{2}} = 23 \text{ minutes}),$$

which, in turn, undergoes beta decay to form plutonium-239:

$$^{239}_{93}Np \rightarrow ^{239}_{94}Pu + ^0_{-1}e \ (t_{\frac{1}{2}} = 2.3 \text{ days})$$

Plutonium-239 is an alpha emitter but decays with a half-life of nearly 25,000 years. Thus, the neutron absorption by U-238 leads to a build-up of the long-lived Pu-239. The significance of this *breeder reaction* is that Pu-239 is fissionable. As a result, huge breeder reactors were built in Hanford, Washington, in which neutrons emitted by a controlled, fissioning core of U-235 were absorbed by a "blanket" of U-238 leading to the production of fissionable Pu-239 within the blanket. Thus were U-235 and Pu-239 produced for America's nuclear arsenal.

Then it was only a matter of time. With sufficient amounts of U-235 and Pu-239 available, a nuclear weapons explosion would result from quickly bringing two slightly *subcritical* masses of fissionable material together. The resulting critical mass would begin an un-controlled chain reaction that would in less than a millionth of a second release tremendous amounts of energy—and destruction. The devasta-tion of Hiroshima and Nagasaki bore witness to the awesome energy locked within the atom's nucleus, and altered the course of history.

### 32.15 Fallout

The new, lighter nuclei formed from fissioning uranium usually range in atomic number from 30 to 64 and are known as *fission products*. The n/p ratio for fissionable uranium is 1.55, somewhat larger than the values for stable nuclei with atomic numbers between 30 and 64. Consequently, the fission products, with n/p ratios around 1.6, are "neutron rich" and undergo beta decay. In nuclear explosions, the most abundant fission products, for example Sr-90, I-131, and Co-137, con-stitute the "fallout," that is, the debris that gradually settles down to the earth's surface. One of the most deadly members of this fallout is the strontium-90 that is absorbed by plants and eventually becomes concentrated in our bones through food, especially milk. Many of the fission products have half-lives of years, so that fallout continues to be a danger to health long after the original explosion.

### 32.16 Nuclear energy and peaceful power

The immense energies liberated during self-sustaining fission reactions are a potential source of almost limitless peaceful power for mankind. Controlled chain reactions in nuclear reactor power plants are providing electricity in areas throughout the world. Nuclear-powered ships of the United States and Russia ply the seas, both on and below the surface.

A great variety of types of nuclear reactors are currently in operation. However, they all have five basic components. (Fig. 32.11.) 1. *Fuel.* This may be either natural uranium or natural uranium en-riched with U-235 or Pu-239. Normally, the fuel is used in the form of metal plates alloyed with aluminum. 2. *Moderator.* Neutrons, being electrically neutral, may be slowed down by passing them through substances that have stable nuclei and that do not react with them. Graphite, water, and $D_2O$ are the most common materials used as *moderators* to slow the fission neutrons to the low velocities at which they are most effective in causing further fissioning. 3. *Control Rods.* Cadmium and boron are used to absorb excess neutrons through nuclear reaction so as to control the rate of the chain reaction. 4. *Coolant.* The coolant conducts away the heat produced during fission so as to keep the temperature within the reactor at a reasonable level. Water, $D_2O$, air, or even a molten mixture of sodium and potassium are used as

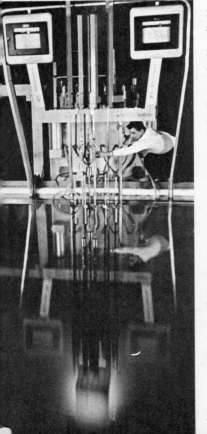

A "swimming-pool" nuclear research reactor. Water serves as moderator, coolant, and radiation shield. A blue glow is emitted in the vicinity of the reactor core, sixteen feet be-low the surface, where intense radiation ionizes the water.

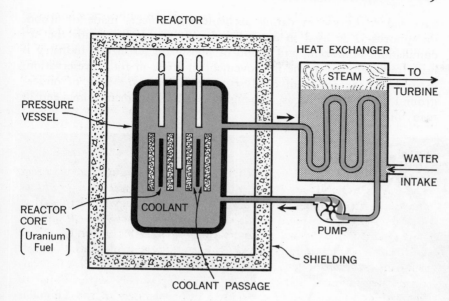

REACTOR

HEAT EXCHANGER

STEAM

TO TURBINE

PRESSURE VESSEL

WATER INTAKE

REACTOR CORE
[Uranium Fuel]

COOLANT

PUMP

SHIELDING

COOLANT PASSAGE

**FIGURE 32.11** A simplified model of a nuclear reactor

coolants. In many reactors, the same water or $D_2O$ serves as both moderator and coolant. In power reactors the coolant carries the heat to a heat exchanger, where it is used to produce steam. This steam in turn is used to drive turbogenerators to produce electricity. *5. Shielding.* Thick layers of shielding serve to absorb the intense radiation produced in the reactor. Shielding is usually accomplished by the use of water, concrete, or both. Often, lead shielding is used around ports used for the insertion of graphite holders into reactors that are used in the preparation of radioisotopes.

## 32.17 Radioisotopes: the plentiful vintage of modern alchemy

Most radioisotopes are produced by exposure of nonradioactive isotopes to neutron irradiation in nuclear reactors. Research in medicine, biology, agriculture, and many other fields has been helped tremendously by the use of synthetic radioactive nuclides.

Radioactive iodine, I-131, for example, is used in the diagnosis and treatment of thyroid disorders. After drinking a liquid containing a measured amount of radioiodine, the rate of movement to the thyroid gland can be accurately determined by use of a scintillation counter. The isotope, having a half-life of eight days, will decay completely before its radiation will cause any appreciable damage to nearby tissue, but it may destroy enough thyroid tissue to stop oversecretion and hyperthyroidism.

The beta active carbon-14 is a wonderful research tool in the study of photosynthesis, human sugar metabolism, and other biochemical reactions. Its natural occurrence and long half-life (5570 years)

Iodine-131 radiation outlines the thyroid gland. The lighter, nonabsorbing areas are "trouble spots."

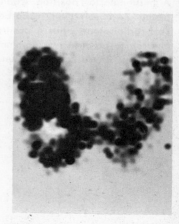

have led to its use in dating archeological objects made of wood. Phosphorus-32 is used in agricultural research dealing with the accumulation, utilization, and action of phosphate fertilizers. Industry is using radioisotopes in the improvement of steel; in food preservation; in studying the action of catalysts; in measuring the flow of underground water, oil, and gas; in gauging thickness of metal films, and in many other ways.

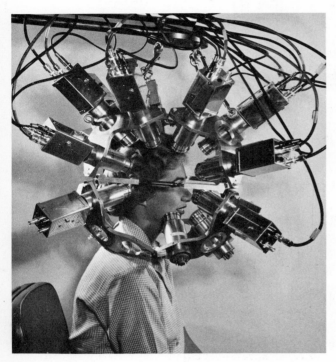

A multi-detector positron scanner. A compound containing arsenic-74 is selectively absorbed by tumorous brain tissue. This radioisotope emits a positron, which combines with an electron to produce two gamma rays that move in opposite directions. These rays are then detected simultaneously by an opposed pair of detectors.

Radioactive isotopes are used to trace the distribution of a new animal-repellent chemical to a Douglas fir seedling. The chemical, "tagged" with a radioactive nuclide, is applied to the soil at the roots and makes its way into the plant through the root hairs.

### 32.18 Nuclear fusion

While nuclear fission is currently used as a source of nuclear power, it is expected that nuclear fusion will be the ultimate source of unlimited nuclear power. As we saw in studying Figure 32.8, nuclear fusion reactions are potentially greater sources of energy than are fission reactions. It is believed that nuclear fusion is the source of the energy released by the sun and other stars.

One series of fusion reactions believed to occur within the sun's interior, where temperatures are of the order of 20 million degrees, is:

$$^{12}_{6}C + {}^{1}_{1}H \rightarrow {}^{13}_{7}N + \text{energy}$$

$$^{13}_{7}N \rightarrow {}^{13}_{6}C + {}^{0}_{+1}e$$

$$^{13}_{6}C + {}^{1}_{1}H \rightarrow {}^{14}_{7}N + \text{energy}$$

$$^{14}_{7}N + {}^{1}_{1}H \rightarrow {}^{15}_{8}O + \text{energy}$$

$$^{15}_{8}O \rightarrow {}^{15}_{7}N + {}^{0}_{+1}e$$

$$^{15}_{7}N + {}^{1}_{1}H \rightarrow {}^{12}_{6}C + {}^{4}_{2}He + \text{energy}$$

$$4\,({}^{1}_{1}H) \rightarrow {}^{4}_{2}He + 2\,({}^{0}_{+1}e) + \text{energy}$$

The total energy released per mole of He-4 nuclei produced may be calculated to be more than 600 trillion calories!

Spectroscopic evidence indicates that about one per cent of the sun's mass is helium. From this it has been calculated that though the energy output of the sun corresponds to a mass loss of four million tons per second, it should continue to radiate at its present rate for another thirty billion years!

Unlike nuclear fission, nuclear fusion requires two positively charged and thereby mutually repulsive nuclei to approach each other close enough to fuse. The probability of a fusion reaction, then, is very small unless nuclei with enormously high energies collide. To attain energies high enough for fusion to occur, atoms must be initially heated to about 200 million degrees! Once nuclear fusion is initiated, however, the heat from this *thermonuclear reaction* yields enough energy to be self-sustaining.

Thus far, scientists have enjoyed only very limited success in achieving controlled nuclear fusion. We are all aware, however, of their success with uncontrolled fusion in the area of thermonuclear weapons. Nuclear fission explosions provided the initial temperatures required to fuse heavy hydrogen nuclei. The resultant energy liberated from the uncontrolled thermonuclear reaction that ensued is almost unimaginable. Nearly 100 million calories were released per gram of heavy hydrogen nuclei fused:

$$^{2}_{1}H + {}^{3}_{1}H \rightarrow {}^{4}_{2}He + {}^{1}_{0}n + \text{energy}$$

## 32.19 Peaceful use of nuclear fusion

The successful production of energy from fusion reactions for peaceful means would be of tremendous importance to the people of the world. The energy that is potentially available from the small amount of heavy hydrogen in ordinary water could supply enough energy to meet the world's requirements for millions of years. Furthermore, fusion, unlike fission, does not yield radioactive products that require expensive precautions for safe storage and disposal.

In order to use fusion energy for creative purposes, the reaction must be sustained for long periods of time with a *controlled* release of energy. At 200 million degrees, however, no material can exist as a solid, liquid, or even as a regular gas. At these extreme temperatures, the electrons have so much energy that the hot gas really consists of positive ions separated from the electrons. This hot gas is an example of the fourth state of matter—*plasma*.

In order to sustain the fusion reaction, it is important that the entire plasma be kept hot. If any of the particles strike a solid wall, enough heat would be lost by transfer to cool the plasma below the reaction temperature, and the walls of the container would be simultaneously melted and vaporized. This problem may be solved by using the matterless walls provided by magnetic fields, that is, by using a "magnetic bottle." A strong magnetic field can prevent the charged particles of the plasma from colliding with the walls by causing the particles to move in a small circle, just as the synchrotron magnets hold a proton beam in a circular path. The field further acts to squeeze the plasma particles together to increase their density sufficiently for continuous fusion to occur. Research in the United States, England, Russia, and India has produced promising results, but present indications are that economical fusion power will require several more decades of research.

While it is true that our knowledge of nuclear fission and fusion grew out of military necessity, that knowledge may now be used for our safety, our health, and many still undetermined benefits. This nuclear age, which began in the darkness of world war, opens before us in brightness and hope.

## SUMMARY

Some atomic nuclei undergo sudden, spontaneous, and random changes marked by the release of charged particles and radiant energy. Whether a nucleus has an even or odd number of protons and neutrons seems to determine nuclear stability, as does the neutron/proton (n/p) ratio. The n/p ratio can be used to predict the type of emission an unstable nucleus will undergo. While radioactivity is by nature a random process, the time it takes for half of a given sample of a radioactive nuclide to decay is constant for that nuclide. The effects of radioactive emanations on matter are used as the basis for designing detection devices necessary to the study of nuclear chemistry.

Using charged particle accelerators, nuclear chemists have synthesized sixteen elements, twelve of which follow uranium in the periodic classification of the elements. Other nuclear transmutation reactions have led to the production of more than 1000 radioactive nuclides of the elements.

From the Einstein mass-energy equivalence, it is possible to calculate nuclear binding energies. Such information leads to the prediction of nuclear fission and, especially, nuclear fusion as major energy sources. The emergence of nuclear fission as such a source is the capstone of one of the great dramas of history. The eventual control of nuclear fusion will be the epilogue of that drama.

## QUESTIONS AND PROBLEMS

**32.1**  **a.** Name and describe the three most common *particle* emissions of naturally radioactive nuclides. **b.** How does each emission affect the parent nuclide? **c.** What is the effect of each type of emission on the n/p ratio?

**32.2**  Write nuclear equations for the radioactive decay of the following nuclides; their mode of decay is given in parentheses. ($\alpha$ = alpha particle; $\beta^-$ = negative beta particle; $\beta^+$ = positron; E.C. = electron capture.)

   **a.** $^{13}_{7}\text{N}$ ($\beta^+$)   **c.** $^{35}_{16}\text{S}$ ($\beta^-$)   **e.** $^{140}_{56}\text{Ba}$ ($\beta^-$)   **g.** $^{167}_{71}\text{Lu}$ (E.C.)

   **b.** $^{7}_{4}\text{Be}$ (E.C.)   **d.** $^{31}_{16}\text{S}$ ($\beta^+$)   **f.** $^{230}_{92}\text{U}$ ($\alpha$)   **h.** $^{257}_{103}\text{Lw}$ ($\alpha$)

**32.3**  The usual required storage time for radioactive wastes is seven half-lives. **a.** What is the required storage time for I-131? ($t_{\frac{1}{2}} = 8.1$ days.) **b.** At the end of that time, what per cent of the original I-131 radioactivity would remain?

   ANS.  **b.** 0.78%

**32.4**  $^{2}_{1}\text{H}$, $^{10}_{5}\text{B}$, and $^{12}_{6}\text{C}$ are stable nuclides. Write nuclear equations for the radioactive decay of $^{3}_{1}\text{H}$, $^{8}_{5}\text{B}$, $^{12}_{5}\text{B}$, $^{10}_{6}\text{C}$, and $^{14}_{6}\text{C}$.

**32.5**  Describe differences among the three most common methods of radiation detection.

**32.6**  Why are particle accelerators necessary?

**32.7**  When the copper-63 nuclide is bombarded with deuterons, six different transmutations may occur. Complete the equations for these:

   **a.** $^{63}_{29}\text{Cu} + {}^{2}_{1}\text{H} \rightarrow \underline{\quad} + \text{neutron}$   **d.** $^{63}_{29}\text{Cu} + {}^{2}_{1}\text{H} \rightarrow \underline{\quad} + \alpha$

   **b.** $^{63}_{29}\text{Cu} + {}^{2}_{1}\text{H} \rightarrow {}^{64}_{29}\text{Cu} + \underline{\quad}$   **e.** $^{63}_{29}\text{Cu} + {}^{2}_{1}\text{H} \rightarrow {}^{62}_{29}\text{Cu} + \underline{\quad}$

   **c.** $^{63}_{29}\text{Cu} + {}^{2}_{1}\text{H} \rightarrow {}^{63}_{30}\text{Zn} + \underline{\quad}$   **f.** $^{63}_{29}\text{Cu} + {}^{2}_{1}\text{H} \rightarrow {}^{65}_{30}\text{Zn} + \underline{\quad}$

**32.8**  Describe the derivation and implications of Figure 32.8.

**32.9** Why has controlled nuclear fission been achieved more readily than controlled nuclear fusion?

**32.10** Neutron capture reactions, occurring in nuclear fission reactors, are the most common types of nuclear transmutations. Write nuclear equations for the neutron capture reactions involving these nuclides: a. $_3^6Li$; b. $_{15}^{31}P$; c. $_{48}^{113}Cd$; d. $_{64}^{157}Gd$; e. $_{95}^{242}Am$.

**32.11** What does each of the following terms mean?

a. nuclide     e. phosphor     i. nuclear chain reaction
b. nucleon     f. artificial radioactivity     j. neutron moderator
c. isotope     g. binding energy     k. magnetic bottle
d. fallout     h. breeder reaction     l. the plasma state

## SUGGESTED READINGS

Bishop, Amasa S. *Project Sherwood: The U.S. Program in Controlled Fusion.* Addison-Wesley Publishing Co., 1958.

Choppin, Gregory R. *Nuclei and Radioactivity* (paperback). W. A. Benjamin, 1964.

Curie, Marie. *Radioactive Substances* (paperback). Philosophical Library, 1961.

Gamow, George. *The Atom and Its Nucleus* (paperback). Prentice-Hall, 1961.

Glasstone, Samuel. *Sourcebook on Atomic Energy.* Van Nostrand, 1958.

Hill, R. D. *Tracking Down Particles* (paperback). W. A. Benjamin, 1963.

Hughes, Donald J. *The Neutron Story* (paperback). Doubleday, 1959.

Overman, R. T. *Basic Concepts of Nuclear Chemistry* (paperback). Reinhold, 1963.

Seaborg, G. T. *Man-made Transuranium Elements* (paperback). Prentice-Hall, 1963.

Wilson, R. R., and R. Littauer. *Accelerators* (paperback). Doubleday, 1960.

CHEMISTRY
Dunham, C. L., "ISOTOPES–Explorers in Medical Science." Jan. 1965
Mellor, David P., "Origin and Evolution of Chemical Elements." Part 1, Feb. 1964; Part 2, Apr. 1964
Seaborg, Glenn T., "Plutonium, the Ornery Element." June 1964
Swart, E., "Chemistry and Archaeology." Feb. 1965

SCIENTIFIC AMERICAN
Ginzton, E. L., and W. Kirk, "The Two-mile Electron Accelerator." Nov. 1961
Marshak, R. E., "The Nuclear Force." Mar. 1960
Puck, T. T., "Radiation and the Human Cell." Apr. 1960
Weinberg, A. M., "Breeder Reactors." Jan. 1960
Woodwell, G. M., "The Ecological Effects of Radiation." June 1963

# APPENDIX I | Table of the Chemical Elements

| Element | Symbol | Atomic Number | Relative Atomic Weight Based on $O = 16.0000$ | Relative Atomic Weight Based on $^{12}_{6}C = 12.0000$ |
|---|---|---|---|---|
| Actinium | Ac | 89 | (227)* | (227)* |
| Aluminum | Al | 13 | 26.98 | 26.9815 |
| Americium | Am | 95 | (243)* | (243)* |
| Antimony | Sb | 51 | 121.76 | 121.75 |
| Argon | Ar | 18 | 39.944 | 39.948 |
| Arsenic | As | 33 | 74.91 | 74.9216 |
| Astatine | At | 85 | (210)* | (210)* |
| Barium | Ba | 56 | 137.36 | 137.34 |
| Berkelium | Bk | 97 | (247)* | (247)* |
| Beryllium | Be | 4 | 9.013 | 9.0122 |
| Bismuth | Bi | 83 | 209.00 | 208.980 |
| Boron | B | 5 | 10.82 | 10.811 |
| Bromine | Br | 35 | 79.916 | 79.909 |
| Cadmium | Cd | 48 | 112.41 | 112.40 |
| Calcium | Ca | 20 | 40.08 | 40.08 |
| Californium | Cf | 98 | (249)* | (249)* |
| Carbon | C | 6 | 12.011 | 12.01115 |
| Cerium | Ce | 58 | 140.13 | 140.12 |
| Cesium | Cs | 55 | 132.91 | 132.905 |
| Chlorine | Cl | 17 | 35.457 | 35.453 |
| Chromium | Cr | 24 | 52.01 | 51.996 |
| Cobalt | Co | 27 | 58.94 | 58.9332 |
| Copper | Cu | 29 | 63.54 | 63.54 |
| Curium | Cm | 96 | (248)* | (248)* |
| Dysprosium | Dy | 66 | 162.51 | 162.50 |
| Einsteinium | Es | 99 | (254)* | (254)* |
| Erbium | Er | 68 | 167.27 | 167.26 |
| Europium | Eu | 63 | 152.0 | 151.96 |
| Fermium | Fm | 100 | (253)* | (253)* |
| Fluorine | F | 9 | 19.00 | 18.9984 |
| Francium | Fr | 87 | (223)* | (223)* |
| Gadolinium | Gd | 64 | 157.26 | 157.25 |
| Gallium | Ga | 31 | 69.72 | 69.72 |
| Germanium | Ge | 32 | 72.60 | 72.59 |
| Gold | Au | 79 | 197.0 | 196.967 |
| Hafnium | Hf | 72 | 178.50 | 178.49 |
| Helium | He | 2 | 4.003 | 4.0026 |
| Holmium | Ho | 67 | 164.94 | 164.930 |
| Hydrogen | H | 1 | 1.0080 | 1.00797 |
| Indium | In | 49 | 114.82 | 114.82 |
| Iodine | I | 53 | 126.91 | 126.9044 |
| Iridium | Ir | 77 | 192.2 | 192.2 |
| Iron | Fe | 26 | 55.85 | 55.847 |
| Krypton | Kr | 36 | 83.80 | 83.80 |
| Lanthanum | La | 57 | 138.92 | 138.91 |
| Lawrencium | Lw | 103 | (259)* | (259)* |
| Lead | Pb | 82 | 207.21 | 207.19 |
| Lithium | Li | 3 | 6.940 | 6.939 |
| Lutetium | Lu | 71 | 174.99 | 174.97 |
| Magnesium | Mg | 12 | 24.32 | 24.312 |
| Manganese | Mn | 25 | 54.94 | 54.9380 |
| Mendelevium | Md | 101 | (256)* | (256)* |
| Mercury | Hg | 80 | 200.61 | 200.59 |
| Molybdenum | Mo | 42 | 95.95 | 95.94 |
| Neodymium | Nd | 60 | 144.27 | 144.24 |
| Neon | Ne | 10 | 20.183 | 20.183 |
| Neptunium | Np | 93 | (237)* | (237)* |
| Nickel | Ni | 28 | 58.71 | 58.71 |
| Niobium | Nb | 41 | 92.91 | 92.906 |
| Nitrogen | N | 7 | 14.008 | 14.0067 |
| Nobelium | No | 102 | (253)* | (253)* |
| Osmium | Os | 76 | 190.2 | 190.2 |
| Oxygen | O | 8 | 16.0000 | 15.9994 |
| Palladium | Pd | 46 | 106.4 | 106.4 |
| Phosphorus | P | 15 | 30.975 | 30.9738 |
| Platinum | Pt | 78 | 195.09 | 195.09 |
| Plutonium | Pu | 94 | (242)* | (242)* |
| Polonium | Po | 84 | (210)* | (210)* |
| Potassium | K | 19 | 39.100 | 39.102 |
| Praseodymium | Pr | 59 | 140.92 | 140.907 |
| Promethium | Pm | 61 | (145)* | (145)* |
| Protactinium | Pa | 91 | (231)* | (231)* |
| Radium | Ra | 88 | (226)* | (226)* |
| Radon | Rn | 86 | (222)* | (222)* |
| Rhenium | Re | 75 | 186.22 | 186.2 |
| Rhodium | Rh | 45 | 102.91 | 102.905 |
| Rubidium | Rb | 37 | 85.48 | 85.47 |
| Ruthenium | Ru | 44 | 101.1 | 101.07 |
| Samarium | Sm | 62 | 150.35 | 150.35 |
| Scandium | Sc | 21 | 44.96 | 44.956 |
| Selenium | Se | 34 | 78.96 | 78.96 |
| Silicon | Si | 14 | 28.09 | 28.086 |
| Silver | Ag | 47 | 107.880 | 107.870 |
| Sodium | Na | 11 | 22.991 | 22.9898 |
| Strontium | Sr | 38 | 87.63 | 87.62 |
| Sulfur | S | 16 | 32.066 | 32.064 |
| Tantalum | Ta | 73 | 180.95 | 180.948 |
| Technetium | Tc | 43 | (99)* | (99)* |
| Tellurium | Te | 52 | 127.61 | 127.60 |
| Terbium | Tb | 65 | 158.93 | 158.924 |
| Thallium | Tl | 81 | 204.39 | 204.37 |
| Thorium | Th | 90 | 232.05 | 232.038 |
| Thulium | Tm | 69 | 168.94 | 168.934 |
| Tin | Sn | 50 | 118.70 | 118.69 |
| Titanium | Ti | 22 | 47.90 | 47.90 |
| Tungsten | W | 74 | 183.86 | 183.85 |
| Uranium | U | 92 | 238.07 | 238.03 |
| Vanadium | V | 23 | 50.95 | 50.942 |
| Xenon | Xe | 54 | 131.30 | 131.30 |
| Ytterbium | Yb | 70 | 173.04 | 173.04 |
| Yttrium | Y | 39 | 88.92 | 88.905 |
| Zinc | Zn | 30 | 65.38 | 65.37 |
| Zirconium | Zr | 40 | 91.22 | 91.22 |
| (Unnamed)† | ? | 104 | (260)* | (260)* |

* Each of these is a radioactive element. The value in each parenthesis denotes the *mass number* of the *isotope* of the element with the longest known *half-life*.
† Discovery of element 104 was reported in 1964.

| # The Metric System

Scientists, universally, have adopted the *metric system* of weights and measures to express quantitative data uniformly. The basic units in the metric system are defined and agreed upon internationally. A great value of the metric system lies in the fact that larger and smaller units are derived as decimal multiples or fractions of the basic ones. Definitions of the basic units of the metric system are:

**Length.** The *meter* is 1,650,763.73 times the wavelength of the orange-red spectral emission line of krypton-86.

**Mass.** The *kilogram* is the mass of a platinum-iridium cylinder kept at the International Bureau of Weights and Measures in Sèvres, France. (See photograph on p. 83.)

**Time.** The *ephemeris second*, or simply the second, is 1/31,556,925.9747 of the tropical year for 1900 January $0^d12^h$ ephemeris time.*

Table II–1 lists the decimal multiple and fractional prefixes commonly used with the basic units of the metric system when scientific data is recorded.

When the kilogram was originally defined, it was intended that it be equal to the mass of a cubic decimeter of water at its maximum density. The *liter*, as the *derived* unit of volume in the metric system, was to have been the volume occupied by a kilogram of water at its maximum density, and, therefore, equal to a cubic decimeter. Later, when more exact measurements were made on the density of water, it

---

* Ephemeris time is a *uniform* measure of time defined by the *orbital motion* of the earth *about* the sun. Until 1956, the second was defined as 1/86,400 of a *mean solar day*. *Mean solar time* is defined by the *rotational motion* of the earth about its axis. Since such motion is irregular, mean solar time is not uniform enough for the very precise measurement of modern scientific research. Thus, it was necessary to define the second more uniformly.

## TABLE II–1 METRIC SYSTEM DECIMAL PREFIXES

| Multiples | | | Fractions | | |
|---|---|---|---|---|---|
| Tera- | — $10^{12}$ units | (T) | deci- | — $10^{-1}$ units | (d) |
| Giga- | — $10^{9}$ ” | (G) | centi- | — $10^{-2}$ ” | (c) |
| Mega- | — $10^{6}$ ” | (M) | milli- | — $10^{-3}$ ” | (m) |
| kilo- | — $10^{3}$ ” | (k) | micro- | — $10^{-6}$ ” | ($\mu$) |
| hecto- | — $10^{2}$ ” | (h) | nano- | — $10^{-9}$ ” | (n) |
| deka- | — $10^{1}$ ” | (dk) | pico- | — $10^{-12}$ ” | (p) |

was found that a cubic decimeter of water at its maximum density weighs slightly less than a kilogram. Thus, the cubic decimeter differs slightly from the liter as originally defined. Until 1964, 1.000000 liter was equal to 1.000028 cubic decimeters—a slight, but significant, difference in high precision work. Therefore, use of the milliliter (1 ml = $1 \times 10^{-3}$ l) and the cubic centimeter (1 cc = $1 \times 10^{-3}$ cubic decimeter) as equivalents of each other was not possible for the most precise work. In 1964, to eliminate the confusion, the liter was redefined to be a volume *exactly equal to* the cubic decimeter. Thus, we may now use *ml* and *cc* as equivalent abbreviations.

Since we live in a country in which the unwieldy English system of weights and measures, rather than the metric system, is more commonly encountered, it is necessary to know some conversion facts relating the two systems. Table II–2 lists some of those facts.

## TABLE II–2 CONVERSION FACTS RELATING THE METRIC AND ENGLISH SYSTEMS OF WEIGHTS AND MEASURES

| Length | Volume | Mass |
|---|---|---|
| 1 km = 0.6214 miles | 1 l = 1.057 quarts | 1 kg = 2.2046 pounds |
| 1 m = 39.37 inches | 1 qt = 0.9463 liters | 1 pound = 453.59 g |
| 1 inch = 2.5400 cm | | |

| # Scientific Notation

Scientists make measurements involving quantitative data that range from the astronomically large to the infinitesimally small. To facilitate the recording and manipulating of such data, numbers are expressed in a special way called *scientific notation*. Scientific notation involves using numbers between 1 and 10 with exponents of 10, as described below.

Any number may be expressed in the form $A \times 10^N$, where $A$ is any number between one and ten, including one but not ten, and $N$ is an integer. When $N \geq 0$, $A \times 10^N$ is a number *equal to* or *greater* than one. Some examples are:

$$7,860,000,000 = 7.86 \times 10^9$$
$$655,000 \quad\; = 6.55 \times 10^5$$
$$6.00 \quad\quad\;\; = 6.00 \times 10^0$$

When $N < 0$, $A \times 10^N$ is a number *less than one but greater than zero*. Some examples are:

$$0.450 \quad\quad = 4.50 \times 10^{-1}$$
$$0.00062 \quad = 6.2 \; \times 10^{-4}$$
$$0.00000039 = 3.9 \; \times 10^{-7}$$

Using scientific notation, the mean distance from the earth to the sun, 93,000,000 miles, can be expressed as $9.3 \times 10^7$ miles. The wavelength of certain gamma rays, 0.0000000001 cm, can be expressed as $1 \times 10^{-10}$ cm. In both of these cases, the mere fact that scientific notation leads to a simplified expression of the numbers involved would have been argument enough for the use of that notation. However, scientific notation finds its greatest use in the mathematical manipulation of scientific data. Some examples will prove this point.

### EXAMPLE

A current of 0.0000500 amp flows for 30.0 hours through an electrolytic cell. How many coulombs pass through the cell?

### SOLUTION

$$Q = It$$
$$I = 0.0000500 \text{ amp} = 5.00 \times 10^{-5} \text{ amp}$$
$$t = 30.0 \text{ hours} \times 3600 \; \frac{\text{sec}}{\text{hour}} = 1.08 \times 10^5 \text{ sec}$$

$$Q = (5.00 \times 10^{-5} \text{ amp})(1.08 \times 10^5 \text{ sec})$$
$$Q = (5.00 \times 1.08)(10^{-5} \times 10^5) \text{ amp-sec}$$
$$Q = (5.40)(10^{-5+5}) \text{ amp-sec}$$
$$Q = 5.40 \times 10^0 \text{ amp-sec}$$
$$Q = 5.40 \text{ amp-sec (or coulombs)}$$

**EXAMPLE**

A solid cube 0.0000200 m on edge weighs 0.0000600 mg. What is the density of the cube expressed in grams per cubic centimeter?

**SOLUTION**

$$D = \frac{w}{V}$$

$$w = \quad 0.0000600 \text{ mg} = 6.00 \times 10^{-5} \text{ mg}$$

$$V = (0.0000200 \text{ m})^3 = (2.00 \times 10^{-5} \text{ m})^3$$
$$= (2.00)^3 (10^{-5})^3 \text{ m}^3$$
$$= 8.00 \times 10^{-15} \text{ m}^3$$

$$D = \frac{w}{V}$$

$$D = \frac{6.00 \times 10^{-5} \text{ mg}}{8.00 \times 10^{-15} \text{ m}^3}$$

$$D = \left(\frac{6.00}{8.00}\right)\left(\frac{10^{-5}}{10^{-15}}\right)\frac{\text{mg}}{\text{m}^3}$$

$$D = (0.750)(10^{[-5]-[-15]})\frac{\text{mg}}{\text{m}^3}$$

$$D = 0.750 \times 10^{+10} \frac{\text{mg}}{\text{m}^3}$$

$$D = 7.50 \times 10^9 \frac{\text{mg}}{\text{m}^3}$$

Since 1 mg = $1 \times 10^{-3}$ g,

and   1 m$^3$ = $(1 \times 10^2 \text{ cm})^3 = 1 \times 10^6 \text{ cm}^3$,

then   $$D = 7.50 \times 10^9 \frac{\text{mg}}{\text{m}^3}\left(\frac{1 \times 10^{-3} \text{ g}}{1 \text{ mg}}\right)\left(\frac{1 \text{ m}^3}{1 \times 10^6 \text{ cm}^3}\right),$$

$$D = 7.50 \times (10^{[9]+[-3]-[6]})\frac{\text{g}}{\text{cm}^3},$$

$$D = 7.50 \times 10^0 \ \frac{\text{g}}{\text{cm}^3},$$

$$D = 7.50 \text{ g/cm}^3.$$

# Significant Figures

Chemistry is an experimental science. Fundamental to its growth, development, and future is the *quantitative* study of matter, energy, and change. The more exact are the measurements that the chemist makes, the more sound are the conclusions he may draw from his experiments. Yet, every measurement made has an *uncertainty* associated with it that is a complex function of human and mechanical factors.*

Most often the chemist uses *measured quantities* in some mathematical way to reach a *derived quantity*. For example, the measured weight of a solid *divided* by its measured volume leads to its density—a derived property of the solid. The amount of current passing through an electrolytic cell is *derived* by multiplying the measured rate of flow of current through the cell, the amperage, by the measured time of current flow. In recording and communicating his measured data, the chemist also records and communicates the uncertainties associated with them. If measured data are uncertain of themselves, then values of properties derived from such data must also be uncertain. In fact, according to the *theory of measurement*, the uncertainties associated with experimental data are *compounded* when new values are calculated, or derived, from that data. There are a number of detailed methods of determining and recording uncertainties in measured and derived data. The simplest method involves the use of *significant figures*. It is the method that is used consistently in this book. The following example will indicate the basis of the method.

Using ruler *A*, the length *xy* is measured to be somewhere between 2.5 cm and 3.0 cm. While from visual observation we would feel quite confident that the length of *xy* is closer to 2.5 cm than to 3.0 cm, we cannot say with certainty what that length is. It *might* be 2.6 cm or 2.7 cm.

If we use ruler *B* to measure the length of *xy*, we now can say with confidence that its value lies between 2.60 cm and 2.70 cm. In this case, we are also able to see that the length of *xy* is closer to 2.60 cm

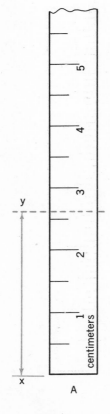

---

* The uncertainty of a measurement is indicative of two different and unrelated deviations. The *precision* of a measurement reflects the reproducibility of that measurement, or its *reliability*. The *accuracy* of a measurement reflects its deviation from a true, known value, or its *validity*. A measurement may be precise—that is, it may be highly reproducible—but it may be highly inaccurate.

than to 2.70 cm. Again, however, we can only *estimate* that *xy* is 2.64 cm or 2.65 cm long.

All the *certain* digits in a measured quantity plus the first estimated, or doubtful digit, are called *significant* figures. In using ruler *A*, we can read the length of *xy* to *two* significant figures. With ruler *B*, the certainty of our measurement increases by one significant figure. With some highly complex measuring system, we might be able to measure the length of *xy* as being 2.6430976 cm, that is, to eight significant figures.

In using data of known uncertainty to arrive at derived values, it is imperative to understand that the **derived values can be no more certain than the original data.** With this understanding firmly in mind, the following rules and examples will help you determine the number of significant figures to be present in a derived value.

**RULE 1.** Numbers used for counting or in exact definitions have an infinite number of significant figures.

**EXAMPLES:**

a. 12 beakers means *exactly* 12.
b. 12 inches per foot means *exactly* 12.

**RULE 2.** Zeros that serve only to place the decimal point are not significant figures. All other zeros in a measured quantity are significant figures.

**EXAMPLES:**

a. 0.002 cm contains *one* significant figure.
b. 0.020 mg contains *two* significant figures.
c. 0.202 cal contains *three* significant figures.
d. 2.020 amp contains *four* significant figures.
e. 202,000 ml contains *at least three* significant figures. If the measurement was made to the nearest ml, then there should be *six* significant figures indicated. This is best accomplished by use of scientific notation and reporting the measurement as $2.02000 \times 10^5$ ml. If the measurement was made to the nearest ten milliliters, it should be reported with *five* significant figures as $2.0200 \times 10^5$ ml. At worst, if *this* measurement was

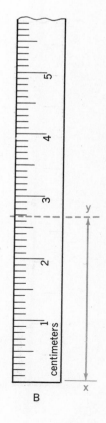

B

made to the nearest thousand milliliters, it should be reported with three significant figures as $2.02 \times 10^5$ ml.

**RULE 3.** In addition and subtraction of measured data, arrange the data in tabular form. Select the data that has its first uncertain figure *farthest to the left.* In all other data, *round off* all figures to the same column containing this first uncertain figure. Add or subtract as usual. (In rounding off, if the figure in the column to be retained is *odd,* and the next figure is *equal to or greater than five,* increase by one the value of the figure in the column to be retained. If the figure in the column to be retained is *even,* increase its value only when the next figure is *greater than five.*)

**EXAMPLES:**

$$42.253 \text{ ml} \rightarrow \quad 42.2 \text{ ml}$$
$$125.6 \quad \text{ml} \rightarrow 125.6 \text{ ml}$$
$$1.75 \quad \text{ml} \rightarrow \quad 1.8 \text{ ml}$$
$$\overline{\text{Sum} \quad \rightarrow 169.6 \text{ ml}}$$

$$127.46 \text{ cm} \rightarrow \quad 127.5 \text{ cm}$$
$$-48.2 \quad \text{cm} \rightarrow -48.2 \text{ cm}$$
$$\overline{\text{Difference} \rightarrow \quad 79.3 \text{ cm}}$$

**RULE 4.** In multiplying and dividing measured data, the derived result can contain no more significant figures than the least certain measurement.

**EXAMPLES:**

a. $Q = It$
   $Q = (4.53 \text{ amp})(2.0 \times 10^3 \text{ sec})$
   $Q = 9.06 \times 10^3 \text{ amp-sec}$
   $Q = 9.1 \times 10^3 \text{ coulombs}$

c. $D = \dfrac{w}{V}$
   $D = \dfrac{4.32 \times 10^{-3} \text{ g}}{2.4739 \times 10^{-3} \text{ ml}}$
   $D = 1.7462 \text{ g/ml}$
   $D = 1.75 \text{ g/ml}$

b. $K_{sp} = [Ag^{+1}][Cl^{-1}]$
   $K_{sp} = (1.3 \times 10^{-5})(1.3 \times 10^{-5})$
   $K_{sp} = 1.69 \times 10^{-10}$
   $K_{sp} = 1.7 \times 10^{-10}$

d. $K_{sp} = [Ba^{+2}][F^{-1}]^2$
   $[F^{-1}]^2 = \dfrac{2.4 \times 10^{-5}}{1.20 \times 10^{-3}}$
   $[F^{-1}]^2 = 2.00 \times 10^{-2}$
   $[F^{-1}] \ = \sqrt{2.00 \times 10^{-2}}$
   $[F^{-1}] \ = 1.41 \times 10^{-1} \text{ m/l}$
   $[F^{-1}] \ = 0.14 \text{ m/l}$

It should be apparent that the *final* results in these examples could have been obtained more *easily* by first rounding off all values to the number of significant figures of the least certain measurement. Therefore, those results could have been obtained most *efficiently* through the use of a simple slide rule. The same can be said of almost all the numerical problems in this book. Use of the slide rule, therefore, is highly recommended.

# ACKNOWLEDGMENTS

ART: **EARL KVAM** *except as noted below*
DESIGNER: Lois Pelaia
COVER ART: Leo and Diane Dillon
PORTRAITS: Joseph Escourido
GRAPHS: Caru Studios, Inc.

**CHAPTER 1:** 8—L. University of Pennsylvania; R. E. I. du Pont de Nemours & Company, Inc. 11—Culver Pictures, Inc. 13—L. Gordon Coster; R. Olin Mathieson Chemical Corporation. 17—J. R. Eyerman, for LIFE.

**ALCHEMY: The Plentiful Vintage:** 23—Eric Lessing, from Magnum. 24—Derek Bayes, courtesy of the British Museum. 25—B.L. David Lees, courtesy of Biblioteca Nazionale Marciana in Venice; T.R. Herbert Orth, courtesy of the Monell Engineering Library, Columbia University. 26-27—Copyright by Rand McNally & Company R. L. 64-GP-40. 28—Manso, courtesy of Prado Museum, Spain. 29—T. Derek Bayes, courtesy of the British Museum; B. Robert Lackenbach for Black Star by courtesy of *Kupferstick Kabinett*, Dahlem Museum, Berlin. 30-31—Derek Bayes, courtesy of the British Museum. 32—T. Bibliothèque Nationale, Paris; B. Herbert Orth, courtesy of the Sidney Edelstein Foundation. 33—Derek Bayes, courtesy of the British Museum. 34—David Lees, courtesy of *Studiolo Di Francesco I De Medici*, Palazzo Vecchio, Florence. 35—Herbert Orth, courtesy of the Burndy Library. 36—Foto Gerhard Rüger, Dresden. 37—Derek Bayes, courtesy of the Derby Museum and Art Gallery.

**CHAPTER 2:** 47—Bettmann Archive. 48—Culver Pictures, Inc. 54—General Mills, Inc. 57—New York *Daily News*. 63—Reproduced from the original copy in the collection of Dr. Roy G. Neville.

**CHAPTER 3:** 83—National Bureau of Standards.

**CHAPTER 4:** 100—University of Pennsylvania. 101—Abstract contributed by *Index Chemicus*, a service of the Institute for Scientific Information, Philadelphia, Pennsylvania.

**CHAPTER 5:** 119—T. Wide World Photos, Inc.; B. National Safety Council. 122—L. Elgin Ciampi; R. J. Fabry. 126—Air Reduction Company, Inc. 127—The Welsbach Corporation. 128—The Franklin Institute Science Museum.

**CHAPTER 6:** 147—The International Nickel Company, Inc. 151—Courtesy of Prof. M. J. Buerger, Massachusetts Institute of Technology. 152—Corning Glass Works. 153—Fig. 6.6 adapted from *College Chemistry, A Systematic Approach*, 2nd Edition © 1961, by Sisler, VanderWerf, and Davidson by permission of The Macmillan Company. 161—The Franklin Institute Science Museum.

**CHAPTER 7:** 169—Hans Arber. 175—Ethyl Corporation. 183—United Press International. 185—T. Standard Oil Company of New Jersey; B. Robert Capa, for LIFE. 186—Corning Glass Works.

**CHAPTER 9:** 211—Air Reduction Company, Inc. 215—Brookhaven National Laboratory. 221—Brookhaven National Laboratory. 224—The Danish Directorate of the Postal and Telegraph Services, stamp designed by Viggo Bang. 229—Yerkes Observatory.

**CHAPTER 10:** 254—Argonne National Laboratory.

**CHAPTER 12:** 293—Fig. 12.7, Ruth Otey; Fig. 12.8, Delos D. Rowe Associates. 294—I. Fankuchen, late professor at the Polytechnic Institute of Brooklyn. 299—French Embassy, Press and Information Division, New York. 300—L. Westinghouse Electric Corporation; R. Argonne National Laboratory.

**CHAPTER 13:** 306—Fig. 13.1, Delos D. Rowe Associates. 312—Fig. 13.4, Leonard Hyams Associates.°

**CHAPTER 16:** 351—Fig. 16.1, Delos D. Rowe Associates; Fig. 16.2, Leonard Hyams Associates. 361—Fig. 16.6, Leonard Hyams Associates. 363—The Borden Company. 365—Delos D. Rowe Associates.

**CHAPTER 17:** 383—Beckman Instruments, Inc.

°*Leonard Hyams Associates commissioned by Rowe Associates.*

**CHAPTER 18:** 392—Fig. 18.1, Delos D. Rowe Associates. 393—Fig. 18.2, Leonard Hyams Associates. 395—Fig. 18.3, Leonard Hyams Associates.

**CHAPTER 19:** 411—Fig. 19.1, Leonard Hyams Associates. 413—Fig. 19.2, Matt Green. 416—Hooker Chemical Corporation.

**SPECTROSCOPY: The Science of Measuring Molecules:** 441—University of Michigan. 444-445—Courtesy of Bausch & Lomb Inc., Rochester, New York. 446-449—The Perkin-Elmer Corporation. 450—L. Courtesy of Prof. M. W. P. Strandberg, Massachusetts Institute of Technology; C. Hewlett-Packard Company. 451—R. Courtesy of Prof. M. W. P. Strandberg, Massachusetts Institute of Technology; B. Hewlett-Packard Company. 452-453—Albert Fenn, for Silver Burdett Company.

**CHAPTER 21:** 458—Fig. 21.1, L. Pelaia; General Electric Company. 460—Fig. 21.2, Leonard Hyams Associates. 461—Fig. 21.3, Leonard Hyams Associates; The Franklin Institute Science Museum. 462—Fig. 21.4, Leonard Hyams Associates. 463—The Dow Chemical Company. 466—Ethyl Corporation. 467—Morton Salt Company.

**CHAPTER 22:** 478—L. National Park Service, United States Department of Interior; R. Italian State Tourist Office, New York. 479—Universal Atlas Cement, a Division of United States Steel Corporation. 480—Portland Cement Association.

**CHAPTER 23:** 485—Fig. 23.1, L. Pelaia; Fig. 23.2, Leonard Hyams Associates. 486—Fig. 23.4, L. Pelaia. 488—Oberlin College Library. 489—Fig. 23.5, Leonard Hyams Associates. 490—Karl Boese.

**CHAPTER 24:** 507—Courtesy of Dr. Zenkevitch. 509—Ben Schnall. 511—L. Copper and Brass Research Association; R. International Minerals & Chemical Corporation. 512—Anaconda Copper Mining Company; Fig. 24.1, Leonard Hyams Associates. 513—Tom Hutchins. 514—L. Robert Crandall Associates for FORTUNE, from the DeGolyer Collection, University of Oklahoma; R. United Press International.

**THE STORY OF STEEL: Red Earth to Master Metal:** 519—Mark Kauffman. 520—Cornell Capa. 521—Ralph Crane. 522—L. Laurence Lowry from Rapho-Guillumette; R. Jerry Cooke. 523—Francis Miller. 524-525—art, Bethlehem Steel Corporation. 526—art, Bethlehem Steel Corporation; United States Steel Corporation. 527—United States Steel Corporation. 528—art, Bethlehem Steel Corporation; United States Steel Corporation. 529—Jones and Laughlin Steel Corporation. 530—L. Grey Villet, for LIFE; R. United States Steel Corporation. 531—United States Steel Corporation. 532—T. Albert Fenn, for LIFE; B. Ralph Morse, for LIFE. 533—Ralph Crane, for LIFE.

**CHAPTER 25:** 539—Fig. 25.2, L. Pelaia. 543—Fig. 25.4, L. Pelaia. 545—Figs. 25.5 and 25.6, Leonard Hyams Associates. 546—Fig. 25.7, Leonard Hyams Associates; Figs. 25.8 and 25.9, L. Pelaia.

**CHAPTER 26:** 552—Fig. 26.1, Leonard Hyams Associates. 555—Esso Research and Engineering Company. 558—Fig. 26.2, Leonard Hyams Associates. 560—L. Western Electric Company; R. Corning Glass Works. 561—Figs. 26.3 and 26.4, Leonard Hyams Associates. 562—Fig. 26.5, Leonard Hyams Associates. 563—L. Culligan Water Institute; R. The Permutit Company, a Division of Pfaudler Permutit, Inc. 564—L. Michigan Chemical Corporation; R. Fig. 26.6 adapted from *Modern Aspects of Inorganic Chemistry*, 3rd Edition © 1960, by Emeleus and Anderson by permission of Routledge & Kegan Paul, Ltd.

**CHAPTER 27:** 571—Nitragin Company. 572—Shell Chemical Corporation. 573—The Edgar Fahs Smith Memorial Collection, University of Pennsylvania. 575—Fig. 27.1, Delos D. Rowe Associates.

**CHAPTER 28:** 582—Figs. 28.1 and 28.3, Leonard Hyams Associates. 583—Fig. 28.4, Delos D. Rowe Associates. 587—Fig. 28.5, Leonard Hyams Associates. 590—Fig. 28.6, Leonard Hyams Associates.

**CHAPTER 29:** 595—T.L. Stauffer Chemical Company; T.R. E. I. du Pont de Nemours & Company, Inc.; Figs. 29.1a and 29.1b, L. Pelaia; Fig. 29.1c, Leonard Hyams Associates. 596—Figs. 29.2a and 29.2b, L. Pelaia. 597—Fig. 29.3, L. Pelaia. 599—Fig. 29.4, L. Pelaia. 602—Fig. 29.5, L. Pelaia. 604—L. The Dow Chemical Company; R. Shell Oil Company. 607—Fig. 29.6, Delos D. Rowe Associates. 608—Fig. 29.7, L. Pelaia. 609—Fig. 29.8, Leonard Hyams Associates. 610—Figs. 29.9 and 29.10, Delos D. Rowe Associates; Ministry of Postal Services, Bonn. 612—Fig. 29.11, Ruth Otey.

**CHAPTER 30:** 616—Fig. 30.1, Ruth Otey. 618—Fig. 30.2, Ruth Otey. 622—Figs. 30.3 and 30.4, Ruth Otey. 623—Figs. 30.5 and 30.6, Delos D. Rowe Associates. 624—Figs. 30.7 and 30.8, Ruth Otey. 627—United Press International; Fig. 30.10, Delos D. Rowe Associates.

**GIANT MOLECULES: Plastics, Fibers, Films, and Feathers:** 631—Courtesy of Prof. F. M. Carpenter, Harvard University. 632—L. R. Van Nostrand from National Audubon Society; B.R. Henry Groskinsky, for Silver Burdett Company. 633—T.R. Photo by E. Guthrie, The American Museum of Natural History; B.L. Boise Cascade Corporation; B.R. Courtesy of Carl W. Rettenmeyer. 634-635—Phil Brodatz. 636-640—Molecular models and bouncing spheres provided by Prof. M. Goodman, Polytechnic Institute of Brooklyn, and photographed by Henry Groskinsky for Silver Burdett Company. 642—art, Phillips Petroleum Company. 643—Ivan Masser, from Black Star. 644—AVCO-Everett Research Laboratory, a Division of AVCO Corporation. 645—T. Albert Fenn, for TIME; B. Spencer Chemical Division, Gulf Oil Corporation.

**CHAPTER 31:** 651—Fig. 31.1, Ruth Otey. 652—Fig. 31.2, Delos D. Rowe Associates; American Heart Association. 653—Fig. 31.3, Ruth Otey; Fig. 31.4, Delos D. Rowe Associates. 654—Fig. 31.5, Delos D. Rowe Associates. 655—Figs. 31.6 and 31.7, Delos D. Rowe Associates. 656—Fig. 31.8, Delos D. Rowe Associates; Fig. 31.9, Ruth Otey. 657—Fig. 31.10, Leonard Hyams Associates; courtesy of Prof. Max Perutz, Laboratory of Molecular Biology, Medical Research Council, Cambridge, England. 658—Fig. 31.12, Ruth Otey. 659—Fig. 31.13, Delos D. Rowe Associates. 660—Fig. 31.14, Ruth Otey. 661—Schwarz Bioresearch, Inc.; Fig. 31.15, L. Pelaia. 662—Figs. 31.16 and 31.17, L. Pelaia. 663—Fig. 31.18, L. Pelaia; Fig. 31.19, Leonard Hyams Associates. 664—Fig. 31.20, Matt Green. 665—Fig. 31.21, Matt Green. 666—Dr. G. Lockard Conley, Johns Hopkins Hospital.

**CHAPTER 32:** 676—Fig. 32.4, Leonard Hyams Associates. 677—Brookhaven National Laboratory; Fig. 32.5, Leonard Hyams Associates. 680—Fig. 32.6, Leonard Hyams Associates; Argonne National Laboratory. 681—Fig. 32.7, Leonard Hyams Associates; Brookhaven National Laboratory. 685—National Archives. 686—Argonne National Laboratory. 687—Figs. 32.9 and 32.10, Leonard Hyams Associates. 688—Union Carbide Corporation. 689—Fig. 32.11, Delos D. Rowe Associates as adapted from "Nuclear Reactors —Putting the Atom to Work" by permission of the Los Alamos Scientific Laboratory, University of California; Picker X-ray Corporation. 690—L. Brookhaven National Laboratory; R. Weyerhaeuser Company.

**APPENDIX 4:** Leonard Hyams Associates.

Page numbers in index that appear in italics refer to illustrations; those in boldface refer to definitions and statements of laws; those followed by an asterisk refer to biographical sketches; and those followed by "n" refer to footnotes.

2  5176